# Tiwanaku and Its Hinterland

# Smithsonian Series in Archaeological Inquiry

Robert McC. Adams and Bruce D. Smith, Series Editors

The Smithsonian Series in Archaeological Inquiry presents original case studies that address important general research problems and demonstrate the values of particular theoretical and/or methodological approaches. Titles include well-focused edited collections as well as works by individual authors. The series is open to all subject areas, geographical regions, and theoretical modes.

# Tiwanaku and Its Hinterland

## Archaeology and Paleoecology of an Andean Civilization

## 1
## Agroecology

EDITED BY ALAN L. KOLATA

SMITHSONIAN INSTITUTION PRESS
Washington and London

Copy Editor: Jane Kepp
Supervisory Editor: Duke Johns
Designer: Janice Wheeler

Library of Congress Cataloging-in-Publication Data
Kolata, Alan L.
Tiwanaku and its hinterland : archaeology and paleoecology in an Andean civilization / Alan L. Kolata.
v. <1 >. — (Smithsonian series in archaeological inquiry)
Includes bibliographical references (p. ) and index.
Contents: v. 1. Agroecology —
ISBN 1-56098-600-X (acid-free paper)
1. Tiwanaku culture. 2. Indians of South America—Titicaca Lake (Peru and Bolivia)—Agriculture. 3. Indians of South America—Titicaca Lake (Peru and Bolivia)—Antiquities. 4. Irrigation farming—Titicaca Lake (Peru and Bolivia)—History. 5. Raised bed farming—Titicaca Lake (Peru and Bolivia)—History. 6. Human ecology—Titicaca Lake (Peru and Bolivia)—History. 7. Titicaca Lake (Peru and Bolivia)—Antiquities. I. Title. II. Series.
F3319.1.T55K63 1995
984′.1201—dc20 95-5837

British Library Cataloguing-in-Publication Data is available

Manufactured in the United States of America
03 02 01 00 99 98 97 96 5 4 3 2 1

♾ The paper used in this publication meets the minimum requirements of the American National Standard for Information Sciences—Permanence of Paper for Printed Library Materials ANSI Z39.48-1984.

*For my parents,*
*Edmund J. and Esther Borowiak Kolata*

*In the memory of my beloved father,*
*Edmund J. Kolata (1916–1989),*
*whose name lives on in the heart of*
*Tiwanaku*

# Contents

# Illustrations

# Tables

# Contributors

Jaime Argollo is a consulting geologist and geomorphologist with the Fundación Wiñaymarka in La Paz, Bolivia.

Michael W. Binford is an associate professor of landscape ecology in the Graduate School of Design, Harvard University, Cambridge, Massachusetts.

Mark Brenner is a senior research associate in the Department of Fisheries and Aquatic Sciences, Institute of Food and Agricultural Sciences, at the University of Florida, Gainesville.

Heath J. Carney is a research associate in the Institute of Ecology, Division of Environmental Studies, University of California at Davis.

Evelyn Gemio is an assistant agronomist with the Fundación Wiñaymarka in La Paz, Bolivia.

Kevin Healy in representative for the Andean region of the Inter-American Foundation, Arlington, Virginia.

Alice B. Kehoe is a professor of anthropology in the Department of Social and Cultural Sciences, Marquette University, Milwaukee, Wisconsin.

Alan L. Kolata is a professor of anthropology and director of the Center for Latin American Studies at the University of Chicago.

Barbara W. Leyden is a member of the graduate faculty and an adjunct research scientist in the Department of Geology at the University of South Florida, Tampa.

Charles R. Ortloff is a principal engineer at the Corporate Technology Center, FMC Corporation, Santa Clara, California.

Juan Carlos Ramírez is chief agronomist with the Fundación Wiñaymarka, La Paz, Bolivia.

Oswaldo Rivera is director of the Instituto Nacional de Arqueología de Bolivia, La Paz.

Leocadio Ticlla is a geoarchaeologist on the staff of the Instituto Nacional de Arqueología de Bolivia, La Paz.

# Preface and Acknowledgments

This book is the first of a two-volume set that draws together data and interpretations from a long-term, University of Chicago–Bolivian National Institute of Archaeology project of interdisciplinary research at the archaeological site of Tiwanaku and its sustaining hinterland. This ongoing research program, in Bolivia called Proyecto Wila Jawira, integrates ecological and archaeological investigations in order to understand the history and character of Tiwanaku society, particularly the relationship between that society's production systems and its risk-prone environmental setting in the Andean high plateau.

This first volume concentrates on the issue of long-term human-environment interactions in the southern Lake Titicaca basin, with a focus on the nature, technology, and social organization of agricultural production. The second volume will present archaeological data and interpretations from the project's intensive excavations in the urban centers of Tiwanaku and Lukurmata and from regional survey and excavations at rural sites in the Tiwanaku and Catari River basins of northwestern Bolivia. Together, the two volumes present the first synthetic statement of the project's investigations into the environmental, historical, and cultural context of Tiwanaku urbanism as an indigenous Andean social process.

I would like to acknowledge the institutions, agencies, corporations, and individuals who underwrote, and continue to underwrite, Proyecto Wila Jawira's research program. In Bolivia, the research is authorized and conducted under the auspices of the Instituto Nacional de Arqueología de Bolivia (INAR), currently under the Secretaría Nacional de Cultura directed by Alberto Bailey Gutierrez. Over the past eighteen years, my research has been authorized through agreements signed by three separate directors of INAR: Carlos Ponce Sanginés, Carlos Urquizo Sossa, and Oswaldo Rivera Sundt. I thank each of them for their commitment to the project.

Our research has been generously supported by grants from the National Science Foundation (BNS-8607541, BNS-8805490, DEB-9212641); the National Endowment for the Humanities (RO-21806-88, RO-21368-86); the Inter-American Foundation (BO-252, BO-273, BO-374, BO-374a); the UNESCO/Man and the Biosphere Program (1753-000566); the National Oceanic and Atmospheric Administration (GC-95-174); the H. John Heinz III Charitable Fund of the Heinz Family Foundation; the Pittsburgh Foundation; the Office of Social Science Research and the Campus Research Board of the University of Illinois at Chicago; the Marion R. and Adolph J. Lichstern Fund for Anthropological Research, Department of Anthropology, University of Chicago; the Division of Social Sciences of the University of Chicago; Tesoro Petroleum Corporation, San Antonio, Texas; Compañía Minera del Sur, La Paz, Bolivia; and Occidental Petroleum Corporation, Los Angeles, California.

Additionally, I wish to thank several people who worked intensively with me to identify and secure funding for the research. They include Ambassador Robert S. Gelbard, Kevin Healy of the Inter-American Foundation, and, in particular, Dr. Robert V. West, Jr., former chairman and CEO of Tesoro Petroleum Corporation, who has supported the project financially from its inception in 1978. I wish also to acknowledge the staunch support of Connie Thrasher Jaquith of Louisville, Kentucky, who contributes generously each year to the work of the project.

Over the past two decades of my research career in Peru and Bolivia, I have incurred many debts, both personal and professional. I cannot possibly acknowledge all of the individuals and scholars who have contributed to my professional and personal development by providing formal academic training and by sharing field experiences, intense discussions, and occasionally heated debate. They have all helped enrich my life. Nevertheless, I wish to thank here my principal collaborators and senior colleagues in Proyecto Wila Jawira: Michael Binford, Mark Brenner, Charles Ortloff, and Oswaldo Rivera. Michael Binford has been the co-principal investigator for the project since 1986, and he, along with Mark Brenner and Charles Ortloff, have contributed inestimably to the intellectual excitement and personal pleasure of doing scientific research in the Lake Titicaca basin and beyond. After sharing a decade of intense, difficult, and rewarding work, we continue to operate as a team.

I owe a special and continuing debt of gratitude to Oswaldo Rivera, current director of the National Institute of Archaeology, La Paz, Bolivia. Oswaldo is the co-director of Proyecto Wila Jawira and has worked closely with me in conceptualizing and organizing our research efforts in Bolivia since I first arrived in 1978. He is both my research collaborator and my *compadre:* I value both roles highly, but the latter is the more important.

Many other scholars in Bolivia and the United States, including a remarkable cohort of current and former graduate students at the University of Chicago, have participated in the project. Several of these colleagues are authors of chapters in the second volume of this set. I thank them collectively for their key contributions to the project's fieldwork. In Bolivia, Carlos Ponce Sanginés first invited me to begin work at Tiwanaku in 1978, never imagining, I am sure, to what lengths this would lead. To him I owe my entrée into Bolivian science and society, and I acknowledge him with gratitude.

Speaking on behalf of all the participants in Proyecto Wila Jawira, our most profound social debt is to the many Aymaras with whom we have worked. This book is about their history and culture, and possibly about their future as well. Without their active collaboration and intense interest in their own cultural heritage, the research on which this book is based could never have been accomplished. The number of people involved in the work of the project is, literally, in the hundreds, and I cannot thank each of them by name here. But the people of the villages of Tiwanaku, Lukurmata, Chojasivi, Lakaya, Lillimani, Quiripujo, Chokara, Korila, Wakullani, Khonko Wankané, Chambi Grande, Chambi Chico, Wankollo, Huaraya, Achuta Grande, Kasa Achuta, Pillapi, Guaqui, Yanarico, Patarani, Andamarca, Yanamani, Pircuta, Corpa, Sullcata, Lacuyo, Kusijata, and Copajira have helped, to various degrees, in the work and life of the research. I thank them all.

In Tiwanaku itself, the Associación de Trabajadores en Arqueología de Tiwanaku provided the highly skilled workers who participated in all aspects of the excavations and analysis of materials. They are truly extraordinary people. In Tiwanaku, César Yurja Callisaya, supervisor of the ruins of Tiwanaku and my closest Aymara friend, collaborator and *compadre,* opens his house to me and the entire research team. The generosity of his family cannot go unremarked in any publication based on the project's research. César's knowledge of Aymara communities and his remarkable diplomatic skills have permitted the project to complete its ambitious research agenda under even the most difficult of political circumstances. He, along with Oswaldo Rivera, are the two people most responsible for the successful completion of the research described in this book.

With regard to publication, I would like to thank, at the Smithsonian Institution Press, the editors of this series, Robert McC. Adams and Bruce D. Smith, as well as Daniel Goodwin and Duke Johns, who guided this complex volume through production. I also wish to acknowledge the constructive suggestions of the two anonymous reviewers of the manuscript. Our copy editor, Jane Kepp of Kepp Editorial in Santa Fe, New Mexico, merits special acknowledgment. Faced with an overwhelming, unwieldy, and highly technical manuscript, Jane did much more than edit copy; she repeatedly encouraged all the authors to clarify their thoughts, to coordinate their text with accompanying graphics, and above all, to check and recheck their chapters for accuracy. The resulting manuscript was immeasurably improved by her skillful eye and sensitive hand. On behalf of all the authors, I thank her.

At the University of Chicago, two of my advanced graduate students, Shawn Welch and Nicole Couture, accepted the monumental job of helping me edit the manuscript, produce and correct illustrations, and compile the master bibliography. Nicole Couture, in particular, invested uncounted hours in preparing the manuscript for publication. She accepted and accomplished the most difficult tasks with grace and wit. Each of the authors of chapters in this book has worked closely with Nicole. Collectively we admire and thank her for her exceptional dedication and good humor.

Finally, I want to acknowledge my wife, Anna, and my daughter, Justine, who tolerated endless, difficult separations and at times endured the rigors of the Bolivian high plateau while research was in progress. Their love sustains me.

Alan L. Kolata

# 1

# Proyecto Wila Jawira

## *An Introduction to the History, Problems, and Strategies of Research*

ALAN L. KOLATA

The ability of irrigation agriculture to support large populations and underwrite the agrarian economies of state-level societies has long been recognized. Most historical and interpretive studies of agricultural reclamation have been concerned with the technological, sociological, and political implications of hydraulic agriculture in arid lands (Wittfogel 1938, 1955, 1957). The interplay between social institutions, political organization, and an agrarian economy based on artificial water distribution has been the subject of a large body of literature (Boserup 1965; Downing and Gibson 1974; Fernea 1970; Mitchell 1973; Price 1971; Sanders 1972; Sanders and Price 1968; Sanders and Webster 1978; and Stewart 1955, among many others). For wetlands environments, however, the potential of intensive drained-field agriculture to provide a similar economic base and sustain demographic growth is little known. In response to this lacuna, recent interest in the problem of agricultural reclamation in perennially or periodically inundated landscapes has expanded dramatically.

The initial product of this emergent interest has been substantial new information on the morphology, functions, and implications of drained- and raised-field agriculture in various regions and culture areas of the Western Hemisphere. A sampling of studies on these subjects reflects the geographical breadth of the distribution of paleohydraulic systems as well as the relatively recent character of scholar inquiry into them: for the Maya, see Adams (1980), Harrison (1977, 1978), Matheny (1976, 1978), Puleston (1977), Scarborough (1983), Siemens (1978, 1982, 1983a), Siemens and Puleston (1972), and Turner (1974, 1978, 1983); for Veracruz, see Siemens (1983b) and Wilkerson (1983); for the Valley of Mexico, see Armillas (1971), Calnek (1972), J. R. Parsons (1976), and Parsons, Parsons, Popper, and Taft (1982); for Venezuela, see Zucchi (1972); for Colombia, see Broadbent (1966), Parsons and Bowen (1966), and R. West (1959); for Ecuador, see Batchelor (1980), Denevan and Mathewson (1983), Knapp (1981), Knapp and Ryder (1983), and J. J. Parsons (1969); for Peru, see Erickson (1984, 1988a, 1988b), Lennon (1983), Parsons and Denevan (1967), and Smith, Denevan, and Hamilton (1968); and for Bolivia, see Denevan (1964, 1966), Erickson and Brinkmeier (1991), and Pflaker (1963). Empirical studies of raised-field agriculture such as these constitute a valuable context of comparative data. In particular, they provide essential insights into the appropriate questions that must be posed of this complex phenomenon of agrarian intensification.

This book, the first of two volumes, concentrates on the issue of long-term human-environment interactions in the southern Lake Titicaca basin, with a focus on the technology and organization of agricultural production in the pre-Hispanic Andean state of Tiwanaku (figs. 1.1, 1.2). The second volume presents archaeological data and interpretations from excavations in the urban centers of Tiwanaku and Lukurmata and from regional surveys and excavations at rural sites in the Tiwanaku and Catari River basins. Both volumes are the products of a long-term, multidisciplinary research project referred to in Bolivia as Proyecto Wila Jawira (after the Wila Jawira River, the local name for the Catari River, an important feature of our study area). Together the two volumes constitute the first integrated, English-language report of research in Tiwanaku and its hinterland undertaken under the aegis of Proyecto Wila Jawira from 1986 to 1994.

Because the research is ongoing, with a substantial new field program that commenced in 1995, this book should not be construed as a final report. Rather, we conceive of it as a substantive progress report on the research accomplished to date. We expect that in time, many, if not all, of the conclusions and interpretations presented here will be significantly changed or perhaps even superseded. But this is the nature of progress in research programs that explicitly test conclusions and seek verification of results. It is particularly the case in a field of study that attempts to open new ground. As noted later in my brief summary of the history of research on Tiwanaku, very

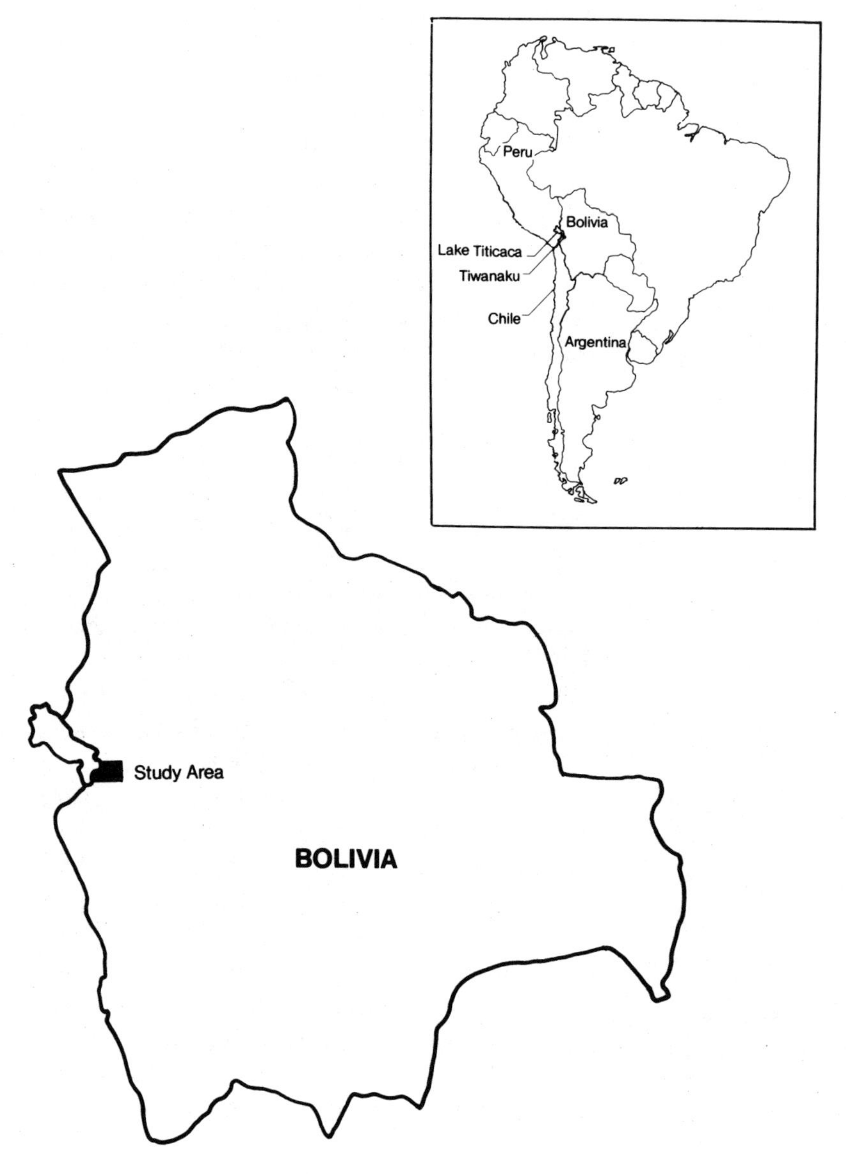


**Figure 1.1.** Location of the study area around the southern shores of Lake Titicaca.

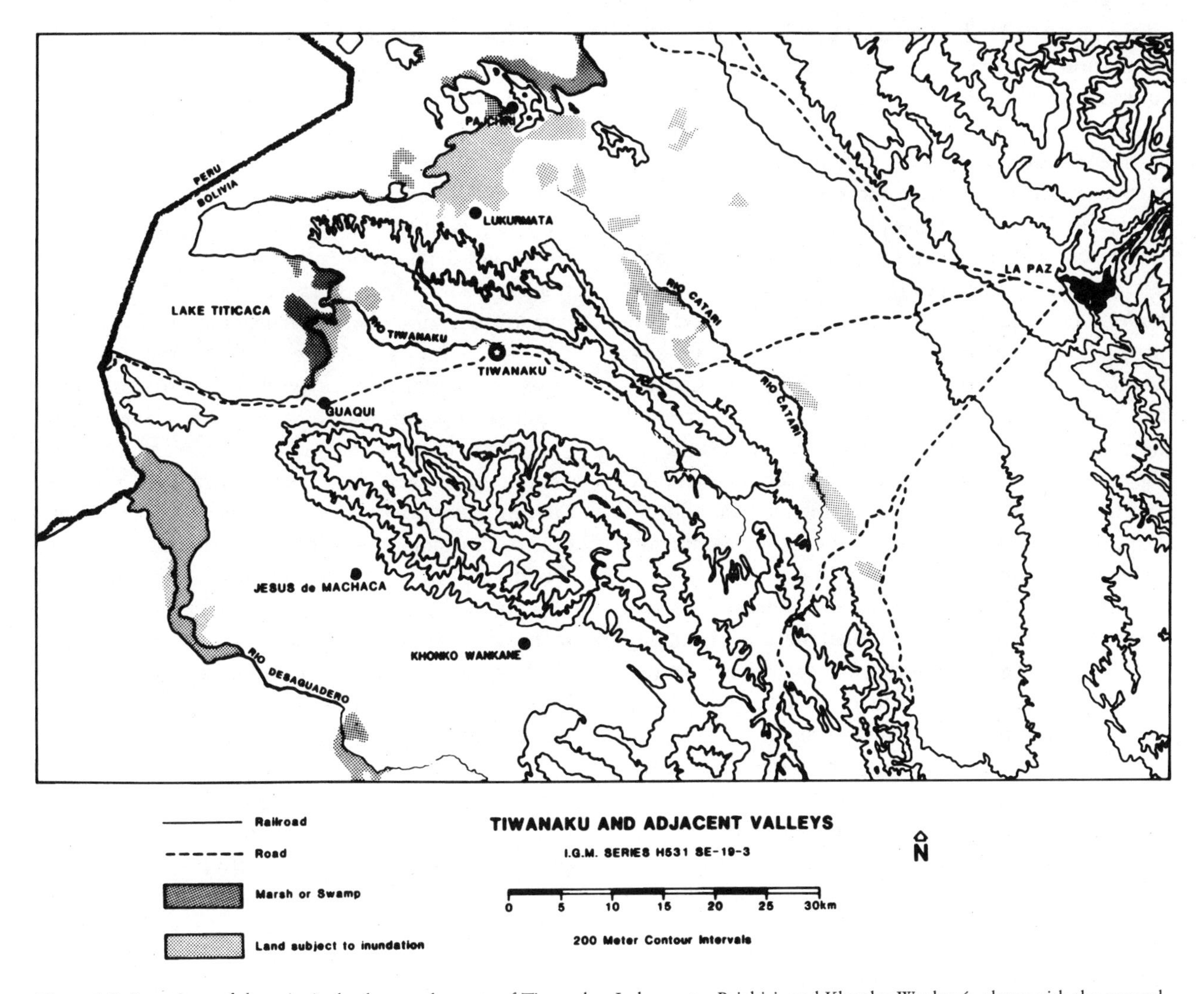


**Figure 1.2.** Locations of the principal urban settlements of Tiwanaku, Lukurmata, Pajchiri, and Khonko Wankané, along with the general topographic and hydrological features of the basins of the Tiwanaku and Catari rivers and portions of the Machaca-Desaguadero region.

little attention has been focused on agricultural landscapes in Tiwanaku's hinterland or, for that matter, on the technological and sociological organization of agricultural production in the Andean altiplano as a whole. As a result, our investigations, although systematic and as comprehensive as the exigencies of logistics and available resources have allowed, are inevitably incomplete. As I phrased this issue elsewhere (Kolata 1993a:32):

> We are forced by the nature of the inquiry to continually respond to fresh information, and to constantly reformulate our analytical perspectives. The archaeologist cannot afford the luxury of dogma. . . . This is not to say that all our current interpretations are merely casual, mutable speculations. Rather they are like a partially completed building with some essential structural elements laid down, but with much more finish work to be done. We have the basic blueprint and, although unforeseen changes and modifications will undoubtedly affect the plan, we can nevertheless envision the principal contours of the final structure.

This publication is intended to incorporate new elements into this "basic blueprint," as well as to commence work on some of the important detailing that will, in time, result in a more complete interpretive structure.

Proyecto Wila Jawira is multidisciplinary, with a strong convergence of research questions among the ecologists, agronomists, and archaeologists participating in the project. We use an ecological model of human-environment relationships to analyze the space-time systematics and productivity of intensive raised-field agriculture in the Lake Titicaca basin of Bolivia. Human populations and environmental conditions interact by dynamic ecological processes. Manipulation of water and nutrient cycles, energy flow, and interactions with other organisms constitute the foundations of a society's exploitation of natural resources. In turn, large-scale human activities such as intensive agriculture and urbanization alter ecological processes. The interaction operates constantly, changing environmental constraints and creating new challenges and opportunities for the reproduction of the biological and cultural bases of human society. The principal anthropological and ecological objectives of our long-term research in the Tiwanaku core area are to explore the role of varying environmental conditions as stimuli for cultural innovation, to determine the environmental consequences of such innovations, and to define the implications of the physical and social organization of an agricultural landscape for the nature of an ancient Andean society.

A collateral focus on the contemporary implications and consequences of rehabilitating Tiwanaku raised fields developed during the early stages of the field research in 1986. The field rehabilitation efforts provided a strong experimental strut for the historically oriented dimensions of the research. That is, we were able to address several questions regarding the physical and technical characteristics of raised-field agriculture in the Tiwanaku region only after successfully implementing the rehabilitation program. The results include new understandings of the thermal, hydrological, and nutrient retention features of the raised-field system in the high-altitude environment of the Lake Titicaca basin (see chapters 5, 6, 7), as well as a large corpus of material that relates to the productivity of this form of intensive agriculture (chapter 9). We are continuing with interdisciplinary experiments in a gradually expanding landscape of rehabilitated raised fields in our research area (Carney et al. 1993).

Many empirical questions are resolved here, particularly with respect to the physical and organizational dimensions of Tiwanaku raised-field agriculture and the contribution of long-term environmental change and consequent agrarian collapse to the decline of the Tiwanaku state. Not surprisingly, many more questions, both narrowly empirical and broadly interpretive, have been raised by the research. For instance, the role of intensive agriculture in the emergence of the Tiwanaku state remains incompletely addressed. The question of state origins and its relationship to agricultural production was not explicitly incorporated in the original formulation of the research project. This was not because of a lack of interest in this fundamental question but because of a pragmatic consideration of research design. Much of the primary archaeological evidence for the formative processes underlying the emergence of the Tiwanaku state, particularly as these relate to the role of wetlands agriculture, is located in deeply buried lacustrine and fluvial deposits. Extracting this information requires spatially extensive, labor-intensive excavations over a number of archaeological sites and agricultural landscapes. This kind of question can be answered definitively only with long-term research of regional scope. In such an enterprise, patience and the ability to marshal the requisite political, financial, and analytical resources become virtues of necessity. Obtaining critical evidence of these formative processes, particularly of the space-time dynamics of raised-field cultivation throughout the Tiwanaku hinterland, is the prime goal of the new phase of field research begun in 1995. We expect the conclusions from this new phase of research to answer at least some of the questions about the origins of intensive raised-field agriculture in the Tiwanaku hinterland.

The focus of this volume, then, is on the nature of intensive wetlands reclamation by the mature, rather than the emergent, Tiwanaku state. Spatially we concentrate on agricultural reclamation in the environmental context of the Lake Titicaca basin of Bolivia. Temporally, we focus principally, but not exclusively, on the period between about 1500 and 900 B.P. Continuing research will permit us to incorporate a longer-term, diachronic perspective with the evidence and interpretations we advance here.

This chapter offers a brief introduction to the central objectives of research at Tiwanaku and its immediate hinterland, particularly as these objectives relate to the structure and organization of intensive agriculture. I begin with a brief, selective history of Tiwanaku studies, summarizing dominant themes that have characterized archaeological interpretations of this Andean state. I then describe the history of our own research project and outline the research agenda and strategies originally developed to examine the role of intensive agriculture in the mature Tiwanaku state.

## A Selective History of Tiwanaku Studies

In 1877, Ephraim George Squier published an epochal monograph on the Andes entitled *Peru: Inci-*

*dents of Travel and Explorations in the Land of the Incas,* in which he included the first sketch maps of Tiwanaku's megalithic ruins. Perhaps more importantly, his impressions of the nature of Tiwanaku as an archaeological site and an ancient community represent the first crystallization of an interpretive theme that has run through Tiwanaku studies ever since—a theme that, although subject to considerable modification since Squier's time, continues to influence, perhaps even dominate, thinking about Tiwanaku. Squier's (1877:300) brief sojourn in the ruins of Tiwanaku led him to conclude:

> We find nowhere in the vicinity [of Tiwanaku] any decided traces of ancient habitations, such as abound elsewhere in Peru, in connection with most public edifices. . . . This is not, prima facie, a region for nurturing or sustaining a large population and certainly not one wherein we should expect to find a capital. Tiahuanaco may have been a sacred spot or a shrine, the position of which was determined by accident, an augury, or a dream, but I can hardly believe that it was a seat of dominion.

Squier's comments are fascinating in that they represent one of the first expressions of the notion that Tiwanaku was not a true city but was, rather, a sparsely populated ceremonial center—a focus of religious pilgrimage but not of dense residential population. Furthermore, Squier attributed the implicit marginality of Tiwanaku as a population center to its location in the rigorous environment of the Andean altiplano, or high plateau. This attitude that Tiwanaku's environmental setting was inherently unproductive and inhospitable and that therefore the site itself never attained true urban proportions or importance as "a seat of dominion" remains a strong theme in the interpretations of some contemporary archaeologists and ethnohistorians (Schaedel 1988:772–73).

Squier's interpretation of Tiwanaku as essentially a vacant ceremonial center recall similar conceptions proposed for many Maya settlements in the tropical rain forest of the Petén in Guatemala. As in the case of Tiwanaku, the conclusion that Maya society was essentially nonurban was generated by the underlying notion that this society had evolved in a difficult and agriculturally unproductive environment (there, the humid tropics characterized by thin, acidic soils and a choking vegetation cover). In the cases of both the Maya and Tiwanaku, these subjective judgments about the relative productivity of the natural environment were reinforced by a paradoxical concern for mapping and exploring only the visible public architecture of their principal settlements. Little effort was made to investigate the circumceremonial precincts for evidence of domestic structures and habitations that might settle the demographic issue once and for all. It is not terribly surprising, then, that the archaeologists and explorers who worked under difficult environmental conditions in the bitterly cold, windswept Andean high plateau or in the suffocating heat of the Mayan tropical jungles, and who concentrated their energies on the magnificent temple mounds and palaces, developed similar images of these civilizations as theocracies organized around a loose congeries of sparsely populated ceremonial centers.

The theme of Tiwanaku as a ceremonial center lacking large resident populations, first voiced by Squier, was recapitulated in the archaeological research of Wendell Bennett during the 1930s. Bennett (1934) conducted the first systematic excavations within the monumental precincts of Tiwanaku and developed a cultural chronology based on changes in ceramic styles over time. His achievement in establishing the first stratigraphically based ceramic chronology for Tiwanaku cannot be overestimated. His quadripartite stylistic sequence of ceramic phases (Primitive Tiahuanaco, Classic Tiahuanaco, Decadent Tiahuanaco, and Post Tiahuanaco/Inca) formed the foundations for contemporary formulations of Tiwanaku cultural chronology.

Nevertheless, Bennett's excavations, which were restricted by the Bolivian government to 10 test pits, each no larger than 10 square meters, were placed exclusively within the area of monumental architecture at the site. On the basis of this work and his discovery of an enormous, intricately carved stone stela in the center of a structure referred to today as the Semisubterranean Temple, Bennett (1934:480) concluded that Tiwanaku was "distinctly a ceremonial site, composed of an aggregation of temples" built sequentially over long periods of time. Bennett came to understand the expansion of Tiwanaku cultural influence into Peru, Chile, and Bolivia as essentially religious in character, a cult of high prestige directed by "priest leaders" whose principal temple and oracle center was the site of Tiwanaku itself. Like Squier, he did not believe that Tiwanaku ever achieved urban proportions. Implicit in Bennett's interpretations of Tiwanaku as a political and economic phenomenon was the notion of the marginality of the city's environmental setting for supporting substantial human communities.

Bennett's perspective on the religious character of Tiwanaku expansion was forcefully restated by Dorothy Menzel (1964, 1968, 1977) in a series of classic papers on the ceramic styles of the Peruvian Middle Horizon. Menzel argued for the essentially sacred nature of Tiwanaku and emphasized Tiwanaku's role as an iconographic (and therefore ideological) model for the state art of the presumptively coeval capital of Wari in the Ayacucho basin of southern Peru. At the same time, she discounted, or perhaps did not contemplate, the potential *political* implications of these iconographic and conceptual borrowings by Wari from Tiwanaku art. Rather, she conceived of Tiwanaku as an essentially passive donor of a developed religious cult focused iconographically on the figure of the so-called Gateway, or Staff God, together with its attendant symbols (see Cook 1983 for other designations for this figure). This interpretation envisioned (unspecified) commercial interactions between Wari and Tiwanaku, brokered by merchant-missionaries who were instrumental in introducing the cult to Wari. There the cult of the Staff God became the catalyst for the formulation of a consciously fostered imperial ideology that was subsequently imposed by force of arms throughout the central Andes (Lumbreras 1974; Menzel 1964, 1968). This perspective on Tiwanaku, and more explicitly on Tiwanaku and Wari interactions, persists in a number of guises in the modern archaeological literature (Cook 1983; Isbell 1983; Isbell and McEwan 1991; Schaedel 1988).

Apart from the pioneering studies of Bennett in the early 1930s, serious archaeological research on a substantial scale at Tiwanaku and its nearby affiliated sites began only during the late 1950s. This work, executed throughout the 1960s and 1970s, primarily by Bolivian nationals under the aegis of the Instituto Nacional de Arqueología de Bolivia (INAR), again focused primarily on the highly visible architectural ensembles of Tiwanaku. The research emphasis on monumental architecture was shaped, in part, by Bolivia's need to promote economic development through tourism and by the desire to document and restore the salient monuments of the country's pre-Hispanic cultural patrimony (Ponce Sanginés 1978). However, this period of large-scale excavations generated considerable new information on the chronological context and architectural form of the city's development (Ponce Sanginés 1972).

Completing deep stratigraphic excavations in the temple of Kalasasaya, the Bolivian archaeologist Carlos Ponce Sanginés elaborated upon the ceramic chronology sketched out by Bennett. Although controversial in some quarters, Ponce's formulation of five phases of ceramic evolution still forms the basis for contemporary chronological interpretations of the Tiwanaku cultural sequence among scholars working in the region (Bermann 1994; Goldstein 1989; Kolata 1983). The most disputed elements of his ceramic chronology relate to the earlier phases of his proposed sequence, specifically Tiwanaku phases I and II. Some authors have suggested that there is insufficient primary evidence to support a subdivision of the early end of the Tiwanaku sequence into two distinct phases (Albarracín-Jordan and Mathews 1990; Arellano 1991). These authors discount, in particular, the cultural reality of the proposed Tiwanaku phase II. Most archaeologists working at Tiwanaku-related sites in the Lake Titicaca basin accept that Tiwanaku I ceramics, although still insufficiently documented from primary archaeological contexts, represent a distinct Formative-period tradition in the region. Nevertheless, there remains considerable debate about the precise chronological and cultural relationships between Tiwanaku I and other, possibly coeval Formative ceramic complexes of the south-central Andes, such as Chiripa, Wankarani, Pukara, Faldas del Moro, and Huaracane.

There is less controversy over the later phases of the Ponce ceramic sequence, particularly Tiwanaku phases IV and V, for which we now have substantial stratigraphic evidence from a variety of secure archaeological contexts. Because the focus of this volume is on the agroecology of the mature Tiwanaku state (that is, Tiwanaku IV and V), we follow the essential framework of the Ponce chronology in the following discussions and interpretations of archaeological sites and agricultural features. However, a reassessment and refinement of the Ponce chronology appears in the second volume of this set. Future research in the agricultural landscapes of Tiwanaku and its predecessors will benefit from the full elaboration of this refined relative chronology.

Cutting against the grain of Squier's and Bennett's concept of the vacant ceremonial center, Edward Lanning (1967) argued that Tiwanaku, Pukara, and Wari were all major, pre-Inca urban centers. Lanning's concept of urbanism was based directly upon that proposed by John Rowe (1963) four years earlier: "Each city consisted of a nucleus of monumental public buildings and plazas, together with extensive residential districts, the whole covering from one to four square miles. Each was the focal point of a synchoritic system that also included rural and urban towns and numerous villages. Any or all of the three major cities may have had populations in excess of ten thousand persons" (Lanning 1967:115).

This view was reinforced by Parsons (1968), who calculated the total area of occupation at 250 hectares and estimated population density at 5,000 to 10,000 people per square kilometer, for a total maximum population of 25,000. With the results of the Bolivian-sponsored research, Ponce was able to establish empirically based warrants for considering Tiwanaku a true urban settlement. Ponce (1972) subsequently suggested a minimum areal expanse of 420 hectares for the city. Furthermore, he conceived of Tiwanaku as a rigorously planned urban settlement with a civic-ceremonial core of temples and elite residences surrounded by domestic areas inhabited by commoners and craftspeople. Ponce's later revision of urban size suggests a peak population of 21,000 to 42,000 for Tiwanaku, according to Parsons's density estimates. Ponce argued that other major Tiwanaku sites in the near hinterland of the capital, such as Khonko Wankané, Lukurmata, and Pajchiri, were also essentially urban in character (Ponce Sanginés 1981:78–83). He envisioned Tiwanaku as an intensely productive, hierarchically organized political formation with a strong economic resource base and a penchant for aggressive expansion.

In sum, the earliest notions of Tiwanaku viewed the site as a ceremonial center without substantial resident populations. This was an interpretation shaped by the common, persistent perception that the natural environment of the Andean altiplano was inherently marginal for agriculturally based populations, and by the assumption that the site of Tiwanaku consisted solely of an isolated ensemble of temple architecture. Recent interpretations of Tiwanaku have gravitated away from this perspective, increasingly accepting the notion that Tiwanaku was, in fact, an urban phenomenon based on a productive endogenous economy (Kolata 1986, 1991, 1992, 1993b).

The data and interpretations presented in this volume demonstrate empirically that the perception of the high plateau as a marginal environment for human production is distorted and ultimately incorrect. Although the plateau lies at an altitude greater than 3,800 meters above sea level, near the upper climatic boundary for viable agriculture, its presumed "marginality" is an illusory concept derived more from anecdotal assumptions about what an agriculturally productive environment should look like than from systematic, empirical research. A principal conclusion of this volume is that, given certain climatic parameters and the appropriate technological and organizational bases, the Andean high plateau offers an enormously rich environment for sustained, intensive agricultural production and therefore the potential for supporting dense concentrations of humans. The data and interpretations presented in volume two of this set establish a case for the urban status of Tiwanaku and vitiate the assumption that Tiwanaku's surface architecture constitutes the total universe of human activity at the site. Taken together, our general conclusions offer a perspective on the nature of Tiwanaku and its political economy entirely different from that first voiced by Squier over a century ago.

## Current Models of Tiwanaku Political Economy

In recent years, a number of scholars have attempted to model the political economy of the Tiwanaku state (Browman 1978, 1980, 1981, 1984; Kolata 1983, 1986, 1991, 1993b; Lynch 1983; Núñez and Dillehay 1979; Ponce Sanginés 1979, 1980; M. Rivera 1976, 1980). Common to the interpretive frameworks of these models is the observation that large indigenous populations in the Andean high plateau were sustained through the operation of three systems of production: (1) intensive cultivation of tubers and chenopod grains in the altiplano homeland; (2) extensive herding of llamas and alpacas in the sierra basins above 2,500 meters and on the cold, semiarid grasslands of the windswept tableland referred to as the puna; and (3) exploitation of the yungas zones, lower, warmer lands to the east, west, and south of the altiplano by establishment of colonial enclaves (Browman 1974; Casaverde 1977; Custred 1974; Murra 1964, 1965, 1968, 1972).

Divergence in interpretation among these models may be analyzed, in part, in terms of the relative weight or emphasis that a researcher places on any single element of this tripartite economy. For instance, David Browman (1980, 1981, 1984) argues that the Tiwanaku state economy was sustained by massive, interregional exchange of bulk and elite commodities through the vehicle of llama caravans. He maintains that these long-distance exchange networks constituted a special "altiplano mode" of economic integration in which "craft specialization, periodic markets, and regular caravan trade" permitted populations on the high plateau to gain access to essential and desired resources from multiple, lower-lying ecological zones (Browman 1981:415).

Browman framed his altiplano mode of economic production in contrast to the "vertical archipelago" model of economic complementarity first elaborated by John Murra (1968, 1972). In the vertical archipelago model, communities of the high plateau directly exploited the economic resources of lower lands by establishing colonial enclaves, or islands of production, with intimate ethnic and political ties to the altiplano homeland. In contrast, Browman reasoned, with considerable justification, that the social costs entailed in maintaining a vertical archipelago mode of economic integration from the altiplano were exceptionally high, and therefore this strategy was unlikely to have been implemented frequently in the pre-Hispanic context. As Browman (1980:107) phrased it: "In some areas of the Andes, the costs of direct exploitation are too great. Populations have had to find other mechanisms to obtain the resources needed. One such area is the Bolivian altiplano. In this high, flat plain . . . the political difficulty and the economic and social costs of trying to control small 'islands' in different ecozones separated by hundreds of kilometers from the home village is immediately evident."

Browman argues that instead of direct exploitation of resources through colonization schemes, the more common pattern for altiplano communities was indirect acquisition of necessary non-altiplano goods through formal and informal mechanisms of exchange. As a logical extension of that view, he states (1980:108) that "the altiplano individual has found that in order to acquire access to resources from other ecological zones he must become either (1) a skilled trader, or (2) a skilled craftsman, with some sort of marketable skill."

Browman (1981:417, 1984:125) suggests that the Tiwanaku state employed both the altiplano and the vertical archipelago modes of economic integration, but at different times. The former was the essential, indigenous pattern that reached its apogee during the Classic Tiwanaku phase (or Tiwanaku IV, ca. A.D. 400–800), whereas the latter appeared only late in the history of the state (or Tiwanaku V, ca. A.D. 800–1000) in response to the economic dislocation occasioned by disintegration of long-distance trade networks that had been brokered in great part by the Wari empire. The implication is that with the decline of the Wari empire around A.D. 800, the disruption of profitable, extra-altiplano trade routes forced Tiwanaku into an economic crisis. Tiwanaku resolved this crisis by quickly colonizing yungas territories, particularly on the western slope of the Andes, from which it could directly extract necessary resources—particularly metals, minerals, and essential warm-lands agricultural commodities such as coca, aji, and maize.

The empirical evidence Browman adduced to substantiate this temporal distinction is not compelling. We have no prima facie evidence that Wari and Tiwanaku ever sustained economic relations of the intensity that Browman requires if his model of Tiwanaku economic crisis is to have credibility. If we examine this issue closely, the most reasonable conclusion to draw is that Wari and Tiwanaku studiously—one might even maintain scrupulously—ignored one another. Their extractive hinterlands and geoeconomic reach never intersected. There are no Wari trade goods in Tiwanaku and no Tiwanaku trade goods in Wari. The only evidence of Wari at Tiwanaku recovered in our excavations was a single sherd of a thick-walled, oversized urn from a mortuary context in the structure we call the Palace of the Multicolored Rooms, adjacent to the Putuni ceremonial complex (Kolata 1993a).

I have always believed that there was a sharp geopolitical boundary between the Wari and Tiwanaku spheres of political action, drawn roughly along La Raya pass in southern Peru, that is, at the point heading southward at which the Andean altiplano begins. The only cases of substantial Wari presence in Tiwanaku country derive from the fortified site of Cerro Baúl and the related complex of Cerro Mejía in the Osmore River valley of southern Peru (Moseley et al. 1991). In the absence of other such settlements in Tiwanaku territory, I consider Cerro Baúl to be anomalous and certainly not indicative of sustained economic and political relationships between Wari and Tiwanaku. Indeed, Moseley and his colleagues' (1991) interpretation of Cerro Baúl as an intrusive and hostile presence in territory intimately related ethnically and socially to Tiwanaku brings into high relief the enormous cultural, perhaps even cognitive, gap between these two expansive polities. More generally, having worked for years both on the north coast of Peru and in the Lake Titicaca basin, it is my conviction that there exists a fundamental social-structural difference, a kind of cultural fault line, between the cumulative historical experiences and cultural traditions of the central Andean and the southern Andean worlds (by southern Andean I mean the area from the Andean high plateau southward).

In sharp contrast to Browman's culture-historical reconstruction, Elias Mujica (1978) and Mario Rivera (1976, 1980) argue vigorously that the economic complementarity between highlands and lowlands envisioned by proponents of the vertical archipelago model constituted an ancient and perduring framework for state formation in the south-central Andes. They apply this argument to the dynamics of state development at both Pukara in Peru and Tiwanaku in Bolivia. From this perspective, the emergence of vertical archipelago modes of economic and political behavior was a key event, or perhaps better phrased, a critical geopolitical process in the coalescence of state formations in the south-central Andes.

Common to both the altiplano and vertical archipelago models of political economy is the perception that the high plateau is a resource-poor, resource-redundant environment that impelled its inhabitants to acquire agricultural products from lower-lying ecological zones for subsistence purposes. Although, as will become clear in this volume, our research group appreciates both the fragility (from the human perspective) and the potential for agroecological disaster inhering in the altiplano environment, we disagree entirely with this pessimistic perception of the primary productivity and subsistence potential of the altiplano. This debate between adherents of radically different perceptions of the Andean altiplano's productivity is central to our understanding of Tiwanaku as a state society. Elsewhere (Kolata 1992:80–81) I framed this debate in the following terms:

> Perhaps the most interesting element of the interaction between highland altiplano and lowland valley populations during the Tiwanaku regnum were the motivations that each side may have had for fostering and perpetuating this relationship. From the perspective of the Tiwanaku state as a high plateau polity, establishing agricultural colonies in regions at lower elevation would, of course, have provided access to crops otherwise unavailable in the high, cold altiplano. But what is most significant is the nature of the two principal crops that were grown at lower elevation: maize and coca. If my estimates of the productivity of intensive grain and tuber agriculture in the high plateau are correct within an order of magnitude, there is reason to believe that altiplano populations during the Tiwanaku regnum had achieved autarcky. That is, the high plateau under Tiwanaku control would not have required a massive influx of bulk food crops from lower elevations to sustain its urbanized populations: with respect to basic subsistence crops, the altiplano was self-sufficient. However, as Murra (1960) has demonstrated, maize and coca were highly valued as ceremonial and prestige crops in the Andes: they were state crops par excellence under the Inca, produced in many areas under the centralized, monopoly control of the government through the labor of forcibly resettled colonists, or *mitmaqkuna* (see, for instance, the remarkable agricultural reorganization of the Cochabamba Valley under the Inca described by Wachtel [1982]). The motive force underlying Tiwanaku agricultural colonization in the yungas zones was expansion of the cultivation of prestige crops, particularly maize, which provided the raw material for the production of ritually important commodities such as maize beer. These crops were used prodigiously during state-sponsored festivals that demanded ritual hospitality and the ceremonial display of abundance. Maize and coca as primary products were undoubtedly channeled into the redistributive networks manipulated by the Tiwanaku elite classes as well, providing a storable, high value, state-controlled medium of exchange that could be used by the elites to "purchase" supplementary labor from peasant populations. In short, the agricultural provinces of the Tiwanaku state in the yungas zones were essential, not as a source of subsistence goods, but as a source of prestige and ritual commodities that fueled the interpenetrating economic and ideological systems articulated by elite-mediated redistribution.

In effect, I argue that the natural resources of the altiplano, when extracted and managed with the appropriate technologies of production, permitted complex human communities to attain economic, if not political and religious, autarky. The motives for Tiwanaku political action and territorial expansion *outside* the productive confines of the Titicaca basin were not, then, related to the subsistence dimensions of the state economy. This does not mean that these motives were entirely noneconomic or in some fashion outside the essential sphere of production. On the contrary, ritual hospitality framed around the large-scale consumption of maize beer and coca (products obtainable only outside the altiplano) was central to the economic, political, and religious life of the Tiwanaku state. But the bulk of the agricultural, pastoral, and lacustrine products that constituted the fundamental food supply for Tiwanaku's rural and urban populations was, in essence, home grown. There was no compulsion to appropriate goods or productive territories beyond the rim of the altiplano engendered strictly by the need to acquire daily subsistence.

Although the vertical archipelago and altiplano models of political economy emphasize different sources and modes of production, they share the characteristic of focusing on what may be termed the exogenous elements of the altiplano tripartite economy:

long-distance caravan trade, transhumance, and the exploitation of lowland colonial enclaves. This focus, of course, derives in great part from the models' shared, pessimistic perception of the altiplano's natural resource endowments. Until recently, the role of *endogenous* elements in the Tiwanaku state economy, particularly intensive agriculture in the heartland of the high plateau, has received little comparable scholarly attention. Apart from a few perceptive observations that certain Tiwanaku settlements were physically associated with raised-field systems (Browman 1978; Denevan 1982; Ponce Sanginés 1980; Smith, Denevan, and Hamilton 1968), the problem of the precise relationship between intensive agriculture and the subsistence base of Tiwanaku society had not been addressed by means of a comprehensive program of research until we organized Proyecto Wila Jawira in 1986.

## Background to Proyecto Wila Jawira

In 1979, Oswaldo Rivera (INAR) and I initiated a pilot project of archaeological survey and test excavations in the Pampa Koani zone of the Tiwanaku sustaining region. The results of this preliminary research established that the combined archaeological and natural resources of this zone constituted a substantial body of data that enabled us to test the nature, scope, and cultural implications of the Tiwanaku state's organization of its agricultural hinterland (Kolata 1986, 1991, 1993a). We chose the greater Pampa Koani zone for investigation after an initial inspection of aerial photographs of the region at 1:40,000 and 1:10,000 scale revealed massive and well-preserved archaeological features (figs. 1.3–1.5). Important elements of the archaeological landscape first observed on these photographs included (1) extensive, continuous tracts of now-abandoned raised agricultural fields that run from the edge of Lake Titicaca to nearly 15 kilometers inland; (2) an intersecting set of linear features crosscutting field segments that subsequent study indicates was a formal network of causeway/dikes; (3) large quadrangular and L-shaped mounds set within the raised-field system, located near or at the terminal points of the causeways; (4) a series of massive agricultural terraces cut into hill slopes bordering the northern edge of Pampa Koani, extending onto the peninsula of Cumana; and (5) an artificial canalization of the Catari River that bisects the Pampa Koani.

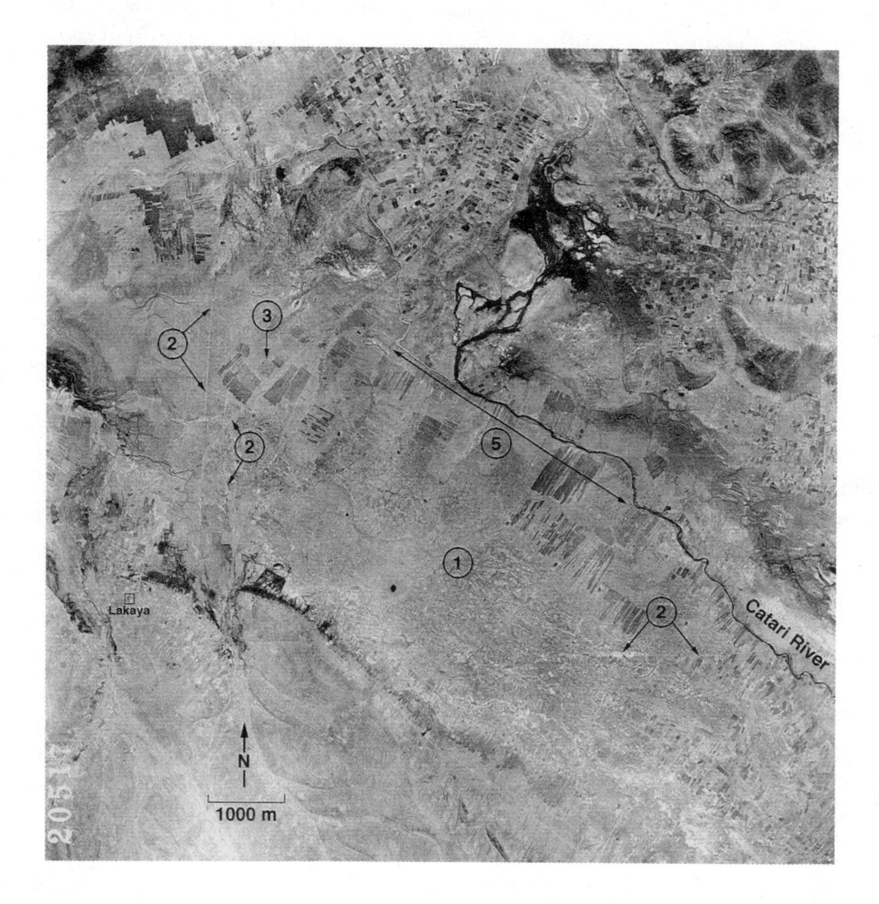


**Figure 1.3.** Aerial photograph of the southern portions of the Pampa Koani study area, showing (1) extensive tracts of raised fields, (2) networks of causeways and dikes, (3) quadrangular and L-shaped mounds, and (5) the artificially canalized section of the Catari River.

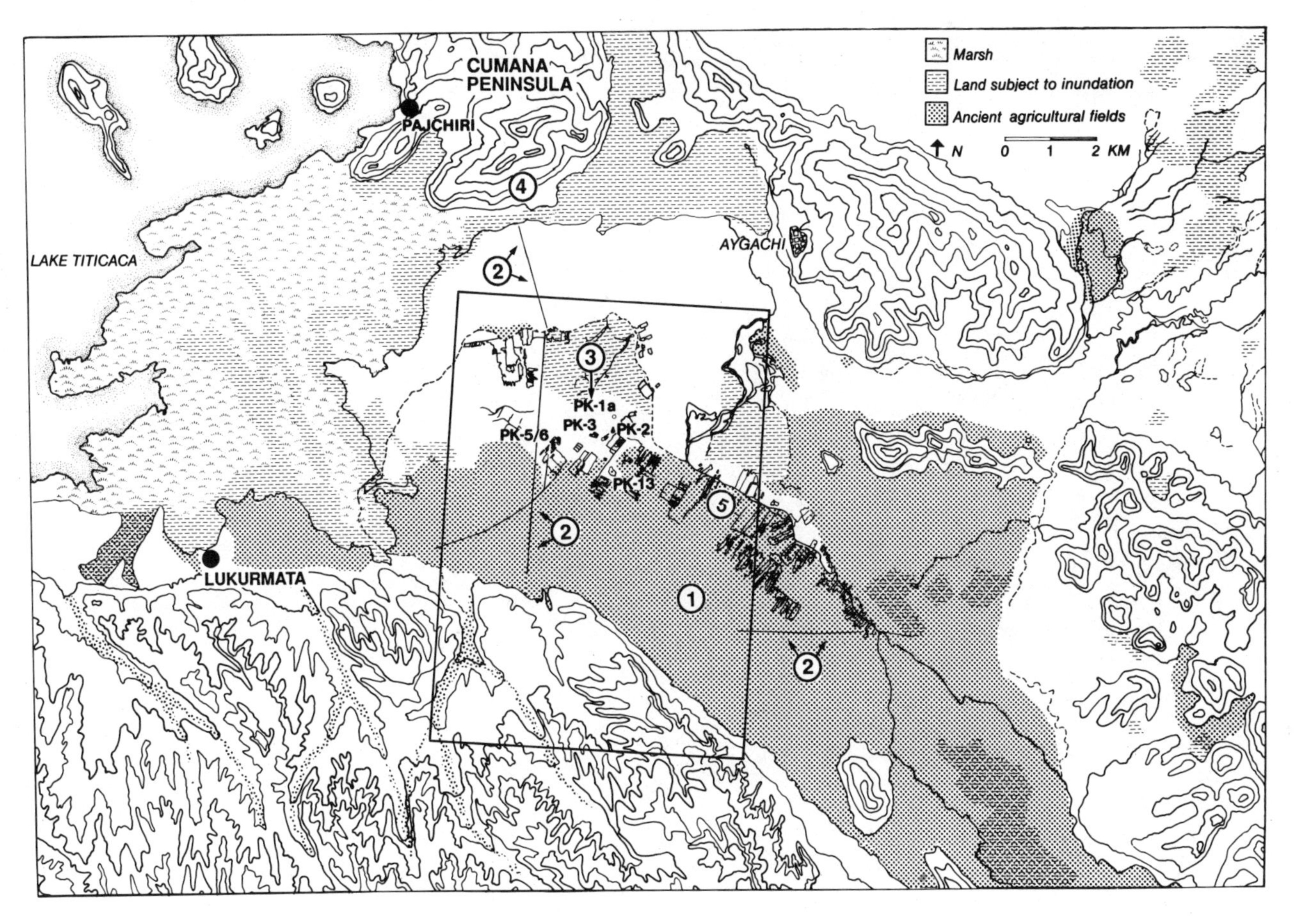


**Figure 1.4.** Principal archaeological features in the Pampa Koani and its vicinity, including (1) an extensive zone of ancient raised fields and (2) a system of causeways that linked (3) local administrative sites with the regional administrative centers of Lukurmata and Pajchiri. Also indicated are (4) agricultural terraces cut into the Cumana peninsula and (5) canalized sections of the Catari River. The box outlines the area enlarged in figure 1.5.

In subsequent years, we have made substantial progress in analyzing and understanding each of these elements of the agricultural landscape, except for the terrace systems. Our investigations to date have concentrated on the raised-field systems and their supporting hydraulic features. Future research will target the terrace systems. Ground survey confirmed the artificial nature of each of the five elements of the cultural landscape and further revealed the presence of numerous smaller habitation mounds dispersed throughout the research zone and a complex set of hydraulic features including dikes, aqueducts, canal systems, and river and quebrada canalizations that were not readily observable from the aerial photographs. The smaller habitation mounds located by ground survey are directly associated with the raised-field systems and, in some instances, are structurally merged with individual field segments (Graffam 1990; Kolata 1986, 1989, 1991).

In their pioneering work, Smith, Denevan, and Hamilton (1968:32) recognized six distinct patterns of raised fields in the Titicaca basin: (1) open checkerboard, (2) irregular embanked, (3) stepladder, (4) riverine, (5) linear or curvilinear, and (6) combed. Although each of these morphological types is found in the Tiwanaku hinterland, the bulk of the fields in the research zone, particularly in the Pampa Koani, appear to conform to the last three categories. A map of the central sector of the Pampa Koani, compiled from a 1:10,000 aerial photograph enlargement, illustrates the sweeping, curved platforms of earth characteristic of these fields (fig. 1.5). The fossil fields of the Pampa Koani exhibit marked differential patterns of preservation. In the western portions of the plain, nearest to the lake edge, old planting surfaces remain intact to elevations that reach 1 meter. In the eastern half of the Pampa Koani, these surfaces are rarely preserved more than 10–20 centimeters above the adjacent swales. There, the existence of some fields may be observed only by subtle differences in soil color and veg-

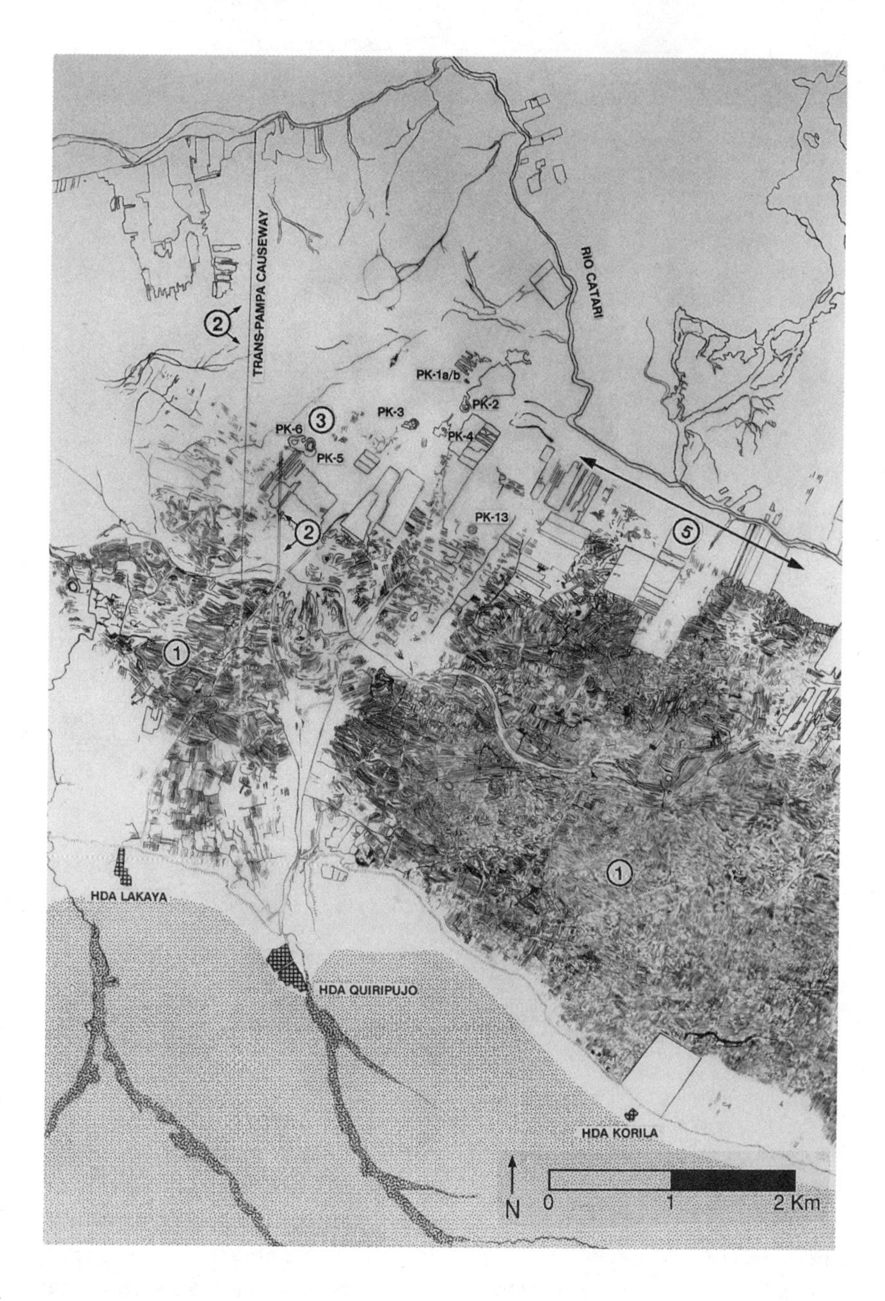


**Figure 1.5.** Detailed map of a portion of the Pampa Koani, compiled from a 1:10,000 aerial photograph enlargement showing (1) systems of raised fields, (2) networks of causeways, (3) Tiwanaku administrative and ritual mound clusters, and (5) the artificially canalized section of the Catari River.

etation. The form and profile of one self-contained field segment located in the lake-edge environment of the western pampa is illustrated in figure 1.6.

In the initial regional survey, the Pampa Koani was divided into quadrants with the intention of producing a controlled surface collection for typological and chronological purposes. It became apparent, however, that only the small habitation mounds and the larger platform mounds produced significant quantities of cultural materials. The field surfaces were essentially devoid of archaeological materials, and, as later test excavations proved, such material was sparse in subsurface levels of the fields as well. In contrast, the exceptionally rich surface collections from the two classes of mounds did provide an important chronological overview of pre-Hispanic human occupation on the Pampa Koani. Table 1.1 presents data on the nature, size, and temporal affiliations of 23 mound structures that were found in this preliminary survey.

In general terms, as this table indicates, the Pampa Koani zone was occupied as early as 1000 B.C. by Chiripa peoples who may have been exploiting the marshy area along the lake edge for its substantial lacustrine resources: waterfowl, fish, rhizomes, and algae. Of course, the intriguing possibility that in Chiripa times the Koani zone was being transformed into an artificial agricultural landscape remains a viable proposition, but one whose confirmation or refutation awaits further testing in the field.

The research results of the pilot project indicated

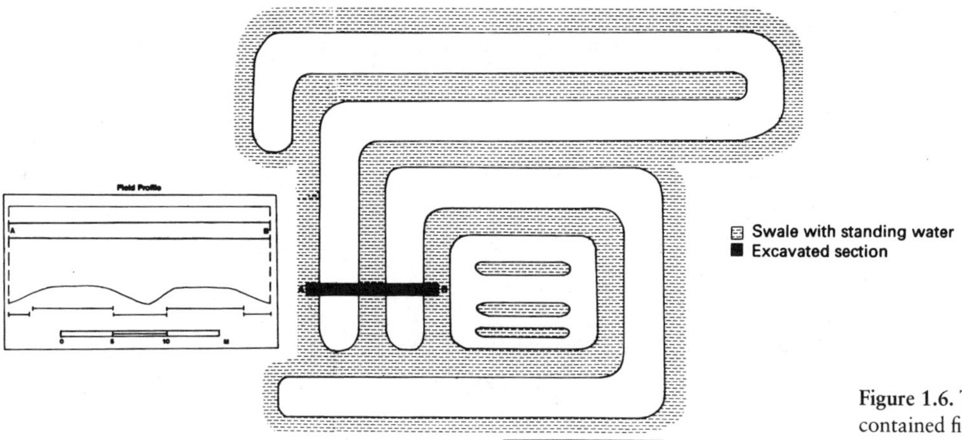


Figure 1.6. The form and profile of a self-contained field segment in the western Pampa Koani.

that the most extensive human activity on the Pampa Koani occurred during Tiwanaku IV and V times (ca. A.D. 400–1000). Several Tiwanaku IV and V habitation mounds can be structurally linked with the construction of raised-field segments. Moreover, the configuration of causeways linking the larger platform mounds dated to Tiwanaku IV–V times was clearly compatible with, and designed around, the spatial and hydraulic requirements of the adjoining raised-field networks (Kolata 1986, 1991). In chapter 8 we argue that in post-Tiwanaku times (post–A.D. 1000) this integrated regional system of agricultural production was abandoned under the pressure of a major climatic shift, specifically chronic drought conditions that progressively reduced groundwater inputs to the system to the point of failure.[1] Further, we argue that this climatic change was the proximate cause for the disintegration of the Tiwanaku state (Ortloff and Kolata 1993).

## Research Objectives and Strategies of Proyecto Wila Jawira

Proyecto Wila Jawira was designed to explore vital aspects of the nature, organization, and impact of large-scale agricultural production in the heartland of the Tiwanaku state—the region incorporating the city of Tiwanaku itself and its sustaining hinterland in Bolivia (see fig. 1.2). As stated in the original proposals for this project, the ultimate objectives of the first phase of the research program were (1) to achieve an empirical understanding of the technology of intensive agriculture in the Andean altiplano, particularly with respect to the critical variables of climate, soils, topography, hydrology, and potential short-term environmental perturbation; (2) to establish a plausible history of agricultural reclamation in the research zone that addressed the interdependent relationships among the variables of agricultural intensification, environmental degradation, population growth, and sociopolitical evolution; and (3) to explore the nature of the relationship between political organization and large-scale agricultural production in the Tiwanaku state and the theoretical implications embedded in that relationship.

The first phase of the project, from 1986 to 1988, concentrated on the first two objectives, which related to the technology and organization of Tiwanaku intensive agricultural production. The second phase of the project, from 1988 to 1991, shifted the focus of fieldwork toward basic research in the urban center of Tiwanaku itself and in its immediate valley hinterland. This redirection of principal field activities toward urban and settlement archaeology was designed to generate information that would permit us to address the third general goal of the project: defining the social linkages between the sustaining agricultural landscapes and the human settlements from which these landscapes were conceived, organized, and sustained. A key element of this second phase of research was a systematic, full-coverage survey of the Tiwanaku Valley with the objective of placing the evolution of intensive agricultural systems in the context of regional settlement history.[2]

This volume focuses on Tiwanaku agroecosystems in the environmental context of the Lake Titicaca basin. Except for an extended discussion in chapter 8, we do not consider other forms of Tiwanaku intensive agriculture established in different ecological zones, such as in the Moquegua Valley of south coastal Peru, where extensive systems of irrigated agriculture are associated with Tiwanaku settlements (Goldstein

Table 1.1. General Characteristics and Tentative Dating of Selected Sites on the Pampa Koani

| Site | Location | Type | Approximate Dimensions (L × W × H in meters) | Phase(s) |
|---|---|---|---|---|
| PK-1a | See figure 1.5 | Small habitation mound: oval | 28 × 20 × 1.50 | Chiripa, Tiwanaku I, Tiwanaku III–V |
| PK-1b | Adjacent to PK-1a | Small habitation mound: oval | 27 × 20 × 1.50 | Chiripa, Tiwanaku III–V |
| PK-2 | See figure 1.5 | Large platform mound: L-shaped | 73 × 65 × 2.10[a] 67 × 19 × 1.50 | Chiripa, Tiwanaku III–V |
| PK-3 | See figure 1.5 | Large platform mound: L-shaped | 75 × 60 × 2.35[a] 16 × 14 × 1.10 | Chiripa, Tiwanaku III–V, Inca |
| PK-4 | See figure 1.5 | Small habitation mound: quadrangular | 16 × 14 × 1.10 | Tiwanaku III(?)–IV |
| PK-5 | See figure 1.5 | Large terraced platform mound: quadrangular with possible sunken court and gateway | 120 × 75 × 3.75 | Chiripa, Tiwanaku III–V |
| PK-6 | See figure 1.5 | Large terraced platform mound: quadrangular, paired with PK-5 | 110 × 67 × 3.10 | Tiwanaku IV–V |
| PK-7a | Approximately 750 m SE of PK-2 | Small habitation mound: oval | 27 × 21 × 2.20 | Tiwanaku IV–V |
| PK-7b | Adjacent to PK-7a | Small habitation mound: oval | 24 × 18 × 1.50 | Tiwanaku IV–V |
| PK-8 | Approximately 1 km SE of PK-2 | Small habitation mound: oval | 32 × 28 × 1.45 | Tiwanaku IV–V |
| PK-9 | Adjacent to PK-8 | Small habitation mound: oval | 28 × 25 × 1.25 | Tiwanaku IV–V |
| PK-10 | Approximately 2 km SE of PK-5 | Small habitation mound: quadrangular | 34 × 30 × 0.90 | Tiwanaku IV–V |
| PK-11 | Approximately 2 km SE of PK-5 | Small habitation mound: oval | 24 × 27 × 1.30 | Tiwanaku IV–V |
| PK-12a | Approximately 2 km SE of PK-5 | Small habitation mound: oval | 26 × 18 × 1.24 | Tiwanaku IV–V |
| PK-12b | Adjacent to PK-12a | Small habitation mound: oval | 12 × 16 × 0.90 | Tiwanaku IV–V |
| PK-13 | See figure 1.5 | Small habitation mound: quadrangular | 60 × 57 × 3.30 | Tiwanaku IV–V |
| PK-14 | Approximately 1.5 km N of Hda. Lakaya, see figure 1.5 | Small habitation mound: oval | 23 × 22 × 1.35 | Tiwanaku IV–V |
| PK-15 | Approximately 1.5 km N of Hda. Lakaya, see figure 1.5 | Small habitation mound: oval | 20 × 13 × 0.90 | Tiwanaku IV–V |
| PK-16 | Approximately 1.5 km N of Hda. Lakaya, see figure 1.5 | Small habitation mound: oval | 13 × 17 × 0.80 | Tiwanaku IV–V |
| PK-17 | Approximately 1.5 km N of Hda. Lakaya, see figure 1.5 | Small habitation mound: oval | 27 × 22 × 1.72 | Tiwanaku IV–V |

*Table 1.1—Continued next page*

Table 1.1.—*Continued*

| Site | Location | Type | Approximate Dimensions (L × W × H in meters) | Phase(s) |
|---|---|---|---|---|
| PK-18 | Approximately 1.5 km NW of Hda. Lakaya, see figure 1.5 | Small habitation mound: oval | 24 × 19 × 1.10 | Tiwanaku IV–V |
| PK-19 | Approximately 1.5 km NW of Hda. Lakaya, see figure 1.5 | Small habitation mound: oval | 20 × 14 × 0.90 | Tiwanaku IV–V |
| PK-20 | Approximately 1.5 km NW of Hda. Lakaya, see figure 1.5 | Small habitation mound: oval | 23 × 21 × 1.10 | Tiwanaku IV–V |

[a]PK-2 and PK-3 are L-shaped mounds, and the two sets of measurements reflect this configuration. The first set refers to the main quadrangular portion of each mound; the second set refers to the narrow terrace that projects from the main portion.

1989; Kolata 1991, 1993a; Ortloff and Kolata 1993; Watanabe, Moseley, and Cabieses 1990). Emphasis is placed on the technical and organizational characteristics of Tiwanaku agriculture in the altiplano and, even more specifically, on intensive raised-field cultivation. We do not here treat the potential use of agricultural terraces or *qochas,* artificial ponds or tanks, by Tiwanaku. Of course, a complete history of Tiwanaku agricultural technologies and forms of organization will require intensive research into these two additional altiplano forms of intensification as well as the non-altiplano systems.

In this volume, we include three chapters on the results of our experimental raised-field rehabilitation program, from both technical (chapters 7 and 9) and social (chapter 10) frames of reference. The data and experiences generated by the contemporary rehabilitation of Tiwanaku raised-field technologies are invaluable for understanding the productivity of this specialized form of production in the pre-Hispanic past. That is, the experiments in raised-field production provide us with an empirical tool for calculating the range of production possibilities in the Tiwanaku sustaining area. With this tool, we have a plausible method for projecting local carrying capacities and demographic potentials (Kolata 1991, 1993a).

Our experiences in raised-field rehabilitation also hold implications for contemporary programs of agricultural development in the Andean high plateau and elsewhere. Abandoned agricultural areas, including raised fields, are globally significant ecosystems in their own right. Recent trends in the design and implementation of sustainable agriculture include programs to rehabilitate ancient and traditional systems to enhance production without massive external infusions of capital (Browder 1989; Erickson 1985, 1988b; Erickson and Candler 1989; Gómez-Pompa et al. 1982). The underlying assumption of such programs is that indigenous systems of intensive agriculture with demonstrable historical viability are environmentally suitable for modern agrarian development. This assumption may be true, but development planners and managers must understand how specific ecological-economic interactions sustained such systems. The results of the experiments reported here contribute to this evolving body of information. Chapters 9 and 10 reflect upon the potential development implications of our raised-field rehabilitation program, and chapter 11 places this program in the broader context of recent trends in "ethnodevelopment" throughout Bolivia.

## The Primary Working Hypothesis

Preliminary data on settlement and agriculture collected by the Pampa Koani pilot project generated a general hypothesis that framed the principal questions of the more comprehensive research program organized in 1986. Briefly, this working hypothesis linked the construction, maintenance, and production of the Pampa Koani field system with a centralized political authority that systematically co-opted land and labor for the benefit of nonlocal populations. The presence and apparent power of this authority is reflected in the archaeological record by massive public reclamation and construction projects such as the artificial canalization of the Catari River, which required a coordinated labor force and a contemporaneous hierarchical settlement network. This settlement hierarchy describes, minimally, a nested, quadripartite division of administrative and primary production responsibilities (fig. 1.7). Intensive survey in the Tiwanaku Valley between 1988 and 1991 confirmed the essential contours of this proposed settlement hierarchy and signaled that hierarchical organization of agricultural production by Tiwanaku extended beyond the confines of the Catari River basin (Albarracín-Jordan and Mathews 1990).[3] Hierarchical settlement systems such as these are a salient characteristic of integrated preindustrial states (Isbell and Schreiber 1978; Wright and Johnson 1975). The presence of such a hierarchy throughout the Tiwanaku sustaining area implies that the Tiwanaku state maintained a high degree of administrative efficiency and control over agricultural production.

The social organization of raised-field agricultural production has emerged recently as a central issue in Lake Titicaca basin archaeology (Erickson 1988a; Graffam 1992; Kolata 1991). The terms of the debate are drawn rather starkly between those who argue that the construction and management of raised-field agriculture always remained the province of small-scale, kin-related corporate groups (Erickson 1988a; Graffam 1990, 1992) and those who argue that the emergence of regional systems of agricultural reclamation clearly signal the action of supracommunity, centralized authorities (Kolata 1986, 1991, 1993a; Kolata and Ortloff 1989; Mathews 1992; Ortloff and Kolata 1989).

Erickson (1988a) offers the best-articulated defense of the first position. He argues that small corporate groups, organized along the lines of traditional Andean principles of kinship, were capable of constructing the immense configuration of raised fields in the Lake Titicaca basin and that centralized, supracommunity authorities were not involved in the management of those fields. Further, he speculates that this agricultural system was originated by, and remained the province of, a wetlands-adapted cluster of ethnic groups that he associates with the ethnohistorically documented Uru- and Pukina-speaking peoples. Erickson (1988a:348) concludes that Andean raised-field agriculture was *never* under the direct control of centralized state governments: "In the Lake Titicaca Basin, the raised fields were associated with relatively small cooperative groups, while the dominant political organization in the basin was at the level of a state. It is unlikely that this highly productive system that functioned efficiently under local management would have been tampered with by the state."

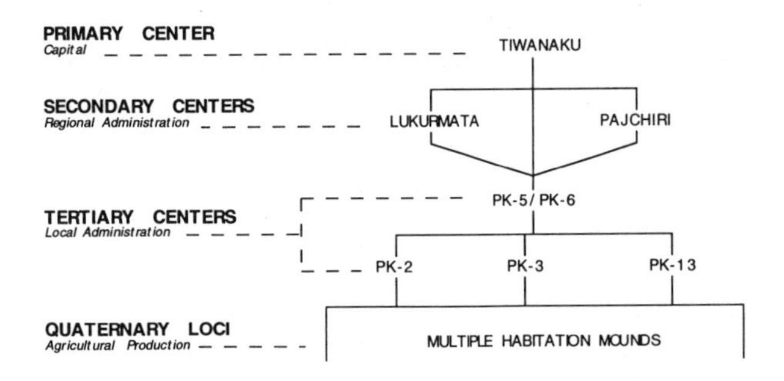


**Figure 1.7.** Schematic representation of Tiwanaku's hierarchical settlement network in the Pampa Koani during the Tiwanaku IV and V periods.

This last statement is not self-evident. It is, however, fully in the fashion of recent Andeanist literature on the Inca state that focuses on concepts of indirect rule and local community autonomy and deemphasizes the managerial role of political hierarchies and elite interest groups in the administration of local and regional-scale economies.

Implicit in this line of argument is the embedded notion that states are invariably repressive, inflexible, and inefficient organizational structures. From this perspective, states are better served pursuing a laissez-faire strategy in their relationships with local communities because these communities are somehow inherently more effective in organizing systems of production. This seems to me a rather uncritical, naive vision of the socially complex terrain in which cities, states, and societies are enmeshed. I believe a better perspective begins with the proposition that states and local communities are often counterpoised in a complex dynamic of mutualism. Although states exert directive control over regional economies, and in the process impinge on the traditional prerogatives and autonomy of local communities, they also introject these communities into more inclusive social and economic worlds. States create interconnections among diverse communities and, in essence, promote a process of accelerated local economic development. States can contribute to the dynamism, social diversity, and organizational strength of local communities.

Such a perspective acknowledges that states can and often do organize themselves as repressive structures that constrain local political autonomy. But political repression at the local level does not necessarily imply economic repression and the inevitable impoverishment of local communities. In this view, state involvement in management of agricultural production is not inherently inefficient. On the contrary, states control enormous organizational and economic capital that can be invested in improvement and management of regional agricultural landscapes on a scale inaccessible to the "small cooperative groups" that Erickson envisions as the maximal unit of production. In these instances, state control and management of production is more efficient than that of local communities and generates significant economic benefits for these local communities, particularly for their dominant lineages.

Other unresolved problems emerge with the kind of interpretation Erickson wishes to make in the case of raised-field production in the Lake Titicaca basin. For instance, he does not indicate what taxation or tribute mechanisms the state employed to acquire agricultural surplus from the lands that were, according to his interpretation, under the complete control of local, kin-dominated corporate groups. But cutting even more centrally to the issue, I have argued, in diametrically opposed fashion, that it was precisely *because* the raised fields were so highly productive that the state "tampered" with them (Kolata 1991, 1993a). Tiwanaku's urban system was heavily dependent upon the surplus generated from intensive cultivation of raised fields. It was in the interest of the state authorities (that is, the elite, ruling lineages resident in the urban centers) to have direct and unambiguous control over land and natural resources in the immediate hinterlands of their urban centers. The extension of authority demands active engagement. No capital of an expansive state can afford to have a rural hinterland weakly or only indirectly consolidated into its internal political economy. The political stability of urban centers is intimately related to dependable and adequate food supplies, and the economics of bulk commodity transport in the preindustrial world dictate that these food supplies derive principally from local sources (D'Altroy 1992; Hassig 1985). These cities come to dominate their hinterlands politically and economically in the concerted attempt to ensure control over the extractive enterprise. If the capital fails to exert political control over its sustaining hinterland and at the same time does not substitute other tangible services to the countryside, such as marketing, critical food supplies for the urban population are threatened. The inevitable result of insecure food supplies is pervasive political instability. No Andean capital—in particular one where the great economic engine of markets did not exist or was weakly developed—could persist for long without effective control of a productive hinterland.

Furthermore, it may be, as Erickson argues, that raised fields were operated efficiently under local management. But this does not mean that they were optimally efficient or that they could not be made even more productive with the planning and labor resources at the disposal of supracommunity authorities. Indeed, primary archaeological evidence presented in this volume for an elaborate hydraulic infrastructure of regional scope associated with raised-field systems in the Tiwanaku hinterland can be interpreted only as attempts to optimize raised-field production through intensive water management (Kolata 1991, 1993b; Ortloff and Kolata 1989; and see chapters 5–6).

Foreshadowing the results of the research we present, I believe the evidence we have generated points ineluctably to an active, pervasive, and nonlocal management of agricultural production in the Tiwanaku hinterland during the period of the mature Tiwanaku state, from about A.D. 400 to 1000. This does not mean that I envision the Tiwanaku state as a monolithic political entity endowed with a formal *Wasserbaubureaukratie* as described by Max Weber and subsequently by Karl Wittfogel. Rather, the "quasi bureaucracy" imposed by Tiwanaku was most likely restricted in geographic scope to certain strategic regions within the capital city's sustaining hinterland. Control over this strategic hinterland demanded a measure of cooperation and collaboration with local leaders. Cooperation may have been essentially extorted by the threat of force, but it seems more likely that the economic benefits that inevitably flowed from capital investments made by the central authorities in the agricultural landscape were sufficient incentive such that local communities readily contributed their labor to enhance the collective forces of production.

Before moving to a description of the specific research objectives of Proyecto Wila Jawira, one additional salient point should be emphasized. The published debate regarding the social organization of intensive agricultural production in the Lake Titicaca basin has been framed in a polarized fashion that does violence to historical verisimilitude. Simply put, it is highly implausible that a single configuration describes and explains the social organization of agricultural production as it was worked out once and for all by the native populations of the Lake Titicaca basin. Organizational forms are highly volatile, mutable, and subject to deformation and change. They exhibit exceptional variability over space and time. One region of a kingdom or empire may be governed in a centralized, bureaucratic fashion while simultaneously another is articulated with the central authorities only indirectly via local rulers—and these relationships are never fixed over the life history of the state. The ways in which arable land, water, plants, and human labor were interrelated at the local level and how they in turn formed a nexus with socially distant political authorities constituted a series of shifting and evanescent patterns. We cannot expect or falsely create uniformity: there never was an organizational once and for all. Rather, we can conjecture that there existed multiple structures of local organization revolving around the social, economic, and ritual acts of farming. These structures were formed and reformed as they came into articulation with nonlocal demands and the social world beyond the parochial horizons of the corporate kin group. I return to these fundamental interpretive issues in the concluding chapter to this volume.

## Specific Research Objectives

Ultimately, confirming or rejecting the general hypothesis on the organization of agricultural production in the Tiwanaku hinterland entailed testing a series of more specific research propositions about the technological dimensions of the raised-field system, about the environmental contexts of agrarian expansion and contraction in the sustaining hinterland, and about the settlement system of the hinterland in relation to the regional urban centers of Tiwanaku, Lukurmata, and Pajchiri. The objectives of our research on raised-field systems in the Tiwanaku hinterland, initiated with the large-scale project, in 1986 included the following.

1. *Documenting the range of variability in field morphology and the concomitant spatial distribution of field types throughout the research zone.* Substantial areas of raised-field complexes are extremely well preserved and are amenable to such documentation. Systematic ground survey keyed into enlargements of aerial photographs provided an efficient means of cataloging the formal and spatial variability of field segments. An overview of the spatial distribution of raised fields in the Tiwanaku hinterland is presented in chapter 5.

2. *Ascertaining variability in raised-field construction techniques and function over time and space.* This objective entailed relatively broad horizontal exposure and careful excavation of extant field surfaces together with their adjacent swales or canals. Because of the remarkable preservation of fossil fields in the research zone, we were able to generate substantial new data on technology and methods of field construction; on processes of soil development and erosion on planting surfaces stemming from both anthropogenic and natural causes; on sequences of swale infilling; and on techniques of field and swale maintenance. These data, in turn, provided key insights into the labor requirements and processes of field construction and field maintenance. Periodic cleaning of nutrient-rich organic materials, such as algae and decayed aquatic plants, from the canals between the fields, coupled with subsequent redistribution of these materials over planting surfaces, has been inferred as a critical element in the maintenance of long-term field fertility (Denevan and Turner 1974; Knapp and Ryder 1983; Wadell 1972). Evidence concerning the existence and extent of this canal cleaning and field fertilizing process (frequently termed "mucking") provides key information for calculating the variables of labor input and potential field productivity. The importance of this maintenance procedure for enhancing agricultural productivity is clearly indicated by Knapp and Ryder's (1983:215) conclusion that its application would have permitted double cropping of potatoes on raised fields in the altiplano around Quito, Ecuador. These technical data bearing on the structure and function of Tiwanaku raised-field systems are reported in detail in chapters 5–9.

3. *Establishing the antiquity of raised-field agriculture and dating field segments with respect to each other and to associated archaeological features such as causeways, river canalizations, and, most importantly, the various classes of mounds.* One of the more intractable empirical problems in archaeology concerns dating of agricultural features. Such features rarely incorporate significant quantities of datable artifacts and only infrequently contain sufficient organic material appropriate for radiocarbon assays. This statement essentially describes the situation in the Tiwanaku hinterland. A number of field segments in the research zone, however, are structurally merged with habitation mounds (fig. 1.8). This structural merging of field surfaces with architectural elements presents a unique opportunity (we are aware of no other example of this phenomenon in the literature) to date field segments *directly* through standard techniques of artifact chronology and absolute dating. For instance, test excavations in one of these merged units

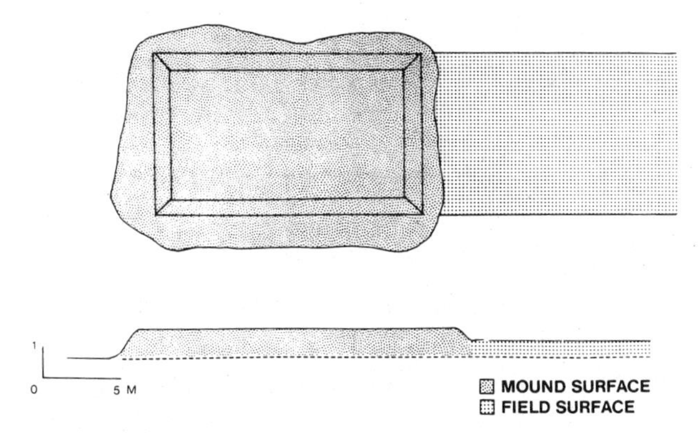


**Figure 1.8.** A sketch map of site PK-15, a small Tiwanaku IV–V habitation mound in the Lakaya region of the Pampa Koani, showing the manner in which raised field segments were frequently merged structurally with the mounds themselves (after Kolata 1986:fig. 6).

on the Pampa Koani in 1979 (PK-15) indicated that the mound element of the unit consisted of substantial occupation floors with hearths, and abundant domestic debris. Ceramics derived from test excavations permitted us to assign the mound and its (structurally merged) raised-field complex to the Tiwanaku IV and V periods.

To date, however, we have not generated evidence for raised-field construction in the Tiwanaku hinterland prior to the Tiwanaku IV period, through either direct ceramic associations or absolute dating techniques. All earlier associations are based on inference from ceramic inclusions in mounds and field surfaces. Inclusions of Formative-period (Chiripa, Tiwanaku I, Tiwanaku III) ceramics in raised fields and their associated sites derive from contexts that cannot incontrovertibly be demonstrated to be of primary origin and undisturbed by postdepositional processes. Pre–Tiwanaku IV period raised fields in the region are plausible, given the arguments for massive Formative-period raised fields in the northern Lake Titicaca basin advanced by Erickson (1988a). However, such early raised-field complexes remain to be demonstrated archaeologically in the southern Lake Titicaca basin.

Our current field research is directed precisely toward enhancing our understanding of changes in the space-time configuration of agricultural landscapes and associated human settlements in the Tiwanaku hinterland. Nevertheless, substantial new information on the Tiwanaku IV–V distribution of raised fields in the study area is presented in chapter 5.

4. *Systematically exploring the set of physical variables indicative of field functions, hydrological processes, and crop productivity.* A central objective of our archaeological and ecological research is to examine how the artificial ecosystem of fields in the study area functioned and how this ecosystem was managed. Critical variables in exploring these questions are field form and dimensions; soil composition, texture, moisture, and fertility; temperature; and hydrological regime (distribution and rates of water flow, evapotranspiration) of field systems (Denevan 1982:192). Analysis of the hydrology of agricultural features provides essential information on the functions of distinct field segments. For instance, certain field forms, such as the "linear" type, function effectively to divert excess water from planting surfaces when their linear axes are arrayed along the direction of slope. Other forms, such as the "irregular embanked," appear to hinder effective drainage and may have been designed to enhance water conservation (Smith, Denevan, and Hamilton 1968:361).

Similarly, our paleohydrological studies have resulted in new evidence bearing on the engineering sophistication of Tiwanaku raised-field systems that functioned as integrated, regional landscapes of agricultural production. In particular, in chapters 5 and 6 we present evidence of the designed multifunctionality of certain hydrological features (aqueducts, dikes, river shunts) incorporated into Tiwanaku raised-field networks (Kolata 1991; Kolata and Ortloff 1989; Ortloff and Kolata 1989). Crucial nonarchaeological evidence pertaining to raised-field function and crop productivity was developed by direct observation and measurement of experimental, rehabilitated raised fields in the study area that we have constructed and maintained in cooperation with indigenous communities since 1987. A comprehensive account of these experiments in rehabilitated raised-field cultivation is presented in chapter 9.

In order to explain the dynamics of agrarian expansion and collapse in the Tiwanaku hinterland, we must gain an understanding of the environmental contexts in which these ancient agricultural landscapes developed. The need for paleoenvironmental research, specifically paleolimnological and paleohydrological studies, is brought sharply into relief by archaeological and environmental evidence for, on the one hand, periodic lacustrine and fluvial inundations of those landscapes (Kolata 1987b; Leyden 1989) and, on the other hand, chronic drought (Ortloff and Kolata 1993a; and see chapter 8). Simply phrased, the altiplano is an environment characterized by rapid change and notorious extremes.

Archaeological evidence of periodic inundation finds tangible confirmation in a recent event: between September 1985 and April 1986, torrential rains affected the Andean altiplano and caused the level of Lake Titicaca to rise approximately 3 meters. This catastrophic inundation, following on the heels of severe drought in 1982–83, destroyed a minimum of 11,000 hectares of agricultural fields on the pampas adjacent to the lake edge. Such inundations would have had substantial negative impact upon agricultural activity in the past as well.

Similarly, as we describe in chapter 8, we now have strong paleoenvironmental and archaeological evidence for a dramatic climatic shift in the study area after A.D. 1000. This climate shift took the form of chronic and severe drought conditions that affected the ability of indigenous populations to sustain raised-field cultivation, at least in the intensive form of regional scope characteristic of Tiwanaku agroecosystems. In short, we believe that we have identified the proximate cause for the decline of the Tiwanaku state after A.D. 1000 and that this cause may be located in the disintegration of Tiwanaku's landscapes of intensive agricultural production under the pressure of regionwide ecological crisis.

Our overarching ecological objective, then, is to reconstruct the general paleoenvironmental landscape of the Tiwanaku hinterland and to define the physical interaction of human populations with that landscape over time, primarily but not exclusively through paleolimnological techniques. Lakes are one of the best indicators of human activities in watersheds. Paleolimnological studies provide the best means of measuring the impact of riparian human populations on their environment over time. In undisturbed ecosystems, the elemental composition of a lake mirrors the relative concentrations of elements in the terrestrial environment. Anomalies in the lacustrine occurrence of particular elements—for instance, disproportionately large or rapidly changing rates of mineral input—frequently reflect human action on a large scale, such as the processes of urbanization or massive agricultural reclamation (Deevey et al. 1979; Rice and Rice 1984). Consequently, the combination of paleolimnological studies with the analysis of raised-field geochemistry and hydrology has enabled us to model, at least in a preliminary fashion, the impact of human populations on the riparian ecosystem of the Pampa Koani zone and, conversely, the effects of natural processes and events on human utilization of that ecosystem for intensive agricultural production. The results of our initial paleoenvironmental research are outlined in chapters 2–4. Related environmental data derived from our analysis of contemporary natural and artificial ecotones are presented in chapter 7.

## Summary of the Research Goals

For nearly a millennium (ca. A.D. 100–1000), Tiwanaku was the paramount city of the Lake Titicaca basin, which in turn was one of the great demographic centers of native Andean civilization. Despite Tiwanaku's fundamental position in the cultural history of the Andes as an early and distinctive center of state formation, until recently we knew little about its economic history and virtually nothing about its important agrarian structure. The three interrelated research components of Proyecto Wila Jawira—analysis of preserved ancient and rehabilitated raised-field systems and their hydraulic infrastructure, analysis of the paleoenvironmental context of agricultural reclamation and collapse, and analysis of the regional settlement system—were designed to generate fundamental new data concerning the history, technology, productivity, and organization of intensive agriculture in the Tiwanaku state. These data, in turn, form the informational corpus against which new interpretations concerning the endogenous political economy of Tiwanaku can be tested.

By "political economy" I mean the aggregate processes of production, distribution, and consumption by which populations reproduce the biological and cultural bases of their society. The core elements of this conception of political economy are the mechanisms of resource production and resource allocation: the stress, in effect, is upon the production and flow of energy through the interaction of human labor, technological capacity, and the physical environment. These generically economic mechanisms may entail and entangle a variety of processes that do not necessarily emerge from or partake intimately in the technoeconomy of production itself. These more purely *social* dimensions of the political economy require from us a sensitivity to the import of ideology, ritual practice, and cognition, even though these are inordinately difficult of access in the archaeological and historical record. I tentatively approach some of these more subtle questions concerning the social interpretation of Tiwanaku's endogenous political economy in the concluding chapter to this volume (chapter 12).

But the principal purpose of this volume is descriptive and more narrowly interpretive. The various contributions to the book address empirical issues relating to Tiwanaku agroecosystems. These chapters are heavily interdependent, although we have purposefully constrained repetitive cross-referencing in order to enhance the flow of the text. Major sections of the volume include (1) extended treatments of the regional physical environment and change in it over time (chapters 2–4); (2) detailed descriptions of the history, distribution, and technology of intensive raised-field agriculture in the Tiwanaku hinterland (chapters 5–6 and 8); and (3) discussion of the productivity and contemporary implications of rehabilitated raised fields (chapters 7 and 9–11).

Changes in patterns of agricultural reclamation and abandonment in the Tiwanaku hinterland are, in some senses, reflective of, if not entirely isomorphic with, broader political and economic developments in the history of the Tiwanaku state. A mutable, risk-prone environment, shifting social relationships among human interest groups, and complex physical interactions between human and natural systems have shaped the character and changing historical role of Tiwanaku's hinterland. This book can be read as our first step toward the larger project in which we are actively engaged: understanding Tiwanaku as a total cultural system within its unique and dynamic physical environment.

## Notes

1. Recently Graffam (1990, 1992), reporting on research in the Pampa Koani sponsored by Proyecto Wila Jawira, concluded that the bulk of the raised fields visible on the surface of the pampa date to *post*-Tiwanaku times. He argues that massive surplus production on raised fields did not cease with the disintegration of Tiwanaku around A.D. 1000 but rather remained a primary economic strategy of small-scale, post-Tiwanaku polities in the region. He implies that this cultivation system continued in use up to the Spanish conquest of the region and that its ultimate disappearance related to demographic collapse of native populations triggered by the trauma of conquest.

We do not find his case for widespread raised-field cultivation in the Tiwanaku region after A.D. 1000 compelling. First, we have presented substantial new evidence of major climatic change in the post-Tiwanaku period that rendered raised-field cultivation increasingly problematic (Ortloff and Kolata 1993; and see chapter 8). This climate change, in the form of chronic drought conditions, dramatically reduced the potential area of raised-field cultivation to increasingly constricted zones of high groundwater. The evidence for severe and chronic drought in the region during the immediate post-Tiwanaku period renders Graffam's historical reconstruction of massive post-Tiwanaku raised-field construction implausible. Second, as noted in Albarracín-Jordan and Mathews (1990), Albarracín-Jordan (1992), Mathews (1992), Stanish (1994), and Seddon (1994), there is simply no primary archaeological evidence for widespread implementation of raised-field systems in the region in the post-Tiwanaku period. Although Graffam (1990) presents convincing evidence for localized, small-scale utilization of raised fields in post-Tiwanaku times, the authors cited above, working independently, are in complete agreement that the lake-edge region from Juli-Pomata in Peru to the immediate hinterland of Tiwanaku experienced massive agrarian collapse in the post-Tiwanaku period, characterized by abandonment of large-scale raised-field cultivation (a position I have argued since 1982 in a number of publications).

What accounts for these radically different culture-historical reconstructions? Leaving aside the more subjective, psychological nuances that generate academic debates, it is clear that the anomalous result obtained by Graffam in the Pampa Koani derived from (1) an insufficient sample of sites generated by his transect survey technique, and (2) logical errors in inference in relating post-Tiwanaku habitation mounds located in his transect survey to adjacent field surfaces. There *was* substantial post-Tiwanaku occupation of mounds in the Pampa Koani, but the great bulk of these occupations were not related to cultivation of adjacent, previously constructed raised fields (Seddon 1994).

2. In the third phase of the field research, which commenced in 1993, we returned our focus to the rural agricultural landscapes surrounding Tiwanaku's principal urban settlements. This phase in the research is designed to increase the resolution of our understanding of changes in the human-environment relationship in the Lake Titicaca basin from approximately 3500 to 800 B.P. (and in certain respects to the present). The objectives of this ongoing phase of the research are (1) to describe lake-level variation during the past 5,000 years, the major period of human occupation; (2) to analyze Holocene climate variation in the altiplano through two different lines of evidence—by using lake-level variation as input to water and energy-budget (climatonomy) models, and by using stratigraphic variations of stable oxygen and carbon isotopes through the past 5,000 years as a direct measurement of the hydrological water balance; (3) to reconstruct the spatial and temporal dynamics of raised-field agriculture in the study area through a program of topographic mapping and systematic test excavations; (4) to model agricultural space-time systematics in the context of hypotheses regarding hydrological and climatic control of raise fields utilizing Geographic Information Systems techniques; and (5) to determine by paleolimnological methods the ecosystem consequences (i.e., erosion and deposition processes, nu-

trient loss from the land and flow to the lake) of distinct types of farming practices. The results of this study will contribute toward more sophisticated, quantitative understanding of the ecological bases of raised-field sustainability.

3. The results of full-coverage survey of the lower and middle Tiwanaku Valley are reported in detail in Albarracin-Jordan (1992) and Mathews (1992). These works describe a settlement hierarchy analogous to the one I have proposed for the Pampa Koani.

# 2

# The Natural and Human Setting

MICHAEL W. BINFORD AND
ALAN L. KOLATA

How did a complex civilization such as Tiwanaku develop in the seemingly hostile environment of the Lake Titicaca basin? The assumptions underlying this question are that humans are embedded in and dependent on the physical environment in which they pursue their activities, and that the natural system of the Andean altiplano is inhospitable to an agrarian society. The first assumption is always true, because the ecological setting, or ecosystem, simultaneously affords civilizations material opportunities and sets physical constraints. Food, shelter, and intellectual stimulation are all dependent to one degree or another on the material world of the natural system. Human capacity to extract materials is dependent on the ability of the system to produce them. The second assumption, specific to the area, must not be completely true because the civilization did develop and flourish. But Tiwanaku ultimately disappeared, and the proximate cause of its collapse had environmental roots. In short, neither Tiwanaku nor any other civilization can be understood without an appreciation of the entire ecosystem in which it developed.

An ecosystem consists of all the interacting biotic and abiotic components within a defined space and time, including, but not limited to, patterns and processes of climate, geology, soils, vegetation, and human activities. Although ecosystems can be any size and can exist over many spatial scales, for methodological purposes hydrological drainage basins are often the appropriate scale for scientific study of human populations (Binford et al. 1987; Likens 1984; Oldfield 1978). Drainage-basin ecosystems can be mapped with discrete boundaries on and below the earth's surface (where aquifer boundaries do not correspond to surface contours). Flow of materials, energy, and organisms, including humans and their goods, into and out of the basin and their standing stocks within the basin can be measured, studied, and explained. If the basin contains a natural lake, it may hold a sedimentary record of environmental history that can be read through well-developed paleoecological techniques (Pennington 1981). This environmental history describes the physical and material context within which humans lived and carried out their activities.

Accordingly, paleoecological and archaeological studies in an area depend on description and understanding of existing and past environmental conditions. While recognizing that precise modern analogs may not exist, we subscribe to the uniformitarian assumption that fundamental physical processes (hydrological, ecological, etc.) functioned in the same manner in the past as they do now, although perhaps with different magnitudes or influenced by factors that have since changed. Our challenge is to describe these factors, how they have changed, and how they influenced the scope and magnitude of environmental processes.

The objective of this chapter is to describe the physical, climatic, biological, and cultural context within which the Tiwanaku civilization carried out its activities. We first describe the general location, geological setting, climate, and weather of the Tiwanaku core area, incorporating considerations of past and present environmental conditions. We then discuss the natural systems of terrestrial and aquatic environments. Finally, we sketch the major contours of Tiwanaku social history, focusing on dimensions such as trends and patterns in human land use and settlement that illuminate long-term human-environment interactions in the Andean altiplano. This summary of Tiwanaku cultural history is intended to provide an armature for the succeeding chapters in this book. Throughout the discussion, we interject commentary on human perception and use of changing physical environments.

In shaping this overview of the natural and human context of Tiwanaku development, we owe a major debt to a volume edited by DeJoux and Iltis (1992). This comprehensive book summarizes nearly all recent environmental work on Lake Titicaca, including geology, climatology, hydrology, limnology, biology, and, to a lesser extent, socioeconomic studies. Readers who wish to learn more about each of our topics are referred to this excellent volume. This chapter is directed more specifically toward describing the local environmental context of Tiwanaku, and it also includes more information that is not specific to the lake than does DeJoux and Iltis's book.

## Natural Systems

The drainage basins of the Tiwanaku and Catari rivers constitute the local ecosystems of the Tiwanaku civilization's core area. These areas have been the subject of our archaeological and paleoecological research over the past nine years (Binford and Brenner 1989; Binford, Brenner, and Engstrom 1992; Kolata 1983, 1986, 1989, 1991, 1993a; Kolata and Ortloff 1989; Leyden 1989; Ortloff and Kolata 1989, 1993). Many other river drainage basins make up the Lake Wiñaymarka (Titicaca) ecosystem. Similarly, the Catari and Tiwanaku basins themselves consist of many smaller ecosystems: tributaries, agricultural and pasture lands, clusters of human settlement, and diverse nearshore lake regions with characteristic littoral vegetation, aquatic invertebrates, and fish. The drainage basin centered on the Jesus de Machaca region in the contemporary Bolivian province of Pacajes, which is tributary to the Desaguadero River, contains significant Tiwanaku sites, such as the settlement of Khonko Wankané, and this region was clearly an important element of the Tiwanaku core area (Kolata 1993a). Although we have conducted preliminary investigations in this region, we do not have sufficient primary data to warrant their inclusion in this discussion. Future investigations are designed explicitly to incorporate this drainage basin into our ongoing analyses of the environmental and human contexts of Tiwanaku's development.

The center of Lake Titicaca is near 16° S, 69° W, at 3,810 meters above sea level in the northern Andean altiplano (fig. 2.1). The altiplano is a high, intermontane basin that lies between the cordilleras Occidental and Oriental (known locally as the Cordillera Real); it stretches over 1,200 kilometers from north to south and nearly 200 kilometers east to west at its widest point. At the extremes, the basin extends from 14°09′06″ to 17°08′2″ S latitude and from 68°03′34″ to 71°01′42″ W longitude, forming parts of the modern nations of Peru, Bolivia, Chile, and Argentina. Lake Titicaca proper lies about 60 percent in Peru and 40 percent in Bolivia. The drainage basin of the entire lake covers 57,340 square kilometers (table 2.1), including the 5,220 square kilometers of the Desaguadero River basin (Boulangé and Aquize Jaen 1981). Of this area, the lake itself covers 8,562 square kilometers, with a total volume of 903 cubic kilometers. Lake Wiñaymarka, the part of the lake in which we are interested, has a surface area of over 1,440 square kilometers and contains 12.36 cubic kilometers of water.

The elevation of the basin floor varies from around 4,500 meters in the north to nearly 3,600 meters in the south. Bordering mountain ranges reach over 6,000 meters high, with the highest peak in the catchment, Nevado Illampu in the eastern cordillera, extending to over 6,400 meters. Various authorities list the altitude of this peak as from 6,300 to over 7,000 meters (7,010 meters on the map in Boulangé, Vargas, and Rodrigo [1981], 6,369 meters on Newell's plate 18 [1949], and 6,322 meters in Wirrmann [1992]). Except for Nevado Illampu, the mountain boundary

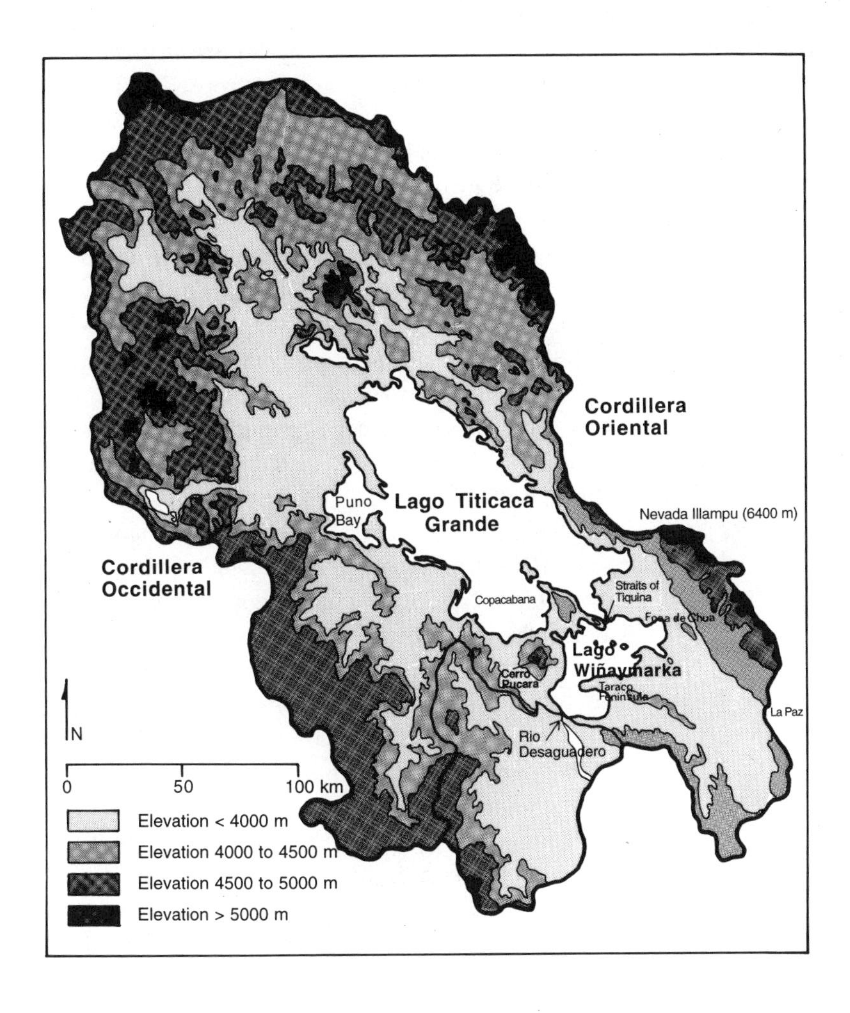


**Figure 2.1.** The Lake Titicaca basin (redrawn from Boulangé and Aquize Jaen 1981).

of Lake Titicaca's drainage basin varies from 4,500 to 5,400 meters.

## Geology and Tectonic Evolution

Bedrock composition and structure influence general geomorphology, are the source of parent material for soil development, and, with the hydrological system, determine basic ecosystem geochemistry. Thus, processes that have continued over millions of years form the fundamental physical and chemical structure of the Tiwanaku area.

The altiplano and Lake Titicaca first formed during the Miocene epoch (23 million to 5 million years ago) as the Andes were created by subduction of the eastward-moving Nazca tectonic plate under the westward-moving South American plate (James 1971). Before this folding and uplift, western South America was covered by sedimentary rocks, perhaps as much as 10 to 15 kilometers thick, deposited during the Paleozoic (mostly upper Ordovician, 500 to 435 million years ago, but also during the Silurian-Devonian, 435 to 360 million years ago, and the Carboniferous and Permian, 360 to 240 million years ago) and early Cenozoic (the present geological era, beginning about 63 million years ago). Volcanism, increased compression, and the resulting folding and faulting deformed the sediments and created the two major mountain belts now called the Cordillera Occidental and the Cordillera Oriental (fig. 2.2). The broad, high plain between the major ranges formed the early altiplano.

The Andean altiplano attained its present form during the strong period of orogenesis (mountain formation) of the Pliocene and early Pleistocene, some 2 million years ago (Lavenu 1981, 1992). Volcanic activity was greatest during this time. Intruded magma caused thrust faulting and folding, especially in the eastern cordillera. More recently, during Quaternary times, reduction of volcanic activity relaxed the compressive stresses and stimulated small-scale tectonic activities such as graben formation. Despite the reduction of volcanism, the Andes are still rising at a

Table 2.1. Morphometric Information for Lakes Titicaca Mayor and Wiñaymarka

| Variable | Lago Titicaca Mayor | Lago Wiñaymarka |
|---|---|---|
| Maximum length (km) | 150 | 64 |
| Maximum width (km) | 43 | 31 |
| Surface area (km$^2$) | 7130 | 1430 |
| Island area (km$^2$) | 49 | 61 |
| Catchment area (km$^2$) | 57340[a] | |
| Maximum depth (m) | 280 | 43 |
| Mean depth (m) | 109 | 7.40 |
| Shoreline length (km) | | 334.10 |
| Shoreline development | | 2.57 |
| Volume (km$^3$) | | 10.01 |
| Hakanson's (1981) lake form | | CxMi |
| Mean slope (%) | | 0.35 |
| Bottom roughness index | | 9.44 |
| Major tributary rivers | | 5 |
| Annual basin precipitation (mm) | | 687 ± 138 |
| Annual mean air temperature (°C) | | 9° |
| Diel air temperature variation | | 12° |
| Annual mean water temperature | | 11–15° |
| Mixing regime | | Polymictic |
| Total dissolved solutes (mg/liter) | | 850 |
| Mean pH | | 8.6 |
| N:P ratio | | >10 |

Sources: Data for Lago Titicaca Mayor are from Boulangé and Aquize Jaen (1981). Data for Lago Wiñaymarka are from measurements made on bathymetric maps published by the Comisión Mixta Peruana Boliviana, Instituto Geográfico Militar, Lima, Peru, in 1978.

[a]Total for both basins.

rate of more than 0.7 millimeters per year, which is probably the most rapid rise of their geological history (Benjamin, Johnson, and Naesar 1987).

Catchment bedrock is mostly igneous basalts and andesites, with some shales and sandstones and small pockets of limestone (Newell 1949). Outcrops of older bedrock (Paleozoic sandstones, quartzites, and mudstones) that occur at the Straits of Tiquina are resistant to weathering and therefore yield low concentrations of dissolved elements. The islands in Lake Wiñaymarka, including Taquiri and Paco and the northern half of Cumana, are also formed of these older rocks. The altiplano, the Cordillera Oriental, the Putina basin to the northeast, and the Cordillera Occidental form four distinct geological provinces within the catchment (Ellison, Klinck, and Hawkins 1989). Fault zones separate the altiplano from the Putina Basin and the Cordillera Oriental, both to the east. The western border is bounded by rhyolitic and andesitic volcanic rocks created during the Miocene through the Holocene.

Much of the bedrock in the basin is igneous rock, and volcanism characterizes much of the western boundary of the Andes mountains. An extinct cone, Cerro Pucara, forms the western boundary of Lake Wiñaymarka, and Newell's map (1949:plate 12) shows at least five sites of igneous rocks. However, there has been no volcanic activity around Lake Titicaca during Holocene times, which includes the periods of human occupation (deSilva and Francis 1991).

The Quaternary has been marked by periodic advances and retreats of higher-altitude glaciers, the lowest of which created moraines that extend down to 3,900 meters (Servant and Fontes 1978). Other Quaternary formations include alluvium in elevated terraces 10 to 20 meters above present rivers, fluvioglacial deposits of stratified drift, and lake sediments. Most of the surficial geology in the pampas of the Catari and Tiwanaku rivers consists of Quaternary sediments derived from weathering of the bedrock and from water deposition.

#### SURFACE GEOLOGY: LACUSTRINE DEPOSITS AND PAMPAS

The pampas consist of fluvial and lacustrine sediments deposited during the Quaternary. Archaeological sites are found mostly in the flat pampas and colluvial terraces that lie between three ridges, the central one of which forms the Taraco peninsula.

The altiplano has been covered by a series of lakes of declining depth during the Pleistocene and Holocene (fig. 2.3). Each of the former lakes left terraces at the elevations indicated in figure 2.3, and sediments from each lake stand are found between the appropriate elevations in the drainage basin. The first lacustrine deposition began in the Late Pliocene and created the Charaña Formation of the eastern altiplano

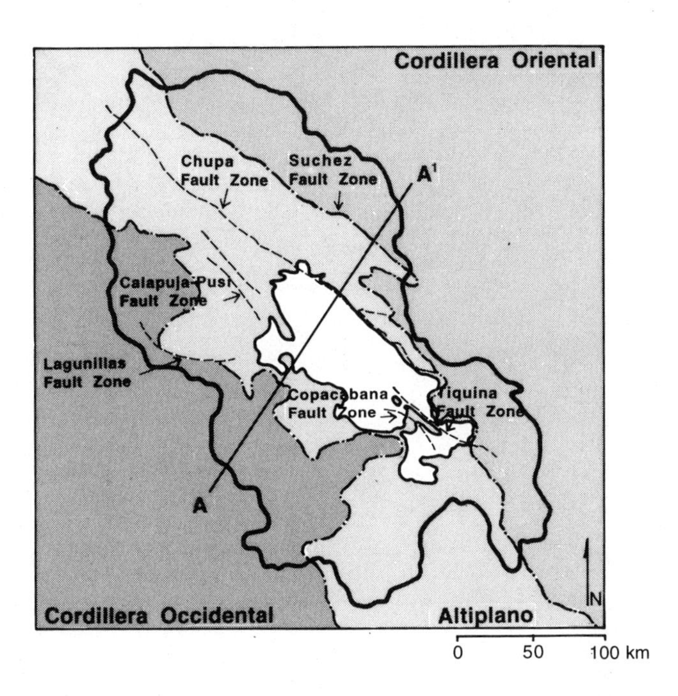


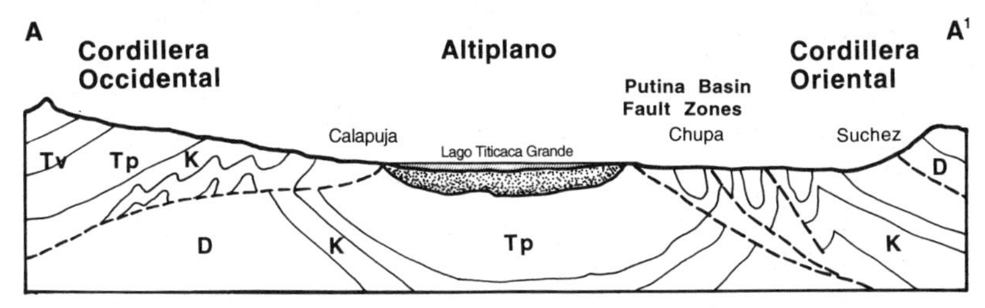


Figure 2.2. Top: Map featuring the major geological provinces and fault zones in the Lake Titicaca basin. Bottom: Schematic geological cross section along line A–A′: D = Devonian, K = Cretaceous, Tp = Puno group, Tv = Tertiary volcanics. Both modified from Newell (1949) and Paul Baker (personal communication).

| Age (Ma) | Epoch | Lacustrine Event | Surface | Glacial and Interglacial Event |
|---|---|---|---|---|
| | Present | Titicaca | t0 | Moraines |
| | Holocene | | | |
| 0.01 | | Tauca | t1 | Choqueyapu II |
| | Late Pleistocene | Minchin | t2 | Choqueyapu I |
| 0.5 | | | | |
| | Early Pleistocene | Ballivian | t3 | Sorata |
| | | | S4 | |
| | | Cabana | | Kaluyo |
| 1.6 | | Mataro | S5 | Calvario |
| | Pliocene | | | |

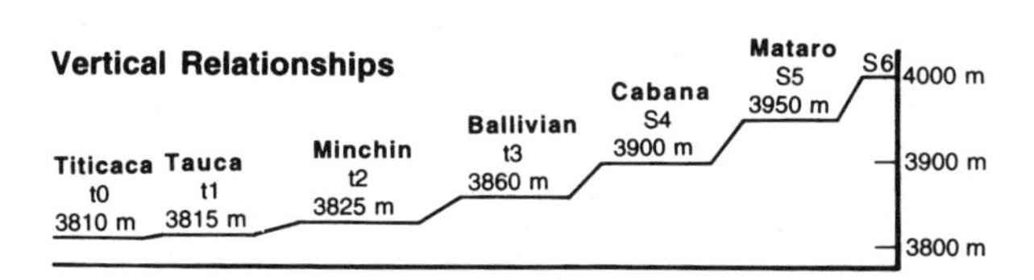


Figure 2.3. The stratigraphy and vertical relationships of lakes in the altiplano during the Quaternary (modified from Lavenu 1992 and Lavenu, Fornavi, and Sebrier 1984).

and the Plio-Pleistocene Azángaro Formation. The Azángaro Formation (called Río Azángaro Lake Deposits in Newell 1949), a complex series of calcareous silts, sandstones, and conglomerates that are often laminated, outcrops at many sites around the lake between the Peruvian villages of Azángaro and Juliaca (Klinck, Ellison, and Hawkins 1986). These deposits are derived from both lacustrine and fluvial sources and occur in some places as much as 100 meters above the current lake level (Newell 1949).

Lake Mataro deposits mostly have been eroded away but are found in the northernmost part of the Titicaca drainage basin and in a few other locations. A small exposure south of Desaguadero is the only Mataro site in the Wiñaymarka area. The pampas in the Wiñaymarka basin are derived partly from Lake Cabana deposits, especially to the west of the lake and in the upper river basins to the east. The major areas of the pampas adjacent to Lake Wiñaymarka are formed of Lake Ballivian deposits.

The Minchin and Tauca lakes occurred sequentially at the end of the Pleistocene and beginning of the Holocene and have been related to the melting of the last of the Pleistocene glaciers (Lavenu 1992). Although Lake Minchin was only about 15 meters deeper than the present lake in the Titicaca basin, it was more extensive to the south of Lake Wiñaymarka, covering the vast area of altiplano that now includes Lake Poopo and the *salares,* or salt flats, of Uyuni and Coipasa. Lake Tauca, 5 meters deeper than the present lake, left peaty terraces throughout the altiplano. The locations of the terraces indicate that the lake had a surface area of about 9,000 square kilometers in the Titicaca basin and at least 43,000 square kilometers in the southern altiplano (Servant and Fontes 1978).

### GEOMORPHOLOGY OF THE TIWANAKU CORE AREA

Plate tectonics, block faulting, and sedimentation in ancient lakes created the general form and elevation of the altiplano and Lake Titicaca's topographic drainage basin. More recently, general geomorphology has been shaped by stream erosion and deposition processes. Three principal ridges define the two major basins (fig. 2.4). The Serranías Lakaya Pata (referred to here as the Taraco Range), which forms the Taraco peninsula, is a low range of mountains of Tertiary origin between the Catari and Tiwanaku basins. Two mountain ranges, the Quimsa Chata and Chilla, form the eastern and western parts of the southern boundary of the Tiwanaku Valley, respectively (these two ranges are referred to collectively as the Tiwanaku Range). The northern and eastern boundary of the Catari River basin is a massif formed of Paleozoic rocks. Both valleys are bordered on the west by Lake Titicaca.

The two drainage basins—the Catari and the Tiwanaku—consist of Quaternary fluvial and lacustrine clay, sand, and gravel deposits with occasional outcrops of Tertiary rock, principally sandstones. The pampas zones are characterized geomorphically by abandoned lakeshore terraces, multiple river meander scars, and large alluvial fans composed of unsorted material ranging from fine-grained sediments to boulders (Argollo and Ticlla 1991; and see chapter 3). Local hydrological conditions within each basin heavily influence contemporary land use and have important implications for interpretation of pre-Hispanic agricultural landscapes. For instance, over 90 percent of the Catari pampas zone is now pasturage, and small-scale dry farming is done only on scattered plots in areas of relatively high elevation such as small hillocks and archaeological mounds (MACA 1974, 1985).

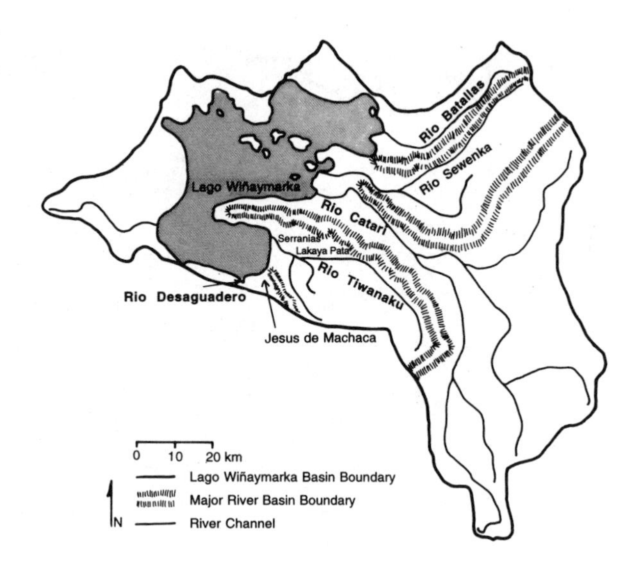

**Figure 2.4.** River basins feeding Lake Wiñaymarka—the central valleys of the Tiwanaku civilization.

Several Tiwanaku sites are found on islands in the lake, most prominently on Isla Cumana. This island is connected to the mainland during periods of low lake water. Its topography is mountainous, with steep slopes and narrow ledges at the water's edge, where most contemporary habitation is situated. It features two southwest-facing basins characterized by rich alluvial sediments with abandoned raised fields and large-scale human constructions on the surface. The island rises to over 4,200 meters, or about 400 meters above the normal lake level.

## Surface Hydrology

At least 16 major and minor rivers flow into Lake Titicaca, although there is only one surface outlet. The larger catchment, including Lake Poopo to the south, is internally drained. The two main basins of Lake Titicaca, the greater lake and Lake Wiñaymarka, are connected through the Straits of Tiquina, with a normal discharge of 20 cubic meters per second from the large basin. Five major streams flow into Lake Wiñaymarka, and the single surface outflow from Lake Titicaca is to the south through the Desaguadero River. In the Tiwanaku study areas, the four major rivers are the Batallas, Catari, Tiwanaku, and Sewenka (fig. 2.4), which drain areas of 365, 3,421, 953, and 850 square kilometers, respectively. None of the rivers has a distinguishable mouth; instead, each discharges into wetlands from which water flows into either the lake or another river. All the rivers except the Batallas run through alluvial substrates that are easily eroded during rainy-season floods. The Tiwanaku, Catari, and Sewenka rivers have sections that were artificially canalized and diverted by the people of Tiwanaku (Kolata 1991, 1993a; and see chapter 5). Thus, stream geomorphology has been altered by direct human activities and cannot be explained strictly by geomorphic processes.

The many springs that emerge from the lower slopes of the three ridges appear to be the dominant sources of water on the pampas during the dry season. Springs and marshy seeps occur with a frequency of about one per kilometer along the road that runs across the northern slope of the Taraco Range. Several dozen springs are shown on the topographic maps both in the footslopes and on the pampas of the Tiwanaku and Catari River valleys. These springs have never been studied, and discharge volumes are unknown. However, they discharge year-round, with copious flows even in August, the driest month of the year.

Springs are surface discharges of groundwater, so their chemistry indicates the mineralogical nature of the aquifer. Rudimentary analyses of spring water from sites between the villages of Lukurmata and Lakaya show that water chemistry is variable over even short distances (see table 4.3). Thus, the aquifers are quite heterogeneous. On the other hand, spring water (with an average specific conductance of 20 milliSiemens per meter) is much more dilute than lake water (130 milliSiemens per meter) (see chapter 4). This relatively fresh water can leach salts from soils in agricultural fields as it passes through them. Slightly brackish lake water left behind after high stands and normal evapotranspiration of soil moisture supply these salts. Excessive soil salinity can constrain or inhibit plant growth, and farmers must avoid salt buildup. Thus, cultivation is dependent on the springs in two ways. First, they provide water during the seven-month dry season, which includes the time of planting. Second, spring water contributes to maintaining salinity levels in the soil below the threshold of damage to crop plants.

Areas with water-saturated soils, wetlands vegetation, and standing water at least part of the year are abundant throughout the pampas. These wetlands are the result of complex interactions between the larger rivers, the springs, and groundwater. Some wetlands occur in locations where the land surface is below the groundwater table. Others may be perched above the normal groundwater table but are fed by river or spring water faster than they can evaporate or drain to the subsurface aquifer. Still others lie in the zones of groundwater discharge.

The pampas are largely a wetland system similar to wet meadows in some places and to marshes in others. Thirty-five percent of the Catari River valley is designated as wetlands on the Aygachi topographic map (fig. 2.5). During the wet season, according to

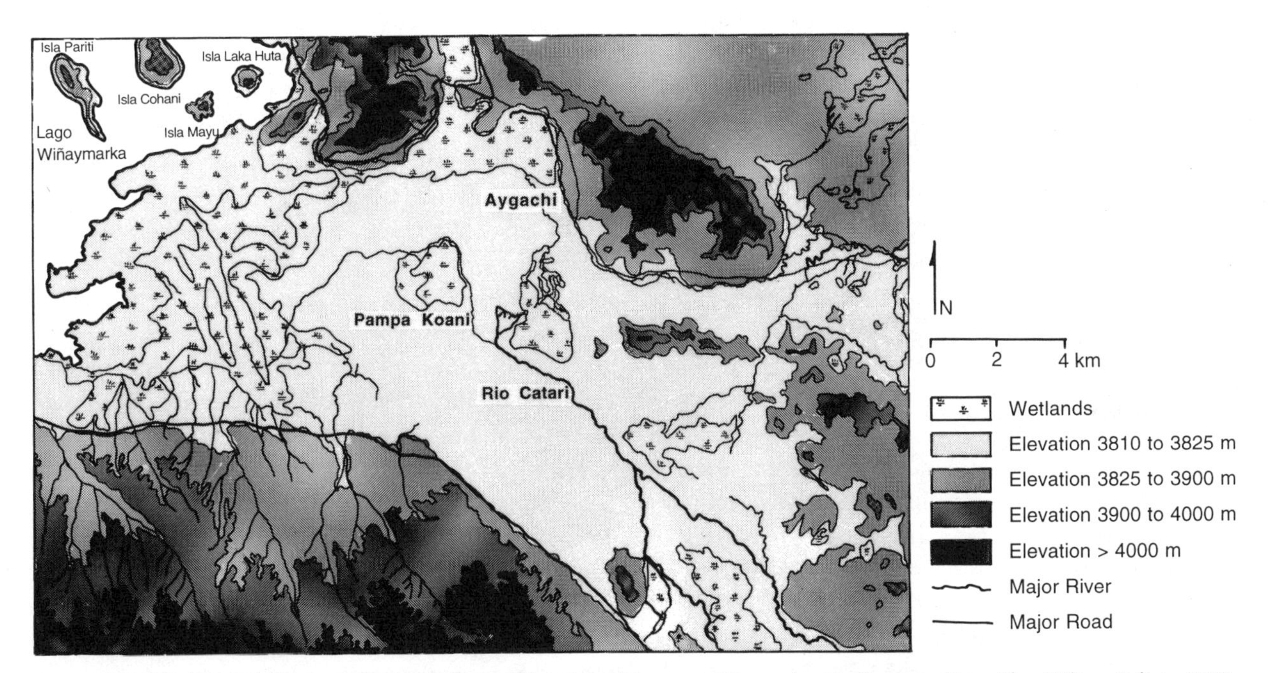


**Figure 2.5.** Wetlands distribution in the Catari River valley (Aygachi topographic quadrangle, Instituto Geográfico Militar, Bolivia, 1961; scale 1:50,000).

our observations, nearly all of the lower Catari River valley is covered with shallow standing water. Twelve percent of the Tiwanaku Valley, shown on the available geological, geomorphological, and land-use maps for Tiwanaku, Taraco, and Guaqui, is designated wetland.

## Groundwater

Water table characteristics of the Catari pampas zone result from the interaction of several geological and climatic features. Of the two principal aquifers in this sub-basin, one is confined in the Tertiary sandstones of the mountainous Taraco Formation, and the other is within the alluvial Quaternary sediments of the pampas zone. Groundwater in the Quaternary aquifer is directly influenced by the nearby lake. The pampas zone is perennially marshy and subject to inundation during the wet season. Throughout the year, intersecting water table and ground surfaces create wetlands and pools of standing water. These pools diminish in size as water evaporates and lake level declines through the dry season (June to September), leaving behind saline crusts consisting mostly of $CaSO_4$, $CaCl_2$, and NaCl.

Under these circumstances, a combination of waterlogging and surface deposition of soluble salts is inevitable, and the absence of constructed drainage systems results in saline soils. Artificial water control systems are required to maintain a locally regulated phreatic surface and to allow drainage and leaching of salts by new freshwater. In some cases, the springs along the footslopes of the hills are the sources of freshwater; in other cases, rivers and streams are the only nearby sources. Thus, raised fields and associated drainage features (canals, dikes, river shunts, and aqueducts) are technological responses to the problem of drainage and regulation of groundwater levels (Kolata 1991, 1993a; Ortloff and Kolata 1989; and see chapters 5–6).

## Meteorology and Climate

The altiplano climate is dominated by typical tropical wet-dry seasons and orographic effects, with influences from both Amazonian and Pacific air masses. Most precipitation comes from the strong easterly trade winds that sweep across the Amazon basin and bring warmer, moister air to the altiplano. Periodically, especially during summer when a coastal temperature inversion is low, local convection currents can drive the cooler and drier Pacific air over the Cordillera Occidental (Johnson 1976). This dynamic interplay between distinctly different air masses, as well as the complicated atmospheric circulation in the western Amazon, results in highly variable climatic conditions in the altiplano. Interpretation of long-term climate averages must be tempered with the understanding that interannual variability is expressed by standard deviations ranging from 20 to 70 percent of the annual means (see table 2.1).

The recent, medium-term climate summary for the Lake Wiñaymarka basin is based mostly on records from the meteorological stations at the international airport at El Alto (table 2.2). Other data are available from stations at Guaqui, Desaguadero, Viacha, and Taquiri Island in Bolivia and from Puno in Peru, but El Alto station has the longest and most complete record on the altiplano for Bolivia. Except for precipitation, variables measured at other stations are not significantly different from those measured at El Alto. Most of the others record higher precipitation because they are located in or on the edge of the lake, where precipitation is more intense.

### TEMPERATURE, MOISTURE, AND WATER BUDGET

Temperature in mountainous regions is controlled primarily by elevation, with warmer temperatures at low elevations and cooler temperatures in the mountains. The exception to this rule is that temperature inversions can occur in which cooler air lies below warmer air, as it does on the western slope of the Andes. There, inversion is caused by air cooled by the cold water of the Peru-Chile (Humboldt) current underlying air warmed adiabatically as it descends the western slope.

The change of air temperature with altitude is called the lapse rate, and in the Bolivian Andes the lapse rate is about −6.5° C per 1,000 meters of elevation between 2,500 and 3,600 meters (Johnson 1976), and about −7.5° C per 1,000 meters at higher elevations (Graf 1981a, 1981b). The freezing point, or 0° isotherm, in the Andes is between 4,800 and 4,950 meters, determined by extrapolating both the lapse rate and measurements by radiosonde (Johnson 1976; Hastenrath 1967). Lapse rate is a useful parameter because it can be used to estimate local mean air temperature simply from the elevation of a site. It also enables us to make paleoclimatic inferences because temperatures in the past can be estimated by measuring past distributions of glaciers and vegetation,

Table 2.2. Temperature and Precipatation Data for Several Stations around Lake Wiñaymarka

| Station | Dates | Variable | S | O | N | D | J | F | M | A | M | J | J | A | Mean or Total |
|---|---|---|---|---|---|---|---|---|---|---|---|---|---|---|---|
| El Alto–La Paz | 1942–1978 | Max. temp. (°C)[a] | 14 | 16 | 16 | 14 | 13 | 13 | 14 | 14 | 13 | 13 | 13 | 14 | 14 |
| (4105 masl) | | Min. temp. (°C)[a] | 0 | 2 | 3 | 3 | 3 | 3 | 3 | 2 | 0 | −2 | −2 | −1 | 1 |
| | | Precipitation (mm)[a] | 34 | 37 | 48 | 76 | 139 | 108 | 56 | 22 | 9 | 5 | 4 | 17 | 555 |
| | 1942–1969 | Days with precipitation[b] | 8 | 8 | 9 | 16 | 20 | 16 | 11 | 6 | 3 | 2 | 3 | 3 | 104 |
| | | Sunshine hours[a] | 189 | 180 | 171 | 186 | 183 | 153 | 149 | 165 | 223 | 240 | 236 | 217 | 2292 |
| | | % Possible sunshine[a] | 52 | 47 | 44 | 46 | 45 | 43 | 39 | 47 | 63 | 72 | 68 | 61 | 52 |
| | 1958–1961 | Measured evaporation[c] | 146 | 160 | 150 | 158 | 152 | 129 | 147 | 126 | 121 | 109 | 118 | 139 | 1654 |
| Viacha | 1957–1976 | Precipitation (mm)[a] | 40 | 30 | 53 | 101 | 135 | 124 | 72 | 41 | 20 | 3 | 6 | 20 | 645 |
| Desaguadero | 1964–1978 | Precipitation (mm)[a] | 23 | 24 | 42 | 103 | 174 | 157 | 94 | 25 | 10 | 4 | 6 | 15 | 676 |
| Guaqui | 1964–1978 | Precipitation (mm)[a] | 22 | 39 | 47 | 91 | 146 | 129 | 60 | 22 | 12 | 3 | 3 | 7 | 581 |

[a]Data compiled from tables in Boulangé and Aquize Jaen (1981).

[b]Data compiled from tables in Johnson (1976).

[c]Mean of two measurements made with a Piche evaporimeter at Desaguadero and on the Isla Taquiri (Kessler 1970: Table 1, p. 243).

which are regulated in part by temperature. Furthermore, if we know the modern distribution of various human activities, such as altitude-dependent agriculture, we can deduce whether the activity would have been possible at the altitude of the core area during Tiwanaku times.

Annual mean air temperature at lake elevation is about 9° C, with a daily variation of about 12° (Boulangé and Aquize Jaen 1981). Diel temperature variation is greater than seasonal, which is typical of tropical climates. Mean nighttime temperature minima of −10° C are commonly recorded in the higher altiplano in June through August, with rare lows of −20° (Johnson 1976). Warmest nights occur during the wet season, and the mean minimum is usually above freezing. Minimum temperatures are higher near the lake because the heat content of the water strongly influences nearshore areas. Mean daytime maximum temperatures range from 16.4° C in July to 19.1° C in November.

Annual precipitation for the entire Lake Titicaca drainage basin averages about 750 millimeters ± one standard deviation of about 20 percent of the mean (Boulangé and Aquize Jaen 1981; Johnson 1976; Kessler and Monheim 1968), and the average potential evapotranspiration is estimated to range from 1,200 to more than 1,700 millimeters (Kessler and Monheim 1968; Roche et al. 1992). Most precipitation falls between December and March (fig. 2.6).

Precipitation varies spatially in two ways. First, because most moisture comes from the east, east-facing slopes have greater precipitation and west-facing slopes are in rain shadow. Second, evaporation from Lake Titicaca provides an enormous amount of moisture to the air, much of which precipitates on or near the lake. No consistent relationship between precipitation and elevation is apparent from available data (Seltzer 1990). There have been several measurements of more than 1,500 millimeters falling annually on and near the lake, which is the prime agricultural area, and as few as 400 millimeters falling on the westernmost ridge of the drainage basin (Boulangé and Aquize Jaen 1981). A long-term average of 945 millimeters falls directly on the large lake, and an average of 792 millimeters falls on Lake Wiñaymarka (Boulangé and Aquize Jaen 1981).

Potential evaporation and transpiration (usually considered together and termed evapotranspiration) are extremely high. The three physical factors that control evapotranspiration are energy input (which drives the phase transition from liquid to vapor), humidity of the overlying air mass, and wind (which blows moist air away from a site). The altiplano is higher than 40 percent of atmosphere. Because the atmosphere absorbs light energy, energy input by insolation is high in the altiplano, varying from 280 watts per square meter in November to 215 watts per square meter in July (measurements taken in Puno, Peru, in 1978 by Boulangé and Aquize Jaen [1981]). Furthermore, the low relative humidity and high wind speeds that occur in the altiplano result in high potential evapotranspiration. Thus, long-term average monthly precipitation is nearly always less than monthly potential evapotranspiration, so that without other sources of water, the soil should always have a moisture deficit, or insufficient moisture to support most vegetation.

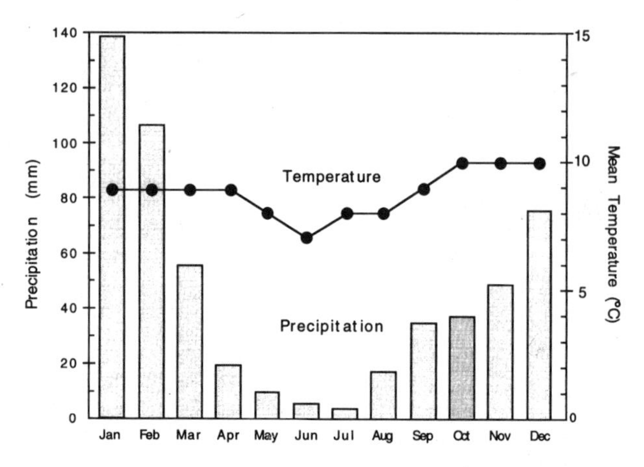


**Figure 2.6.** Average annual precipitation and temperature for the Lake Titicaca drainage basin, 1933–69 (data from the international airport at El Alto, Bolivia).

This deficit results in a large difference between potential and actual evapotranspiration. If the moisture is not there to evaporate or be transpired, no amount of additional energy input or wind will increase water loss. Actual evapotranspiration has been estimated by Roche and colleagues (1992) by water balance calculations to be about 563 millimeters per year for the terrestrial drainage basin. Actual evapotranspiration from different river basins varies from 490 to 660 millimeters per year. When actual terrestrial evapotranspiration is added to evaporation from the lake surface, which is equal to the potential amount because water is always available, 91 percent of all losses of water from the entire drainage basin is via evapotranspiration. All in all, an equivalent depth of more than 1.6 meters of water (with an uncertainty of ± 8 percent) evaporates or is transpired from the drainage basin.

The El Niño–Southern Oscillation (ENSO) is an episodic change in the distribution of warm water in the equatorial Pacific Ocean that causes transient changes in global weather patterns. The major phenomenon in ENSO events is the overriding of the cold Peru-Chile current, which travels northward along the western coast of South America, by warm water from the central Pacific Ocean. Cold coastal water and the atmospheric circulation pattern in the Pacific normally create extreme aridity along coastal Peru and Chile. ENSO events usually correspond to both rainfall and flood peaks along the normally arid Peruvian coast (Waylen and Caviedes 1986, 1988).

ENSO events have occurred throughout the Holocene (DeVries 1987) and therefore have been a significant part of the human environment. Until the very strong 1983 ENSO that demonstrably affected much of the world's weather, most attention was paid to the coasts of Ecuador and Peru, where direct effects were strongest. There the most evident human consequence was that the normally productive Peruvian anchovy fishery periodically collapsed because the usual nutrient-rich upwelling along the coast was replaced by relatively sterile warm water, reducing food supplies for the fish. Wildlife in the Galapagos Islands and along the coasts is affected in similar ways.

Climatic response to ENSO events in the altiplano is less well understood. There are several apparent correlations between rainfall and ENSOs or between lake-level changes and ENSOs, but the only statistically significant pattern detected in the existing data is indirect. Precipitation data from several stations in the region indicate that precipitation in very strong ENSO years is somewhat less than that in the average year (436 ± 126 millimeters and 618 ± 79 millimeters [95 percent confidence limits], respectively), but that moderate ENSO years are not different from the average year (641 ± 163 millimeters; see fig. 2.7). Additionally, during the twentieth century, ENSO years have typically been years of low lake-level rise, but not in every case (fig. 2.8). The level of Lake Titicaca increased more than the average in the five-year periods immediately following five of the seven twentieth-century ENSOs ranked as "strong" or "very strong" by Quinn, Neal, and Atúñez de Mayolo (1987) (fig. 2.8). Similarly, the few years before ENSOs have typically been years of lake-level decline. A statistically significant correlation between precipitation and lake-level rise exists during the relatively short-term record of precipitation at Guaqui ($r = 0.428$, $df = 39$, $p < 0.01$). Because lake level rises somewhat less during strong ENSO years, and low precipitation results in small rises, a connection between lake level and ENSO may exist.

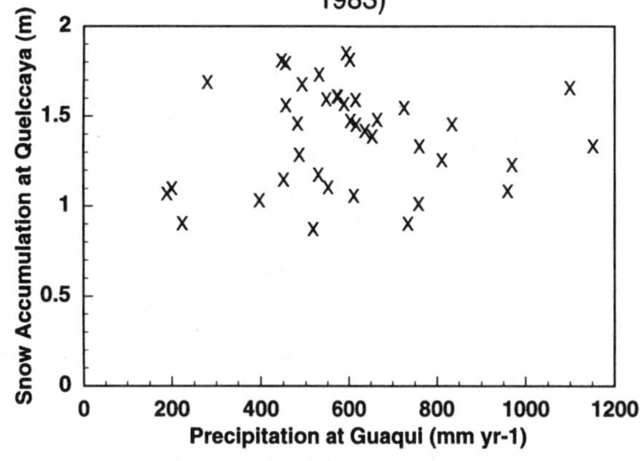


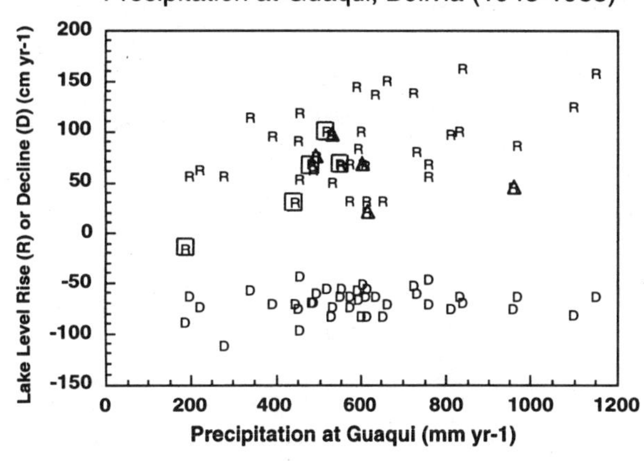


Figure 2.7. *Top:* Relationship between precipitation measured at Guaqui, on the southeastern shore of Lake Wiñaymarka, and snow accumulation at the Quelccaya ice cap (data from Thompson et al. 1985). The lack of relationship calls into question the suggestion by Thompson et al. (1985) that the Quelccaya glacier is a "reasonable" climatic proxy for Lake Titicaca. *Bottom:* Relationship between precipitation at Guaqui and the annual rise or decline of Lake Titicaca. Squares indicate years of strong or very strong ENSOs; triangles are years with moderate ENSOs (data from Quinn, Neal, and Atuñez de Mayolo 1987). There is a statistically significant correlation between precipitation and annual rise in lake level, but no correlation between precipitation and decline.

## Paleoclimate

The one constant of climate is that it always changes. Understanding the nature of these changes is a major

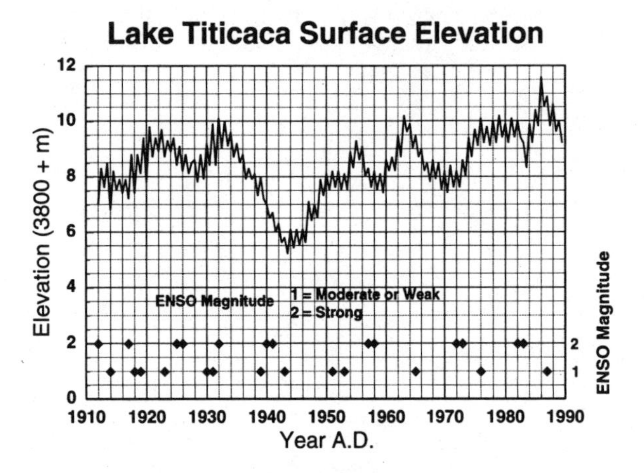


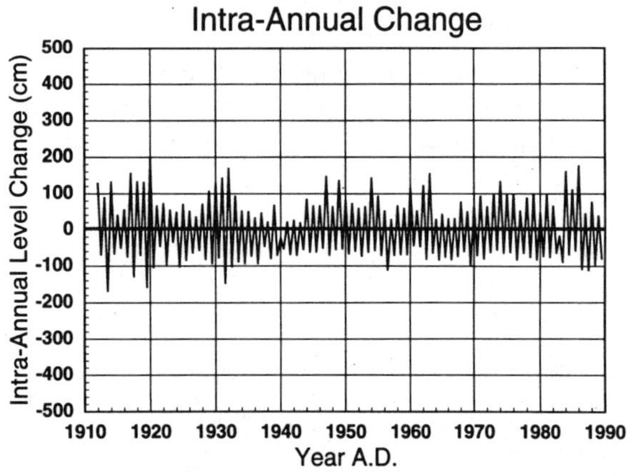


**Figure 2.8.** *Top:* Twentieth-century lake-level curve with occurrences of ENSO events. Lake-level data were originally collected at Puno, Peru, by the Servicio de Hidrografía de Puno–Peru. Note that periods of ENSO activity tend to be periods of relatively lower lake levels but that there is no perfect coincidence. *Bottom:* Magnitude of intra-annual lake-level change. Note that the long decline in the 1930s and 1940s was a result of low or no annual increases, while the annual declines were not different from the long-term average. The rise in the mid–1980s was a result of abnormal annual rises and normal declines.

component of describing the environmental context within which a civilization developed, prospered, and collapsed. This section describes general Andean climate changes for the past 12,000 years (the period of human occupation) and then reviews the results of paleoclimate studies in the Tiwanaku core area. Although stratigraphic studies of pollen assemblages are normally major sources of paleoclimatic information, the most useful lines of evidence for this discussion are studies of former lake-level fluctuations, fluctuations of glacial extent, and changing accumulation rates of ice in high-altitude glaciers.

Pollen studies have been less important than other avenues of research in the central Andes for several reasons. First, few studies have been done, and these have produced ambiguous results because of the high spatial variability of both climate and vegetation. Second, the high-altitude vegetation that produces pollen has low diversity. Different species of the same genus are distributed in various ways relative to climate, and most plant species cannot be distinguished by their pollen. This problem is especially acute for studies of human activities because cultivated plants and natural vegetation are often of the same genera. Third, high beta diversity (the diversity gradient across spatial transects) in the Andes and low density of sampling sites preclude development of the quantitative relationships between climatic parameters and pollen assemblages that exist for European and eastern North American regions (Markgraf 1989). Fourth, relationships between plant frequencies and pollen frequencies are unknown. At best, paleoclimatic inferences from pollen stratigraphy are only semiquantitative, and they depend on knowledge of the biogeography and natural history of many different plant species. Such biogeographical studies are not well developed in the region.

Glacial and lake-level studies are also constrained because of the uncertainty about causes of variation. Authorities have argued for years about whether changes in precipitation, temperature, or processes that drive evapotranspiration have been the factors controlling these water bodies (Lynch 1990). Increased precipitation, with the other factors held constant, leads to glacial expansion, thicker annual ice accumulation, and higher lake levels. Decreased temperature can also cause expansion because a smaller amount of water evaporates from the system. Finally, decreased insolation and wind speed with increased relative humidity form a third possible cause of expansion of the water systems.

### GLOBAL CLIMATE AND LOCAL HUMAN ACTIVITIES

Climatic discontinuities and episodes of greater global climatic variation sometimes occurred at dates similar to those of periods of change in the Tiwanaku culture (Bradley 1985:14). The transition from subboreal to sub-Atlantic time (about 2760 to 2510 years before present [B.P.], where "present" is A.D. 1950) was roughly contemporaneous with the initiation of lacustrine and fluvial floodplain agriculture in the altiplano (3500 to 2000 B.P.). A period of high global climate variability around 1680 B.P. was contemporaneous with the initiation and expansion of raised-field systems. Finally, abandonment of most fields occurred near the period of high climate variability about 850 B.P.

We do not infer cause and effect from these periods of global change because we have insufficient data for the altiplano and the region. Despite several decades of effort, paleoclimatological study sites are sorely deficient in Central and South America (Binford et al. 1987; Colinvaux 1987; Kutzbach and Street-Perrott 1985; Lynch 1990; Markgraf 1989; Street and Grove 1979). Recent evidence from South American glaciers suggests that precipitation and temperature in the altiplano have not necessarily varied in concert with global averages but exhibit independent patterns (Seltzer 1990; Wright, Seltzer, and Hansen 1989). However, the apparent temporal correspondences between periods of major climate change or high variability and periods of cultural change in the Tiwanaku region are provocative.

### ANDEAN PALEOCLIMATES

Despite the uncomfortable level of uncertainty, some informative work has been done recently at sites in the Peruvian, Bolivian, and Chilean Andes, including the Lake Titicaca basin. Results from this work are not in complete agreement, but broad patterns emerge. In general, climates throughout Central and South America were 4° to 5° C cooler during full and late glacial times (18,000 B.P. to 12,000 B.P.) than today, but moisture patterns varied in different regions (Markgraf 1989). Most areas were significantly drier than at present, but the southern subtropics and high latitudes were substantially moister.

The transition from Pleistocene to Holocene climate occurred everywhere between 12,000 and 10,000 B.P. (Bradbury et al. 1981; Hansen, Wright, and Bradbury 1984; Markgraf 1989), with most authors leaning toward the later date. Lakes in the lowlands and in northern South America filled as water formerly sequestered in both high-altitude and high-latitude glaciers was released by warming and conveyed to the lakes by global atmospheric circulation or directly by local glacial meltwater.

The early Holocene, from 10,000 to 8000–7000 B.P., was generally warmer and moister than now. This warm, moist period was followed by a period of warmer climate that lasted for 3,000 to 4,000 years in the Altoandean region, 5,000 years in the Paramo, and as little as 1,000 years in the higher-latitude southern lands (Markgraf 1989). Just as the period, sometimes called the hypsithermal in North America and Europe, varied in time depending on the location, different regions experienced different moisture regimes as circulation patterns and local topography influenced precipitation. Most of the continent was warmer and wetter. However, the Paramo and sub-Paramo regions of Venezuela, Colombia, and Peru were cooler and drier, as was the Altoandean region in which Lake Titicaca is located (Markgraf 1989).

Regional climates, however, do not necessarily follow the widespread general patterns, especially in areas of high altitude and diverse microenvironments like the altiplano. Along with lake-level fluctuations (discussed later), the major sources of paleoclimate information are pollen studies in Lake Titicaca and several other nearby lakes and studies of local glacier behavior over the past 20,000 years.

#### POLLEN STUDIES

Stratigraphy of pollen and aquatic plant remains in sediment cores taken from Lake Wiñaymarka, Lake Poopo, and several smaller lakes from higher elevations in the Wiñaymarka basin show great variations in vegetation communities through time and, by inference, wide variability in past climates. The most useful sources of information for interpreting pollen stratigraphy are the modern elevation distributions of different terrestrial plant species and the associations of aquatic plants with water depth and sediment type in the large lake.

A paper by Ybert (1992) summarizes many years of work on altiplano paleoecology based on palynology and studies of diatoms, animal microfossils, and other organismal indicators. Ybert divides the stratigraphy of two cores taken from about 20 meters of water in Lake Wiñaymarka near the Bolivian-Peruvian border into five zones. Each zone is characterized by an assemblage of pollen, aquatic plant microfossils (mostly remains of phytoplanktonic algae), and aquatic plant macrofossils (seeds, leaves, recognizable fragments).

The first zone represents the time before 21,000 years B.P. Terrestrial pollen is from a community now found at about 4,500 meters, which is about 3° to 5° C cooler than the elevation at lake level now. Aquatic fossils indicate a shallow lake not vegetated by the currently widespread totora (sedges) but by another macrophyte, *Isoetes,* which is not now recorded in the lake. Pollen and microfossils in the second zone, from about 21,000 to 17,500 B.P., indicate cooler temperatures than those of the previous zone by about 2° to 5° C. The lake became shallower early, then deepened to about 15 meters at the core site in the later part of the zone. Temperatures increased to roughly modern levels in the third zone, from 17,500 to 11,000 B.P., and the lake level was about 5 meters higher. This zone corresponds to the deeper lakes Minchin and Tauca described from geomorphological evidence. The top of the zone, from 12,000 to 11,500 B.P., shows a cooling trend accompanied by the beginning of a drop in lake level.

Lake level declined through the fourth zone, from 11,000 to 4100 B.P., at first rapidly to a depth of 0 to 1 meter, with the lowest levels attained between 7700 and 6500 B.P. and again at 4500 B.P. The temperature was 1° to 3° C cooler throughout the zone. Aquatic microfossils are typical of more saline conditions and resemble the modern phytoplankton of the saline Lake Poopo. The uppermost zone, from about 4100 B.P. to the present, has a rapid increase in aquatic microfossils, indicating rapid rise of lake level. According to Ybert (1992:60), "the water level was 10 to 15 meters below the present level between about 3000 and 2000 B.P., then at the same level from 2000 to 1500 B.P. A well-marked drop occurred about 2500 B.P. together with oscillations of an amplitude of about 5 meters marked by sharp increases in the percentage of *Pediastrum,* a common planktonic algal microfossil that indicates deeper water." The upper part of this zone is especially interesting because it shows the expansion of pollen representation of Cyperaceae, most if not all of which is totora. The logical interpretation is that totora was not widespread, or possibly even present, in the lake until about 3,000 years ago.

Recent palynological work by Barbara Leyden (chapter 4) agrees generally with Ybert's interpretations. However, a core taken in only 2 meters of water near the village of Lukurmata on the northern side of the Taraco peninsula apparently contains 6,000 years of uninterrupted sedimentation. If the lake level was exceptionally low at 4500 B.P., then the site should have been dry and far from the shoreline of any large lake. In chapter 4, Binford, Brenner, and Leyden speculate that the core site could have been something like the many small ponds (*qocha,* in Quechua, or *kkota,* in Aymara) that are widespread in the Lake Titicaca drainage basin today.

### LOCAL GLACIAL STUDIES

Glacial geologists and paleoclimatologists use the chronology of advances and retreats of local glaciers as an index of local climate change. Generally, glacial advances indicate periods of increased precipitation or decreased temperature, and retreats indicate the reverse. Glacial advances and retreats cannot be measured continuously. Instead, they are measured by mapping and radiocarbon dating end-moraine deposits, which record the time of the maximum advance, and by dating basal organic sediments in tarn and cirque lakes and peat deposits, which indicate the time of retreat from a given point. Glaciers depend on a net accumulation of annual snowfall. At the latitude of the altiplano, freezing temperatures occur only at altitudes high enough for the mean annual temperature to be below 0° C. The Bolivian Andes have been high enough for glacier formation since the late Pliocene or early Pleistocene, and high-altitude glaciers have been present during the entire period of human occupation.

Notwithstanding our earlier comments about the uncertainties of regional causes of glacial advances and retreats, Seltzer (1990) makes a convincing argument that, at least locally in the Peruvian-Bolivian Andes, permanent snowline follows precipitation. For a local example, a 50-millimeter-per-year increase in precipitation results in a 100-meter lowering of the snowline in the Cordillera Apolobamba, directly to the north of Lake Titicaca (Jordan 1985).

Four major and several minor Quaternary glacial advances have been documented in the basin (Servant 1977; and see fig. 2.3). The major advances are named, from oldest to most recent, Calvario (2.8 million years ago), Kaluyo (age uncertain), Sorata (age uncertain), and two stages of Choqueyapu (stage I is of uncertain age; stage II was from about 28,000 to 14,000 years ago, but see below). Each left behind interglacial erosion surfaces at elevations from 3,900 to 4,400 meters.

Higher-elevation glaciers (currently terminating at between 4,700 and 4,920 meters) in the Cordillera Real, less than 40 kilometers east of Lake Wiñaymarka, reached as low as 4,200 meters at the glacial maximum between 18,000 and 14,000 B.P. as a result of higher precipitation and temperatures 3.5° ± 1.6° C cooler than at present (Seltzer 1992). Deglaciation began about 12,000 B.P. as the local climate became drier and warmer. A short-lived neoglaciation began about 1300 B.P., with several readvances and recessions (Seltzer 1990, 1992). Since then, the glaciers have steadily retreated. Therefore, at least during the Quaternary the floor of the altiplano in the Lake Titicaca basin has not been covered by glaciers. Moreover, it is unlikely that it has *ever* been glaciated because prior to the major periods of orogenesis its elevation was even lower. The most recent (1300 B.P.) neoglaciation and retreat correspond to a period of increased, then decreased, precipitation that is recorded in the Quelccaya ice cap (Thompson et al. 1985, 1988) and reflected in the rise and collapse of hydraulically dependent agricultural systems (Ortloff and Kolata 1993; and see chapter 8).

### QUELCCAYA ICE CORE DATA

The most highly resolved record of regional paleoclimates comes from 200 kilometers to the northwest at the Peruvian Quelccaya glacier (Thompson et al. 1985, 1988). The record clearly indicates wetter periods during Tiwanaku times at A.D. 610–650 and 760–1040 and periods of decreased precipitation at A.D. 540–730 and 1250–1310. Our own preliminary studies indicate that between A.D. 350 and 510 (just before the published Quelccaya record and coincident with the widespread development of raised-field agriculture) the lake level was significantly higher than usual (Binford and Brenner 1989:Appendix A; and see chapter 4). This period is also bracketed by the South American and Antarctic neoglacial advances of 3000–2000 B.P. and 1300–1000 B.P., which were probably influenced more by increased precipitation than by temperature variation (Clapperton and Sugden 1988; Seltzer 1990). Two periods of major earth-moving activity, including raised-field construction, are indicated by high dust concentrations in the Quelccaya ice cap, with peaks around A.D. 920 and 600 (Thompson et al. 1988). Although we do not agree completely, Thompson and colleagues argue that the Quelccaya record is a reasonably good proxy for Lake Titicaca level.

A recent analysis of the Quelccaya data may help explain the termination of raised-field agriculture. Ortloff and Kolata (1993; and see chapter 8) demonstrate conclusively that long-term average ice accumulation declined by about 15 percent shortly after 1000 B.P. The sharp decline was preceded by several hundred years of high accumulation that began nearly coincident with the initiation of raised fields and was followed by approximately 400 years of reduced precipitation. Ortloff and Kolata expand their analysis to the rest of the Central Andean region and argue that such a drought would have led first to decreased rainfall, then to decreased spring discharges and loss of groundwater resources as aquifers were not recharged. The effects of the drought seem to have spread throughout Tiwanaku's hegemony and coincided with the abandonment of several other hydraulically intensive agricultural practices.

### LAKE-LEVEL FLUCTUATION

The fluctuation of lake levels offers another line of evidence for investigating paleoclimatic variation. The altiplano is endorheic; the single outlet from Lake Titicaca drains to Lake Poopo and then to the immense salt flats farther south. Lake Titicaca itself lies in a semiclosed basin because of the relatively tiny discharge through the Desaguadero River. Consequently, the lake responds rapidly to climate changes as its level fluctuates in response to precipitation (Carmouze and Aquize Jaen 1981; Carmouze, Arce, and Quintanilla 1984; Hastenrath and Kutzbach 1985).

Lake stands during the Pleistocene have already been discussed and are not relevant to human activities until the time of the late Pleistocene lakes Minchin and Tauca. Although the levels of Lake Tauca are not well dated, there was a high stand from 12,500 to 11,000 B.P. in response to a precipitation increase of approximately 200 millimeters per year, or 30–50 percent (Servant and Fontes 1978; Wirrmann, Ybert, and Mourguiart 1992). Although apparently large, this increase is within the normal range of variation in the instrumental record and therefore plausible as a long-term environmental change (Hastenrath and Kutzbach 1985).

The large basin of Lake Titicaca may have undergone fluctuations of +10 to –50 meters during the Holocene, while Lake Wiñaymarka dried up completely (Wirrmann and Oliveira Almeida 1987; Wirrmann, Ybert, and Mourguiart 1992). The entire lake declined rapidly beginning about 10,500 to 11,000 years ago and reached its minimum elevation between 7700 and 7250 B.P., when the two basins became separated. This low stand was followed by a rise in Lake Wiñaymarka to about 10 meters below its present level by 6000 B.P., then by another decline beginning about 4500 B.P. After 4000 B.P., the lake rose gradually, reaching its present level at about 2000 B.P. Wirrmann, Ybert, and Mourguiart (1992) cite historical records of a rapid rise and fall about 350 B.P. Our more recent work is refining the lake-level curve for the past 3,500 years, and we find major fluctuations that are correlated with significant cultural changes.

This interpretation has clear implications for regulation of human activities in the basin. The first agriculture in our study area is recorded at a time of increasing lake level, which implies increasing precipitation. The initiation of raised-field agriculture occurred around the time that the lake level became relatively stable. The outlet elevation at the Desaguadero River determines the near-maximum elevation of the lake, and the more recent fluctuations of several meters are the result of hydrological balance between the rate at which water enters the basin and the rate at which it leaves through the outlet. Consequently, if the lake attained its present elevation about 2000 B.P., then the general extent of available moisture, wetlands, and periodic flooding at that time would have been about the same as it is today.

Present climate, however, is hardly stable. The lake level has varied over 6.4 meters during the twentieth century (Carmouze and Aquize Jaen 1981; Roche et al. 1992; and see fig. 2.8). The continuous decline from 3810.1 meters in 1933 to 3805.2 meters in 1943 is singular in this century and is twice the magnitude of the next greatest decline, in the period 1964–70. The greatest continuous rise was between the lowest level at 3805.2 meters in 1943 and 3809.3 meters in 1955. From 1985 to 1986 the lake rose about 3 meters to the highest level of the twentieth century. On the average over the twentieth century, the lake rose about 80 centimeters during the rainy season and fell 78 centimeters during the dry season. There have been only two years in which the lake failed to rise during the rainy season (1940 and 1983, both years of strong ENSO), and the lake always falls during the dry season.

The mean high level is 3808.8 ± 1.2 meters (standard deviation), and the mean low level is 3808.0 ± 1.1 meters. An analysis of recurrence intervals for lake levels indicates that whereas the annual high stand is greater than 3807.0 meters in 90 percent of the years, the lake is higher than 3810.1 meters in only 10 percent of the years. Conversely, the annual low stand is lower than 3806.5 meters in only 10 percent of the years and lower than 3809.4 meters in 90 percent of the years.

## The Lake

We describe the physical, chemical, and biological nature of Lake Titicaca because the lake and its biota are resources for people as much as are the soil and the water from rivers and springs. Unfortunately, only a few ecological studies have been done in the terrestrial sector of the drainage basin, and what we know of natural systems comes mostly from investigations carried out either as part of more general studies of Andean ecosystems or as part of limnological or paleoecological studies that included terrestrial components. Lake Titicaca has attracted many limnological studies because its size and elevation make it an interesting laboratory that has physical conditions within which to test both general hypotheses developed in more common situations and hypotheses unique to the site. From our perspective, the description of the lake is very much a part of the description of the natural and human context of Tiwanaku civilization.

Seventy percent of the 1,430-square-kilometer Lake Wiñaymarka is greater than 10 meters deep, and 58 percent of the lake bottom is covered by macrophyte beds (bathymetry from 1:100,000-scale map produced by the Dirección de Hidrografía de la Marina de Bolivia and the Instituto Geográfico Militar de Peru; macrophyte data from Collot, Koriyama, and García 1983). The slope of the bottom and nearby pampas is so slight that the lake can cover many square kilometers with a rise of only a few meters. A 1-meter excursion in lake level (about normal annual variation) can affect 250 square kilometers of the total lake area, which in turn can mean as much as a 5-kilometer change in the location of the shoreline. A 5-meter lake level change would result in a 7- to 18-kilometer migration of some sections of the eastern shoreline. A 20-meter decline from the July 1977 level, which could result from a long-term, 25-percent decrease in precipitation (and may, in fact, have occurred during the mid-Holocene [Hastenrath and Kutzbach 1985]), would move the eastern shoreline 28 kilometers, nearly to the present border in the lake between Bolivia and Peru.

### WATER BUDGET AND WATER CHEMISTRY

Calculating the water budget for Lake Titicaca seems to have been a popular occupation for hydrologists. Multiple water budget studies have been attempted for a variety of purposes: as an academic exercise in a hydrologically unique basin (Carmouze, Arce, and Quintanilla 1977, 1984; Kessler and Monheim 1968); as a prerequisite for paleoclimatological modeling (Hastenrath and Kutzbach 1985); and even to provide the basic information required for decisions about exploiting the water resources of the basin (Bourges, Cortes, and Salas 1992). Water budgets describe the input, storage, and outputs of water, and consequently of materials borne by water such as sediments and dissolved ions. The physico-chemical condition of the lake is dependent first on the nature of its water budget.

In the annual water balance for the lake and the basin for the years 1968 to 1987, precipitation added about $7.47 \times 10^9$ cubic meters per year directly to the lake and an additional $36.13 \times 10^9$ cubic meters per year to the basin, for a total of $43.6 \times 10^9$ cubic meters per year (Roche et al. 1992). Evaporative losses accounted for 91.1 percent of the precipitation. Little water leaves by the Desaguadero River (less than 0.5 percent of the input in wet years) or by deep seepage (about 9 percent, but note that this figure was calculated by difference and therefore is suspect; see Winter 1981).

The effect of the predominance of evapotranspiration on the water budget is that dissolved salts in river water and precipitation tend to stay in the system; they do not flow out through the outlet (Carmouze, Arce, and Quintanilla 1992). Consequently, the lake water is slightly brackish, which has major implications both for lake biota and for agriculture around the lake. Water in the large lake has a high concentration of total dissolved solutes (about 850 milligrams per liter), dominated by $Ca^{2+}$, $Na^+$, $Cl^-$, $HCO_3^-$, and $SO_4^{2-}$. Average pH is 8.6 (Richerson et al. 1977). The ions are supplied mostly by river inflow, which has an average total dissolved salt concentration of between 5 and 10 millimoles per liter (Carmouze, Arce, and Quintanilla 1992). According to Meybeck (1979), the average value for all inland waters is about 2 millimoles per liter, which makes the inflowing rivers especially concentrated by chemical weathering in the drainage basin. There are no published measurements of ion chemistry in rainfall. Ion losses balance income, resulting in stable lakewater chemistry, at least during the twentieth century. Chemical sedimentation and losses to seepage account for 88.6 percent of the losses of ions from the water column. Only 11.4 percent of the ions are lost to the outflow (Carmouze, Arce, and Quintanilla 1992).

#### HEAT BUDGETS AND MIXING

Mean temperature of surficial waters is 11° to 15° C. The large basin (Lake Titicaca) is warm monomictic, as are most large tropical lakes, and it stratifies from October to June, when the epilimnetic temperature reaches its peak of 14° to 15° C (Richerson et al. 1986). Despite its great depth, the water mixes to the bottom during the brief period of July and August in some years, although the strength of mixing is variable between years (Kaiser and Richerson 1988; Richerson 1992). In contrast, Lake Wiñaymarka is polymictic and stratifies only in the deep Fosa de Chua during the austral summer (Carmouze, Arce, and Quintanilla 1984).

The daily pattern of thermal stratification is also typical of large tropical lakes. By midafternoon the water surface can become as much as 1° C warmer than water at 10–15 meters (Powell et al. 1984). Heating of 0.4° C can reach down as far as 6 to 7 meters below the surface during the day. The heat is lost rapidly during the night, however, and the epilimnion (at least to about 25 meters) is usually isothermal by early morning.

Mixing regimes are important because they regulate the recycling of biologically important elements. The movement of particles downward into the hypolimnion (lower waters separated by density differences from the upper water in the lighted zone) carries nutrients out of reach of photosynthesizing organisms. When the lake mixes, the nutrients, which often have been transformed from organically bound to inorganic, biologically available forms in the anoxic environment of the lower waters, are circulated back into the zone of primary production. Furthermore, the pattern of diurnal stratification inhibits epilimnetic mixing, which enhances the transfer of nutrients downward.

#### PRIMARY PRODUCTION

Primary production in an ecological sense is the conversion by plants of nutrients and sunlight into biomass through the biochemical process of photosynthesis. This biomass becomes the basis of food webs that include all the other living organisms in the ecosystem. Limnologists and ecosystem scientists measure the primary production of the total community, not of individual species or groups of species, and report results in grams of carbon incorporated into biomass per unit area or volume per unit time (usually day or year). Primary production in any ecosystem is variable in space and time, and the factors that control its magnitude and variation are important to understand.

Several studies of primary production have been done in both basins of Lake Titicaca. Richerson and colleagues (1992) have summarized the interesting patterns that emerge. The rate and temporal variability of primary production are typical for tropical lakes, although decreased slightly by the extreme altitude. The four-year average value for primary production in the large lake basin is 1.13 grams of carbon per square meter per day, in Lake Wiñaymarka 0.56 g C per $m^2$ per day, and in the Bay of Puno 0.82 g C per m$^2$ per day. There is essentially no seasonal variation, in part because of the low variability of physical forcing factors. On the other hand, interannual variability is large, some years having periods of very high productivity and other years very low.

There is wide spatial variability in primary production, both vertically and horizontally. High light intensities at the surface of the lake inhibit photosynthesis, so the zone of maximum productivity is often below 5 meters. Algal biomass, which is correlated with productivity, is generally higher in Lake Wiñaymarka than in the large lake (Iltis 1988, 1992), probably because of the proximity of nutrient-rich sediments. There seems to be a rough correlation between water depth and biomass in both the large and the small lake, with shallower water having higher biomasses (see maps in Iltis 1988).

#### TROPHIC STATUS AND NUTRIENT LIMITATION

Trophic status is a combined expression of plant biomass in the water column and rate of primary production by photosynthesis. Generally, only phytoplankton biomass and photosynthesis are considered, although some authors argue that macrophyte biomass and production should be considered as part of trophic state. A lake is described as oligotrophic, mesotrophic, or eutrophic, in increasing magnitude of phytoplankton biomass and rate of primary production. Lake Titicaca is considered meso-oligotrophic (Carney, Richerson, and Eloranta 1987; Lazzaro 1981; Vincent et al. 1984, 1985), except in productive areas such as the Fosa de Chua and the Bay of Puno, which are meso-eutrophic and eutrophic, respectively (Lazzaro 1981).

Primary production supports higher trophic levels such as fish and humans. Lakes of different trophic statuses harbor different assemblages of aquatic plants and animals, some of which are more useful to humans than others. One of the major results in limnology during the twentieth century has been the demonstration that primary production, and consequently biomass, in lakes is usually limited by the availability of one or more nutrient elements. The rate of supply of nutrients, especially nitrogen and phosphorus, controls the rate of primary production. Manipulating the rate of supply is the most effective method for lake management, whether the objective is to increase or decrease productivity.

Primary production in most north-temperate lakes in formerly glaciated areas is usually limited by a scarcity of phosphorus. Because most earlier studies of nutrient limitation were done in these kinds of lakes, this generalization about phosphorus limitation has been mistakenly applied to lakes all over the world. Many subtropical and tropical lakes, as well as lakes in regions with phosphorus-rich sedimentary bedrock, have been shown to be limited by nitrogen availability. In fact, tropical lake productivity may be more often limited by nitrogen than by phosphorus (Vincent et al. 1984).

Nutrient conditions in Lake Titicaca's water column are generally deficient, except during mixing episodes, because of the biomass of algal phytoplankton. Nitrogen availability usually limits phytoplankton photosynthesis, although when thermal stratification is prolonged, phosphorus drops to low levels and becomes the limiting nutrient (Wurtsbaugh et al. 1985). Several micronutrients, including molybdenum and iron, can also limit photosynthesis at times.

When nitrogen-phosphorus ratios (N:P) in lake water drop below 30, cyanobacteria (blue-green algae) often dominate a lake's phytoplankton because many of those species can carry out nitrogen fixation, which is the transformation of inert, gaseous nitrogen to inorganic ammonium and then to nitrate compounds that can be used in photosynthesis (Smith 1982; Tilman 1982). N:P ratios in Lake Titicaca are usually around 11 and often less than 10. Nitrogen fixation by cyanobacteria is therefore a significant source of biologically available nitrogen for primary production (Carney 1984; Lazzaro 1981; Vincent et al. 1984, 1985; Wurtsbaugh et al. 1985). Nitrogen fixation also depends on the availability of other nutrients, including phosphorus and iron. Thus, low phosphorus concentrations (generally about 10 $\mu$g per liter in Lake Titicaca) may limit nitrogen fixation. However the interactions among nutrients affect primary production, the fact remains that overall primary production in Lake Titicaca is probably limited by nitrogen availability. If the input of biologically available nitrogen to the lake were to increase, or if the nitrogen-phosphorus ratio were to increase, an increase in overall productivity of the lake would be expected.

#### AQUATIC VEGETATION

Phytoplankton in the main basin is dominated by chlorophytes (green algae) and diatoms, with about 5 to 20 percent of the total algal biomass represented by cyanophytes (Carney et al. 1987; Vincent et al. 1986).

Cyanophyte dominance and maximum nitrogen fixation occur during thermal stratification. Until recently, no cyanophytes had been recorded in Lake Wiñaymarka (Lazzaro 1981). Studies in 1985–87 found an increasing biomass of cyanophytes in the smaller lake (Iltis 1988), perhaps owing to the flooding of soils relatively rich in phosphorus.

For the most part, the algal species found in the lake are widespread forms, and only a few endemics exist (Iltis 1992; Servant-Vildary 1992). Floral diversity of algae is low, with no inventories counting more than 260 species, a small number considering the size and physical diversity of the lake (Iltis 1992). There is no apparent seasonal cycle of population sizes as there is in temperate lakes. Instead, interannual variability, perhaps governed by interactions with higher trophic levels or competition with other algae, regulates temporal patterns (Richerson et al. 1986).

One of the most striking characteristics of Lake Wiñaymarka is its vast beds of totora, the emergent sedge (sedges are plants of the family Cyperaceae). This plant, either *Schoenoplectus totora* or *Scirpus totora*, depending on the authority, is the source of food, fodder, fiber for clothing, and building material for houses, boats, even islands. The beds also provide habitat and food for many other species of plants and animals, including fish. There are several other species of higher aquatic plants in the lake, and with only a couple of exceptions they are all exploited by humans. Earlier we noted that paleoecological studies by Ybert (1992) demonstrate that totora was not widespread, and may not even have been present, in the lake until about 3,000 years ago. Several authors (summarized in Levieil and Orlove 1992:508) describe the recent spread of totora as principally the result of planting and transplanting by local shore-dwelling humans. These two observations, together with the archaeological evidence that intensive human activities did not begin in the basin until about 3,000 years ago, support the hypothesis that the colonization and spread of totora in Lake Titicaca may have been anthropogenic.

The total higher plant flora of Lake Titicaca is represented by only 10 families encompassing a total of 12 species (table 2.3). An additional 11 species of macrophytes belong to the family Characae, which is a group of algae with a growth form resembling that of higher plants. Deeply submerged beds of *Chara*, the dominant genus of the family, cover about 32 percent of the total surface area of Lake Wiñaymarka, making this the dominant plant in the lake (Collot, Koriyama, and García 1983). Other total coverages listed by Collot, Koriyama, and García (1983) are *Elodea* (water weed), 16 percent; *Myriophyllum* (water milfoil), 16 percent; *Potamogeton*, 23 percent; *Schoenoplectus*, 13 percent; and no vegetation, 44 percent.

This listing is a little misleading, however, because it implies monospecific stands of plants, whereas the different species actually occur in associations distributed according to several ecological factors, the most important of which seems to be water depth (fig. 2.9). According to Collot, Koriyama, and García (1983), the emergents *Hydrocotyle* and *Lilaeopsis* occur from 0 to about 20 centimeters deep. *Myriophyllum*, *Elodea*, *Potamogeton*, and *Ruppia* (the assemblage commonly used today as livestock feed) dominate from 0.2 to 2.5 meters. *Schoenoplectus tatora*, interspersed with *Potamogeton* or *Chara*, dominates from 2.5 to 4.5 meters. *Chara* is found in monospecific stands below the totora zone, from 4.5 to about 7.5 meters. Finally, there is a zone of nearly pure *Potamogeton* from 7.5 to 8 or 9 meters.

This characterization of plant association distribution is also slightly misleading because the different associations are actually found arranged in a complicated mosaic, with weaker control by water depth than that implied by Collot and colleagues (1983). We routinely encountered, at depths ranging from 1 to 7 meters, *Chara* beds—supposedly deep-water forms in Collot, Koriyama, and García's scheme—directly adjacent to the *Myriophyllum*, *Elodea*, *Potamogeton*, and *Ruppia* assemblages, which are supposed to be in shallower water. We have also dredged some *Chara* species from as deep as 15 meters in locations near Huatajata. Clearly, Collot, Koriyama, and García's description is valuable as a first approximation, but the actual distributions of both individual species and associations of species are much more complicated.

Because of its correlation with water depth, the distribution of aquatic plants is bound to change with changing lake level, which in turn must affect the ability of humans to harvest the plants. A better characterization of the factors that regulate aquatic plant distribution in Lake Titicaca would be a major contribution not only to aquatic science but also to the understanding of how humans might manage their exploitation of the resource, both in modern times and in the past.

High light levels, low diversity, and high density and extent of macrophytes results in extraordinarily

**Table 2.3 Higher Plant Taxa Recorded in Lake Titicaca.**

| Family | Species | Uses |
|---|---|---|
| Azollaceae | *Azolla* sp. | Nitrogen fixation by ectosymbiotic cyanobacteria *Anabaena azollae* |
| Ranunculaceae | *Ranunculus trichophyllus* | None: toxic |
| Haloragaceae | *Myriophyllum elatinoides* | Livestock fodder, handicrafts, fuel |
| Umbelliferae | *Hydracotyle ranunculoides* | None, possibly fodder |
| | *Lilaeopsis andina* | None, possibly fodder |
| Hydrocharitaceae | *Elodea potamogeton* | Livestock fodder, handicrafts, fuel, major $O^2$ producer |
| Potamogetonaceae | *Potamogeton strictus* | Livestock fodder, handicrafts, fuel |
| Ruppieceae | *Ruppia maritima* | Livestock fodder, handicrafts, fuel |
| Zannichelliaceae | *Zannichellia palustris* | None |
| Lemnaceae | *Lemna gibba* | Possibly fodder |
| | *Lemna* cf. *aequinoctialis* | |
| Cyperaceae | *Schoenoplectus* (or *Scirpus*) atora | Food, fodder, fiber, boats, building materials; major economic importance for Lake Titicaca dwellers |

Sources: The taxonomic treatment is from Raynal-Roques (1992) and the list of uses is from Levieil and Orlove (1992).

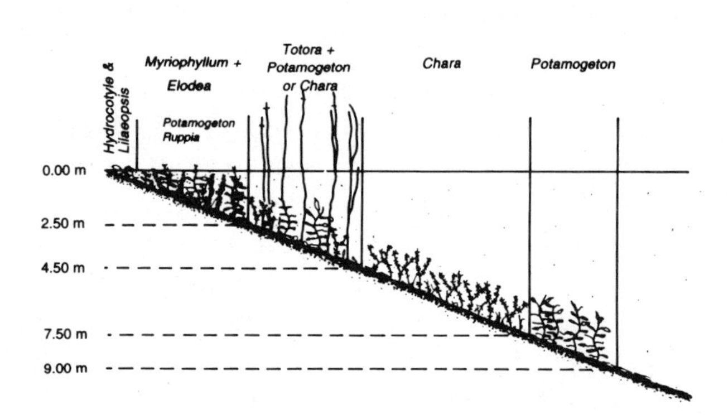


**Figure 2.9.** Aquatic macrophytes and their general relationship to water depth (redrawn from Collot, Koriyama, and García 1983).

high levels of primary production. Rooted plants have their roots in the nutrient-rich sediments and their leaves in the air (emergents), on the surface of the water (floating leaves), or in shallow water (submergents). The relatively low seasonal variability of physical factors, including lack of freezing in the lake, results in maximum potential for photosynthesis by these high-altitude plant communities. For example, Collot, Koriyama, and García (1983) measured the mean production of *Chara* alone to be 11.6 grams dry weight (DW) per square meter per day, which each year between 1978 and 1980 added about 5,000 metric tons of biomass to the system in Lake Wiñaymarka. The same studies measured a production of between 0.2 and 1.5 g DW per m$^2$ per day for totora (120 tons [T] per day), or about 44,000 tons per year (in Lake Wiñaymarka, 265 T per day, and in Puno Bay, about 97,000 T per yr), and between 0.8 g (175 T) and 10 g (2,200 T) DW per m$^2$ per day for *Myriophyllum* and *Elodea*, respectively.

Production measurements can be compared with extraction estimates to determine the degree to which the macrophyte resources are exploited. Unfortunately, there are no estimates of extraction rates for the *Myriophyllum-Elodea-Potamogeton* assemblage, collectively called *llachu* and used extensively for livestock feed and to some extent for industrial purposes such as mattress stuffing and fuel (Levieil and Orlove 1992). The production measurements for totora are about double the contemporary extraction rates by humans, which have been estimated at about 50,000 tons per year in Puno Bay (Levieil and Goyzueta 1984, cited in Levieil and Orlove 1992). No estimates are available for Lake Wiñaymarka, but because the human population density is lower there than around Puno Bay, the extraction rate is probably a lower absolute amount, but an unknown percentage of total production. The average totora harvest in Puno Bay was only about 18 percent of total biomass (50,000 T out of 275,900 T; total biomass from Iltis and Mourguiart 1992). Again, the total totora harvest from Wiñaymarka should be a smaller absolute amount of the estimated 131,700 T of total totora biomass.

#### INVERTEBRATES

Invertebrates occupy nearly every possible niche in Lake Titicaca and include both endemics and cosmopolitan species. Diversity at the class and order level is high, and many scholars have studied the different groups. Despite the long interest in the taxonomy and biogeography of the invertebrate fauna of the lake, there have been only a smattering of ecological studies.

Zooplankton, tiny animals that cannot swim strongly enough to avoid transport by currents and that make up a major part of the diet of small fishes, are rather common and have densities that equal or exceed those of most temperate and low-altitude tropical lakes (Pinto 1992). According to Pinto's maps (his fig. 5), zooplanktonic animals are less abundant in the zones of high macrophyte density, except for a zone just north of the Taraco peninsula, where both of the two major crustacean zooplankton genera, *Copepoda* and *Cladocera,* reached their highest densities.

As in the case of phytoplankton, there seems to be no definite seasonal variation in the zooplankton community in either Lake Wiñaymarka or the large lake. Studies done in different years report maximum densities in different months, with a small tendency toward peaks in the late wet season (March and April) and sometimes in January–February (Moreno 1983; Pawley and Richerson 1992; Pinto 1992). In all cases, the variation of different zooplankton taxa was characterized by unpredictability.

*Orestias ispi,* a small pelagic fish, actively feeds on zooplankton during the day and can depress the population size of all zooplankton (Leblond 1983, cited in Pinto 1992). *O. ispi* are predominantly plankton feeders and do not seem to select among the crustacean groups (Vaux et al. 1988). Several other fish, especially other species of *Orestias,* along with *Basilichthys bonariensis* (*pejerrey*) and *Salmo gairdneri* (rainbow trout), depend on zooplankton at one or several stages of their life cycle (Loubens 1989; Loubens and Osorio 1988; Vaux et al. 1988).

The benthic fauna are animals that live on or in the sediments on the bottom of the lake or on plants. This group is also an important component of the diet of different fishes. Like those of zooplankton, the taxonomy and biogeography of several different benthic groups have been studied in some detail, but useful ecological studies have been done only on the Ostracoda, or seed shrimp. These studies have described the distribution of different species of ostracods in relation to plant associations and water depth (Mourguiart 1992). The information is valuable for inferring past environments because the carapaces of the animals preserve in sediments and can be identified to the species level (e.g., Mourguiart et al. 1986; Wirrmann, Ybert, and Mourguiart 1992).

Currently, rudimentary taxonomic studies exist for many other groups of invertebrates, including the Amphipoda, Mollusca, Oligochaeta, Porifera, Bryozoa, Coelenterata, Tricladida, Hirundinea, Hydracarina, and even the insects (see chapters in DeJoux and Iltis 1992). Members of each of these groups carry out important functions in ecosystem processes, ranging from shredding large particulate organic matter into fine particulates that can be decomposed by bacteria to providing food for higher trophic levels, including humans.

The two ecological studies that exist describe the habitat relationships of benthic species assemblages and short-term temporal variations in the population densities of different taxa (DeJoux 1992a). Mollusks and amphipods are the most abundant groups in both parts of the lake, although this may be an artifact of sampling methods. Of the two parts of the lake, Lake Wiñaymarka is far more densely populated by benthos. The density of benthos in the smaller, shallower lake is highly variable spatially, which, when coupled with temporal variability, seems to make predicting the density of benthos at a particular place and time difficult, if not impossible.

### FISH

Aquatic habitats in the central Andes are an excellent evolutionary and biogeographical laboratory (Parenti 1981). Although there are 24 endemic species of the fish genus *Orestias* in the lake (Parenti 1984), other aquatic animals seem to be no more diverse than at higher latitudes. There are only two fish genera that occur naturally in the lake, *Trichomycterus* and *Orestias,* both of which are endemic to the altiplano. The only other two species, *Salmo gairdneri* and *Basilichthys bonariensis,* were introduced into the lake in 1941–42 and 1955–56, respectively. Thus, only the two native genera and any genera that may have gone extinct in the last 1,000 years were part of the human environment of Tiwanaku.

*Trichomycterus,* a genus of the Trichomycteridae catfish family that is widespread in South America, has only two species, *T. rivulatus* and *T. dispar,* in Lake Titicaca. Almost nothing is known about their ecology, although they form a small part of the lake's fishery. *Orestias* is an extraordinarily interesting genus with 24 different species in the lake (Lauzanne 1992). Parenti (1984) lists 46 possible species (including one hybrid) from the Andes of Peru, Bolivia, and Chile but argues that the genus does not form a "species flock" because it is not monophyletic. According to Lauzanne (1992), the different species partition the Lake Titicaca habitat into several vegetation zones, called "biotopes," and the pelagic, or deep-water, zone. Juveniles and small adults of many species inhabit the nearshore littoral with its floating-leaf plants and shallow open water. The totora zone harbors the highest diversity of *Orestias* species, and the deeper *Chara, Potamogeton,* and unvegetated zones have fewer species. In the case of deep water, only three zooplanktivorous species, including the abundant *O. ispi,* are common. Deeper water surveys have not been accomplished, and more species may be encountered.

### AMPHIBIANS AND REPTILES

Although the neotropical amphibian fauna is among the most diverse in the world, only four genera representing three families are found in Lake Titicaca (Vellard 1992). All species are either frogs or toads, and we know of no reports of salamanders, newts, or other amphibians. Environmental conditions at high altitudes are not optimal for most amphibians, which usually must breed in warm water and live in areas with high humidity. The amphibians that do live in the drainage basin all are adapted in interesting ways to the harsh conditions.

*Bufo spinulosus,* the only toad, is widespread in the Andes from Chile and Argentina to Ecuador. Very little is known of its ecology. *Gastrotheca bolivian,* a member of the tree-frog family Hylidae, is widely distributed in the basin of the lake. This frog is interesting because the females incubate their eggs in brood pouches, which allows them to breed in dry areas. Specimens have been collected as far from the lake as Tiwanaku, Calacoto in southern La Paz, and even Potosí. The third minor amphibian genus is represented by two species of the family Leptodactylidae—*Pleuroderma cinerea* and *P. marmorata*—both of which live in damp habitats. They are aquatic only during breeding and are both distributed widely in the Andes.

The most important and well-known amphibian genus is another leptodactylid, *Telmatobius,* which is widespread in the Andes. The taxonomy of this genus is indistinct, but Vellard (1992) defines 17 species living in the Lake Titicaca basin. One group of five species (called the *marmoratus* group) lives mostly in marshes, springs, along the lake margin, and in streams leading to the lake. The second group of 12 species comprises mostly lacustrine forms. Some of these species live in the different macrophyte zones, and others, which can reach sizes of over 130 millimeters long and almost as broad, are usually found in deeper water, perhaps more than 20 meters deep.

These frogs and toads have been part of the human environment for millennia and have been used for medicinal and ritual purposes (Vellard 1992). Infusions made from *Telmatobius* and *Paludicola* are used to treat several internal diseases, and living frogs and toads are applied locally for inflammation and skin diseases. During droughts or at the end of the dry season just prior to the anticipated onset of the rains, Aymaras of the Lake Titicaca region frequently collect toads (*jamp'atu*) from different sources of water such as rivers, ponds, and marshy seeps at the foot of mountains. They place the toads in ollas which they carry to places of offering, frequently an earth shrine on a mountain peak. The toads are left there to "cry out" (that is, to begin croaking) as the hot sun beats down upon them and evaporates the moisture that protects their skins. One of our informants, Policarpio Flores from the village of Qorpa in the Tiwanaku Valley, understands this croaking as the toads' "crying" tears that are intended to encourage the onset of the rains by evoking pity for the toads from the spirits of nature. Tschopik (1947:567) provides a similar description of toads used as vehicles of ritual communication among Aymaras on the northern shores of Lake Titicaca.

Very few reptile species live in the high Andes, and only a few have been reported from the Lake Titicaca basin. Small lizards of the genus *Liolaemus* can sometimes be found under rocks and occasionally in the open (Mann 1969). The only time the lizards can be found on the surface is when environmental conditions are optimal and they seek heat from solar radiation. The only snake reported from the Lake Titicaca basin is the small (40–50 centimeters total length), rear-fanged colubrid *Tachymenis peruviana,* which is widespread in the Peruvian and Bolivian Andes between 3,000 and 4,000 meters (Vellard 1992). The snake is venomous but not usually fatal to humans, although its bite "provokes a moderately serious effect with local oedema, moderate swelling and fever" (Vellard 1992:459). This snake feeds mostly on small amphibians and lizards and is not aggressive toward humans unless harassed or handled. Despite its abundance, it is not seen often because it is nocturnal, lives in protected, damp areas under rocks, and is not particularly active.

#### BIRDS AND MAMMALS

The avifauna of the Lake Titicaca basin are derived from widespread Andean species. DeJoux (1992b) lists 13 orders, 27 families, and 50 species recorded in the basin. Several species, especially the rails (three species), ducks (five species), and the Andean goose, were used for food by the people of Tiwanaku. There is currently little hunting of birds around the lake.

Several different groups of mammals, which are of primary importance to humans, are found in the Andes and altiplano. The dominant group with human importance consists of members of the family Camelidae, which includes llamas (*Lama glam*), alpacas (*Lama paco*), and vicuñas (*Lama vicugna*). Other mammals include deer (*Odocoileus* sp., *Hippocamelus antisensis*), wild cats (*Telis jacobita* and the mountain lion or puma, *Felis concolor,* both now possibly extinct in the altiplano), foxes (*Conepatus chinga res, Dusicyon culpaeus, Dusicyon griseu*), many rodents, including the edible guinea pigs, *Microcavia niata, Cavia aperea,* and *Galea musteloides,* and finally the viscacha, *Lagidium viscacia.* Many of these animals have important economic and cultural uses for indigenous people living at elevations higher than that at which cattle can be raised. For example, the camelids are sources of protein, wool, and transport. Moreover, they are avidly exploited for ritual purposes. Guinea pigs are eaten as delicacies as well as employed in divination and the taking of auguries.

## Terrestrial Ecology

Lake Titicaca is located in a relatively little-known biome: the high-altitude tropics. High altitudes in the tropics offer replicates of low-altitude systems with different means but similar ranges of climatic variables. With the exception of the fish genus *Orestias* and the amphibian *Telmatobius,* biological diversity in the Titicaca basin and the altiplano is not as great as that in lowland tropical areas and other ancient lakes. Terrestrial vegetation and aquatic macrophyte species diversity is low.

#### TERRESTRIAL VEGETATION

Early European explorers, including Alexander von Humboldt, observed that the altitudinal zonation of different plant communities in the tropics resembled their global latitudinal zonation. More recently, this simplified idea of correspondence has been modified by the understanding that the nature of seasonal variation differs greatly between altitudinal and latitudinal transects (Troll 1968). Nevertheless, the actual vertical variation of climate and vegetation and its changes in historical and paleoecological time have led to a great volume of work that attempts to define human environments in these terms (Masuda, Shimada, and Morris 1985).

The importance of altitudinal variation for the Tiwanaku core area is that its elevation is in a narrow band within which temperature and moisture are benign enough that humans can raise food crops and animals. Our earlier discussion of paleoecology described a highly variable climate over the past 10,000 years. A seemingly slight change in average annual temperature or precipitation can change the effective climatic elevation. A change in effective elevation of only a few hundred meters could bring impossibly harsh conditions to the level of the altiplano. This means that any agriculturally dependent society would have to adapt to the change by altering subsistence technologies or by migrating over the cordilleras to lower elevations in order to carry out the same cultivation practices. Ortloff and Kolata (1993; and see chapter 8) discuss the decline of Tiwanaku as an integrated, preindustrial state precisely in terms of an environmentally generated agricultural crisis of this kind.

The modern vertical distribution of general ecological communities in the Peruvian and Bolivian Andes in the region of Lake Titicaca is illustrated in figure 2.10. Although the lake is just over 3,800 meters above sea level, it exerts a strong climatic effect on agriculture near the shoreline, creating an environment that is similar to that at least 450 meters lower (Vacher, Thuy, and Liberman 1992). For example, barley and wheat are normally grown below 3,350 meters, but because of the lake's thermal effects, these crops can be grown near the lakeshore.

Much of the recent descriptive vegetation ecology of the Bolivian Andes was compiled by Ellenberg (1975), who divided the country into 12 ecoregions based on climate, elevation, and vegetation. The Ellenberg ecoregions found in the Tiwanaku area are the Altoandean zones (dry and semihumid) and the Puna zone. The Altoandean zones extend from about 4,400 meters up to the permanent snow line. The Puna zone spans the rest of the elevations in the altiplano.

Plant species in the dry Altoandean zone, mostly in the Cordillera Occidental, are characterized by adaptations to cold, desiccating conditions and thus are not very useful for grazing livestock. The exception to this is that camelids can live for short periods while feeding on hard forage. Cushion plants (e.g. *Azorella*) and tough grasses (*Festuca, Stipa,* and *Calamagrostis*) dominate the assemblages. There are a few small evergreen shrubs (*Baccharis, Parastrephia, Adesmia,* and *Senecio*). Rarely, small groves of the tree *Polylepis* are encountered, sometimes in sheltered areas as high as 5,200 meters.

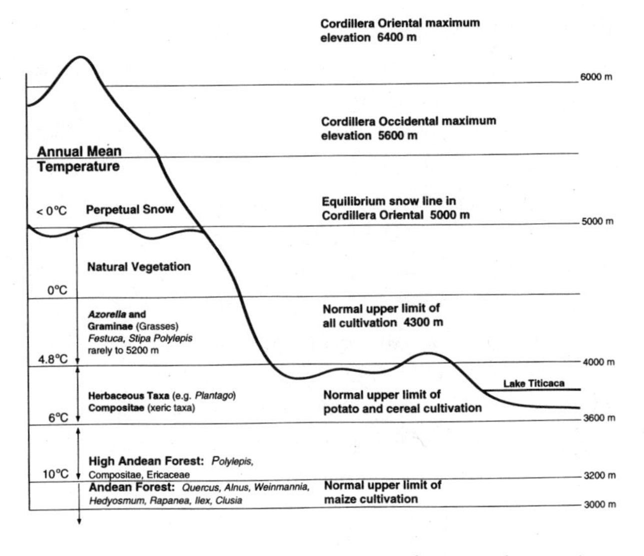


**Figure 2.10.** Modern vertical distribution of terrestrial vegetation communities in relation to annual mean temperature, along with normal limits of cultivated crops in the Lake Titicaca basin (data from Markgraf 1989; Morales 1990; Troll 1980; Seltzer 1992).

The semihumid Altoandean zone, mostly in the Cordillera Oriental, is characterized by plant communities with distributions strongly controlled by the aspect of the mountainside and microrelief at a particular spot (Morales 1990). The dominant species are again tough grasses (*Stipa*) and several shrubs (*Baccharis, Parastrephia*), but various herbaceous plants and other grasses can be found where microedaphic conditions are appropriate.

There are small, boggy spots, termed *bofedales,* found in both the Altoandean and Puna zones. Although dominated by hard cushion plants (e.g., *Distichia*), these small wetlands harbor much more diverse vegetation assemblages that include several grasses (e.g., *Poa*), aquatic and semiaquatic plants (*Carex* and *Juncus*), and other plants that provide useful animal forage (Morales 1990). Palacios Ríos (1977:155) offers a fascinating description of artificial bofedales maintained by contemporary Aymara communities in nonagricultual zones of extreme altitude. These bofedales are used to generate high-quality forage for the communities' camelid herds. The Aymaras develop and expand these artificial bofedales through irrigation channels fed by local springs and snowmelt. In order to sustain these wetlands, large areas must be inundated abundantly and permanently. If irrigation water is diverted or reduced, the bofedal may shrink dramatically as high evapotranspiration rates deprive colonizing vegetation of essential moisture. According to Palacios

Rios's Aymara informants from Chichillapi in the Department of Puno, Peru (1977:162), if the bofedal is deprived of water, the sun will burn the vegetation to the roots and the artificial wetland cannot be restored for years. It is likely that many if not all of these bofedales are only partially anthropogenic, reflecting human manipulation of localized, naturally occurring wetlands. Artificial bofedales were almost certainly a technological and cultural feature of the pre-Hispanic social landscape of the altiplano.

The Puna zone is divided into two distinct regions in the altiplano: the semihumid puna in the north, which is the Tiwanaku region, and the dry puna in the central and southern altiplano. The semihumid puna is amenable to cultivated plants and trees such as *Buddleia, Polylepis,* and *Cantua.* Introduced eucalypts are widespread in isolated patches.

On the floors of Lake Titicaca valleys, terrestrial associations consist of composites, grasses, legumes, and solanaceous plants, varying with local precipitation. The *Fabiana densa–Psila bolivensis–Adesmia horridiuscula* association generally prevails, with infrequent woods of *Polylepis tomentella* (Cabrera 1968). The *Psila bolivensis* consociation is less frequent, as is *Oreocereus celsianus.* Many edaphic communities can be found in areas of sandy, moist soils or high groundwater table.

#### PRINCIPAL CULTIVARS

Modern crops are segregated altitudinally in the Tiwanaku core area (Bowman 1916; Galdo Pagaza 1981). Corn, barley, and wheat are normally grown below 3,350 meters, but barley and wheat especially are produced in zones around the lake. Potatoes can be grown to 4,200 meters and quinoa (*Chenopodium quinoa*) to around 4,000 meters. Kañiwa (*Chenopodium pallidicaule*) is readily grown to 4,300 meters, and the upper limit of cultivation approaches 4,400 meters in protected areas. Two other tuberous crops, oca (*Oxalis tuberosa*) and ullucu (*Ullucus tuberosus*), and a legume, tarwi (*Lupinis mutabilis*), are grown in the study area. Apart from occasional plots of kañiwa, no crops are grown above 4,300 meters, and the sparse natural vegetation is used for grazing camelids. Most contemporary agriculture is practiced on hill slopes and, to a lesser extent, on broad plains that once supported raised fields. Chapter 9 discusses the range of native and introduced cultivars that we are currently producing on rehabilitated raised-field systems. We have successfully produced a broad range of non-Andean food crops, such as lettuce, carrots, onions, and radishes, on these experimental plots at altitudes around 3,800 meters. From these experiments, it is clear that raised-field technology can reduce the normal altitude limitations on certain food crops.

## Human Systems

Local culture history is summarized in table 2.4. From the perspective of significant changes in agroecosystems, important dates in this timeline are 3500 B.P., when agriculture began in the area; 1800 to 1600 B.P., when intensive raised-field cultivation became widespread; 900 to 800 B.P., when raised-field agriculture was effectively abandoned; and 400 B.P. to the present, after which European activities became important. Each date is the beginning of a period of land-use change that is reflected in the paleoecological record.

All evidence points to a date of around 3500 B.P. for the emergence of relatively widespread agriculture in the southern Lake Titicaca region. This does not mean that no agriculture was practiced on the shores of the lake and its associated river systems before that time. It is possible that nonintensive forms of cultivation appeared as early as 5000 B.P. However, the first archaeological evidence in the study area for a relatively well-developed form of lacustrine and fluvial floodplain agriculture appears around 3500 B.P. Further research may modify this picture, but given our interpretations of the environmental history of the southern Lake Titicaca region, we do not believe that raised-field agriculture was widely developed before about 3500 B.P. This conclusion contradicts Erickson's (1988a) speculation that raised-field agriculture in the Lake Titicaca basin was an ancient agricultural technology that emerged as early as 6000 B.P. In sum, the probability of intensive agriculture on the shores and fluvial plains of Lake Titicaca by as early as, but no earlier than, 3500 B.P. is a strong one. We should detect evidence of land-use change, vegetation disturbances, or influx of allochthonous materials into the lake around this time (see chapter 4).

We agree with Erickson's (1988a) suggestion that the earliest expression of intensive raised-field agriculture was restricted to the zone near the lake's edge. The lacustrine zone is the most obvious candidate for initial experimentation with this wetlands form of cultivation in the Lake Titicaca basin. Inland, river-oriented raised fields were most likely a later adapta-

**Table 2.4. Summary of Human Activities in the Catari and Tiwanaku Valleys**

| Date | Culture | Land Use | Human Population |
|---|---|---|---|
| 5000–6000 B.P. | Preceramic | No archaeological evidence of large-scale agriculture | 200–500 in small, mobile bands |
| 3500–2000 B.P. | Chiripa and Tiwanaku I | Initiation of lacustrine and fluvial floodplain agriculture (raised fields) | 10,000–15,000 in 40–60 small villages along Lake Titicaca shore |
| 1800–1200 B.P. | Tiwanaku III<br>Tiwanaku IV | Expansion and integration of raised fields into regional systems; articulation of raised fields with large hydraulic structures: aqueducts, canalized rivers, quebradas | 200,000–350,000 in regional urban centers, rural zones, and city of Tiwanaku |
| 1200–1000 B.P. | Tiwanaku V | Peak of raised-field construction and maintenance | Population reaches maximum: 285,000–570,000 |
| 950–850 B.P. | Early Pacajes | Collapse of raised fields as an integrated system; raised fields abandoned as major economic activity | Population decline and break-up of Tiwanaku macrostate into smaller, regional polities |
| 800–700 B.P. | Early Pacajes | Initiation of terrace agriculture systems on steep slopes on mainland and on islands. | Dispersal of population into numerous villages and fortified settlements |
| 500 B.P. | Pacajes/Inca | Peak of terrace agriculture | |
| 400 B.P. | Spanish conquest | Abandonment of major terraces; collapse of intensive agricultural systems | Massive demographic collapse: local population declines 65–90% |
| 300 B.P. | Colonial to modern period: Aymara speakers | Small-scale subsistence farming; shallow-furrow dry farming on gentle slopes and valley bottoms | Slow population recovery |

Sources: Based on published and unpublished data collected by Proyecto Wila Jawira. Published sources for population projections include Albarracín-Jordan and Mathews (1990), Kolata (1983, 1986, 1989, 1991), Kolata and Ortloff (1989), and Ortloff and Kolata (1989).

tion from this precocious lake-edge reclamation. In our study area, the first evidence for inland (10 to 15 kilometers from lake edge) expansion of raised-field systems occurs in late Tiwanaku III and early Tiwanaku IV times, or around A.D. 300 to 500. Note, however, that the evidence for Tiwanaku III raised-field cultivation in inland zones is largely inferential and not as secure as the abundant evidence for subsequent Tiwanaku IV and V associations. This expansion entailed both large-scale construction of raised fields themselves and development of a suite of agriculturally related public works projects: causeways, dikes, empoundments, reservoirs, aqueducts, and quebrada canalizations. This process of massive agricultural construction continued in the southern Lake Titicaca region throughout the late Tiwanaku IV period and into Tiwanaku phase V (approximately A.D. 800 to 1000). The peak of raised-field construction and maintenance occurred during the 400-year period from about A.D. 600 to 1000 (see chapter 5).

Between A.D. 1000 and 1100, the archaeological record indicates major population shifts throughout the Tiwanaku sustaining area, marked most dramatically by the effective abandonment of Tiwanaku urban centers such as Lukurmata and Tiwanaku itself. This period was characterized by significant disaggregation and dispersion of populations throughout the Tiwanaku sustaining area. By the end of the Tiwanaku V period, raised-field agriculture was no longer a major economic activity in the region. We correlate these regional-scale changes in agricultural technology, demography, and human settlement patterns with a significant deterioration in climate, specifically with the onset of chronic drought conditions that rendered intensive, groundwater-dependent, raised-field agriculture infeasible (Ortloff and Kolata 1993; and see chapter 8).

There may have been a hiatus in intensive agricultural activities in the Tiwanaku core area from about A.D. 1000 to 1200, but this possibility requires additional empirical investigation and verification. It is clear, however, that after A.D. 1100 there was a major shift in agricultural technology in the Tiwanaku sustaining area. Intensive agriculture in the study area reemerged in the post-Tiwanaku social environment not as alluvial-plain, wetlands-adapted agriculture but rather in the form of terraced agriculture.

We believe that the replacement of continuous tracts of raised fields in the pampas zones along the lake with small-scale, irrigated terrace systems in the immediate post-Tiwanaku environment was an adaptation to chronic drought conditions. These smaller-scale terrace complexes are concentrated in protected quebradas and, unlike the virtually continuous tracts of Tiwanaku-period raised fields, they are not integrated into regional-scale production complexes. Rather, they occur as independent, discontinuous, microdrainage basin systems. They draw water from specific, single-point sources (typically higher-altitude springs) rather than from multiple and more geographically generalized sources (such as the groundwater inputs to raised fields). In essence, the post-Tiwanaku agroecological landscape appears as fragmented pockets of production or, to change the simile, as a differentiated mosaic of discrete, quebrada-based systems.

This physical dispersion and differentiation of agricultural production zones holds implications for the nature and organization of post-Tiwanaku political economy in our study area. When conjoined with our evidence for disaggregation and dispersion of human populations into previously unexploited ecological zones during the post-Tiwanaku period (which we will discuss later), this change in land-use patterns strongly implies a dramatic shift in the social and political organization of agricultural production. The most central dimension in this shift was movement away from a tightly hierarchical organization of production. With the "Balkanization," or political fragmentation, of the Tiwanaku macrostate into smaller-scale, competing polities, there was an apparent truncation of the hierarchy of extraction, correlated with a significant reduction in geographical scope of the agricultural hinterlands that post-Tiwanaku political units were able to exploit. The geography of power of the post-Tiwanaku period was one of movement from stability to instability, from centralization to decentralization, and from monopolized to multipolar expressions of authority. The concluding chapter to this volume considers in greater detail the social implications of these changes in indigenous political economy.

Terrace agriculture in the study area continued through the Inca conquest of the Lake Titicaca basin sometime around A.D. 1450. Inca-period terraces appear prominently in the forms of both irrigated and rainfall-fed terraces. Terrace-based production appears to have continued into the early Spanish colonial period (up to about A.D. 1560 or so), after which the effects of massive depopulation due to disease, trauma, war, and Spanish labor demands for the mines of Potosí resulted in virtually complete and permanent abandonment of major terrace systems (see Sánchez-Albornoz 1978 for a document-based study of the catastrophic, early-colonial-period decline in native populations).

A third pre-Hispanic intensification technology, that of *qochas,* clearly played an important role in the Lake Titicaca basin (Flores-Ochoa 1983). Qochas are essentially artificial ponds excavated into the phreatic zone to exploit groundwater and to capture and store seasonal rainfall. These features, similar in many respects to the pre-Hispanic *mahames,* or sunken gardens, of coastal Peru, were intended for cultivation purposes but may have been designed to provide forage and sources of drinking water for camelid herds as well. In this latter aspect, qochas were functionally equivalent to the forage-producing, anthropogenic bofedales described by Palacios Ríos. We have strong circumstantial, but no incontrovertible, evidence that qochas were part of the repertoire of Tiwanaku farmers and herders, at least during the Tiwanaku IV and V phases. We suspect that qochas became increasingly important as an intensification device in the post-Tiwanaku social environment, which was subject to and shaped by significant problems of cultural adaptation to drought conditions.

Dug into the phreatic zone above the water table, qochas supported crop production on their shallow-angle sidewalls and pit bottoms. They offered a simple technological response to drought conditions: they could be continuously excavated to follow a dropping water table. Although less vulnerable to drought than rain-fed and raised-field cultivation systems, by their nature qochas have limited planting surface areas and offer a low rate of agricultural return relative to labor invested (Ortloff and Kolata 1993). Rather than being a direct source of agricultural produce, post-Tiwanaku qocha systems may have been intended principally to support intensive investment in camelid herds. That is, after the collapse of Tiwanaku raised-field agriculture in the region, human populations may have shifted the mix of their agropastoral activities to place increasing emphasis on camelid pastoralism in order to replace lost food resources. Such a shift would have entailed dramatic changes in the logistics of subsistence and, correlatively, in the structure of the prevailing social order toward a more dispersed, mobile (and perhaps aggressive) society. As we have already indicated, and consistent with this scenario of drought-induced change in subsistence strategies, population disaggregation and dispersion and the effective abandonment of urban centers are dramatic hallmarks of the post-Tiwanaku social environment.

## Demography and Settlement Patterns

Human population size is directly correlated with the history of agricultural intensification in the Lake Titicaca basin (Kolata 1983, 1986, 1991). Table 2.4 summarizes estimates of population size in the research area over time. These numbers are general, *order-of-magnitude* estimates based on intensive archaeological survey in the Tiwanaku and Catari River basins and on surface survey and excavations in Tiwanaku-period urban centers. We offer these population estimates as first-order approximations subject to future modification, and we emphatically intend no attribution of precision.

Current archaeological evidence indicates that from 3,500 to 2,000 years ago, population in the Tiwanaku hinterland was distributed in some 40 to 60 hamlets and villages representing from 10,000 to 15,000 people. Many of these settlements are located on or near the current shoreline of Lake Titicaca or in closely adjacent uplands. Because many small sites from these early, Formative-period complexes may be deeply buried under sediments in the active floodplains of the river basins and therefore missing in our survey sample, we cannot profile the complete population size and distribution of this period with great confidence or accuracy.

The period between 1800 and 1100 B.P. in the research area witnessed significant processes of population aggregation and urbanization. It was at this time that substantial populations concentrated at Tiwanaku and other regional urban centers such as Lukurmata, Pajchiri, and Khonko Wankané in the Machaca-Desaguadero basin. In addition, in the Tiwanaku and Catari basins at least, large, village-sized settlements developed along colluvial terraces immediately adjacent to virtually continuous raised-field complexes on the valley floors (Albarracín-Jordan and Mathews 1990; Kolata 1993a). For instance, in the Tiwanaku IV and early Tiwanaku V phases, the lower and middle valley of Tiwanaku was organized into an integrated agricultural production zone characterized by a distinct settlement hierarchy similar in many respects to that described by Kolata (1986, 1991, 1993a) for the Pampa Koani area of the Catari basin. During this time, a series of sites was established along the colluvial terraces on both the north and south sides of the valley, immediately above the Tiwanaku River's floodplain. These Tiwanaku settlements are spaced regularly, approximately 2 kilometers apart, along the adjacent terraces from the city of Tiwanaku itself to the shore of Lake Titicaca some 17 kilometers away (Albarracín-Jordan and Mathews 1990). They vary in size from 1 to 10 hectares and show evidence of dense occupation. Several have elaborate, stone-faced terraces on which houses and craft workshops were constructed. Some of the larger sites were substantial villages associated with the administration of agricultural production on raised fields in the adjacent river plain (Albarracín-Jordan and Mathews 1990). Frequently, these settlements were linked with raised-field complexes via causeways.

This 700-year period was unquestionably the time of greatest population growth and organizational complexity in the research area. The expansion of this population was directly associated with the integration of raised-field and supporting hydrological technology into a complex regional landscape of agricultural production. Human population reached a maximum in the region between 1200 and 1000 B.P. Based on recent systematic archaeological work in Tiwanaku, its secondary urban settlements, and its hinterland, we estimate that the overall peak population for the immediate Tiwanaku sustaining area (the three-valley system of Pampa Koani–Tiwanaku–Machaca) during this period approached approximately 365,000, distributed into a concentrated, urbanized component of some 115,000 and a more dispersed, rural component of 250,000 (Kolata 1993a). By "rural component" we mean simply all population that maintained primary residence outside the four major urban centers of this area—Tiwanaku, Lukurmata, Pajchiri, and Khonko Wankané. As Stanish (1989) recognized for the Taraco peninsula, this distinction between urban and nonurban populations is partly arbitrary, considering that populations were almost continuously distributed along the extensive colluvial terraces between urban nodes in the Tiwanaku region. During this "peak period," city and countryside both were densely populated and interconnected in a hierarchically organized network of settlement and production (see the concluding chapter to this volume for additional consideration of this point).

In sharp contrast, the immediate post-Tiwanaku settlement pattern in the region exhibits a nearly complete disintegration of this organized exploitation of the valley for the purposes of intensive agricultural production. Although there are still substantial numbers of sites in Tiwanaku's hinterland dating after 900 B.P., they are widely dispersed across the landscape and few exceed 1 hectare in size (Albarracín-Jordan and Mathews 1990). Most dramatic of all in terms of settlement pattern transformations, the cities of Tiwanaku and Lukurmata themselves were virtually abandoned at this time. (We suspect that Pajchiri and possibly Khonko Wankané suffered the same fate, but at present we have no primary archaeological evidence to substantiate this conjecture.) Radiocarbon dates on Tiwanaku V–phase households in these cities cluster between A.D. 750 and 950, and *no* radiocarbon dates on domestic occupations are associated with these urban centers past A.D. 1000 (table 2.5). There was, in short, a dramatic redistribution of population in the Tiwanaku hinterland characterized by complete deurbanization. If, as Saalman (1968:11) suggests, "there is only one criterion of failure for cities: depopulation," then after about A.D. 1000 Tiwanaku and its secondary urban centers were clear failures. As a

**Table 2.5. Radiocarbon Dates from Sites of the Tiwanaku V Phase**

| Site | Laboratory Designation | Radiocarbon Years | Calibrated Years | Tiwanaku Phase |
|---|---|---|---|---|
| Tiwanaku | SMU-5639 | 1170 ± 60 B.P. | A.D. 860 ± 80 | V |
| Tiwanaku | ETH-6306 | 1460 ± 60 B.P. | A.D. 590 ± 60 | IV |
| Tiwanaku | SMU-2330 | 1080 ± 210 B.P. | A.D. 950 ± 110 | V |
| Tiwanaku | SMU-2367 | 1150 ± 80 B.P. | A.D. 880 ± 80 | V |
| Tiwanaku | ETH-5680 | 1170 ± 65 B.P. | A.D. 860 ± 85 | V |
| Tiwanaku | SMU-2468 | 1390 ± 50 B.P. | A.D. 640 ± 35 | Late IV |
| Tiwanaku | SMU-2467 | 1130 ± 60 B.P. | A.D. 900 ± 70 | V |
| Tiwanaku | SMU-2472 | 1200 ± 115 B.P. | A.D. 830 ± 130 | V |
| Tiwanaku | SMU-2465 | 1110 ± 50 B.P. | A.D. 930 ± 60 | V |
| Tiwanaku | SMU-2466 | 1170 ± 60 B.P. | A.D. 860 ± 80 | V |
| Tiwanaku | SMU-2289 | 1185 ± 60 B.P. | A.D. 840 ± 80 | V |
| Tiwanaku | SMU-2290 | 1120 ± 70 B.P. | A.D. 910 ± 85 | V |
| Tiwanaku | SMU-2276 | 1070 ± 60 B.P. | A.D. 960 ± 60 | V |
| Tiwanaku | SMU-2277 | 1130 ± 60 B.P. | A.D. 900 ± 70 | V |
| Tiwanaku | SMU-2469 | 1190 ± 100 B.P. | A.D. 830 ± 115 | V |
| Lukurmata | SMU-2165 | 1000 ± 230 B.P. | A.D. 1020 ± 220 | V |
| Lukurmata | ETH-3180 | 990 ± 95 B.P. | A.D. 1045 ± 100 | V |
| Lukurmata | ETH-3179 | 1180 ± 110 B.P. | A.D. 840 ± 115 | V |
| Lukurmata | SMU-1920 | 1201 ± 96 B.P. | A.D. 818 ± 110 | V |
| Lukurmata | ETH-3178 | 1085 ± 90 B.P. | A.D. 950 ± 100 | V |
| Lukurmata | SMU-2117 | 1090 ± 60 B.P. | A.D. 950 ± 70 | V |
| Chen Chen | HV-1076 | 1040 ± 65 B.P. | A.D. 999 ± 32 | V |
| Chen Chen | HV-1077 | 930 ± 65 B.P. | A.D. 1105 ± 78 | Late V |
| Loreto Viejo | HV-1091 | 980 ± 70 B.P. | A.D. 1024 ± 84 | V |
| Omo | Beta-26650 | 1120 ± 60 B.P. | A.D. 897 ± 53 | V |
| Omo | Beta-26649 | 1170 ± 70 B.P. | A.D. 883 ± 93 | V |

corollary to this proposition, we might add that when cities and urban culture fail, so do the state political systems in which they are embedded.

There is some evidence for localized raised-field cultivation in the post–A.D. 1000 environment (Albarracín-Jordan and Mathews 1990; Graffam 1990; Seddon 1994). However, despite subsequent periods of relatively higher precipitation that would have made this form of cultivation again technologically feasible, the earlier regional system of large-scale agricultural production was never reactivated. Perhaps this serves to illustrate that societies possess thresholds of irreversibility. Once fragmented, the precarious structures of organizational complexity characteristic of expansionary polities like Tiwanaku never permit a return to the original state.

In sum, after 1000 B.P. there was a marked spatial shift in populations with the dissolution of the Tiwanaku state and its apparent break-up into smaller, regional polities. Whether this redistribution of population was accompanied by an aggregate population decline as well is still unclear. That is, the salient question becomes, is the archaeologically evident depopulation of Tiwanaku cities also reflective of at least partial rural depopulation? Although in absolute terms there are hundreds of archaeological sites in the Tiwanaku Valley in the immediate post-Tiwanaku social environment, virtually all of these sites are of small scale, with few exceeding 1 hectare in size (Albarracín-Jordan and Mathews 1990). These sites can be interpreted best as dispersed household-sized and hamlet-sized population clusters. Given the previous scale of population concentrations in urbanized clusters during the Tiwanaku IV and V periods, we believe that there was, in fact, an episode of post-Tiwanaku population decline in the research area. Our archaeological evidence, however, is currently of insufficient resolution to enable us to generate a detailed profile of the magnitude of this decline. Nevertheless, all archaeological evidence points to the fact that the high levels of population attained during the Tiwanaku period in the southern lake basin were never achieved again, even during the Inca reign.

The sixteenth-century Spanish invasion and subsequent reorganization and exploitation of native populations in the region induced a catastrophic demographic collapse associated with virtual cessation of intensive agricultural activities. Terraced agriculture as well as extensive camelid pastoralism effectively disappeared in the study area by the close of the sixteenth century and was replaced by small-scale subsistence farming. By this time, camelid herds in the southern lake basin were displaced by European livestock, and the agricultural landscape was reduced to highly localized expressions of nonintensive cultivation, a pattern of indigenous economy that persists to the present.

In the early decades of colonial governance, the Spaniards established a system of large landholdings concentrated in elite-dominated estates. The earliest expression of these landed estates was the encomienda system. An encomienda was essentially the grant of a tract of land, together with the labor service of natives living on the land, made by the Spanish Crown to an individual and, in some cases, his heirs for a number of generations. As Robinson (1964:8) has pointed out:

> The institution of the *encomienda* carried with it the seeds of its own destruction because the tribute that the crown allowed the *encomenderos* to exact from the natives was a fixed amount. Therefore, there was no incentive for the *encomenderos* to improve production, to maintain existing facilities, or care about the welfare of the Indians. The *encomiendas* and tribute were a powerful force in changing economic and land patterns. Many Indian communities were broken down and dispersed when the Indians lost control of their lands.

Because the encomienda was as much a grant of people as of land, the encomienda holders jealously asserted their rights to labor services from the native communities within their concession. Not surprisingly, this exercise of encomienda prerogative to exclusive labor service generated considerable tension with the Spanish Crown and its colonial arms of governance. The cumulative effects of catastrophic decline in native populations brought on by disease, civil strife, and the oppressive demands of the colonial version of *mita* labor tribute, particularly in the savage mines of Potosí, exacerbated a perennial economic problem of the postconquest social environment: a tremendous scarcity of native labor. At the same time, it should be noted that not all native communities were reduced or encapsulated within encomiendas or the estates of the Spanish Crown. Despite the onslaught of tribute demands and the European appropriation and redistribution of native lands, many indigenous communities, particularly those in isolated and economically marginal lands, managed to retain much of their identity and cultural practices, including indigenous forms of land tenure and usufruct rights.

By the later part of the sixteenth century, the encomienda system began to disintegrate under pressure from the Spanish Crown. Large, landed estates, however, persisted in different sociological forms into the twentieth century. During the Republican period and into the modern era, these estates were organized as the latifundio, or hacienda, system (Klein 1992). Latifundios, like encomiendas, exploited the labor of landless workers alienated from their traditional communities. Living conditions for natives on altiplano haciendas varied enormously. In the aggregate, however, there is little question that the system was profoundly repressive and reduced the indigenous populations to an invidious form of indentured servitude. After centuries of increasing conflict and violence between the *patrones* (estate owners) and workers, the latifundio system of landed estates was dissolved in Bolivia by implementation of various agrarian reform laws instituted by the government of the Movimiento Nacional Revolucionario (MNR) beginning in 1952 (Klein 1992). The great estates were broken up into small, native-owned agricultural plots farmed by individuals and small family groups. This form of *minifundismo* remains the principal pattern of land use today.

## Contemporary Land Use in the Research Area

The ultimately negative effects of the contemporary minifundismo pattern of land tenure from the perspective of agricultural production is evident in certain economic diagnostics that characterize indigenous communities within our study area. (All economic and census statistics cited here are drawn from Fernández 1989 and from our own localized census work.) In the province of Los Andes, which includes great portions of the Pampa Koani and Catari basins, the majority of the population supports itself by small-scale agriculture and livestock production. Production is principally for local, internal consumption and not for export; that is, this is a classic subsistence economy. Only 10 percent of the population lives in small villages. The majority of the population lives in dispersed, isolated households and small hamlets. Ninety-two percent of the population in Los Andes province derives its income from agriculture, livestock, and, to a lesser, localized extent, fishing. Of the remaining population, 3.5 percent derives its principal income from small shopkeeping and the sale of prepared food, 2.5 percent from production and sale of arts and crafts, and 2 percent from other services.

The principal agricultural crop is the potato, with quinoa, wheat, barley, and oats as complementary products. Lack of access to sufficient productive land is one of the principal determinants of extremely low family income and subsistence levels in the study area. The average area of cultivable land held by families in Los Andes province is 1.8 hectares, with the following distribution: 0 hectares, 2.5 percent of families; 0–1 hectares, 36.2 percent; 2–5 hectares, 42 percent; 6–10 hectares, 16 percent; 11–20 hectares, 3 percent; and 20 hectares and up, 0.3 percent. According to recent Bolivian government statistics, a farm in this area of the altiplano requires a minimum of 10 hectares of land cultivated with traditional, nonintensive techniques to produce sufficient food for average family consumption. Clearly, most families in Los Andes province (nearly 97 percent) fall well below this benchmark.

One technological and environmental product of this precarious landholding situation is that local farmers have shortened or even abandoned necessary fallow periods and changed crop rotation cycles on the land they do possess. In some cases, the more entrepreneurial farmers have obtained grants through aid programs or have used scarce discretionary income to purchase chemical fertilizers to intensify production on small landholdings. Overall, the end product of these processes has been declining agricultural production and slow degradation of soils and groundwater. Low productivity and a consequent low income stream from agricultural activities induces another negative element in the dynamics of rural social reproduction. Because of low income levels and poor transportation infrastructure, local producers are unable to gain direct access to urban markets. Instead, they use local markets to sell the small quantities of produce they themselves do not consume. These markets are frequented by intermediaries who purchase local products at low prices for resale at substantial premiums in the urban markets. Local producers have insufficient organizational capacity to influence price levels in the markets. Consequently, in a system of unequal exchange values, local producers suffer from the low prices offered for their products but at the same time are subject to high prices for products they desire from the city.

In order to supplement low income from traditional agricultural activities, Aymara families of the region dedicate substantial time and energy to livestock production. Livestock is produced for local consumption but perhaps more importantly for sale in rural and urban markets. Temporary wage labor in rural towns, in the city of La Paz, and in other regions of Bolivia, such as the coca-and citrus-producing yungas zones of the Department of La Paz, by one or more family members is a common strategy for enhancing total income. Two sociological results of these pressures to diversify sources of income have been long-term and permanent fragmentation of family structures in rural zones and an accelerating pace of rural depopulation. Temporary wage labor outside the rural reaches of the altiplano frequently transforms itself into chronic separation from the home community as migrants take up permanent residence in towns and cities.

Demographic profiles are shifting in rural zones as well, as a result of migration patterns. Adolescents and young adults (82 percent) and males (79 percent) constitute the dominant migratory group from Los Andes province, resulting in dramatically skewed age and sex profiles in the rural zones. This pattern most likely applies to the other provinces of the altiplano as well, at least in the Department of La Paz (Franqueville and Aguilar 1988). It should be noted that there are substantial incidences of temporary and oscillating migration among men; that is, men frequently hold dual residences in the city and countryside and rotate residence. Despite this oscillating pattern of migration, the direction of net population flow is overwhelmingly from country to city. Virtually abandoned "ghost towns" and villages dot the landscape of Los Andes province (and the whole of the altiplano), testifying to the powerful economic and social forces of modernity in contemporary Bolivian society. In concert with the human settlements, the altiplano's agricultural landscape is undergoing a wrenching, and perhaps permanent, process of gradual abandonment by its original inhabitants.

## Conclusions

We began this chapter with the question of how Tiwanaku civilization emerged and flourished in the seemingly harsh environment of the Andean altiplano. Our description of ecosystems and their potential economic uses by humans should demonstrate that this environment is not as difficult as it appears from casual observation. In fact, the altiplano, particularly in the Lake Titicaca–oriented sustaining area of Tiwanaku, supplies many resources that are readily extracted and processed for human use. This environment, however, *is* near the edge of easy human habitation based on an agrarian economy. The climate, determined in part by orogenesis and in part by tropical latitude, is nearly too cold and dry to support sufficient cultivable vegetation for large-scale human communities. Small changes in climate can make the altiplano virtually uninhabitable for concentrated human populations, as it was only 4,000 years ago. Only the presence of water, in the lake, in wetlands, and as shallow groundwater and springs, permits viable agriculture. This critical point is brought into sharp relief by the likelihood that Tiwanaku culture collapsed as a result of a prolonged drought that rendered its hydraulically based agricultural systems useless nearly 1,000 years ago.

Despite superficial appearances to the contrary, the altiplano is potentially a resource-rich, productive environment for complex human activities, given the development of appropriate exploitative technologies. Yet even in circumlacustrine areas that enjoyed the moderating environmental influence of Lake Titicaca, the altiplano is, at the same time, an inherently risk-prone ecosystem for agrarian societies. Limiting factors for effective agriculture in the altiplano include frost, drought, nutrient-deficient soils, and periodic meteorological phenomena such as hail and torrential seasonal rainfall (Morlon 1978; ONERN 1965; Unzueta 1975). Of these environmental risks, frost is generally considered to be the principal limiting factor for effective agriculture in the altiplano (Morlon 1981:24). In this hierarchy of risks, regional conditions such as periodic drought and, to a lesser extent, nutrient-poor soils rank behind frost but ahead of localized aleatory phenomena such as hail in terms of their destructive capabilities. What is important to note here is that the three major limiting factors to effective agriculture in the altiplano (frost, drought, and nutrient-poor soils) are problems of regional, rather than local, scope. But at the same time, these environmental risks are perceivable and even predictable through long-term empirical observation; therefore, they are amenable to human management and amelioration.

In the context of the Andean highlands, the two principal strategies of agricultural risk management take the form of (1) maximum diversification of production over multiple altitudinal, edaphic, and microclimatic zones, and (2) maximum environmental modification of single production zones with the potential for intensification. In general, along a hypothetical risk/return spectrum, the first strategy can be characterized as a lower risk–lower return proposition, whereas the latter is higher risk–higher return. Unless there is complete political domination of diverse environmental zones, the former strategy offers lower return because access to productive resources is constrained by local competition. The latter strategy results in higher risk because the hyperdeveloped resource base lacks diversity and therefore is exceptionally sensitive to significant environmental (or, for that matter, social and political) perturbation.

Most pre-Hispanic Andean states pursued these two strategies of agricultural risk management simultaneously and with varying degrees of intensity. Contemporary peasant agriculturalists in the Andes opt predominantly for a diversification strategy, which, in addition to the agricultural dimensions of zonal diversification, includes seasonal wage labor, dual residence in city and country, and partial insertion into regional and national market economies. Few indigenous altiplano farmers today have sufficient labor or capital resources to invest in a maximum modification strategy of risk management. As noted in chapter 11, many innovative modification strategies (such as solar greenhouses) are currently being pursued in the altiplano, but they depend almost exclusively on external support from government agencies and nongovernmental development organizations. Even these intensification strategies are of relatively small scope and cannot address pervasive problems of food production on a regional scale.

Before complex agrarian societies could emerge in the Andean altiplano, technological and cultural solutions to management of environmental risks had to be well developed and articulated with the social organization of production. In this light, it is not surprising that the most intense expressions of social complexity in the Andean altiplano are uniquely concentrated in the Lake Titicaca region, where subsistence and surplus production risks are most easily managed, and that these expressions of social complexity emerged only after Lake Titicaca approached its modern level (that is, after 3500 B.P.). The broader problems of regional food supply in the altiplano were, indeed, resolved by the state of Tiwanaku (and most likely by earlier Formative-period societies on a smaller scale) through diversification strategies, but more importantly by means of efficient single production zone modifications. That is, in the Tiwanaku state at least, the maximum-modification strategy of risk management was the predominant means of ensuring food supply stability. Raised fields, qochas, and terraces were all highly successful technical innovations that emerged from and were embedded in a cultural matrix that focused on the hyperintensification of production in the circum–Lake Titicaca altiplano.

Several hypotheses about human-environment interactions have been developed in this chapter from a multidisciplinary literature review and from our own ongoing research. First, we propose that the Lake Titicaca basin could not have sustained concentrated, agriculturally dependent human populations before about 3500 B.P. because it was far too dry. Until the lake reached near its present level at around 3000 B.P., agriculturally based societies were unable to colonize the altiplano on a large and intensive scale. Second, and of particular interest to ecologists, ancient humans may have caused the colonization and spread of totora in the lake, beginning about 3,000 years ago. Third, wetland systems are essential for intense human habitation of the altiplano. These wetlands harbor many species of biogeochemically important organisms (e.g., nitrogen-fixing cyanobacteria), provide nearly permanent water for livestock and human use, store heat in areas away from the main body of the lake, and supply freshwater to an environmental region in which soils are subject to debilitating concentrations of salts because of high evapotranspiration rates. The original raised-field systems appear to have been sophisticated cultural techniques for exploiting these environmental characteristics.

Reflection on these hypotheses leads us toward a new and more accurate perception of the Andean altiplano's agroecological potential. In Bolivia and Peru, Western-trained agronomists and other development specialists routinely perceive the altiplano as a marginal environment. They characterize the altiplano as possessing soil unfit for agriculture and suitable only for extensive and temporary grazing (Morlon 1981:27). Not surprisingly, the overwhelming majority of significant agricultural development projects in these two countries are situated in humid tropical and subtropical environments far from the arid plains of the high plateau. Even eliminating the abnormal geographic clustering of development projects in Bolivia and Peru in tropical and subtropical zones induced by the coca-cocaine focus of international entities such as the United States Agency for International Development (USAID), it is clear that the common perception of the Andean altiplano environment is shaped by superficial understanding of its high local variability and underlying potentials, and that this distorted image has substantially and negatively affected economic investment in the altiplano.

Yet what these agronomists and development specialists are perceiving of the altiplano environment is a historical artifact. Their vision is not retrospective but rather focuses on the present and the near past, perhaps at best the last three or four decades. They see a recent history of human underutilization of the altiplano and then assume that it stems from inherent environmental limitations. They have not yet appreciated that the more relevant determinants of underutilization are sociological, historical, and economic. Catastrophic demographic collapse, internal migration driven by national and international economic forces, loss of traditional cultural practices, a numbing history of racially based oppression—these are the more germane elements for explaining recent underutilization of the Andean altiplano. The environmental and agroecological image of the development specialists remains uninformed by long-term historical and cultural perspectives on human utilization and realization of altiplano ecosystems potentials. As Morlon (1981:27) notes:

> Frequent assertions about the impossibility of improving agriculture on the altiplano arise from the confusion between the physical and biological *potential* of the environment and its realization, which is largely influenced by history and the functioning of societies. If tens of thousands of hectares of pre-Columbian ridge backs [raised fields] and terraces have been abandoned, is this because of climatic changes or because of a change in social organization and finalities (short-term profit or preoccupation with the long term)? How, in fact, can a plain covered with the remains of ridge backs constructed for agriculture, and where it is not difficult currently to obtain good yields, be classed as 'soil unfit for agriculture, suitable only for extensive and temporary grazing'? Either this provides an alibi to those who are profiting from the present situation, or one must generalize the case cited by Romero (1928:386) and Monheim (1956) of travellers who based all their conclusions on a sejour on the altiplano in the dry season [emphasis in the original].

Morlon's acerbic comments rightly emphasize the need to understand the full range of environmental potentials in the altiplano *as these have been acted upon and developed by human societies.* In this regard, we hope that this book will contribute to a deeper and more subtly nuanced historical perspective on human-environment interactions in the altiplano. From the human frame of reference, at various historical conjunctures, the altiplano has been underutilized to varying degrees and for different reasons. For instance, prior to 3500 B.P. the Lake Titicaca basin was environmentally unsuitable for large-scale, concentrated human populations. After early-sixteenth-century European colonization, the altiplano was marginalized economically and organizationally, and its current underutilization is the product of complex social, not natural, forces. Between these two poles of pervasive underutilization, one environmentally and the other socially determined, the altiplano experienced episodes of intense natural resource development occasioned by the emergence and expansion of complex human societies from about 3500 to 1000 B.P.

Of course, human activities have also altered the natural systems. Cultivation (both terrestrial and aquatic), herding, urbanization, hydraulic engineering, and other activities changed the hydrological system, the distribution and abundance of different plant species and consequently animal species, and the availability of groundwater. Cultivation, first on flat fields in alluvial floodplains and along the edges of Lake Titicaca and later on raised fields with adjacent canals, changed the nutrient dynamics of the whole system in ways as yet unknown, possibly making biologically available nitrogen more abundant in the system (see chapter 7). We have only scratched the surface in our attempts to analyze and interpret these complex and exceedingly dynamic interactions. Exactly how and at what scale these human-driven alterations reciprocally influenced natural processes is currently unknown. The answers to these essential questions of long-term human-environment interaction await further multidisciplinary research in this fascinating ecosystem.

# 3

# Geology, Geomorphology, and Soils of the Tiwanaku and Catari River Basins

JAIME ARGOLLO, LEOCADIO TICCLA, ALAN L. KOLATA, AND OSWALDO RIVERA

The pre-Hispanic culture of Tiwanaku created a complex agricultural system structured in terms of three technologies of water management: raised fields, *qochas* (artificial ponds), and terraces. The spatial arrangement and organization of these artificial agricultural landscapes were based on the distribution of natural resources in distinct microenvironmental zones. With respect to raised fields and qochas, surface and groundwaters and soils were the resources of principal concern. Raised fields and qochas were developed by Tiwanaku in areas where the flow of surface and groundwaters created wetlands characterized by seasonally or perennially inundated soils.

This chapter provides a descriptive overview of the geology, geomorphology, soils, and water resources of the Tiwanaku and Catari River basins, the two principal physiographic zones studied by the Wila Jawira research project. Understanding the distribution and character of these basic environmental variables is fundamental for a systematic interpretation of Tiwanaku agroecology. The results of the field research described here have relevance both for an interpretation of the long-term history of raised-field cultivation in the Tiwanaku region and for ongoing attempts by contemporary Aymara communities to rehabilitate paleoagricultural landscapes.

## Methods

Photointerpretation of geological and geomorphological features and processes in the Tiwanaku and Catari River basins—a study area of approximately 1,380 square kilometers—was an essential first step in our analysis. For the research presented here, we combined laboratory analysis of aerial photographs (42 stereoscopic image pairs at a scale of 1:40,000) with extensive fieldwork. The stereo pairs utilized in this research were analyzed by means of a Wild ST4 mirror stereoscope with 3X binoculars.

We collected both primary and secondary data for the present investigation. Primary data are those we obtained directly through our photointerpretation and field studies. They include descriptions of lithological features and geomorphological units and information on strata trend and dip, types of erosion, and the stratigraphic position of different geological formations in each basin of the study area. Secondary data are those obtained from previous laboratory research and field studies by public and private institutions in Bolivia. We compiled a 1:50,000-scale base map (fig. 3.1) from four separate sheets of the na-

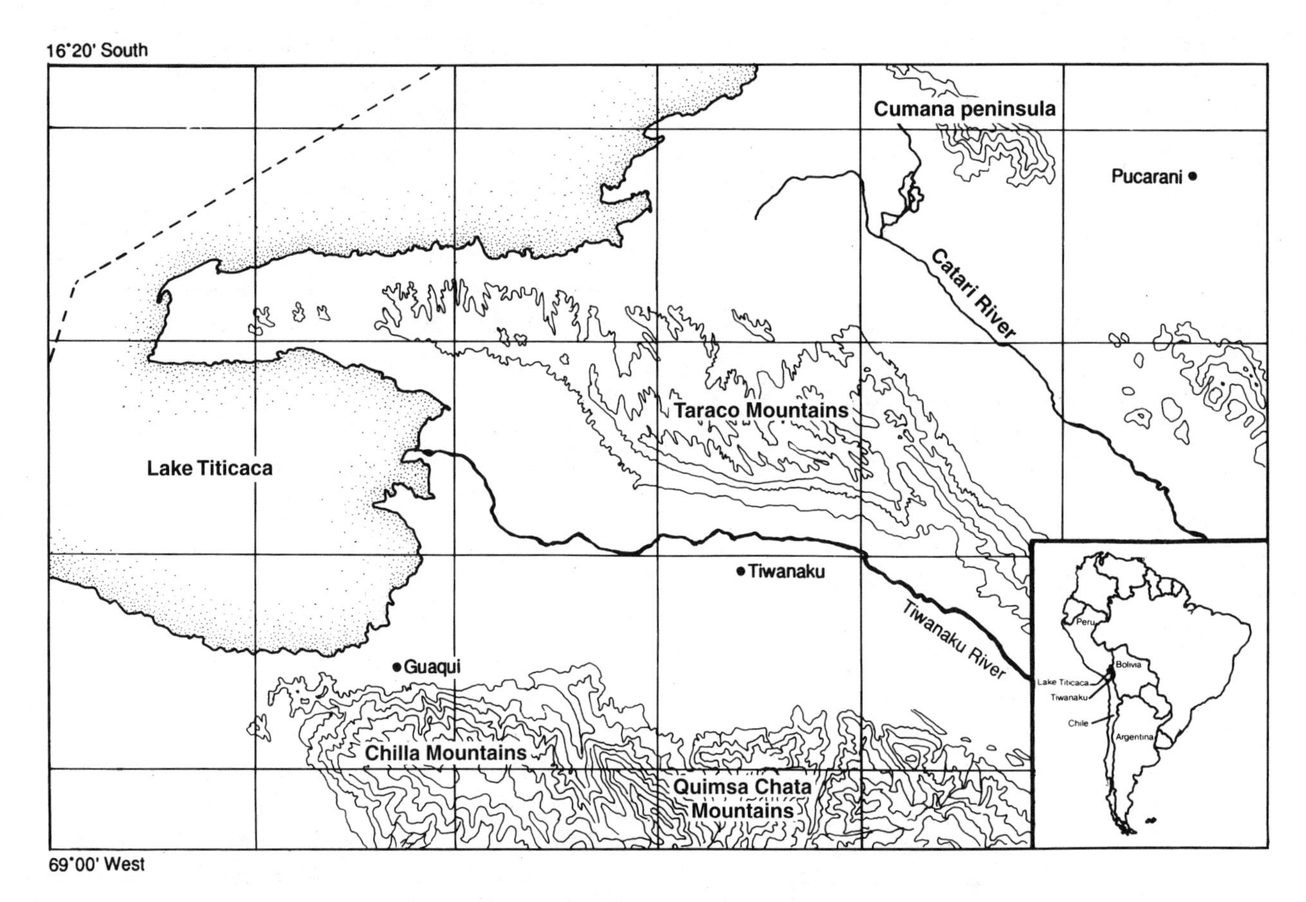


**Figure 3.1.** Topographic map of the Tiwanaku and Catari basins, showing the locations of the most important contemporary human settlements (based on four separate sheets of the national map published by Bolivia's Instituto Geográfico Militar).

tional map published by Bolivia's Instituto Geográfico Militar (IGM). In order to simplify this base map, we eliminated the extreme cartographic detail found in IGM maps. The topographic features of the two basins are delimited in 100-meter contour intervals. This map serves as the base for additional thematic maps presented here.

The fundamental criteria for identifying and demarcating geomorphological units were established as the following landscape components: topographic relief, slope, lithology, degree of erosion, vegetation, and contemporary land use. Each can be derived directly from aerial photographs. Other environmental parameters, such as soil type and permeability, were deduced from stereo pairs and later verified in the field. The specific tonalities of aerial photographs enabled us to identify natural erosional surfaces as well as human-generated or human-altered surfaces such as those related to land use and anthropogenically altered vegetation cover. The photointerpretation of erosional features in our study area was complicated by the scale and quality of the images with which we worked: subtle differences were frequently obscured by lack of fine resolution. Consequently, most of the data on erosional surfaces and soils were derived from direct field observation.

Field studies were conducted after initial landscape interpretations were compiled from the aerial photographs. Fieldwork entailed a general survey followed by detailed study of areas that were difficult to interpret on the basis of the aerial photographs alone. The survey transects were oriented perpendicular to the general strike of the geological structures. This allowed us to define the limits of geological contacts and of lithological and structural variations. During the survey, we noted the primary physical characteristics of geological structures, such as stratigraphic composition and sequences, sedimentary structures (cross, graded, and laminated stratification), degree of metamorphism, grain size, color, form, and hardness, and type of detritus.

In addition, we described the following landscape characteristics: sediments and detrital material transported by the principal rivers and streams; evidence of erosional surfaces and mass wasting; degree, form, and length of local slopes; vegetation cover; and incidences of human activity that have had an impact on landforms and environment. We collected soil samples from representative areas for sediment analyses and water samples from rivers, streams, and springs to determine chemical compositions. The soil and water analyses have a direct bearing on current projects to rehabilitate portions of the paleoagricultural landscape. In selected locations in the two river basins, we recorded schematic profiles of sedimentary columns and collected samples of organic sediments (peats), charcoal, and ceramics and other human artifacts to aid in the characterization of the evolutionary dynamics of the Tiwanaku and Catari basins.

The principal fieldwork took place during a 50-day season between January and May 1991. Supplemental fieldwork was conducted in October–December 1991 and August 1992. After completing the field studies, we reinterpreted the aerial photographs on the basis of these primary data, rectifying our maps of the geological, geomorphological, and erosional contacts.

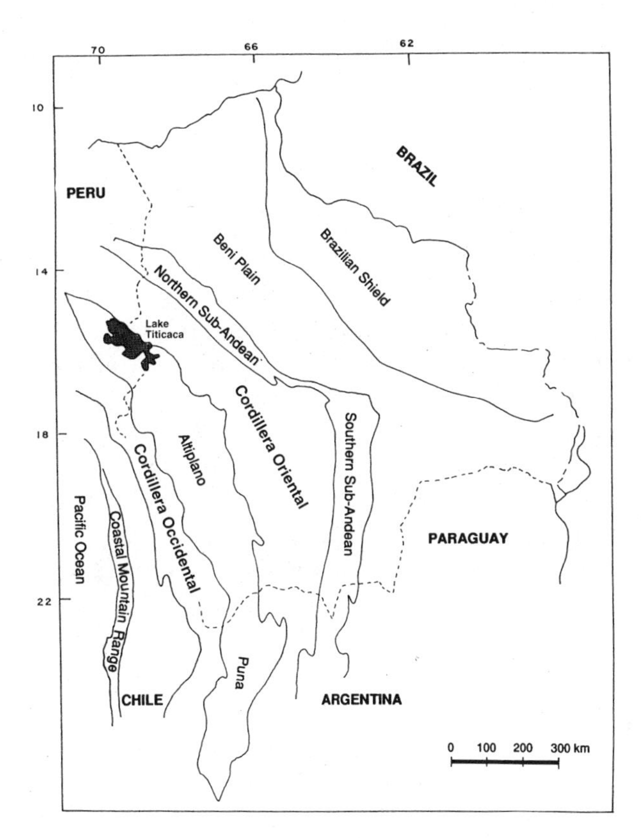


Figure 3.2. The Tiwanaku and Catari River basins between the Cordillera Occidental (western mountain range) and the Cordillera Oriental (eastern mountain range).

## Geomorphology of the Tiwanaku and Catari River Basins

The research area is located between 16°10′ and 16°40′ S latitude and 68°30′ and 60°00′ W longitude. The area includes parts of the Bolivian provinces of Ingavi and Los Andes in the Department of La Paz. The Tiwanaku and Catari River basins are situated in the altiplano morphostructural unit, which is delimited by the Cordillera Occidental and the Cordillera Oriental to the southwest and northeast, respectively (figs. 3.1, 3.2). The Tiwanaku basin has the Tiwanaku (Quimsa Chata and Chilla) mountain range as its southern margin and the Taraco Range as its northern margin. The Catari basin is bordered on the south by the Taraco Range and on the north by the Aygachi and Cumana ranges. Lake Titicaca is in the northwestern sector of the research area. The Tiwanaku basin takes the form of a horseshoe with its opening to the northwest. This configuration is fundamentally due to structural and tectonic factors. The Catari basin is part of a great plain of structural-tectonic type characterized by an aggradational regime.

### Physiography of the Research Area

Physiographically, this area presents landscapes of mountains, hills and erosional surfaces, volcanic domes, alluvial and lacustrine plains, and glacial deposits. Following a south-to-north profile of the research area, we can differentiate four major physiographic zones

The Tiwanaku mountain range trends in a southeast to northwest direction. This chain exhibits a highly folded structure (anticlines and synclines) formed by sandstones and red mudstones of the Lower Tertiary Tiwanaku Formation. These rocks have also been affected by igneous activity. The Tiwanaku Range has the highest elevations in the research area. Chilla peak, formed of sedimentary and volcanic rocks, reaches 4,800 meters above sea level. It is in dike contact with rocks of the Tiwanaku Formation. Quimsa Chata Peak (4,600 meters) in the Tiwanaku Range is formed by andesitic rocks dating to the Upper Miocene. These peaks have been affected by glacial episodes, and it is possible to observe glacial cirques and small moraine deposits (lateral moraines). The Tiwanaku Range has been dissected by a series of rivers that flow orthogonally to it. The principal permanent rivers flowing from the Tiwanaku Mountains include the San Bartolomé, Chilla, Cucuota, and Chusicani. There are also numerous intermittent streams that develop during the rainy season.

The Tiwanaku Valley plain is cut by the Tiwanaku River, referred to locally as the Guaquira River at its headwaters, from which it trends in a SE-NW direction. In the middle of the Tiwanaku basin, the river takes an E-W course, at which point it is renamed the Tiwanaku River. It eventually empties into Lake Titicaca (3,810 meters above sea level). The valley floor of the Tiwanaku basin presents erosional, alluvial, and lacustrine surfaces that have been dissected by fluvial action, resulting in a series of alluvial terraces at different altitudes. Noncontinuous strips of colluvial terraces also occur at the bases of slopes on both the south and north sides of the Tiwanaku Valley. The Tiwanaku basin is narrower (approximately 2 kilometers N-S) toward its head and widens toward its mouth, approaching 16 kilometers wide near the shore of Lake Titicaca.

The Taraco Mountains delimit the Tiwanaku basin to the north and maintain an orientation parallel to that of the Tiwanaku Range. The Taraco Range is formed of conglomerate rocks of the Coniri, Kollu Kollu (Oligo-Miocene), and Taraco (Pliocene) formations. The central portion of this mountain chain exhibits a syncline structure with an axis oriented SE-NW. The highest peaks of this heavily eroded range do not exceed 4,100 meters above sea level. These mountains are drained to the south by intermittent streams that carry their water into the Tiwanaku River during the rainy season. Some of this water was diverted into aqueduct structures by Tiwanaku farmers in order to control drainage and groundwater inputs to local areas of raised fields (see chapters 5 and 6). On the north face of the Taraco Mountains, periodic rivers and intermittent streams flow into the Catari–Pampa Koani basin and subsequently into Lake Titicaca. The Taraco Range exhibits an asymmetric transverse profile with high, steep, heavily dissected slopes to the south (20–40 percent gradient) and moderate slopes to the north (4–8 percent gradient).

Continuing north, the Pampa Koani plain of the Catari basin constitutes the next important physiographic feature. The Pampa Koani is an alluvial plain of Quaternary deposits cut by the Catari River in an east-west trending direction. The southern limit of this plain is affected by a series of inverse faults that have thrust Tertiary and Paleozoic rocks into juxtaposition. This endogenous process originated an alignment of small isolated hills and a well-defined escarpment between the plain and the mountains that are among the visually salient features of the Pampa Koani zone. The northern limit of the study area is defined by the Aygachi and Cumana mountain ranges, which have maximum elevations of approximately 4,200 meters above sea level. These ranges consist of Paleozoic rocks dated to the Devonian, Carboniferous, and Permian periods.

## Geomorphological Units

In the process of conducting field surveys in the Tiwanaku and Catari basins, we differentiated several geomorphological units. The distribution and configuration of these units are illustrated in figure 3.3. Here we summarize the character of these geomorphological units according to the following attributes: relief, slope, degree of dissection, lithology, vegetation and land use, soil type and quality, and soil permeability.

#### I. UNITS OF FLUVIAL ORIGIN

RELIEF: Relief is low, from nearly flat to slightly rolling, and the topography includes alluvial fans, terraces, and plains with extensive wetlands, or *bofedales*.
SLOPES: Slopes are of moderate length and are flat to slightly inclined.
DEGREE OF DISSECTION: Low to medium.
LITHOLOGY: Gravels, sands, and silts.
VEGETATION AND LAND USE: Abundant vegetation, Gramineae; intensive agricultural use.
SOILS: Well developed.
SOIL PERMEABILITY: High.

#### II. UNITS OF LACUSTRINE ORIGIN

RELIEF: Relief is low, flat, and dissected by rivers.
SLOPES: Slopes have moderate length and are flat.
DEGREE OF DISSECTION: Low.
LITHOLOGY: Sands, silts, and clays; low consolidation.
VEGETATION AND LAND USE: Abundant vegetation, mainly Gramineae; intensive agricultural use.
SOILS: Deep.
SOIL PERMEABILITY: Low.

#### III. UNITS OF GLACIAL ORIGIN

RELIEF: Relief is very high, formed by eroded, U-shaped valleys or moraines.

SLOPES: Slopes are long and steep.
DEGREE OF DISSECTION: Low to medium.
LITHOLOGY: Unconsolidated detrital material, poorly selected, with erratic sandstone and volcanic blocks in a silt-clay matrix.
VEGETATION AND LAND USE: Dense vegetation, mainly Gramineae. No land use.
SOILS: Shallow and very rocky, blocks predominate.
SOIL PERMEABILITY: Medium to high.

### IV. UNITS OF EROSIONAL ORIGIN

RELIEF: Low, horizontal forms, concave in higher areas.
SLOPES: Short to medium length, slight slopes.
DEGREE OF DISSECTION: Medium.
LITHOLOGY: Poorly consolidated gravels of Plio-Quaternary age, developed over Tertiary sandstones.
VEGETATION AND LAND USE: Abundant vegetation, intensive agricultural land use.
SOILS: Well developed.
SOIL PERMEABILITY: Medium to high.

Other forms of erosional origin in the research area are debris cones located at the bases of hill slopes. These are formed by gravitational effects. Block flows, which in the study area are small deposits, are located on hill slopes. These forms originate through gravitational action as well as through water saturation, which leads to subsidence of materials. These units of erosional origin also include the landforms produced by different types of water-driven erosion: sheet, rill, and gully erosion.

### V. UNITS OF TECTONIC ORIGIN

RELIEF: Very high, with homoclinal structural crests.
SLOPES: Short, moderate to very steep.
DEGREE OF DISSECTION: High.
LITHOLOGY: Undifferentiated volcanic and sedimentary rocks; also Permo-Carboniferous calcareous rocks and Cretaceous red sandstones.
VEGETATION AND LAND USE: Gramineae; very little agricultural use.
SOILS: Poorly developed and shallow.
SOIL PERMEABILITY: Medium.

Other forms of tectonic origin in the research area are the anticlinal and synclinal structures produced by compressive forces. We also observed linear deformations produced by inverse, normal, and transverse faults.

### VI. ERODED FORMS OF TECTONIC ORIGIN

*VI-a*

RELIEF: High, slightly rounded forms and crests.
SLOPES: Short and straight, low to moderately steep.
DEGREE OF DISSECTION: Medium to high.
LITHOLOGY: Strongly consolidated Tertiary sandstones.
VEGETATION AND LAND USE: Isolated vegetation, dense in certain regions, mainly composed of Gramineae. Limited land use.
SOILS: Shallow.
SOIL PERMEABILITY: Low to medium.

*VI-b*

RELIEF: Moderately high, with rounded forms.
SLOPES: Straight, inclined and steep.
DEGREE OF DISSECTION: Medium to high.
LITHOLOGY: Tertiary compacted conglomerates.
VEGETATION AND LAND USE: Medium vegetation density, mainly Gramineae. Limited to intense land use.
SOILS: Shallow to moderately deep.
SOIL PERMEABILITY: Medium.

*VI-c*

RELIEF: High, with steep forms.
SLOPES: Straight, strongly inclined and steep.
DEGREE OF DISSECTION: High.
LITHOLOGY: Undetermined volcanic and sedimentary rocks, Mesozoic calcareous sandstones.
VEGETATION AND LAND USE: Little vegetation (Gramineae). No land use.
SOILS: Shallow.
SOIL PERMEABILITY: Low.

*VI-d*

RELIEF: Moderately low, rounded forms.
SLOPES: Short and concave.
DEGREE OF DISSECTION: Low to medium.
LITHOLOGY: Compact conglomerates and Tertiary conglomeratic sandstones.
VEGETATION AND LAND USE: Moderately dense vegetation in some sectors to very poor in others. Limited to intense land use.
SOILS: Localized shallow to deep.
SOIL PERMEABILITY: Medium to high.

**Figure 3.3.** Geomorphological units in the Tiwanaku and Catari basins.

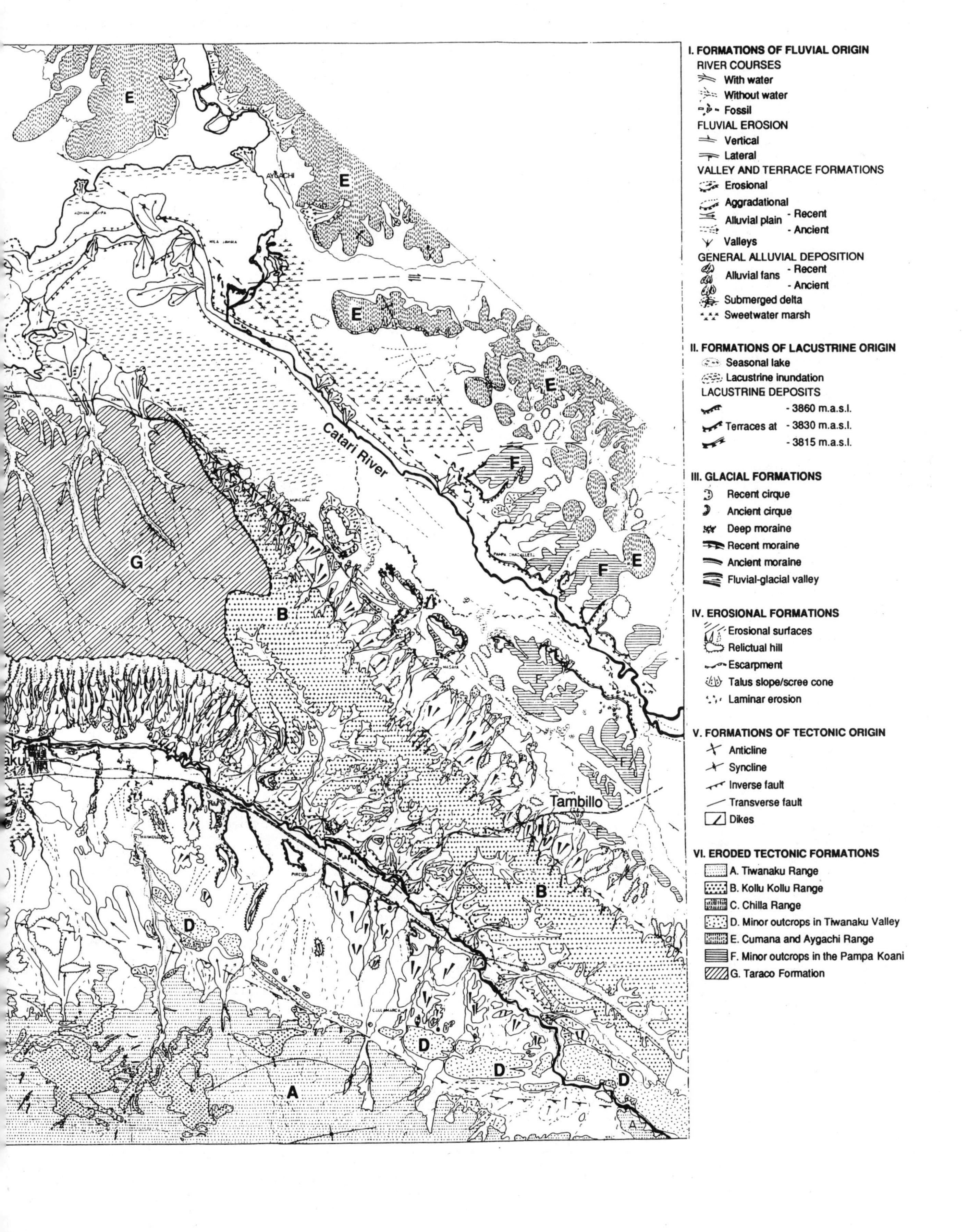

I. FORMATIONS OF FLUVIAL ORIGIN
RIVER COURSES
With water
Without water
Fossil
FLUVIAL EROSION
Vertical
Lateral
VALLEY AND TERRACE FORMATIONS
Erosional
Aggradational
Alluvial plain - Recent
- Ancient
Valleys
GENERAL ALLUVIAL DEPOSITION
Alluvial fans - Recent
- Ancient
Submerged delta
Sweetwater marsh
II. FORMATIONS OF LACUSTRINE ORIGIN
Seasonal lake
Lacustrine inundation
LACUSTRINE DEPOSITS
- 3860 m.a.s.l.
Terraces at - 3830 m.a.s.l.
- 3815 m.a.s.l.
III. GLACIAL FORMATIONS
Recent cirque
Ancient cirque
Deep moraine
Recent moraine
Ancient moraine
Fluvial-glacial valley
IV. EROSIONAL FORMATIONS
Erosional surfaces
Relictual hill
Escarpment
Talus slope/scree cone
Laminar erosion
V. FORMATIONS OF TECTONIC ORIGIN
Anticline
Syncline
Inverse fault
Transverse fault
Dikes
VI. ERODED TECTONIC FORMATIONS
A. Tiwanaku Range
B. Kollu Kollu Range
C. Chilla Range
D. Minor outcrops in Tiwanaku Valley
E. Cumana and Aygachi Range
F. Minor outcrops in the Pampa Koani
G. Taraco Formation
E
AYGACHI
E
E
E
F
Catari River
G
B
F
E
Tambillo
B
D
D
D
D
A

*VI-e*

RELIEF: Moderately high with rounded and steep forms.
SLOPES: Inclined to steep.
DEGREE OF DISSECTION: Medium to high.
LITHOLOGY: Paleozoic sandstones, mudstones, and limestones.
VEGETATION AND LAND USE: Sparse vegetation, mainly Gramineae. Limited land use.
SOILS: Shallow.
SOIL PERMEABILITY: Low to medium.

*VI-f*

RELIEF: Low, flat and rounded forms.
SLOPES: Short, straight and slightly inclined.
DEGREE OF DISSECTION: Medium to high.
LITHOLOGY: Paleozoic and Tertiary sandstones, calcareous rocks, and conglomerates.
VEGETATION AND LAND USE: Sparse vegetation. Limited land use.
SOILS: Poorly developed.
SOIL PERMEABILITY: Medium.

## Erosional Processes in the Tiwanaku and Catari Basins

Erosion is a complex morphodynamic process that results from the interaction of lithologic, pedologic, orographic, and hydroclimatic factors. The effects of these interacting factors vary according to the natural conditions of the area, vegetation cover, and the characteristics of present-day land use. Accordingly, the intensity of erosion is highly variable across time and space. The relief of the Tiwanaku and Catari basins is a case in point. In general, as one might expect, erosional processes in these two basins are more marked and intense in areas with greater relief than in areas with less relief. The distribution of distinct erosion surfaces in these basins is shown in figure 3.3.

Geologic erosion, also termed normal erosion, is caused mainly by natural forces such as gravity, water, and wind. Normal erosion acts upon rocks previously altered by weathering and by chemical or biological processes such as oxidation, hydration, and the interaction of mineralogical components with water or the atmosphere. Although this type of erosion affects nearly all of the study area, erosion of varied intensity can be observed particularly in the river gullies and quebradas. A second form of erosion in the study area—accelerated erosion—works at a faster rate than normal erosion, as the name implies. The principal causes of accelerated erosion are large-scale human activities, such as intensification of agriculture, urbanization, and pastoralism, and certain natural agents such as radical meteorological or climate changes (inundations, droughts) and catastrophes (landslides, mass wasting). Such processes can generate significant loss of soils.

The Tiwanaku and Catari basins are being affected by accelerated erosion in some sectors. Water, the main agent of erosion, originates as rainfall and begins the erosional cycle by impact with the land surface, breaking soil structure into smaller particles that are subsequently removed by runoff. Runoff occurs in two forms: (1) a free or diffuse form, generating laminar or sheet erosion, and (2) a concentrated form, provoking erosional furrows, or gullies. Such concentrated erosional features can enlarge over time and produce mass displacements or mass wasting. Both erosional processes occur in the study area. Sheet erosion is produced when superficial soil is saturated by pluvial waters and subjected to diffuse runoff that removes soil, particularly in areas devoid of vegetation cover. In the research area, sheet erosion occurs most extensively in areas with heavy agricultural activity and where local slopes are steep. Concentrated erosion also occurs in areas of agricultural activity where landforms take a convex shape, and it decreases in intensity when the configuration is concave.

Severe erosion in which runoff concentrates and accumulates in narrow canals during short periods of time can rapidly promote gully development. In zones of gully development, the resultant topography takes the form of deep, ramified ravines characterized by short, steep slopes. In the study area, gully developments are located particularly in the Chilla Range, on the southern side of the Tiwanaku basin, and at the headwaters of the San Bartolomé, Cucuota, Ojra Jawira, and Callijipina rivers.

Fluvial action is the third principal erosional process in the study area. Fluvial erosion works in two ways: (1) vertical incision, restricted to the higher parts of the basins, a consequence of steep slopes producing a V-shaped transverse profile, and (2) lateral erosion, which occurs principally in the larger rivers of the study area such as the Tiwanaku River and Catari River. Lateral erosion is produced by the drift or meandering of watercourses that typically redeposit sediments downstream. Lateral erosion is a serious problem during the altiplano rainy season and can provoke substantial loss of arable land. Tiwanaku's farmers were sensitive to the problems of destructive watercourse meanders on the Tiwanaku and Catari rivers and developed elaborate systems of channel diversion, dikes, and river shunts to counteract them (see chapters 5 and 6).

Mass wasting, the movement of great quantities of unconsolidated rock downslope under the combined action of gravity and water saturation, also occurs in the study area. Water saturation in a deposit of loose material, generally in contact with an impermeable layer, can generate landslides. The types of mass wasting that we have observed in the study area are landslides, earth and mud flows, and mudflows. Landslides are prevalent during the rainy season. The sectors particularly affected by landslides are in the Tiwanaku mountain ranges (both Quimsa Chata and Chilla). They are highly localized and of small extent, owing to the permeability of the rocks in these areas.

Earth and mud flows move relatively slowly but at a perceptible pace. They are characteristic of arid to semiarid zones with sparse vegetation and a marked rainy season characterized by frequent torrential rains. Mudflows develop currents that move relatively fast because of higher water content. In the research area, these flows are small.

## Geology of the Tiwanaku and Catari Basins

### Paleozoic Geology

Paleozoic deposits are exposed in the Pucarani mountain range and in the Cumana peninsula. In the latter area, these deposits take the form of a wide syncline composed of Devonian, Carboniferous, and Permian sediments. These rocks have a general northwestern-southeastern strike.

#### DEVONIAN SYSTEM

Sediments of the Devonian system are found at the base of the hills that form the Pucarani Range. These sediments are fundamentally composed of sandy facies and in lesser proportion by phyllitic facies. The sandstones present a whitish and light brown coloration on fresh surface. If the surface is altered, coloration is dark brown to violet. The sandstones that are close to contact with the Carboniferous deposits are dark violet, dark red, and dark brown, in both fresh and altered surfaces. These colorations are so strong that they can be used as a horizon guide for the top of this unit. Generally they present beds of 10 centimeters to 10 meters thick, formed by thin-grained sands, subangular to subrounded, moderately sorted, embedded in a sandy-ferruginous matrix. Some beds have thin laminations and are cross-bedded.

The stratigraphic sequence exhibits the following lithology, from top to base:

- 25 meters of beds 2 centimeters to 1 meter thick, composed of dark brown ferruginous sandstones, fine grained, poorly sorted, and angular. Compact clayish matrix with medium porosity.
- 70 meters of beds 15 centimeters to 1 meter thick, of yellow to brown fine-grained sandstones, compact clayey matrix, regular porosity. Small silex veins, with cross-bedding and fine lamination.
- 12 meters of beds 15 centimeters to 1 meter thick, composed of dark brown, fine-grained ferruginous sandstones. Compact clayish matrix, fine lamination.
- 50 meters of light brown, fine-grained sandstones, well sorted. Clayish matrix, fine lamination and cross-bedding.
- 100 meters covered by colluvio-fluvial Quaternary deposits.
- 40 meters of white-yellow sandstones, well sorted. Fine lamination and cross-bedding, with beds 3 centimeters to 3 meters thick.

The base of this sequence does not outcrop in the research area. The top is in erosive discordance with the Kasa Formation (Carboniferous system). This sequence has been assigned a Middle to Upper Devonian age by virtue of its stratigraphic position with respect to neighboring deposits.

#### THE CUMANA FORMATION (CARBONIFEROUS SYSTEM)

The Carboniferous system is well exposed in the research area; indeed, the Cumana (base) and Kasa (top) formations were defined there. The Cumana Formation presents intercalated layers of conglomerates, sandstones, limonites, diamictites, and clays (mudstones and siltstones). The conglomerate sandstones are generally dark brown to dark red, 5 to 10 millimeters maximum grain size, subangular, poorly sorted, in a well compacted ferruginous clay matrix. The sandstones are dark brown to dark red; toward the top they are light brown and then yellowish, angular to subrounded, fine to medium grained, in a ferruginous-clayish matrix. Some beds present a fine stratification and at times cross-bedding.

The diamictites are dark violet in color and very fragile. They exhibit pseudonodules and quartzite clasts smaller than 15 centimeters. Toward the top of this formation, these diamictites have colors similar to those of the sandstones. There are a total of three diamictitic horizons. The observed lithologic sequence is as follows, from top to base:

- 40 meters of light brown sandstones, fine to thick grained, well sorted, clayish matrix, finely laminated. The beds are 20 centimeters to 3 meters thick. In the central part there are lateral passages to conglomeratic sandstones.
- 10 meters of light brown and gray mudstones.
- 75 meters of yellowish and gray sandstones, fine to medium grained, well sorted, finely laminated clay matrix. The beds are 20 centimeters to 3 meters thick.
- 4 meters of light brown diamictites, with 1-centimeter maximum-diameter clasts. The matrix is differentiable.
- 10 meters of brown mudstones.
- 20 meters of dark brown sandstones, medium grained, poorly sorted, angular, clayish matrix, with beds up to 1 meter thick. The upper portion presents conglomerates with 2-centimeter maximum clasts.
- 6 meters of yellowish and light brown mudstones.
- 25 meters of dark brown and violet diamictites with pseudonodules and clasts smaller than 15 centimeters, sandy matrix.
- 16 meters of fragile mudstones.
- 18 meters of dark brown sandstones, fine grained, subangular, clayish matrix. The beds are 5 to 15 centimeters thick.
- 8 meters of light brown mudstones.
- 40 meters of brown sandstones, very similar to the light brown mudstones, with 1- to 2-meter-thick beds of brown and whitish to gray siltstones.
- 23 meters of whitish siltstones with beds of light gray mudstones.
- 51 meters of dark brown sandstones. The middle and lower portions of this series present conglomerates with 5-millimeter to 2-centimeter grains.

The base of this formation is in erosive discordance over the Devonian rocks. The top of the formation is in concordance with the Kasa Formation. The age of this system is attributed to the Lower Carboniferous (Mississippian).

### THE KASA FORMATION (CARBONIFEROUS SYSTEM)

The Kasa Formation is a homogeneous series of feldspar sandstones interbedded with small mudstone beds. The sandstones are gray, yellowish to light brown, with medium to small grains at the base; they are whitish and rose colored with medium grains in the central and upper portions of this formation. These beds are well sorted, with a clayish matrix.

The stratigraphic column exhibits the following lithologic sequence, from top to base:

- 24 meters of reddish to rose sandstones, medium subrounded grains in a clayish matrix, 20-centimeter- to 1-meter-thick beds, fine laminated.
- 9 meters of light brown mudstones interbedded with small fine-grained sandstone beds.
- 25 meters of Quaternary colluvial cover.
- 23 meters of rose, dark red, light brown, and yellow sandstones, fine to medium grained, subangular, with clayish matrix. There are some interbeddings of green mudstones, and some exhibit cross-bedding.
- 46 meters of Quaternary cover.
- 16 meters of greenish gray sandstones, fine to medium grained, subrounded, clayish matrix, with 50- to 60-centimeter-thick beds and interbeddings of mudstones.

The base of this formation lies concordantly over the Cumana Formation; its top rests in erosive discordance with the Copacabana Formation of the Permian system.

### THE COPACABANA FORMATION (PERMIAN SYSTEM)

The Permian system is characterized in this area by the two formations of the Titicaca group: the Copacabana Formation at the base and the Collasuyo Formation at the top. Limestones predominate in the Copacabana Formation. The Collasuyo Formation is identified by interbeddings of limestones, marls, sandstones, and limonites.

The base of the Copacabana Formation presents rose and greenish sandy levels with small clasts, usually smaller than 2 millimeters, subrounded, in a clayish matrix. Superimposed over the sandy levels are dark gray mudstone interbeddings. Moving upward, the predominant lithology is calcareous, in which the limestone beds are very compact and massive, usually with small veins of whitish diaclastic calcite.

The stratigraphic sequence from top to base is the following:

- 15 meters of greenish, black, and gray hard silicified mudstones, with compact gray marls.
- 78 meters of dark gray, light gray, and light brown diaclastic limestones. Some beds have chert nodules and 20- to 30-centimeter mudstone layers. Some beds are also fossiliferous.
- 13 meters of black mudstones with 2-meter-thick dark gray calcareous deposits and green marls.
- 20 meters of green and light gray mudstones. In the central portion there are compact black limonites in 10- to 20-centimeter-thick beds.
- 10 meters of rose sandstones, with grains of more than 2 millimeters in diameter, forming 1- to 2-meter-thick beds.

This unit lies in erosive discordance over the Kasa Formation (Carboniferous). The top lies in sedimentary discontinuity with the Collasuyo Formation. These deposits are dated to the Lower Permian (Wolfcampian) by their abundant content of animal fossils, their stratigraphic position, and their lithostratigraphic correlations.

#### THE COLLASUYO FORMATION (PERMIAN SYSTEM)

The Collasuyo Formation is characterized by the interbedding of mudstones, marls, calcareous limonites, sandstones, and limestones. Near the top of this formation, a well-preserved, light gray stromatolite was found. The particular characteristic of this unit is the interbedding of limestones, sandstone with or without calcareous cement, limonites, mudstones, and marls.

The base of the Collasuyo Formation presents an interbedding of mudstones, limonites, and sandstones. Toward the top of the formation, limestones are interbedded with marls, calcareous sandstones, and limonites. The mudstones are greenish, dark gray, and black. The sandstones are green to rose, with fine to medium grains, generally subrounded, calcareous cement, and clayish matrix. The limestones are dark brown, gray, rose, and greenish; they exhibit small calcite lodes and are fossiliferous. The sandy limestones occur in fine laminated beds. The processes of both dolomitization and silicification are common. The marls are rare and have colors similar to those of the limestones. The calcareous limonites are also similar to the limestones in color and texture, which makes identification difficult.

The stratigraphic sequence, from top to base, is as follows:

- 15 meters of rose fossiliferous limestones, in beds 20 to 40 centimeters thick.
- 18 meters of sandy calcareous limonites and gray marls, with beds 20 centimeters to 1 meter thick.
- 5 meters of green sandstones, medium grained, subangular, with clayish matrix and cross-bedding.
- 25 meters of rose and gray calcareous limestones, the lower beds fossil bearing.
- 5 meters of rose calcareous sandstones, fine grained, clayish matrix.
- 30 meters of light to dark gray sandy limestones, with 20-centimeter- to 10-meter-thick beds.
- 20 meters of greenish calcareous sandstones, medium to fine grained, subrounded, clayish matrix, interbedded with green or gray mudstones, with beds up to 2 meters thick.
- 46 meters of greenish and rose chalks, with green mudstone interbeddings in the central part and light brown mudstones and limonites in the lower part.
- 8 meters of fossiliferous limestones with small calcite lodes.
- 7 meters of calcareous sandstones, fine to medium grained, clayish matrix, with cross-bedding.
- 10 meters of dark brown fossiliferous limestones, with beds 30 centimeters to 1 meter thick.
- 18 meters of green calcareous sandstones, fine grained, clayish matrix, 5- to 30-meter-thick beds. In the upper part there are light brown mudstones.

The deposits of this sequence are in sedimentary discontinuity with the Copacabana Formation. This formation corresponds to the Lower Permian.

## Mesozoic Geology

The Mesozoic is exposed in the Tiwanaku mountain chain, in the area of Mount Chilla, and near Guaqui. The Mesozoic deposits are composed of sediments of the Cretaceous system. Only two Upper Cretaceous formations outcrop in the study area: the Chaunaca and Molino formations, both of which are restricted in areal scope and bed thickness.

#### CHAUNACA FORMATION (CRETACEOUS SYSTEM)

The type site of the Chaunaca Formation is located east of the village of Chaunaca, in the Ravelo and Betangos syncline. This formation begins with a thick-grained basal conglomerate. Most of the clasts correspond to the rocks underlying this conglomerate deposit. There are also quartz clasts with a milky rose-colored matrix. The sizes of the clasts approach a maximum of 15 centimeters. They are subangular, with compact sandy, clayish, and calcareous matrix. This basal conglomerate is followed by a series of greenish gray mudstones with an intervening calcareous sandstone bed in the middle.

The stratigraphy presents the following lithologic sequence, from top to base:

- 80 meters of rose mudstones interbedded with light gray, thin, diaclastic limestone beds.
- 20 meters of light gray calcareous sandstones, well sorted and rounded, compact, in a calcareous matrix exhibiting cross-bedding.
- 106 meters of greenish gray mudstones.
- 40 meters of conglomerate, with clasts of dark, metamorphosed rocks in a sandy-clayish matrix.

#### EL MOLINO FORMATION (CRETACEOUS SYSTEM)

The eponymous site of the Molino Formation is located southeast of the town of Aroifillas, in Potosí. This formation lies over the Chaunaca Formation. The sediments that lie above also show an apparent concordance. The Molino Formation can be identified by the alternation of thin beds of light gray limestone with gray marls darker than the limestone and quite diaclastic and friable. This sequence has a thickness of 90 meters.

### Cenozoic (Tertiary) Geology

In the research area, the best-exposed materials (in terms of both extent and thickness) are the Cenozoic period deposits. These rocks outcrop in the Tiwanaku and Taraco mountain ranges that surround the Tiwanaku and Catari basins and correspond to the Lower and Middle Tertiary (Oligocene and Miocene epochs).

#### TIWANAKU FORMATION (TERTIARY SYSTEM)

The Tiwanaku Formation is composed of a group of fine sandstones and red mudstones that grade into gray limonites near the top. These sediments lie in pseudoconcordance over the Cretaceous El Molino Formation and are covered in discordant superposition by the Coniri Formation. Swanson et al. (1987) assign ages of 29 to 57 million years ago to the Tiwanaku Formation.

In the different Tiwanaku Formation facies there are always beds of iron oxide grains (magnetite, ilmenite) that impart to this formation a characteristic aspect of volcanic influence. The deposits of the Tiwanaku Formation in the Tiwanaku mountain range derive from an ancient anastomosed river draining from south to north, emerging from the volcanic massifs of the Chilean border and constantly transporting ilmenite. This river flowed into a lacustrine basin located partly within the present-day Lake Titicaca basin. The sedimentation of the Tiwanaku Formation took place in a period of tectonic stability between 57 and 29 million years ago. Volcanic activity, even though reduced, is evident in the deposition of acidic tuffs.

#### CONIRI FORMATION (TERTIARY SYSTEM)

The Coniri Formation is composed of massive, polygenic conglomerates with green or white Paleozoic quartzite and with Permian calcareous and Precambrian granite clasts. Generally the clasts are subangular and large (90 centimeters). Precambrian clasts occur in the lower Coniri beds (C1), associated with Permian calcareous clasts, which are particularly prevalent in the upper beds (C2) of the Coniri Formation. The radiometric dates obtained by Swanson et al. (1987) on materials from both the top and the base of the Coniri Formation indicated an Upper Oligocene–Lower Miocene age.

The C1 sequence of the Coniri Formation is found in contact with the Coniri fault. These sediments are red and well stratified. They lie in angular discordance over the Tiwanaku Formation. From a petrographic perspective, the presence of many Precambrian granite clasts that give way to Permian calcareous clasts can be observed from base to top. The C1 sequence can be divided into four third-order sequences. The first of these has clasts smaller than 30 centimeters and corresponds to alluvial fan environments. The following three indicate mudflows, with fewer clasts toward the upper portions of the sequences. After that, a proximal fluvial system developed.

The C2 sequence is the thickest (1,200 meters). It is characterized by third-order sequences increasing in grain and layer size toward the top of the sequence, where there are 90-centimeter blocks. Permian calcareous clasts are more abundant in the C2 sequence than in the C1 sequence, and they grade into Paleozoic green quartzites near the top. The C2 sequence corresponds to prograding alluvial fans. During the sedimentation process, the climate must have been arid. Aridity is indicated by the presence of numerous channels filled with clays, along with mudflows and the appearance of evaporites toward the interior of the Tiwanaku basin.

#### THE KOLLU KOLLU FORMATION (TERTIARY SYSTEM)

The Kollu Kollu Formation was defined by Ascarrunz (1973). It is composed of conglomerates, red sandstones, clayish mudflows, and alluvial clays intercalated with acid tuffs. Clasts are subangular to subrounded, and Paleozoic quartzites and Permian calcareous clasts are encountered. Swanson et al. (1987) assigned radiometric dates of 18.3 to 16.6 million years to this formation. This series lies over the Coniri Formation.

#### THE TARACO FORMATION (TERTIARY SYSTEM)

The Taraco Formation in the Taraco peninsula consists of conglomerates approximately 200 meters thick lying in discordance over the Middle Miocene Kollu Kollu Formation. Gravels predominate in clasts with diameters of up to 20 centimeters embedded in a sandy-clayish matrix. In the upper portion of the Taraco Formation there is a volcanic or sedimentary-volcanic level.

The Taraco deposits have been accumulated by watercourses in permanent anastomosed canals. There seems to be an evolution of the deposits from north to south: the sediments located in the south of the peninsula are more clayey and finer than those in the north. The clasts are formed of Devonian mudstones, quartzites, vein quartz, Permian calcareous rocks, and granodiorites. The small quantity of Cordillera Oriental granites indicates that during the deposition period of these conglomerates the granites were little exposed by erosion. These conglomerates have not been dated. Nevertheless, we know that they have been excised by deposits from Lake Ballivian (Ulloma Formation), for which they serve as a substratum. In short, these conglomerates are earlier than Lake Ballivian. By correlation, it has been assumed that these deposits belong to the Pliocene, dated in other locations to 5.4 million years.

### Undifferentiated Rocks

At Mount Chilla we observed a series of rocks that began with a 35-meter-thick basal andesitic extrusion. These rocks have a high hornblende content. Above these sediments there is an accumulation of greenish polymictic conglomerate 20 meters thick. The components of this conglomerate are granitic clasts of a rose color (possibly Precambrian), quartz, and whitish quartzites in a cloritic hematite cement. On top of these sediments there is a 30-meter-thick andesitic extrusion with a high pyroxene content. Another conglomerate bed, 30 meters thick, lies over the volcanic rocks. Immediately above, there is a 35-meter-thick deposit of andesite with pyroxene and hornblende, followed by a 30-meter-thick conglomerate similar to the previous one, and finally an andesitic extrusion with abundant hornblende.

The entire series is affected by a strong metamorphism evident in schist flows and in the conglomerates in which clasts are extruded along the direction of flow. These rocks were first attributed to the Paleozoic (Saavedra 1964) and were later described specifically as Lower Mesozoic in age (Mogravejo 1969).

## Quaternary Geology of the Tiwanaku and Catari Basins

The Quaternary geology of the altiplano and the piedmonts of the Cordillera Oriental and Cordillera Occidental is characterized by extensive lacustrine deposits. These can be found from Peru to Argentina. Three major lacustrine deposits have been identified in the altiplano: Lake Ballivian, Lake Minchin, and Lake Cabana (see fig. 2.3).

Lake Ballivian, known in Bolivia as the Ulloma Formation, was described by Troll (1927), Newell (1949), and Ahlfeld and Branisa (1960). The deposits are composed essentially of fine sands and well-laminated clays. Locally there is a diatomaceous level in the upper part. This formation is well exposed in the northern altiplano of Peru and Bolivia. To the south it is delimited by the topographic formations of Ulloma and Callapa. The precise age of this formation is unknown, but by morphology and correlations with glacial periods we assume that it can be dated to the Middle Pleistocene (200,000 to 250,000 B.P.).

Lake Minchin lacustrine deposits were described in 1882 (Bowman 1909). These deposits are well developed in the central and southern portions of the altiplano. The Minchin deposits have two different facies: calcareous crusts (stromatolites) and gravelly sands. Together these deposits are 50 meters thick.

Lake Cabana deposits are a detritic lacustrine series composed of bluish and reddish clays and sands with small gravel bars. They may also have a thickness of approximately 50 meters. In the Pando and Ulloma stations of the area of Viacha (Bolivia), there are sediments older than the Ulloma Formation (Lake Ballivian). These deposits present a detrital facies composed of gravel, sands, and muds and could be equivalent to the Cabana lacustrine deposit.

## Quaternary Glacial Episodes

In the Bolivian Cordillera Oriental, mainly in the La Paz region, an erosion surface cuts the Pliocene sediments (La Paz Formation). Above this surface are found glacial or fluvial deposits reaching a thickness of some 500 meters. Several authors have established four glacial episodes for the Bolivian Quaternary: the Calvario, Kaluyo, Milluni-Sorata, and Choqueyapu glaciations. Each of these is separated from the next by an interglacial period.

The Calvario glaciation was defined by Dobrovolny (1962) in the La Paz region. These deposits have a thickness of 80 to 100 meters and are composed of faceted and ridged clasts and of blocks with a dark gray or grayish yellow clayey matrix. The morphology of these deposits has been completely erased by later glacial events. In the La Paz region, overlying the Calvario glaciation there are fluvial deposits called the Purapurani Formation (Dobrovolny 1962). These deposits of the first interglacial episode can reach 300 meters in thickness and are formed by conglomerates. They include interlayers of clay and paleosoils.

The second glacial episode, termed the Kaluyo Formation by Servant (1977), ranges from 100 to 150 meters thick and exhibits fluvio-glacial gravels. After the Kaluyo glaciation, the piedmont region of the Cordillera Oriental experienced strong erosion, exhibited in a surface that cuts several types of rocks: Paleozoic, Pliocene, and Quaternary. The development of this surface implies tectonic and climatic stability. This surface was subsequently dissected by an erosional phase represented by the construction of downstream alluvial fans 10 to 40 meters thick (Argollo 1980).

The third glacial episode, the Sorata glaciation, overlies these alluvial fans. These glacial deposits still preserve their morphology. The lateral moraines are rounded hills of great dimensions. Their lithology is of blocks and striated clasts in a clayish matrix. After the Sorata glaciation, the piedmont region of the Cordillera Oriental was dissected by fluvial erosion. This erosional episode may have been related to a lowering in the level of Lake Titicaca. This third interglacial is represented by fluvial fans at the valley mouths.

Individual valleys were differentially affected by the fourth, or Choqueyapu, glacial episode. Glaciers advanced into these valleys in two distinct phases, Choqueyapu I (27,000 B.P.) and Choqueyapu II (18,000 B.P.), which were separated by an interstadial characterized by phases of erosion and accumulation of alluvial fans. After the Choqueyapu glacial episode there were smaller glacial advances, the last of which occurred between the fifteenth and nineteenth centuries A.D., in the period referred to as the Little Ice Age.

## Fluvial Sedimentation

The Quaternary of the Bolivian altiplano and cordillera is marked by complex processes of erosion and fluvial accumulation that acted mainly during the interglacial periods. These erosion and accumulation phases during the early Quaternary are visible as distinct surface development phases locally called Glacis I and II and as paleosoils and thick gravel accumulations such as that of the Purapurani Formation in the La Paz region.

For the Middle Quaternary, these erosion and accumulation phases are visible as a vast erosion surface, Glacis III, which is well represented in the entire altiplano, and by a smaller erosional surface, Glacis IV. These surfaces exhibit an important, altered red paleosoil development over the erosional surfaces. The development of alluvial fans can be observed at the bases of mountains and hills. Alluvial terraces are evident at different levels.

For the Late Quaternary, these erosion and accumulation phases are better preserved and can be reconstructed on the basis of geomorphological features. This recent period is characterized by active development of alluvial fans associated with permanent and impermanent streams and of alluvial terraces of varied composition at several heights. In some valleys it is possible to find fluvial sediments in swampy environments characterized by development of peats. In other valleys there are only terraces formed by alluvial gravels. Each valley has evolved in a different way depending upon lithology, length of watercourse, magnitude of basin or sub-basin, and slope configurations, among other variables.

## Quaternary Stratigraphy in the Research Area

In the research area, the early Quaternary is represented by two terrace levels (T-7 and T-6) or erosion surfaces (S-I and S-II), located at 3,940 and 3,900 meters above sea level, respectively (fig. 3.4).

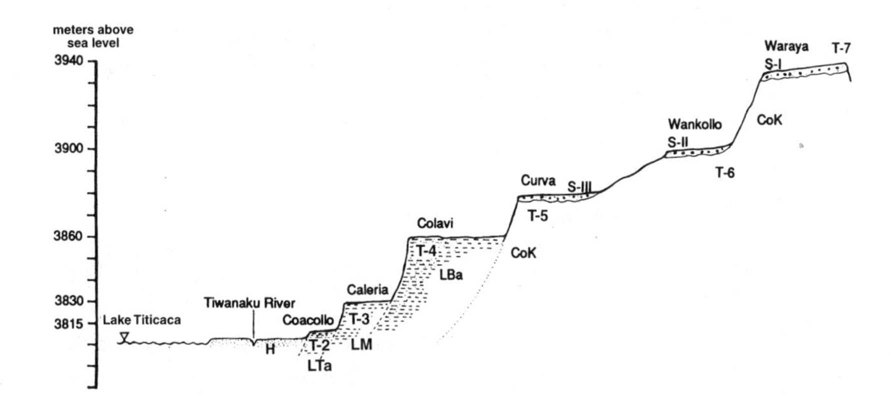


**Figure 3.4.** Geological cross section in the Tiwanaku Valley, illustrating terraces and erosional surfaces. SI, SII, and SIII are erosional surfaces; T-1 through T-7 are lacustrine terraces. H indicates Holocene fluvial deposits; LTa, Lake Tauca deposits; LM, Lake Minchin deposits; LBa, Lake Ballivian deposits; and CoK, Coniri and Kollu Kollu formations.

Relicts of terrace T-7 (surface I) are visible in different areas of the Tiwanaku and Catari basins. The terrace is best represented to the east of the community of Waraya. The following lithologic sequence can be observed in this terrace. The upper portion of the stratigraphic column is composed of red soil approximately 80 centimeters thick that is highly porous and has polyhedral structures. Underlying this soil is an accumulation of poorly transported fluvial gravels composed of red and whitish sandstones and Quimsa Chata and Chilla mountain igneous clasts in a sandy-silty matrix. This accumulation has a thickness ranging from 2 to 6 meters. These gravels represent a fluvial accumulation phase under torrential hydrological conditions. Later, this accumulation plain was dissected, possibly as the result of local tectonic effects that provoked a period of river incision. This gravel deposit lies over a formation of sandstones, mudstones, and levels of volcanic ash, with a NW strike and NE dip. These rocks correspond to the Coniri and Kollu Kollu formations of Middle Miocene age.

Relicts of terrace T-6 (surface II) can also be detected in different locations of the study area. The terrace is best represented to the east of the community of Wankollo. T-6 exhibits the following lithologic sequence. The upper portions consist of 4 to 6 meters of gravels composed of red and whitish sandstone clasts and Quimsa Chata igneous clasts, underlying a well-developed soil. This soil is dark brown in color with a sandy-silt character. The gravels are deposited over more ancient rocks, red sandstones and conglomerates that, as in the case of the T-7 surface, also correspond to the Middle Miocene Coniri and Kollu Kollu formations. This gravel deposit corresponds to a later phase of fluvial accumulation during the process of river incision.

The two lacustrine episodes of the early Quaternary, known in Peru as Lake Mataro and Lake Cabana, cannot be identified in our research area, even though the terrace levels described here correspond to the heights of those lacustrine deposits as defined in Peru. Likewise, the glacial episodes of the early Quaternary, well known in the La Paz region and in the eastern cordillera, have not been observed in the research area. It is likely that the cirques located in the Tiwanaku mountain chain were active during the ancient glacial episodes (Calvario, Kaluyo), but their deposits have been erased by later events.

During the Middle Pleistocene the research area was the situs of a complex sequence of erosion and accumulation phases, higher lacustrine levels, and glacial activity restricted to the elevated portions of the Tiwanaku mountain chain. This evolution has been reconstructed by studying several geological and geomorphological sections and profiles located along the Chilla, Cucuota, Chusicani, Tiwanaku, and Katari rivers. These reference sections define the principal geological and geomorphological units of the study area.

### CHILLA RIVER SECTION

This section is located on the right margin of the Chilla River, near the community of San Antonio. The stratigraphic sequence of the section is as follows:

- A conglomerate deposit of fluvial origin approximately 10 meters thick that exhibits in its upper part 80 centimeters of dark brown silts that correspond to the present-day soil; 3 meters of gravels with reddish sand lenses; 3 meters of fluvial gravels composed of sandstones and green clasts from Mount Chilla; 15 centimeters of fine reddish sand; and 3 meters of gravels composed of Mount Chilla sandstones and green clasts with a maximum diameter of 20 centimeters.
- A dissection phase.

- A laminated deposit of sands and silts that represents a lacustrine episode. The maximum elevation of this deposit is 3,860 meters above sea level.
- Another dissection phase.

KOLLU KOLLU–KALLAMARKA SECTION

This section is located between the communities of Kallamarka and Curva, where the following stratigraphic sequence can be observed (fig. 3.5):

- A substratum of sandstones and conglomerates of the Coniri and Kollu Kollu formations. These rocks are cut by an erosional surface (S-III, or Glacis III) located at 3,880 meters above sea level. On top of this substratum there are 30 centimeters of sandy, light red soil.
- A dissection phase.
- A lacustrine deposit composed of fine sands, silts, and clays reaching a maximum elevation of 3,860 meters.

CHAMBI CHICO SECTION

This section is located near the community of Chambi Chico and reflects a stratigraphic succession similar to those previously described:

- A substratum of sandstones, mudstones, and levels of volcanic ash. This substratum takes a slope of 5 percent. In its upper portion there is a 1- to 2-meter-thick accumulation of fluvial gravels. Over these gravels has developed a sandy red soil some 60 centimeters thick.
- A dissection phase.
- Lacustrine deposits composed of silts and whitish clays. These deposits are at 3,850 meters above sea level. The lacustrine deposits in this section are more eroded than those encountered in the previous sections.
- Another dissection phase.

KOLLU KOLLU SECTION

On the lower slopes of the Taraco mountain range, colluvio-fluvial accumulations lie over the Kollu Kollu Formation rocks. The following stratigraphic sequence can be identified, from top to base:

- 80 centimeters of light gray sands and gravels with quartzite and sandstone subrounded clasts taking a maximum diameter of 20 centimeters.
- 80 centimeters of gravels and red sands (paleosoil) with subrounded quartzite and sandstone elements with a maximum clast size of 10 centimeters. This paleosoil represents a soil-formation phase that affected both the gravel deposits and the red sandstones of the Kollu Kollu Formation. This phase of pedogenesis can be associated with the S-III/Glacis III surface.

GUAQUI ALLUVIAL FAN SECTION

The principal quebrada that descends from the Tiwanaku Range toward the town of Guaqui exposes a 20-meter-thick outcrop in which the following lithologic sequence is visible, from top to base:

- 80 centimeters of present-day dark gray silts.
- 6 meters of fluvial gravels with blocks up to 80 centimeters in diameter, characterized by red and whitish subrounded sandstone clasts.
- 2 meters of heterogeneous material with clasts up to 40 centimeters in diameter, in a silt-clay matrix. This probably reflects a phase of flooding.

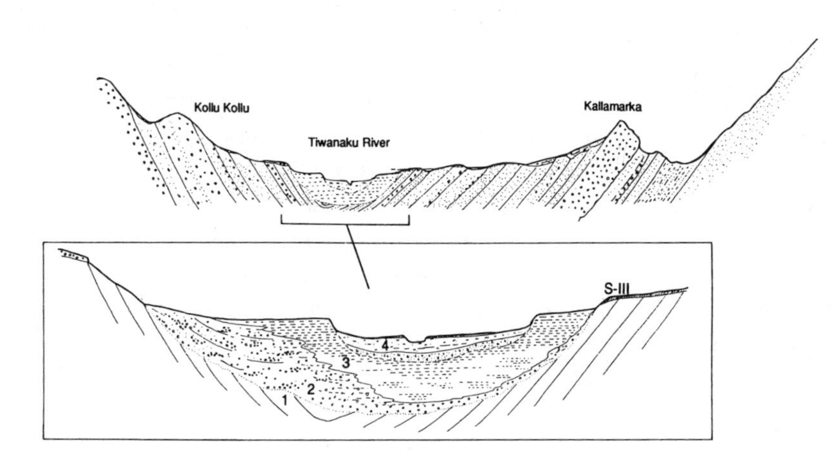


**Figure 3.5.** Kollu Kollu and Kallamarka geological section, illustrating the erosional surface at 3,880 meters above sea level (S-III), the Coniri and Kollu Kollu substratum (1), the erosional surface (2), a dissection phase (3), and a lacustrine deposit (4).

- 8 meters of fluvial gravels with dark gray sand lenses.

## Synthesis of Middle Pleistocene Stratigraphy

The Middle Pleistocene in Bolivia begins with a broad erosion surface (S-III/Glacis III) formed during the interglacial period between the Kaluyo and Sorata glaciations. Field study of the sections and profiles shows the existence of this surface in the research area, but there it takes rather small dimensions. The S-III surface cuts Tertiary rocks in the Kallamarka and Tambillo regions. It can also cut early Quaternary deposits, as it does in the Chilla region. The slope of the S-III surface is variable, normally ranging between 1 and 2 percent but approaching 5 percent in some areas, as in the Chambi Chico region. The S-III erosion surface (Glacis III) has been affected by an erosion phase, evidenced by a difference of 20 meters in elevation between this surface and the highest lacustrine surface of the area. The detrital cover overlying the S-III surface at 3,880 meters above sea level, or 70 meters above Lake Titicaca's present-day level, is very small and sometimes nonexistent. We did not observe tectonic deformations of this surface like those that occur on the western flank of the Cordillera Oriental. A phase of pedogenesis over the S-III erosional surface is geographically generalized even though the thickness and extent of individual deposits are quite small. Alluvial fans developed on the lower parts of quebradas and rivers of the Tiwanaku and Taraco mountain ranges as a consequence of a prior phase of erosion and redeposition. These alluvial deposits were later reworked by the waters of Lake Ballivian.

The Sorata glacial episode, which characterizes the Middle Pleistocene, is well represented along the Cordillera Oriental. In the Tiwanaku mountain range, however, we observed only limited glacial activity, principally in the form of small cirques. We could distinguish small deposits of heterogeneous material that most likely correspond to this glacial episode. Because of the small magnitude of identifiable glacial activity in this region, it is difficult at the moment to establish an adequate correlation with the glacial episodes established in the Cordillera Oriental.

The lacustrine deposits observed in both the Tiwanaku and Catari basins are related to the Ballivian lacustrine episode. The top of these lacustrine deposits is located in the northern region of the altiplano at 3,860 meters above sea level. In the Tiwanaku basin there are only small deposits belonging to this episode. These are greatly altered by subsequent phases of erosion. Similarly, there are very few deposits in the Catari basin. Nevertheless, east of Tambillo there are broad surfaces of Ballivian lacustrine deposits, cut by the Catari and Pallina rivers.

The Sorata-Choqueyapu interglacial represents the end of the Middle Pleistocene. This interglacial episode is characterized in other regions by an important phase of dissection and the development of another erosional surface (S-IV/Glacis IV). In our research area, it has been possible to differentiate only one phase of erosion and one phase of accumulation. In certain upstream sectors, this erosion phase has built alluvial terraces (labeled T-4 in fig. 3.4), while downstream the effects of this phase of dissection include the formation of large alluvial fans.

## Late Pleistocene Stratigraphy

The topography of the research area was established by the end of the Middle Pleistocene. During the Late Pleistocene, lakes much bigger than present-day Lake Titicaca occupied a great portion of the Tiwanaku and Catari basins. The evolution of the valleys during the Late Quaternary (Late Pleistocene–Holocene) has been reconstructed on the basis of sections and geological and geomorphological profiles throughout the study area.

### SAN BARTOLOMÉ RIVER SECTION

The San Bartolomé River exhibits, in its upper portion, a marshy sedimentation that lies over Tertiary rocks of the Tiwanaku Formation. These deposits present the following lithologic sequence, from top to base (fig. 3.6):

- 20 centimeters of dark brown silts that form the present-day soil.
- 1 meter of dark gray silts with levels of burnt peat.
- 60 centimeters of whitish gray sandy silts.
- 10 centimeters of alternating red silts and gravel. Gravels have a maximum clast diameter of 5 centimeters.
- 60 centimeters of peat formed of Gramineae stems and roots.
- 15 centimeters of light gray silt.
- 60 centimeters of red silts with interdigitation of subangular gravels.
- 60 centimeters of intense reddish silts.
- 11 centimeters of red silt.

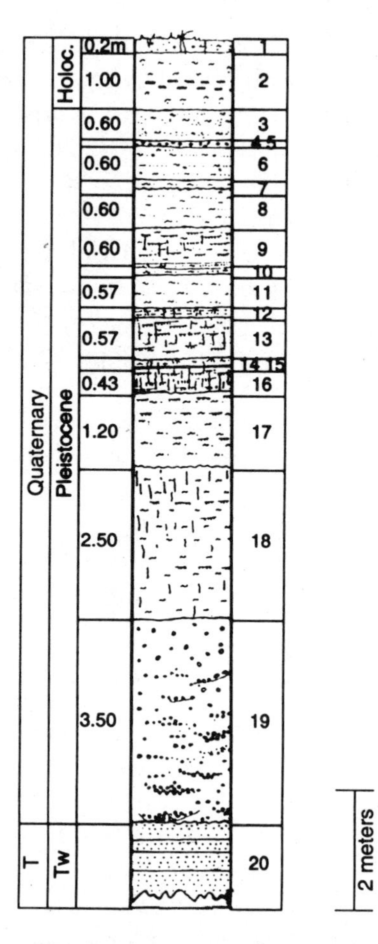


**Figure 3.6.** San Bartolomé River lithologic sequence. From top to bottom: (1) 20 cm of dark brown silts, (2) 1 m of gray silts and peat, (3) 60 cm of whitish gray sandy silts, (4) 10 cm of red silts and gravel, (5) 5 cm of gravel, (6) 60 cm of peat, roots, and stems, (7) 15 cm of light gray silt, (8) 60 cm of red silts and subangular gravel, (9) 60 cm of red silts, (10) 11 cm of red silt, (11) 57 cm of dark gray silt and heavy organic matter, (12) 17 cm of dense black grayish peat, (13) 57 cm of dark gray silt with peat interbedding, (14) 7 cm of red silt and plant roots, (15) 2 cm of carbonized organic matter, (16) 34 cm of peats, (17) 1.2 m of dark brown silts, (18) 2.5 m of dark gray organic silts, (19) 3.5 m of colluvial gravels, and (20) red sandstones.

- 57 centimeters of dark gray silt with abundant organic matter.
- 17 centimeters of dense black, clayish peat.
- 57 centimeters of dark gray silt and peat interbedding.
- 7 centimeters of red silt with plant roots.
- 2 centimeters of carbonized organic matter.
- 34 centimeters of compact peat.
- 1.2 meters of dark brown silt with small beds (5 centimeters thick) of peat.
- 2.5 meters of dark gray organic silt.
- 3.5 meters of colluvial angular gravels in contact with Tertiary red sandstones.

#### WANKOLLO SECTION

A natural outcrop was observed above the San Bartolomé River near the church in the community of Wankollo. There, the following lithologic sequence is visible, from top to base:

- 40 centimeters of present-day silt and sandy soil, light gray in color.
- 18 centimeters of dark gray silt and sandy soil.
- 28 centimeters of light gray sand and silt.
- 25 centimeters of gravels with igneous rock and sandstone clasts reaching 10 centimeters in diameter. Paleochannel structures are visible in this deposit.
- 55 centimeters of dark gray paleosoil, toward the base of which there is a concentration of shells.
- 35 centimeters of whitish gray silt with many calcareous concretions.
- 12 centimeters of silt and oxidized sands.
- 40 centimeters of gravels with igneous and sandstone clasts up to 5 centimeters in diameter.

A second natural outcrop is visible 1 kilometer downstream. There, the following lithologic sequence can be determined:

- 20 centimeters of present-day soil composed of dark brown silts.
- 60 centimeters of coarse sands and dark gray silts.
- 30 centimeters of dark gray silt.
- 20 centimeters of dense, dark gray silts.
- 10 centimeters of dark brown paleosoil.
- 30 centimeters of dark gray silts.
- 20 centimeters of whitish gray silts. In this level there are abundant shell concentrations and calcareous concretions.
- 50 centimeters of fine sands and red silts.
- 50 centimeters of subrounded fluvial gravels with clasts reaching a maximum of 15 centimeters in diameter.

#### QUEBRADA CALLIJIPINA SECTION

This quebrada has an intermittent stream that reworks a glacial cirque in its highest parts, where there are small moraine deposits. In a natural outcrop, the following lithologic sequence is visible, from top to base:

- 20 centimeters of light gray present-day soil.
- 40 centimeters of dark gray silts with substantial organic matter.
- 6 meters of heterogeneous materials with blocks up to 1 meter in diameter. The sandstone clasts

and blocks exhibit angular forms in a silt-clay matrix.

- 20 centimeters of light gray silts with a noticeable degree of lamination, interbedded with peats. This horizon is substantially disturbed by the weight of the overlying deposits.
- 4 meters of altered clayish silt, with some evidence of stratification. These rocks pertain to the Tiwanaku Formation (Tertiary).

### QUEBRADA PILLAPI SECTION

The intermittent stream that courses through the quebrada of Pillapi near the community of the same name reworks conglomerates and sandstones from the Coniri and Kollu Kollu formations. This quebrada exhibits the following lithologic sequence, from top to base:

- 40 centimeters of silt and dark gray gravels representing the present-day soil.
- 55 centimeters of light brown paleosoil with calcareous concretions. In the lower portion of this deposit there is a fine gravel layer.
- 30 centimeters of gravels composed of sandstone clasts with maximum diameters of 15 centimeters. Structures of small paleochannels are evident in this deposit.
- 2.2 meters of thick sand with clasts of 10-centimeter maximum diameter. There are small paleochannels with well-rounded granite clasts of 5-centimeter maximum diameter.
- 1.1 meters of alternating sand and silt. There are calcareous concretions in the central portion of this deposit.
- 85 centimeters of loose thick sands with well-rounded igneous clasts of 3 to 5 centimeters in maximum size. There are small paleochannel structures evident in this deposit.

### TARACO SECTION

Two lacustrine terraces can be differentiated morphologically in the Taraco region near the Cerro Yunga Apacha: one is located at 3,850 meters above sea level and the other at 3,830 meters (fig. 3.7). The higher terrace (labeled Lba in fig. 3.7) is formed by gravels well rounded and polished by wave action. These gravels are composed of sandstone and quartzite clasts with diameters that reach a maximum of 6 centimeters. The thickness of this outcrop is 20 meters. The lower terrace cuts into the higher one and is com-

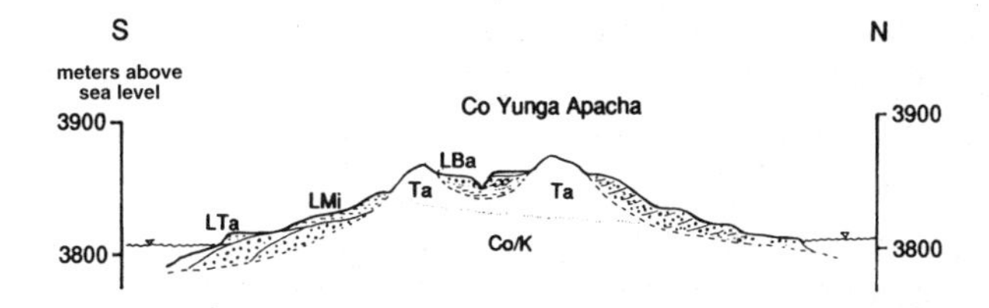


Figure 3.7. Two lacustrine terraces in the Taraco region, showing Lake Tauca deposits (Lta), Lake Minchin deposits (LM), Lake Ballivian deposits (LBa), the Taraco Formation (Ta), and the Coniri and Kollu Kollu formations (Co/K).

posed of laminated sediments alternating between white and reddish silts. Even though these laminations are extremely eroded, they can be followed along most of the Taraco peninsula. These lacustrine deposits have a thickness of some 10 meters.

### MUNCAÑA SECTION

The Muncaña section is located near the community of Muncaña in a quebrada that drains rocks of the Coniri Formation. The intermittent stream in this quebrada flows toward the pampas region of the Catari basin. The following lithologic sequence is observable in this quebrada, proceeding from top to base:

- 50 centimeters of light gray silt that forms the present-day soil.
- 50 centimeters of gravels with clasts up to 10 centimeters in diameter formed of sandstones and quartzites of the Coniri Formation.
- 2.5 meters of compact, light brown silts and gravels.
- 1 meter of gravels, usually of parent materials composed of sandstones, with clasts 10 centimeters in maximum diameter.
- 60 centimeters of red paleosoil formed by silt and altered gravels.
- 4 meters of gravels interbedded with sand lenses. The central portion of this deposit presents red compact sands. Toward its lower part, the deposit turns into gravels with sandstone clasts 20 centimeters in maximum diameter.
- 1.2 meters of laminated, multicolored silts (greenish, whitish, and reddish) with evidence of bioturbation.

### CATAVI SECTION

At the bases of isolated hills of Permo-Carboniferous age near the community of Catavi there are lacustrine terrace deposits located at 3,830 meters above sea level. On the upper part of this terrace, a 2-meter whitish silt layer can be found. Near the top of this deposit, there are two levels of diatomaceous deposits, each approximately 20 centimeters thick, separated by a 30-centimeter light brown silt layer.

## Synthesis of Late Pleistocene Stratigraphy

The Late Pleistocene stratigraphy begins with the last glacial episode, characterized by the Choqueyapu I and II advances. This glacial advance is documented in both the Cordillera Oriental and the Cordillera Occidental. In the Tiwanaku mountain range this glacial activity is manifested in small cirques that probably were active during the four major glacial events known in Bolivia. At the bases of some glacial cirques there are small lateral moraine deposits. The most external glacial moraine could be related by its morphology to this period of glacial advance.

There was no glacial activity below 4,600 meters above sea level. In these lower elevations, the Late Pleistocene is marked by development of fluvial sedimentation and erosion of earlier landscapes. The interstadial period between the Choqueyapu I and II glacial advances lasted approximately 40,000 years. This interstadial is characterized by fluvial deposits identifiable as alluvial terraces and fans. It is possible that these fans had been active since Choqueyapu I times.

Lake Minchin is well represented in the southern altiplano basins but is also visible at the margins of present-day Lake Titicaca, especially in the Taraco peninsula and at the foot of the low Permo-Carboniferous hills of the Catari basin. Evidences of this lacustrine episode are located at 3,830 meters above sea level. These deposits are formed, in the Taraco peninsula, by silt and clay of several colors, and in the Pampa Koani by silt and diatomaceous soils. These lacustrine deposits cut other, older lacustrine levels. The Minchin lacustrine episode is dated between approximately 27,000 and 22,000 B.P.

The Choqueyapu II glacial advance is the last maximum glacial extent known in Bolivia. In the small glacial cirques of the Tiwanaku mountain range, and particularly in the Callijipina glacial cirque, there is a small lateral moraine that can be related to this last maximum. The age of this advance can be estimated at approximately 18,000 B.P.

After the last glacial maximum (Choqueyapu II), a process of deglaciation commenced with marked retreat of glacial ice sheets. Nevertheless, it is possible to observe small fluctuations or stabilizations during this period of deglaciation. While the glacial ice melted in the upper parts, in the lower areas there was fluvial sedimentation together with valley incision. This erosion built alluvial and lacustrine terraces and alluvial fans on both permanent and intermittent rivers and streams. It is possible that this erosion and accumulation phase took place entirely after the Choqueyapu II glaciation.

During the Terminal Pleistocene, another episode of lacustrine development is evident in the research area. This episode is reflected in lacustrine terraces related to Lake Tauca, at 3,815 and 3,818 meters above sea level (fig. 3.4, LTa:T2). These terraces are quite small in the research area and are visible only in the Taraco peninsula. This episode is dated around 11,000–11,500 B.P.

## Holocene Stratigraphy

Overall, the Holocene is represented in the research area by fluvial deposition along the courses of all of the principal rivers. This deposition forms the lower terraces in the research area, with a thickness of accumulation from 2 to 6 meters. These terraces are composed of gravels, sand, and silt, with interbedding of organic matter (peats). In some locations, human activities are identifiable by the presence of bones, vegetal charcoal, ceramics, and ash.

### CHUSICANI RIVER SECTION

This section is near the community of Chusicani, on the river of the same name. Here there is a natural outcrop with the following lithologic sequence, from the top of the section to the base (fig. 3.8):

- 30 centimeters of present-day dark gray soil with flat sandstone clasts of the Tiwanaku Formation, obtaining a maximum diameter of 20 centimeters.
- 26 centimeters of black silt with charcoal and ceramic fragments.
- 18 centimeters of whitish gray silt mixed with anthropogenic ash.
- 12 centimeters of well-compacted, dark gray silt and sand.
- 10 centimeters of dark brown sandy silt.
- 70 centimeters of dark gray silt with gravel lenses.

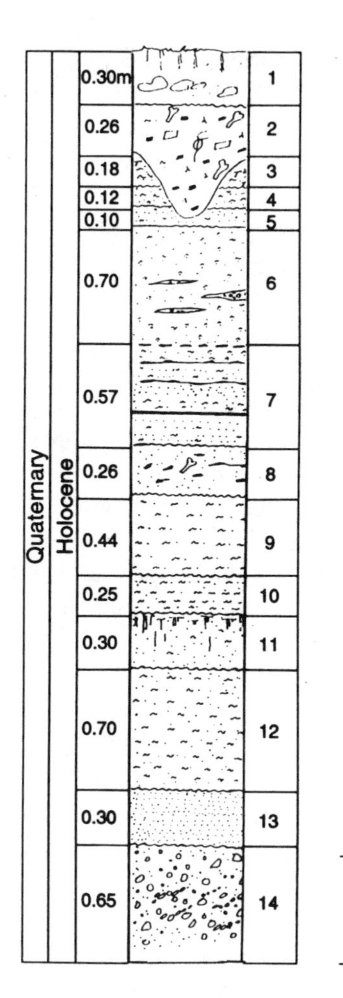


**Figure 3.8.** Chusicani lithologic sequence. From top to bottom: (1) 30 cm of dark gray soil, (2) 26 cm of black silt with anthropogenic deposits, (3) 18 cm of gray silt and ash, (4) 12 cm of compacted dark gray silt and ash, (5) 10 cm of dark brown sandy silt, (6) 70 cm of dark gray silt and gravel, (7) 57 cm of gray sandy silts interdigitated with charcoal horizons, (8) 26 cm of black paleosoil, (9) 44 cm of dark gray silt, (10) 25 cm of gray silt and sand, (11) 30 cm of black paleosoil, (12) 70 cm of black clayish silt, (13) 30 cm of gray clayey silt, and (14) gravels.

In the higher portion there are inclusions of vegetal charcoal.

- 26 centimeters of black paleosoil with remains of roots, charcoal, and bone.
- 44 centimeters of dark gray silt.
- 25 centimeters of dark gray silt and sand.
- 30 centimeters of black paleosoil of high porosity, with remains of ancient roots.
- 70 centimeters of black clayish silt.
- 30 centimeters of gray clayey silt.
- 65 centimeters of subangular gravels formed by sandstone clasts with 20-centimeter maximum diameters, in a clayish silt matrix.

#### TIWANAKU RIVER SECTION

On the Tiwanaku River 200 meters upstream from the K'araña plain, within the archaeological site of Tiwanaku, the following lithological sequence can be observed, from top to base (fig. 3.9):

- 15 centimeters of dark brown silt.
- 70 to 100 centimeters of dark gray silt mixed with anthropogenic ash, bone, ceramics, and charcoal fragments and with stone clasts.
- 20 centimeters of dark gray silt with abundant organic matter.
- 30 centimeters of reddish silt with carbonates.
- 20 centimeters of dark gray silt with abundant organic matter.
- 20 centimeters of dark brown silt, quite friable.
- 30 centimeters of reddish silt with compacted calcareous concretions.
- 10 centimeters of gravels with clasts 5 centimeters in maximum diameter, and silt and sand lenses.

## Fluvial, Lacustrine, and Glacial Sequences of the Holocene

#### FLUVIAL DEPOSITS

Holocene fluvial sedimentation is well preserved in most of the valleys of the Bolivian Andes. Geomorphological and sedimentological study suggests that surface flows have evolved during the Holocene from a pluvial regime favorable to erosion to an aggradational regime favorable to sedimentation of fine materials. The Andean valleys investigated to date are situated between 3,800 and 3,900 meters above sea level in geological contexts characterized by longitudinal slopes of 1 to 8 percent, and they present a generally embanked transverse profile. The drainage basins are usually small and not higher than 4,800 meters above sea level.

Present-day environment is controlled by a seasonal regime of torrential precipitation. Lateral valley erosion, incision and deepening of the valley bottoms, and great alluvial fan development are the principal geomorphological characteristics. Yet during the Holocene, significant modifications of this geomorphology took place through fluvial sedimentation visible as two or three continuous sequences of relatively fine deposits with interbedded peats. These deposits are composed of clay, silts, sands, and gravel. Valley floor deposition conditions have been defined by detailed

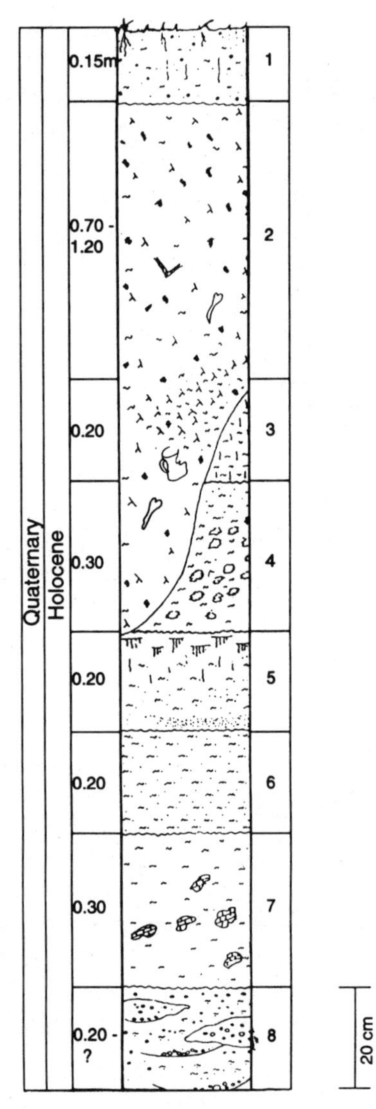


**Figure 3.9.** Tiwanaku River lithologic sequence. Top to bottom: (1) 15 cm of dark brown silt, (2) 70 to 100 cm of dark gray silt with anthropogenic deposits, (3) 20 cm of dark gray silt and organic matter, (4) 30 cm of reddish silt and carbonates, (5) 20 cm of dark gray silt and organic matter, (6) 20 cm of dark brown silt, (7) 30 cm of reddish silt and calcareous concretions, and (8) 10 cm of gravels, silt, and sand.

analysis of layer and sedimentary structure geometry, as well as by correlation with the valley sides.

Schematically, these deposits are related to anastomosed rivers in small meandering channels. The detritus was produced by moderate laminar erosion of valley sides, which produces a local accumulation of thin, flat alluvial fans at the bases of slopes. In the valley bottoms, laminated sediments are frequent. These layers can be classified according to their granulometry. Granulometric classification is related to small seasonal variations in the volume of flowing water. The peats interbedded in these deposits are frequently associated with wetlands areas fed by surface water flows originating from springs located at the bases of the hills and by groundwater flows through permeable deposits. Some peat levels seem to extend across the length and breadth of the valley bottoms, which indicates a greater extent of wetlands in the past than in the present.

Two major fine-sediment accumulation phases were observed in the Holocene deposits: one in their lower portion and the other in their upper portion. In the lower portion, it is possible to observe that the valley bottom was fed by contributions of relatively fine detritus derived from lateral valley erosion. Peat interbeddings are present in the lower Holocene deposits but are dispersed and thin. This weak, fragmentary peat development suggests that the valley bottoms during the early Holocene were not permanently wet and that the distribution of bofedales, or permanent wetlands, was not extensive. After a period characterized by river dissection, the Upper Holocene deposits (the second phase of fine material sedimentation) exhibit a substantial development of peats throughout the valley bottoms, accompanied by lateral valley erosion. Subsequently, the uppermost Holocene deposits indicate a return to less humid conditions and a retraction of wetlands to contemporary conditions.

These sequences of relatively fine material deposition are separated by erosion surfaces and/or levels of discontinuous gravels associated with ancient dissection of the valley sides. These dissections fed alluvial fans, which are particularly well developed in regions where the outcropping geological formations are conglomerates with poorly consolidated rocks. Two principal phases of generalized erosion were observed in all the investigated sites. These are located in the lower and upper portions of the Holocene deposits, intercalated with the episodes of fine material sedimentation.

Holocene accumulations are present in all the valleys located between 3,810 and 3,900 meters above sea level. Generally, these deposits are of gray silt or fine sands with interbedded hydromorphic soils. Toward the margins of the basins these deposits grade into coarser gravels. From this we deduce that processes of erosion and accumulation occurred in these areas throughout the Holocene. Unfortunately, the absence of a substantial series of radiocarbon dates prevents us from establishing an absolute chronology for these erosion and accumulation phases.

#### HOLOCENE LACUSTRINE DEPOSITS AND OSCILLATIONS

Sedimentological research by Oliveira (1986), Wirrmann (1986), and Mourguiart et al. (1986) on cores obtained from the northern and southern Lake Titicaca basins demonstrates that after the Pleistocene-Holocene transition, the waters of Lake Titicaca partially dried in the southern basin (Lake Wiñaymarka), while in the north basin lake levels were substantially lower than present-day levels. Between approximately 7000 and 3500 B.P., lake levels were very low, as indicated by gypsum precipitation. From approximately 4000 to 2000 B.P., water levels increased rapidly until they stabilized. Around 2200 B.P. the lake level was 10 meters below the present-day level. After 2000 B.P. Lake Titicaca slowly reached its present-day level (see chapters 2 and 4).

#### HOLOCENE GLACIAL FLUCTUATIONS

The Pleistocene-Holocene transition is evidenced by substantial deglaciation. Our research into cordilleran glacial activity indicates that since the initial Holocene the positions of glaciers have been virtually identical to present-day locations. Globally, glaciers have been located in similar positions from the initial Holocene to approximately 500 B.P. However, the general stability of glacier positions does not exclude the hypothesis of smaller oscillations during this period. For instance, a last glacial episode provoked the advance of an ice mass in the upper parts of the valleys extending down from the Cordillera Oriental, where a group of glacial moraines is located approximately 1 kilometer in front of present-day glaciers. This event probably occurred at some point during the Little Ice Age, between about A.D. 1500 and 1700. Subsequent to this advance, glaciers receded and have continued to do so into the twentieth century. We did not detect this Little Ice Age glacial episode in the Tiwanaku area, suggesting that the advance was of short duration and restricted to higher elevations.

## Soils of the Tiwanaku and Catari Basins

After water, soil is the most vital, primary natural resource for agricultural production. From an economic frame of reference, soil development is the most important consequence of rock weathering. Five principal factors condition soil development: (1) climate, particularly temperature and amount and type of precipitation; (2) topography, particular the manner in which slope variations affect internal and external patterns of drainage; (3) soil biota, including both surface vegetation cover and subsurface organisms; (4) source rock, including material texture, structure, and composition (both mineralogical and chemical); and (5) time, during which edaphic processes occur.

Conventionally, a soil profile can be divided into three horizons: A, B, and C. We define the A horizon as the surface and immediate subsurface humic soil. The B horizon is that zone of soil development, distinct from the A and C horizons, into which materials from the A horizon migrate and are redeposited. In the soils of the research area, iron and aluminum minerals, calcium carbonates, salts, and clays accumulate and concentrate in the B horizon. The C horizon, in contrast, does not manifest a high degree of alteration. The A and B horizons together are referred to as "solum," or the zone in which soil formation processes have greatly modified parent materials. In the research area, the distinctiveness of the boundaries between A, B, and C horizons varies considerably, although it is always possible to distinguish with some precision the boundary between the B and C horizons. In contrast, the boundaries between A and B horizons are, in some cases, rather indistinct and difficult to distinguish.

In general, a mature soil profile presents well-developed horizons. If soil formation processes have not been occurring for a long time, the soil profile will be imperfect and some horizons may be missing. Of course, time also has an impact on the depth to which soil formation processes have penetrated. Similarly, topography deeply affects soil profiles. On steep slopes, the profile will never reach maturity because erosion removes weathered products as soon as they form. Paleosoils—soils that have been buried after formation—are frequently encountered in the study area. The most notable paleosoils are those that formed during interglacial periods and were buried by glacial till, alluvial fans, or colluvio-fluvial deposits. Paleosoils and polygenetic soils provide information for reconstructing ancient climatic and topographic conditions.

The research area is situated in the subhumid environment of the altiplano. The contemporary landscape is flat to gently undulating with medium-texture soils. The most common soils exhibit an accumulation of organic matter in the surface layer and are associated with shallow rendzinic soils over hard rock. Other soil types in the region include hydromorphic, organic, and poorly developed volcanic ash soils. Some soils have a strong salt content or are sodium saturated.

## Texture Analysis of Soils in the Study Area

In order to characterize soils in the study area granulometrically, we analyzed 20 standard 50-gram samples extracted from selected locations in the Tiwanaku and Catari River basins. The following section summarizes the character and texture of these samples, the source locations of which are indicated in figure 3.10.

### TIWANAKU VALLEY SOILS

*Sample S-1*

This sample, extracted near the community of San Antonio, represents a well-developed dark brown soil some 30 centimeters thick that overlies a lacustrine deposit. This soil exhibits the following composition: 1 percent gravel, 51 percent sand, 36 percent silt, and 12 percent clay. Judging from these proportions, the sample may be characterized as a sandy-silt soil.

*Samples S-2 and S-3*

These soils developed over alluvial fans of the Chilla River. Sample S-2 is a dark brown and highly porous soil with the following granulometric composition: 39 percent sand, 43 percent silt, and 18 percent clay. Sample S-3 has a distinct composition characterized

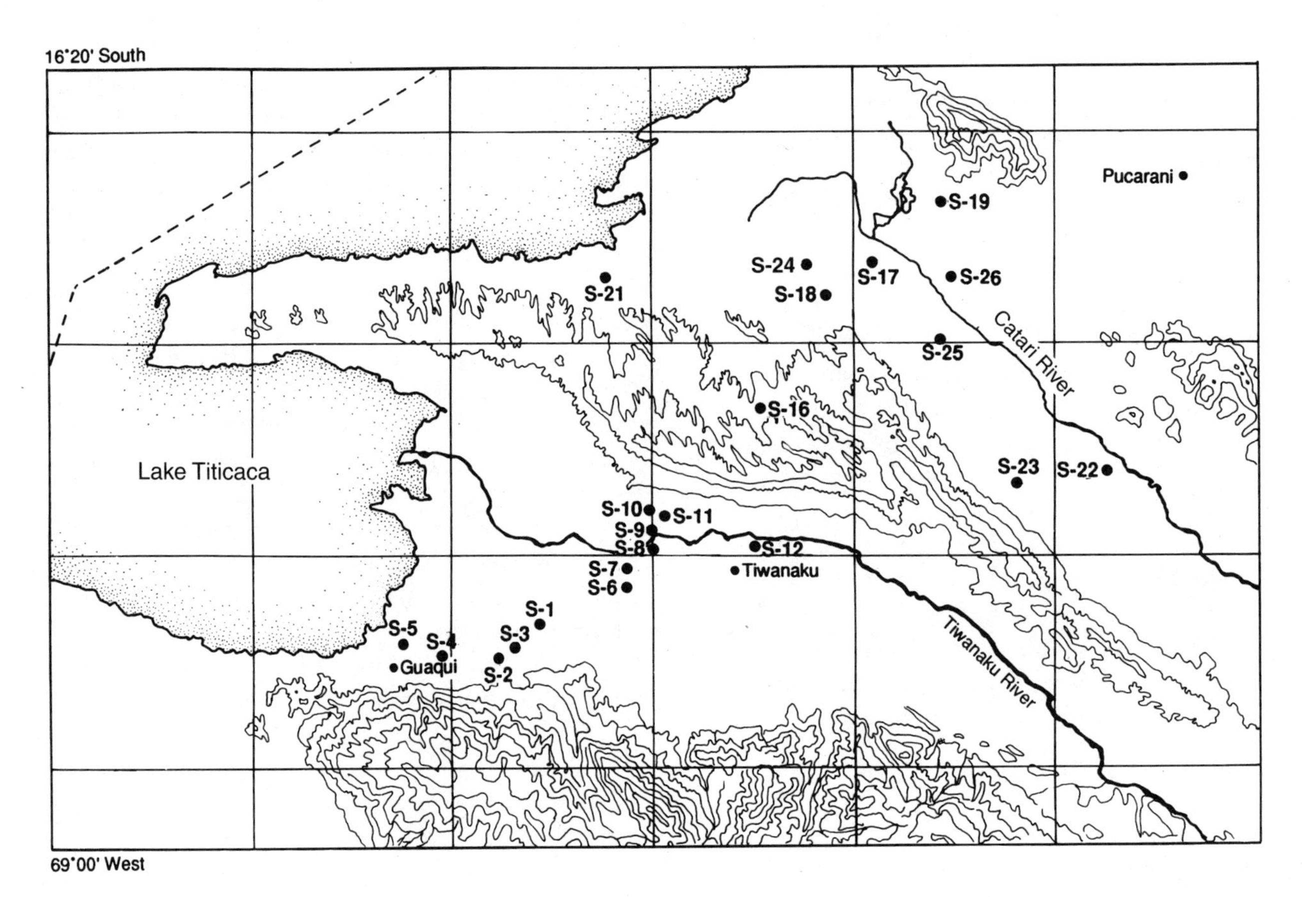


**Figure 3.10.** Locations of soil samples taken from the Tiwanaku and Catari River basins.

by a substantial gravel admixture: 22 percent gravel, 36 percent sand, 34 percent silt, and 8 percent clay. Samples S-2 and S-3 are formed from weathered volcanic-sedimentary rocks and Tiwanaku Formation sedimentary rocks derived from Mount Chilla.

*Sample S-4*

Sample S-4 is a whitish sediment extracted between two alluvial fans in the Chilla River–Guaqui region. The granulometric composition of this soil is 24 percent sand and 76 percent silt and clay. The soil is derived from allocthonous volcanic ash. It represents a highly altered material with substantial calcium carbonate content.

*Sample S-5*

This sample was extracted from a bofedal near the town of Guaqui. It is rich in organic matter and presents the following texture: 53 percent sand, 42 percent silt, and 5 percent clay.

*Samples S-6 and S-7*

Sample S-6 was extracted from the lower portion of the Ojra Jawira river fan. This is a predominantly sandy-silty soil exhibiting the following texture: 2 percent gravel, 51 percent sand, 32 percent silt, and 15 percent clay. Sample S-7 came from approximately 2 kilometers north of S-6. It presents the following component proportions: 37 percent sand, 49 percent silt, and 14 percent clay.

*Sample S-8*

This sample was extracted from a small, inactive canal near the Tiwanaku River. This canal once formed part of a larger hydraulic network that fed freshwater to Tiwanaku-period (Tiwanaku IV and V) raised fields. The texture of this sample was 58 percent sand, 30 percent silt, and 12 percent clay.

*Sample S-9*

This sample was extracted adjacent to the banks of the Tiwanaku River at a point under a bridge in the community of Chambi Grande. Overall, the soil can be characterized as sandy-silty with the following proportions: 2 percent gravel, 58 percent sand, 35 percent silt, and 5 percent clay.

*Sample S-10*

This sample, extracted 1 kilometer north of the Chambi Grande bridge, revealed a porous soil with polyhedral structures. The soil is light brown, with the following textural proportions: 32 percent sand, 45 percent silt, and 22 percent clay.

*Sample S-11*

Sample S-11 came from near the Chambi Grande community's school. This soil developed over a colluvial fan descending from the Taraco mountain range, specifically at the foot of Cerro Quitatupo. Texture analysis reveals the following composition: 4 percent gravel, 64 percent sand, 22 percent silt, and 9 percent clay.

Samples S-6, S-7, S-9, and S-11 were taken along a south-to-north transect orthogonal to the Tiwanaku River. These samples exhibit a marked granulometric variation from the valley margins toward the center of the basin. At the margins, soils are mainly sandy-silty grading into gravels, whereas in the central portion they are silty-sandy to clayish. As might be expected, valley bottom soils exhibit massive structure and distinct laminations in some areas.

*Sample S-12*

This sample was extracted from a section of the archaeological site of Tiwanaku referred to locally as K'araña. It is a dark gray, compact, clayey soil with high organic matter content. Granulometric analysis revealed the following texture: 8 percent sand, 37 percent silt, and 55 percent clay.

The Tiwanaku River basin has two sources of sedimentary input. To the south, the Tiwanaku mountain range, composed of sandstones, conglomerates, and volcanic rocks, provides sediments and minerals to the southern portions of the river plain. To the north, the older, highly weathered Taraco mountain range, composed of conglomerates and sandstones of the Coniri, Kollu Kollu, and Taraco formations, provides the parent material for sediments along the northern margins of the Tiwanaku River. Our granulometric analysis enabled us to identify a number of minerals in the extracted soil samples, including transparent and translucid quartz with well-rounded grain structure, white feldspar, white and black laminar mica, tourmaline, zirconium, epidote, and chlorite. There are also carbonate fragments. The percentages of these minerals in each soil sample are highly variable, depending on the source location of the samples.

### CATARI BASIN SOILS

*Sample S-16*

This sample is located over an erosion surface that cuts through Taraco Formation conglomerates in the mountains above the community of Lukurmata. This sandy-silty soil presents the following granulometry: 2 percent gravel, 58 percent sand, 35 percent silt, and 5 percent clay.

*Sample S-17*

Sample S-17 was taken in the pampas zone of the Pampa Koani 1 kilometer south of the Catari River. This is a well-developed, highly organic soil with a mean thickness of 30 centimeters. Textural analysis revealed the following component proportions: 22 percent sand, 73 percent silt, and 5 percent clay.

*Sample S-18*

Sample S-18 is located 3 kilometers due south of S-17, near the community of Chokara. Like S-17, this soil is well developed and highly organic. Anthropogenic charcoal and ceramics were recovered from this sample, indicating significant human alteration of the soil. The sample presents the following granulometry: 3 percent gravel, 32 percent sand, 53 percent silt, and 12 percent clay.

*Sample S-21*

Sample S-21 was taken from an area of contemporary raised-field rehabilitation on an alluvial plain north of the community of Wakullani. The soils of this plain are compact with a massive structure and are highly organic. Granulometric analysis of the sample revealed the following texture: 2 percent gravel, 30 percent sand, 54 percent silt, and 14 percent clay.

*Sample S-22*

S-22 was extracted on the southern margin of the Catari River along the road to the town of Pukarani. It revealed a sandy-silty soil with the following texture: 50 percent sand, 43 percent silt, and 7 percent clay.

*Sample S-24*

S-24 was extracted in an area of ancient and contemporary raised-field cultivation near the community of Lakaya. The sample presents the following textural proportions: 51 percent sand, 42 percent silt, and 7 percent clay.

*Sample S-25*

Taken from the floodplain of the Pampa Koani near the community of Korila, this sample revealed a well-developed silty soil with the following texture: 22 percent sand, 74 percent silt, and 3 percent clay.

*Sample S-26*

S-26 was extracted from an area of ancient raised-field cultivation on the floodplain near the community of Iquiaca Grande. This area is characterized by significant bofedales, or marshlands. Textural analysis of the sample indicated the following component proportions: 12 percent sand, 66 percent silt, and 22 percent clay.

Sample S-16 represents a shallow soil developed over Taraco Formation conglomerate rocks. Samples S-17, S-18, S-21, S-22, S-24, S-25, and S-26 were extracted from the floodplain of the Pampa Koani. Sediment input to this alluvial plain derives from the Catari and Pallina rivers, which maintain an east-west course. The Sewenka River, which trends in a NE-SW direction, also inputs sediments to the northwest sector of the Catari basin. The Catari and Pallina rivers rework ancient lacustrine deposits of sand, silt, and clay that date to the Lake Ballivian episode. The granulometry of most of these pampas soils is fine, and component elements are well rounded. The majority of component minerals in these soils are quartz, feldspar, white and black mica, tourmaline, zirconium, and some carbonates. Mineral input derives from the Taraco mountain range and from Paleozoic rocks that border the Pampa Koani plain.

### Summary

Granulometric analysis of soil samples indicates that the Tiwanaku and Catari basins have three principal sedimentary input sources: the Tiwanaku and Taraco mountain chains and isolated outcrops of Paleozoic rocks. Most of the soils of the study area are immature. These are transported soils, mostly of Quaternary and Holocene age. Textural analysis indicates a heterogeneous granulometric composition. Soil texture is either predominantly sandy-silty or silty-sandy. Because the valley bottoms of these two basins were the locuses of significant agricultural reclamation projects, most of the analyzed soils show significant human alteration. Some samples, particularly S-17, S-18, and S-21, might even be considered true anthrosols.

## Water Resources of the Tiwanaku and Catari Basins

Water is the key resource for the development of an efficient regional agricultural landscape. Subsequent chapters in this volume provide a detailed portrait of the various techniques employed by Tiwanaku farmers to conserve and manipulate water from natural sources such as rivers, both permanent and intermittent, springs, and groundwater. In this section, we briefly summarize the drainage features of the Tiwanaku and Catari River basins and describe the results of a series of chemical composition tests on water samples from these two basins. We should note that these tests were directed primarily toward a preliminary assessment of water quality for the purposes of the raised-field rehabilitation efforts in these basins (see chapter 9). That is, these tests of chemical composition were intended to identify sources of freshwater that could be employed in irrigating newly rehabilitated raised fields. It is clear, however, that these results are also useful for understanding the water resources that were available to the state of Tiwanaku during its reclamation of the Tiwanaku and Catari river valleys for intensive agricultural production.

### Drainage Patterns

The Tiwanaku River basin incorporates an area of approximately 835 square kilometers with a perimeter of 163 kilometers. The source of the Tiwanaku River lies some 70 meters above its eventual point of discharge into Lake Titicaca. The river runs close to the Taraco mountain range on the north side of the valley through most of its course, resulting in an extensive alluvial plain on the south side. Near the archaeological site of Tiwanaku, the river appears to have been artificially canalized into a straight course, presumably during the Tiwanaku period, although this has not been determined empirically. Elsewhere in the valley, the river behaves in a manner consistent with the valley's relatively mature stage of geomorphological evolution, exhibiting significant meanders.

The principal, permanent tributaries of the Tiwanaku River include the Sainata, Chamaca, Chusicani, San Bartolomé, and Chilla rivers, which drain the Tiwanaku mountain range on the south side of the valley, and the Arapata and Sequeri rivers on the north side of the valley. All other rivers and streams are intermittent, cross only short distances from their point of origin, and achieve significant flow only during the rainy season. In years of low seasonal rainfall, many of these streams remain completely dry. At the same time, it is important to note that in both the Tiwanaku and Catari basins there are significant numbers of springs, especially at the bases of the Tiwanaku and Taraco mountain ranges, which, because of their lithological characteristics, constitute excellent reservoirs of subsurface water. These two mountain ranges possess enormous quantities of water in extensive Tertiary aquifers. Springs were an important source of freshwater for Tiwanaku-period canals that distributed water to raised fields.

As can be seen in figure 3.11, the drainage regime of the Tiwanaku Valley can be characterized generally as dendritic, a feature determined principally by the valley's lithology. Within this general dendritic regime, however, it is possible to distinguish localized anomalies such as radial drainage patterns associated with zones of ancient volcanic activity and dome-shaped structures. Similarly, there are significant occurrences of channel anastomosis. The 680 rivers and streams of the Tiwanaku basin can be classified in the following manner: 522 streams of first order, 128 streams of second order, 25 rivers of third order, 4 rivers of fourth order, and 1 river (the Tiwanaku River) of fifth order.

The drainage regime of the Catari basin is rather different from that of the Tiwanaku Valley (fig. 3.12). The Catari River itself is artificially canalized for approximately 20 kilometers upstream from the point of its discharge into Lake Titicaca. During the Tiwa-

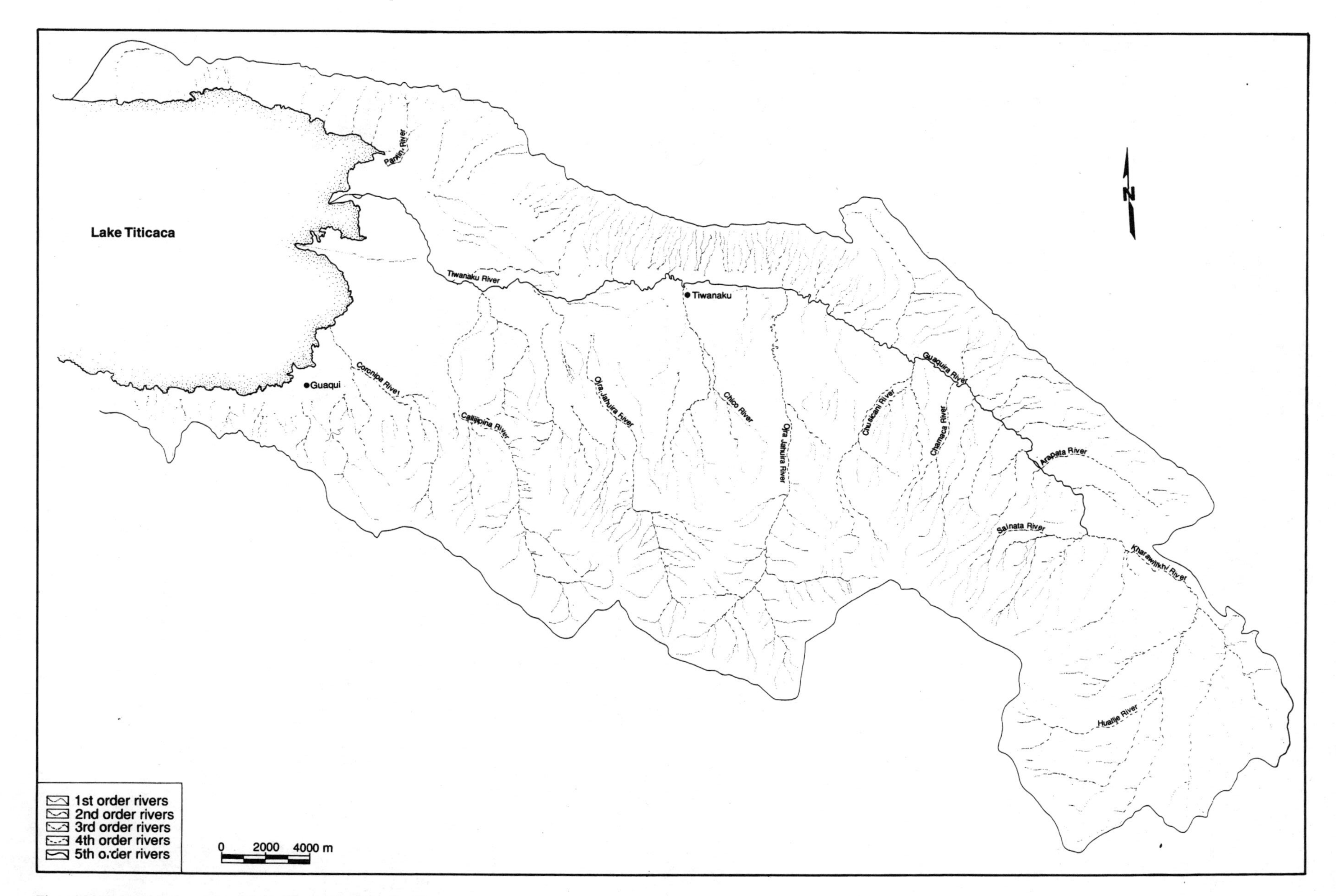


Figure 3.11. Drainage patterns in the Tiwanaku River basin.

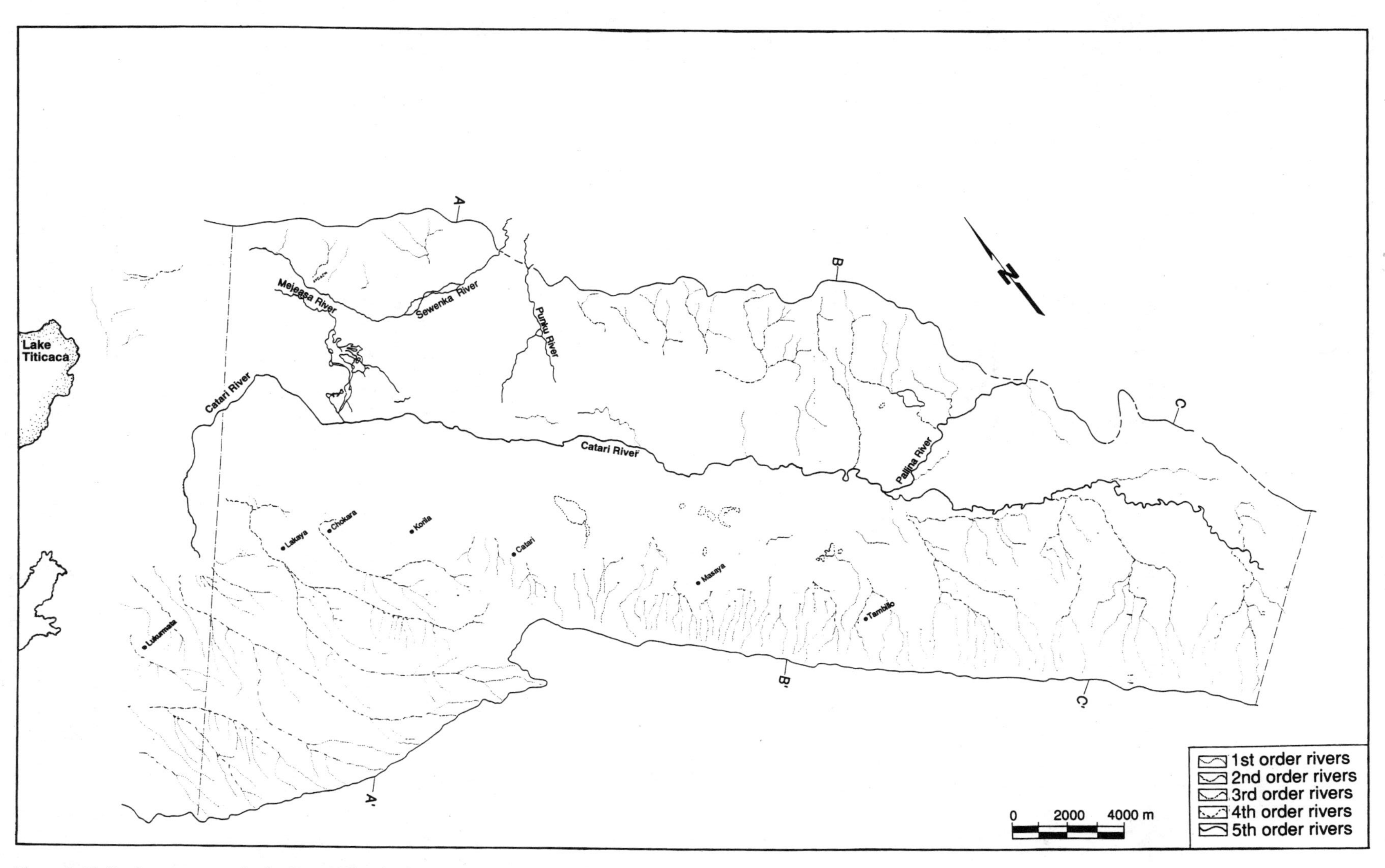


Figure 3.12. Drainage patterns in the Catari River basin.

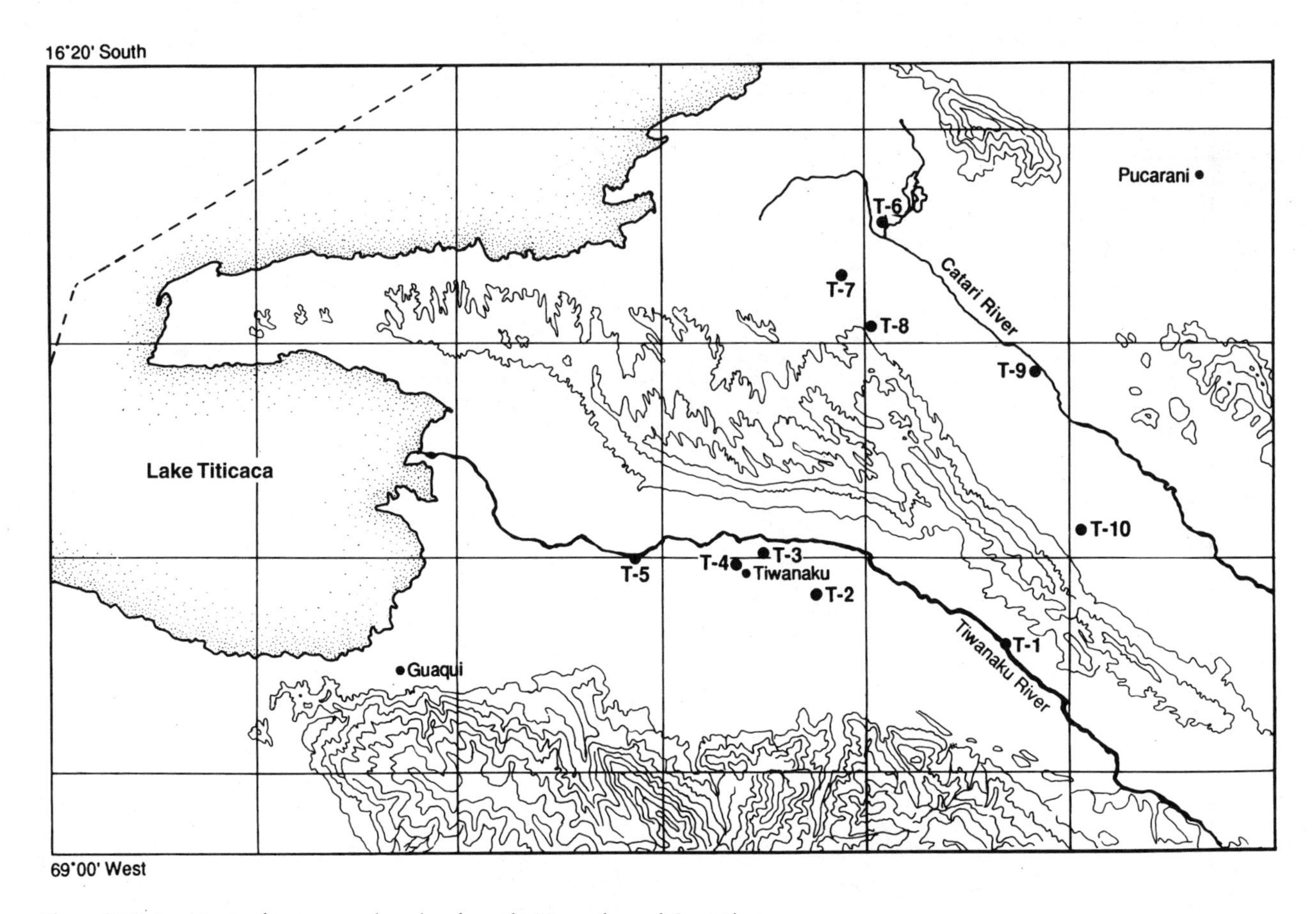


**Figure 3.13.** Locations of water samples taken from the Tiwanaku and Catari basins.

naku period, this section of the river was diverted northward to open up significant quantities of land for agricultural development (see chapter 5). The source of the river is outside the study area, to the east and southeast. From its point of entry into our study area, the Catari River is elevated approximately 10 meters above its point of discharge into Lake Titicaca.

Unlike the Tiwanaku River, the Catari River possesses virtually no significant tributaries in the study area from Tambillo in the east to Lake Titicaca in the west. Over this section of the river's course, none of the small, intermittent streams that originate in the dissected slopes of the Taraco Range on the south side of the basin reach a confluence with the Catari River. Only three intermittent streams descending the isolated hill slopes on the north side of the basin feed the Catari River, and the volume of inflow is insignificant. The water from these intermittent streams flows onto the permeable Quaternary deposits of the pampas zones and percolates into the water table before reaching confluence with the Catari River. Not surprisingly, under these edaphic conditions the groundwater in the pampas zone frequently intersects the surface, resulting in huge pools of standing water during the rainy season.

As in the case of the Tiwanaku Valley, the overall drainage pattern for the Catari basin can be characterized as dendritic, with localized variations generated by distinct lithological conditions. Variations include anastomosis and areas of parallel drainage channels associated with conglomerates. The Catari basin incorporates an area of approximately 546 square kilometers with a perimeter of 121 kilometers. Within this drainage basin, there are 303 rivers and streams that may be classified in the following manner: 224 streams of first order, 56 streams of second order, 14 streams of third order, 2 rivers of fourth order, and 1 river (the Catari River) of fifth order.

## Water Samples

In order to assess water composition and quality in the study area, we drew a set of 10 water samples from the Tiwanaku and Catari rivers, from smaller

Table 3.1. Element Concentrations in Selected Water Samples from the Tiwanaku and Catari Rivers

| Sample | Sodium (mg/L) | Potassium (mg/L) | Calcium (mg/L) | Magnesium (mg/L) | Iron (mg/L) | Chloride (mg/L) | Sulfur (mg/L) | Carbonate (mg/L) | Bicarbonate (mg/L) | Phosphate (mg/L) | Nitrate (mg/L) | Boride (mg/L) |
|---|---|---|---|---|---|---|---|---|---|---|---|---|
| T-1 | 2.96E+01 | 1.48E+00 | 7.35E+01 | 1.03E+01 | 1.00E−01 | 1.72E−01 | 9.00E+01 | 0.00E+00 | 2.45E+02 | 4.17E−01 | 0.00E+00 | 0.00E+00 |
| T-2 | 2.06E+01 | 1.12E+00 | 7.65E−01 | 1.15E+01 | 1.00E−01 | 1.72E+01 | 9.00E+01 | 0.00E+00 | 2.24E+02 | 4.97E−01 | 2.14E−01 | 3.56E−014 |
| T-3 | 4.20E+01 | 1.21E+02 | 8.50E+01 | 2.20E+01 | 1.00E−01 | 2.27E+01 | 2.20E+02 | 0.00E+00 | 3.43E+02 | 3.77E−00 | 2.14E−01 | 1.34E+00 |
| T-4 | 4.97E+01 | 2.29E+00 | 1.13E+20 | 2.20E+01 | 1.00E−01 | 3.92E+01 | 2.25E+02 | 0.00E+00 | 2.42E+02 | 4.57E−01 | 2.14E−01 | 6.31E−01 |
| T-5 | 2.92E+01 | 1.80E+00 | 8.60E+01 | 1.30E+01 | 1.00E−01 | 1.86E+01 | 1.20E+02 | 5.64E+00 | 2.45E+02 | 2.97E−01 | 2.14E−01 | 0.00E+00 |
| T-6 | 8.11E+01 | 6.02E+00 | 4.30E+02 | 1.30E+01 | 1.00E−01 | 9.08E+01 | 1.20E+02 | 1.00E+01 | 1.11E+02 | 6.98E−01 | 2.28E−01 | 1.36E−01 |
| T-7 | 1.54E+02 | 1.73E+01 | 3.45E+01 | 1.48E−01 | 1.00E−01 | 9.97E+01 | 1.45E+02 | 3.50E+00 | 2.29E+02 | 7.11E+00 | 2.14E−01 | 1.23E+00 |
| T-8 | 7.30E+01 | 1.77E+01 | 6.00E+01 | 2.25E+01 | 1.00E−01 | 5.02E+01 | 1.05E+02 | 0.00E+00 | 3.25E+02 | 8.59E−01 | 2.14E−01 | 4.11E−01 |
| T-9 | 8.17E+01 | 5.16E+00 | 3.78E+01 | 1.33E+01 | 2.00E−01 | 9.22E+01 | 1.10E+02 | 5.00E+00 | 1.31E+02 | 5.78E−01 | 2.14E−01 | 6.84E−01 |
| T-10 | 8.17E+01 | 1.04E+01 | 1.02E+02 | 4.40E+01 | 1.00E−01 | 8.94E+01 | 4.00E+02 | 3.15E+01 | 1.57E+01 | 7.78E−01 | 0.00E+00 | 2.32E+00 |

Table 3.2. Total Salt Concentration (TS) in Water Samples from 10 Stations in the Tiwanaku and Catari Rivers

| Station | Grams per Liter |
|---|---|
| 1 | 0.554 |
| 2 | 0.501 |
| 3 | 1.005 |
| 4 | 0.877 |
| 5 | 0.557 |
| 6 | 0.602 |
| 7 | 0.762 |
| 8 | 0.555 |
| 9 | 0.587 |
| 10 | 0.960 |

permanent rivers, from intermittent streams, and from springs (see fig. 3.13 for the locations of sample sites). Tables 3.1 and 3.2 summarize the relevant data from our analyses. Table 3.1 illustrates selected element concentrations in the water samples, including sulfur, potassium, calcium, magnesium, iron, and chlorine, as well as sulfates, carbonates, bicarbonates, phosphates, nitrates, and boride.

One of the most important characteristics of water quality from the frame of reference of irrigation is the total concentration of soluble salts. In general, taking into account all existing ions, total soluble salt concentrations that exceed 1 gram per liter are considered deleterious to irrigation agriculture. Calculations on our 10 water samples yield the results given in table 3.2.

From these calculations we can observe that station 3, representing water taken from a spring in the K'araña sector of the archaeological site of Tiwanaku, is the only sample that exceeds the standard limit of 1 gram per liter of total soluble salts. Stations 4, 7, and 10 also exhibit slightly higher total salt concentrations than the other stations. These results indicate that, overall, total soluble salt concentrations do not play a significant role in limiting water quality; except for station 3, all the samples tested issue from sources that are usable for irrigation agriculture.

# 4

# Paleoecology and Tiwanaku Agroecosystems

MICHAEL W. BINFORD,
MARK BRENNER, AND
BARBARA W. LEYDEN

Humans interact with their environment through dynamic, complex ecological processes. People manipulate and modify water and nutrient cycles, redirect energy flow, and interact with other organisms. Activities such as intensive agriculture and urbanization clearly transform natural landscapes. Although humans are capable of shaping the environment to meet their needs, both natural and anthropogenically modified ecosystems impose significant constraints on cultural development. The interaction between humans and their environment operates constantly, changing environmental constraints and creating new challenges and opportunities for the reproduction of the biological and cultural bases of human society.

A central question for both anthropology and ecology is, how did some societies flourish for many generations in harsh, variable, and even degraded environments? Addressing this question requires a clear picture of the environmental conditions during the development of the society as well as an understanding of the human activities and environmental modifications that permitted cultural perseverance. Political, social, religious, and other explanations for cultural development and change must be considered in light of the environmental context in which the culture existed. Likewise, explanations for environmental changes must consider the role humans play in modifying ecosystems.

Ecosystems are defined as the sum of all the interacting biotic and abiotic components of the environment in space and time. The biogeochemical structure and function of ecosystems is controlled by the cycling of energy and materials (e.g., water and nutrients), which are in turn controlled by physical processes such as erosion and sedimentation as well as biological processes including production and decomposition (chapter 7). All interactions between regional bedrock, soils, hydrology, vegetation, animals, and humans shape ecosystem characteristics (Aber and Melillo 1991). The food and fiber that support human populations are products of biogeochemical processes.

As part of a multidisciplinary study to understand the interaction between the Tiwanaku civilization and the altiplano environment of highland Bolivia, we applied a model based in ecology and ecosystem science. Human activities in lake drainage basins alter the transfer rates of nutrient and non-nutrient materials from the land to the water. We used paleolimnological methods to measure the accumulation rates of these materials on the lake bottom through time (Binford et al. 1987). In turn, our results are used to estimate changing delivery rates of nutrient and non-nutrient materials from the terrestrial to the aquatic environment.

The specific objective of this study was to reconstruct altiplano ecosystem structure and function (i.e., vegetation, limnological conditions, climate, nutrient cycles, and sediment fluxes) before, during, and after the Tiwanaku period. In order to attain this objective, we measured concentrations of nutrients (carbon, nitrogen, phosphorus) and non-nutrient materials in soils as well as in water and dated sediment cores from Lake Titicaca. We used these data to calculate historical fluxes of these materials from land to the lake. Additional studies, including counts of pollen in lake sediments, yielded information on changing terrestrial and aquatic vegetation and the net hydrologic balance of the lake. These data serve as proxy measures of paleoclimate.

The basic tenet of paleolimnology is that lake sediments preserve a continuous, historical record of environmental conditions that prevailed in and around the lake (Frey 1969; Pennington 1981). Materials such as eroded soil and terrestrial organic matter are transferred to the water, where they ultimately settle on the lake bottom and are preserved in an ordered manner (i.e., younger sediment deposits overlie older ones). Stratigraphic study of dated sediment profiles, combined with a thorough knowledge of modern biogeochemical and sedimentological processes, permits reconstruction of the environmental conditions under which the ancient sediments were deposited. The historical record encoded in lake sediments can prove to be superior to historical documents on environmental conditions and in many cases may provide the only data for paleoenvironmental reconstruction.

We present results of paleoenvironmental studies at sites in the southeastern basin of Lake Titicaca, Bolivia. The investigations were conducted at locations near archaeological sites discussed elsewhere in this volume. We present the stratigraphy of sediment cores taken from several areas of the lake, describe changes in material flux from the land to the lake, and discuss these shifting rates of lake sediment deposition with respect to archaeologically documented land-use changes. We use other stratigraphic information to infer lake-level and climate changes and compare our findings with results obtained from other nearby sites. Finally, the paleoecological data and interpretations are used to generate hypotheses that might explain the persistence of Tiwanaku culture in the apparently inhospitable altiplano environment.

## Methods

### Field Methods

Stratigraphic soil samples were collected either with a soil tube sampler with a 20-centimeter bucket 2 centimeters in diameter or with a trowel from the cleaned walls of trenches. Surficial lake sediments were collected with an Ekman benthos dredge along transects in different water depths and near different assemblages of aquatic vegetation. The topmost 1 to 2 centimeters of sediment were removed with a spoon and stored in a Whirl-Pak bag. Short, sediment-water interface cores were taken with a piston corer with a 1.9-meter plastic core barrel 4 centimeters in diameter. Cores were extruded and sampled immediately in a vertical position to prevent sediment mixing. Cores were sampled in 2-centimeter contiguous segments from the sediment-water interface to 10 centimeters in depth, in 1-centimeter segments from 10 to 30 centimeters in depth, and in 4-centimeter segments thereafter to the bottom of the section. Deeper deposits were collected with a square-rod piston corer (Wright et al. 1984) in approximately 1-meter-long segments. Core segments were extruded, described, photographed, sampled (for radiocarbon dates and other geochemical analyses), and wrapped immediately in plastic and aluminum foil and were then stored for subsequent transport in rigid sections of PVC pipe.

### Laboratory Methods

Volumetric subsamples of sediment were taken either with a syringe or with a spatula and steel-barrel volumetric device, depending on the water content of the sediments. Samples were dried at 105° C for 24 hours to determine water content and dry mass. Organic matter was determined by loss on ignition at 550° for two hours. Total carbon was measured coulometrically (Huffman 1977) on a UIC/Coulometrics Model 5011 coulometer attached to a System 120 preparation line. Combustion temperature was set at 950° C. Inorganic carbon was measured on the coulometer in conjunction with a System 140 preparation line that employed 2N $HClO_4$ to generate $CO_2$ from carbonates. Nitrogen was measured by autoanalyzer following sediment digestion according to Parkinson and Allen (1975). Samples for total phosphorus, sulfur, and cations (calcium, magnesium, iron, sodium, potassium, manganese) were ashed and digested according to Anderson (1976). Total phosphorus in the digestate was measured spectrophotometrically following ascorbic acid–ammonium blue color development (APHA 1975). Total sulfur was assessed turbidimetrically (APHA 1975). Cations were measured on a Jarrell-Ash Inductively Coupled Argon Plasma (ICAP) 9000 Spectrophotometer.

Radiocarbon dating was done by Geochron Laboratories in Cambridge, Massachusetts, and by Herbert Haas of Southern Methodist University. Lead-210 ($^{210}Pb$) was assayed by Dan Engstrom at the Limnological Research Center of the University of Minnesota by distillation of the daughter radionuclide, $^{210}Po$, dissolution in weak HCl, and plating on silver planchettes for alpha spectrometry (modified from Eakins and Morrison 1978). A known amount of $^{208}Po$ was added to the original sample as a yield tracer. Dates were calculated by the constant-rate-of-supply model without mixing terms (Appleby and Oldfield 1978, 1983), as modified by Binford (1990) for error estimation.

For pollen analysis, 1-cubic-centimeter subsamples from both core and surficial sediments were treated with KOH, HCl, HF, and acetolysis and then stained with basic fuchsin and suspended in tert-Butyl alcohol (Whitehead 1981). Quantitative subsamples were mounted on microscope slides in silicone oil. At least 200 grains were counted on each slide at 400X magnification. Relative abundance of charcoal was noted but not quantified. Identifications were based on comparison with both reference material and literature descriptions (Graf 1977, 1986; Heusser 1971; Markgraf and D'Antoni 1978; Salomons 1986; van der Hammen and Gonzales 1960; Ybert 1981, 1984).

Samples for scanning electron microscopy (SEM) were air-dried onto circular glass cover slips. After marking the grains of interest by light microscopy, the cover slip was mounted on an EM stub, coated with gold-palladium, and examined at magnifications up to 30,000X with a Jeol JSM 840 SEM.

# Results and Discussion

## Cores and Gross Stratigraphy

We raised three long and seven short sediment-water interface cores from bays near the villages of Lukurmata and Pajchiri (fig. 4.1). Two long cores and five sediment-water interface cores were also collected at offshore sites near the towns of Guaqui and Huatajata. Gross stratigraphy of the cores is presented in figure 4.2. The following discussion is concerned primarily with results from Lukurmata short core 22-VIII-86-1 and Lukurmata long cores 26-VIII-86-1 through 6 because they are the most completely studied sections.

All the short cores have a mixed layer in the upper few centimeters, and deeper sediments consist of sections characterized as brown, organic-rich deposits mixed with plant fragments, marls (carbonates), snail shells, clays, or irregularly laminated sediments. Lithologies of short cores from different nearshore regions of the lake, such as Lukurmata and Pajchiri, do not correlate stratigraphically. This is not surprising because the cores are from different drainage basins with different geomorphologies and land-use histories. With the exception of Pajchiri core 27-VIII-87-4, all the shallow-water short cores from Pajchiri and Lukurmata contain sections of coarse organic material made up of aquatic plant remains.

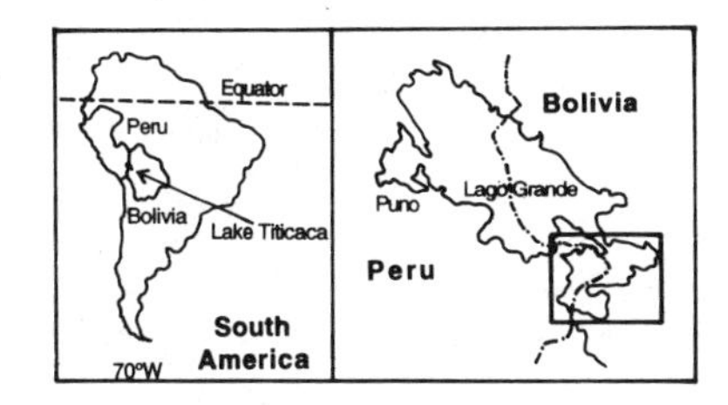


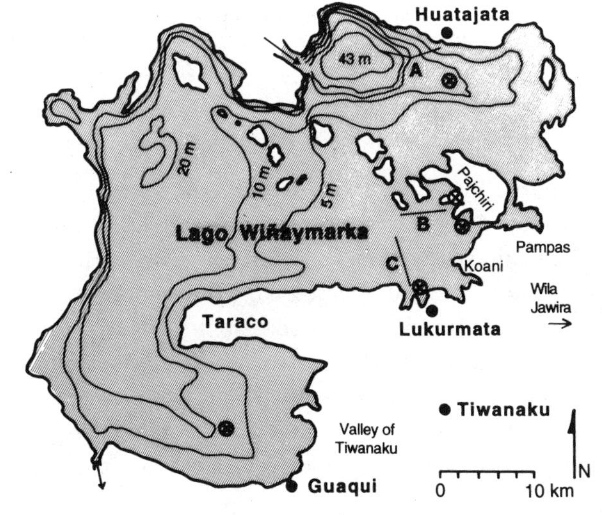


**Figure 4.1.** Coring sites, denoted by circled *x*s, near the towns of Lukurmata, Pajchiri, Guaqui, and Huatajata along the southern shores of Lake Titicaca. Surficial sediment transects are indicated by solid lines next to the letters A, B, and C. Unlabeled contour lines are shown at 10-meter intervals.

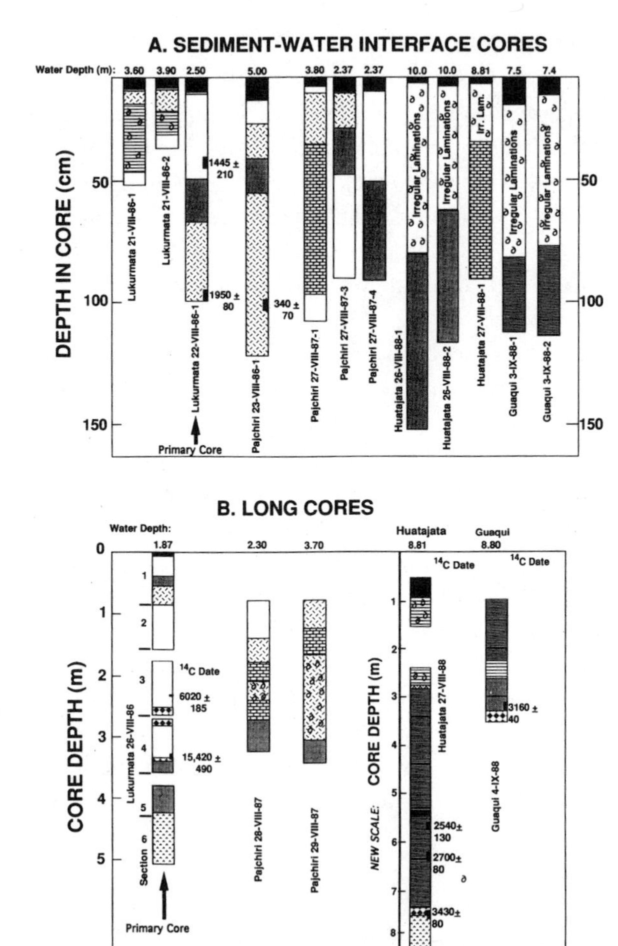


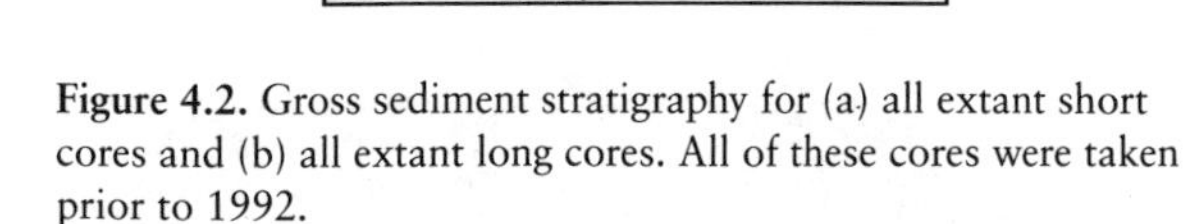


**Figure 4.2.** Gross sediment stratigraphy for (a) all extant short cores and (b) all extant long cores. All of these cores were taken prior to 1992.

Short cores taken from deeper water near Huatajata and Guaqui are more easily correlated stratigraphically despite the great distance between the two sites (more than 40 kilometers). These short cores all contain irregularly laminated sections, rich in ostracod and gastropod shells, that overlie clay- or marl-rich deposits. The base of the Guaqui sediment-water interface cores penetrated into the laminated deposits that characterize the upper half of the Guaqui long cores.

Stratigraphy of long cores taken at shallow-water sites also cannot be correlated on the basis of lithology. The two long cores from near Pajchiri both contain organic matter at the top and marly clay at the base but differ from one another in their middle sections (fig. 4.2). Although the topmost and bottommost portions of the two cores are almost certainly contemporaneous, their middle sections probably differ because of the different land-use histories in their respective drainages.

Although the Huatajata and Guaqui cores were collected far from each other and differed in length (8.36 and 3.27 meters, respectively), their stratigraphies are easily matched. Both sections were collected in 8.8 meters of water and bottomed on stiff sandy clay that stopped the coring device. They are dominated by laminations of alternating light and dark bands (fig. 4.3) with intermittent layers of large particulates that may be gypsum crystals. If the laminations prove to be annual or seasonal (e.g., Pilskaln and Johnson 1991) or to indicate some other event of regular periodicity, then the sediments may yield a paleoecological record with remarkable time resolution (O'Sullivan 1983).

## Sediment Chronology and Bulk Sediment Accumulation Rates

Radiocarbon dates for the cores are presented in figure 4.2. All radiocarbon dates are adjusted for fractionation effects by correcting to a $\delta^{13}C$ of –25‰ (Bradley 1985:60–62) but are not corrected for variations in atmospheric $^{14}C$. Radiocarbon results of $^{210}Pb$ dating of Lukurmata core 22-VIII-86-1 are presented in table 4.1 and figure 4.4, and temporal patterns of sediment accumulation for this core will be briefly summarized. A more complete discussion of changing sedimentation at Lukurmata is presented in Binford, Brenner, and Engstrom (1992).

The two cores that have been analyzed in detail

**Figure 4.3.** Laminated sections of (*top*) the Huatajata core 27-VIII-88-7, 6.65–6.78 meters below the sediment-water interface, and (*bottom*) the Guaqui core, 4-IX-88-3, 3.15–3.27 meters below the sediment-water interface.

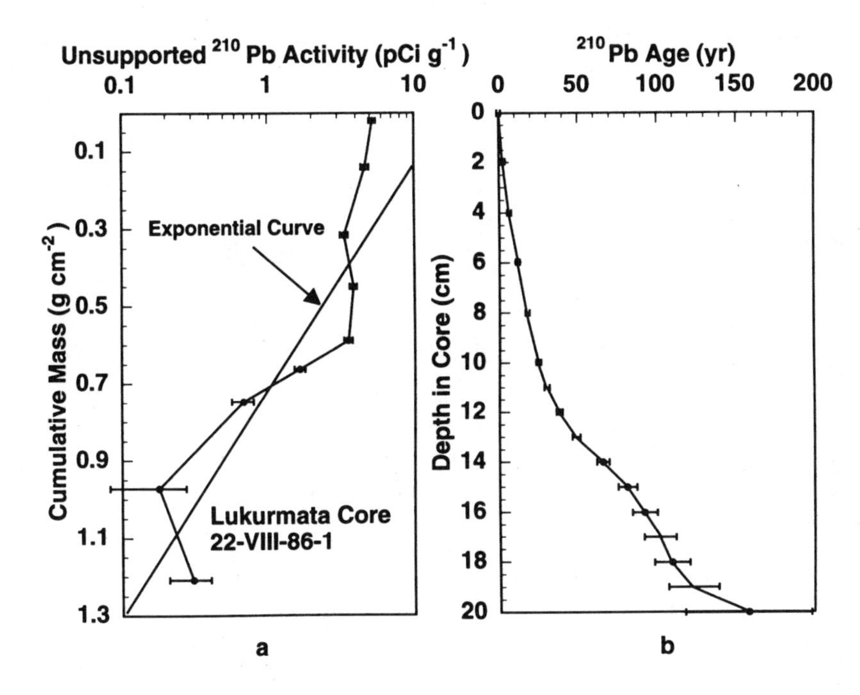


**Figure 4.4.** Graphs of $^{210}$Pb data for Lukurmata core 22-VIII-86-1. The horizontal bars associated with each data point represent one standard deviation of counting error. Cumulative mass of 1.3 grams per square centimeter is equivalent to 20.5 centimeters below the sediment-water interface. The expected curve is logarithmic, based on a core depth measurement of cumulative mass and not on depth in centimeters. (After Binford, Brenner, and Engstrom 1992.)

were taken from a small bay near the archaeological site of Lukurmata (fig. 4.1). The short core was dated by both $^{210}$Pb and radiocarbon. The radiocarbon date at the base of the short core (90–98 cm) is 1950 ± 80 B.P. (GX-13052) (Binford and Brenner 1989). Between 40 and 44 centimeters the sediments display a shift in the concentrations of several elements, and these deposits yielded a radiocarbon date of 1445 ± 210 B.P. (GX-13510). There is no evidence that the date is confounded by hard-water lake error, which can develop in watersheds that possess carbonate bedrock (Deevey and Stuiver 1964). Dissolution of ancient limestones leaks $^{14}$C-depleted bicarbonate into the lake, where the dissolved carbon is available for photosynthetic uptake by aquatic algae and macrophytes. If this occurs, the plants can fix carbon that is in disequilibrium with the atmosphere, and dates on the organic matter will be older than their true radiocarbon age. The average $\delta^{13}$C for carbonates is 0‰, for terrestrial wood –25‰, and for algae about –17‰ (Peterson and Fry 1987). Values for $\delta^{13}$C lighter than –17‰ (i.e., more negative than –17‰) imply, but do not prove (see Aravena et al. 1992), that the dated material was dominated by terrestrial organics or that the aquatic organic matter was uncontaminated by hard-water error. The stable isotope ratio for the dated material at 40–44 centimeters was –22.1‰, suggesting a reliable radiocarbon age. Sediments from this horizon were apparently deposited during the peak of Tiwanaku raised-field agriculture (Binford, Brenner, and Leyden 1987; Kolata 1991, 1993a).

Lead-210 ($^{210}$Pb) activity decreases strictly logarithmically with depth by means of radioactive decay if (1) sediment accumulation rate has been constant, (2) $^{210}$Pb flux to the sediment has been constant, and (3) there has been no postdepositional movement of $^{210}$Pb. The $^{210}$Pb plot for Lukurmata core 22-VIII-86-1 is not straight (fig. 4.4a), suggesting that at least one of the foregoing conditions has not been met. There is no reason to suspect that $^{210}$Pb flux has varied, and it is unlikely that there has been significant sediment mixing because many chemical constituents show pronounced concentration variation. The distribution of unsupported $^{210}$Pb is best explained as a consequence of changing bulk sedimentation rate. Consequently, we used the constant-rate-of-supply model to calculate $^{210}$Pb dates because it takes into account shifts in sediment accumulation rate (Appleby and Oldfield 1983). The bottommost reliable $^{210}$Pb date is 123 ± 16 years at 19 centimeters below the mud-water interface. The nonlinear age/depth plot (fig. 4.4b) reflects both changing bulk sedimentation rate and increased compaction at deeper levels in the profile.

Organic matter at 2.35–2.40 meters in the Lukurmata long core 26-VIII-86-1 (fig. 4.2) yielded a radiocarbon age of 6020 ± 185 B.P. (GX-13053), and

Table 4.1. Lead-210 Data for Lukurmata Core 22-VIII-86-1

| Segment (cm) | | Total $^{210}Pb$ | S.D. TotAct. | Unsupp. $^{210}Pb$ | rho | Prop. | Cum. Mass ($g/cm^2$) | | Date at Top | S.D. | Date at Bottom | S.D. | Sed. Rate | S.D. | Cum. $^{210}Pb$ |
|---|---|---|---|---|---|---|---|---|---|---|---|---|---|---|---|
| Top | Bottom | (pCi/g) | (pCi/g) | (pCi/g) | (g/g) | Organic | Bottom | Middle | (yrs) | Date | (yrs) | Date | ($g/cm^2/yr$) | Sed. Rate | ($pCi/cm^2$) |
| 0.0 | 2.0 | 6.47 | 0.28 | 5.21 | 0.02 | 0.51 | 0.04 | 0.02 | 0 | 1 | 3 | 1 | 0.020 | 0.006 | 2.73 |
| 4.0 | 6.0 | 5.92 | 0.29 | 4.65 | 0.04 | 0.40 | 0.18 | 0.14 | 6 | 1 | 12 | 1 | 0.010 | 0.006 | 2.24 |
| 8.0 | 10.0 | 4.62 | 0.20 | 3.35 | 0.05 | 0.41 | 0.36 | 0.32 | 18 | 1 | 25 | 2 | 0.010 | 0.006 | 1.57 |
| 11.0 | 12.0 | 5.13 | 0.22 | 3.86 | 0.06 | 0.42 | 0.48 | 0.45 | 30 | 2 | 38 | 2 | 0.010 | 0.005 | 1.06 |
| 13.0 | 14.0 | 4.82 | 0.23 | 3.56 | 0.07 | 0.32 | 0.62 | 0.59 | 49 | 3 | 66 | 4 | 0.004 | 0.004 | 0.60 |
| 14.0 | 15.0 | 2.93 | 0.14 | 1.67 | 0.08 | 0.36 | 0.70 | 0.66 | 66 | 4 | 81 | 6 | 0.005 | 0.006 | 0.35 |
| 15.0 | 16.0 | 1.95 | 0.12 | 0.69 | 0.09 | 0.40 | 0.79 | 0.75 | 81 | 6 | 92 | 8 | 0.008 | 0.009 | 0.22 |
| 17.0 | 18.0 | 1.44 | 0.10 | 0.18 | 0.14 | 0.36 | 1.04 | 0.97 | 102 | 10 | 109 | 11 | 0.018 | 0.022 | 0.12 |
| 19.0 | 20.0 | 1.57 | 0.10 | 0.31 | 0.13 | 0.34 | 1.27 | 1.21 | 123 | 16 | 158 | 40 | 0.004 | 0.011 | 0.06 |
| 21.0 | 22.0 | 1.21 | 0.03 | 0.00 | 0.14 | 0.33 | 1.54 | 1.47 | | | | | | | |
| 23.0 | 24.0 | 1.32 | 0.05 | 0.00 | 0.14 | 0.35 | 1.82 | 1.75 | | | | | | | |

deeper material at 3.30–3.39 meters produced a date of 15,420 ± 490 B.P. (GX-13511). Neither sample appears to be affected by hard-water lake error, as $\delta^{13}C$ values for the 2.35–2.40 meter and 3.30–3.39 meter samples were −25.5‰ and −27.3‰, respectively. Sediments in the lower part of the profile were thus deposited during the late Pleistocene. Several layers of coarse, dry material between the two dated horizons appear to be soils and indicate hiatuses in lacustrine sedimentation. After 6020 B.P. the stratigraphy suggests continuous deposition of lake sediment.

Assuming that the 6020 B.P. age at 2.35–2.40 meters is correct, the core represents a continuous sedimentary record spanning the preagricultural period and Tiwanaku times to the present. Because the core was collected in about 1.9 meters of water, the continuous record of sedimentation implies no significant lake-level depression during the last six millennia. These data are at odds with those of Wirrmann and Oliveira Almeida (1987), who found evidence of lowered lake level between 7700 and 3650 B.P. Their lake-level reconstruction indicates a lake 50 meters lower at 4500 B.P.

Organic matter from 98–106 centimeters in the Pajchiri short core has a radiocarbon age of 340 ± 70 B.P. (GX-13051). The core was collected below steep slopes on the nearby lakeshore and indicates very high net sediment accumulation at the coring site. Because the core represents only post-Columbian deposition, it provides no information on Tiwanaku environment and will not be discussed further.

Three radiocarbon dates provide a chronology for the Huatajata long core. Sediments at 5.71 meters depth yielded a radiocarbon age of 2540 ± 130 B.P., material at 6.30 meters was 2,700 ± 80 years old, and sediments from 7.55 meters, just above the marly base of the section, were 3,430 ± 80 years old. The 3.27-meter-long Guaqui core has a similar date at its bottom contact with basal marly clay (3,160 ± 40 radiocarbon years at 3.20 meters). Bottom dates from the two cores suggest that the fine marls were deposited until a little more than 3,000 years ago, when lake level was lower and the core sites were in shallow water. These findings are consistent with the lake-level reconstruction of Wirrmann and Oliveira Almeida (1987). In any event, the dates suggest that the lithologies from the two distant sites can be correlated temporally, at least with respect to the age of the contact with basal marls. These basal dates are coincident with the first archaeological evidence of widespread regional agriculture (Kolata 1993a; and see chapter 5). We hypothesize that the expansion of agricultural activities in this part of the Lake Titicaca basin after 3500 B.P. was related to increased moisture availability that we infer from rising lake levels.

The findings at Guaqui and Huatajata contradict the information from the Lukurmata core site. If coring sites at Guaqui and Huatajata, both in 8.8 meters of water, were dry prior to about 3500 B.P., why do we find a continuous record of sedimentation at the Lukurmata core site, currently under only about 1.9 meters of water? One possibility is that the Lukurmata site was in a depression that was supplied by local groundwater springs and remained wet despite being cut off from the rest of the considerably reduced lake. We cannot resolve this question without a detailed reconstruction of past lake-level variation, and this will require collection and study of cores along a transect extending from the lake shore into deep water.

## Radiocarbon Age/Depth Curves

Age/depth curves for the long cores from Huatajata, Lukurmata, and Guaqui are presented in figure 4.5. Ages between dated levels were calculated assuming constant mass accumulation rate of sediment (i.e., grams per $cm^2$ per year) rather than constant linear rate of sedimentation (grams per cm per year). The slope of the line indicates the rate of net sediment accumulation: the more vertical the age/depth line, the faster the sedimentation rate. Because sediments older than 6,000 years in the Lukurmata core show evidence of depositional hiatuses, the age/depth line between 6000 and 15,400 B.P. is plotted as a dashed line. The age/depth line for the Lukurmata core between about 3,000 and 6,000 years is tentative because of the evidence for a low lake stand discussed earlier.

Long-term sediment accumulation proceeded most rapidly at the deep-water Huatajata site and most slowly at the nearshore Lukurmata site. Expressed as linear sediment accumulation rates, deposition at the Huatajata site averaged 2.2 millimeters per year, the mean rate at Guaqui was 1 millimeter per year, and Lukurmata registered 0.5 millimeter per year since 1950 B.P. In many lakes, sediment accumulation rates in the vegetated littoral zone are higher than offshore rates because inshore areas receive great amounts of macrophyte remains (Carpenter 1981) as well as allochthonous material including eroded soils and allu-

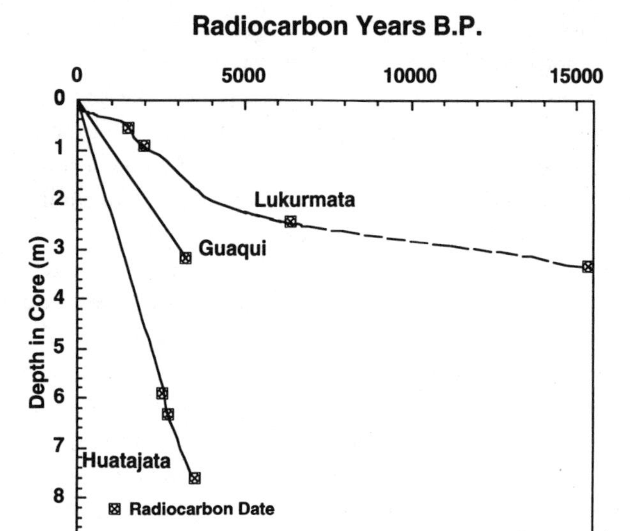


**Figure 4.5.** Age/depth curves for all three long cores.

vial sediments. Such material transported from the drainage basin can be trapped by littoral vegetation (Boulange, Vargas, and Rodrigo 1981; Carpenter and Lodge 1986; Howard-Williams and Lenton 1975; Mackereth 1965, 1966).

In some cases, sediments in shallow areas can be resuspended and transported into deep water, where they are redeposited, accounting for high net rates of accumulation in the profundal zone (Anderson 1990; Davis and Ford 1982). This phenomenon is most pronounced in cone-shaped basins with appreciable bottom slopes (Håkanson and Jansson 1983; Lehman 1975) and would not be expected to be a factor in the pan-shaped Wiñaymarka basin. However, prevailing winds, currents, water movements through the Straits of Tiquina, and delivery of river-borne sediment can all influence spatial variations in net sedimentation within the Wiñaymarka basin. Major differences in sediment lithology at shallow- and deep-water sites may provide clues to the spatial variation in net sediment accumulation rates. Nearshore sediments are made up of organic matter composed largely of aquatic plant remains, and the inorganic component appears to be eroded basin soils. In deep-water locations, sediments are dominated by calcium carbonate ($CaCO_3$) that is probably the product of bio-induced carbonate precipitation. Thus, different mechanisms of sediment genesis may well explain the different measured rates of sediment accumulation.

The Lukurmata short core reveals interesting shifts in nearshore sedimentation during the last two millennia. Mass sediment accumulation, which accounts for changes in sediment compaction, is plotted against time in figure 4.6. Changes in net sediment accumulation before and after 1400 B.P. reflect abrupt shifts in long-term average rates because they are based on only three dates: radiocarbon ages at 90–98 centimeters and 40–44 centimeters, and the $^{210}$Pb age at 19–20 centimeters. The mean sediment accumulation rate from 1950 to 1400 B.P. was an order of magnitude higher than the rate from 1400 B.P. to the present. The 1400 B.P. date corresponds to the peak period of Tiwanaku raised-field agriculture, suggesting that this farming technique slowed soil erosion and material flux to the lake. In more recent deposits, there is an increase in sediment accumulation about 100 years ago and again in the last decade. These recent high sediment accumulation rates are, nevertheless, about half the rate measured for the period prior to 1400 B.P. Recent shifts in net sediment accumulation rates were shown to have been temporally correlated with land-use changes during the last

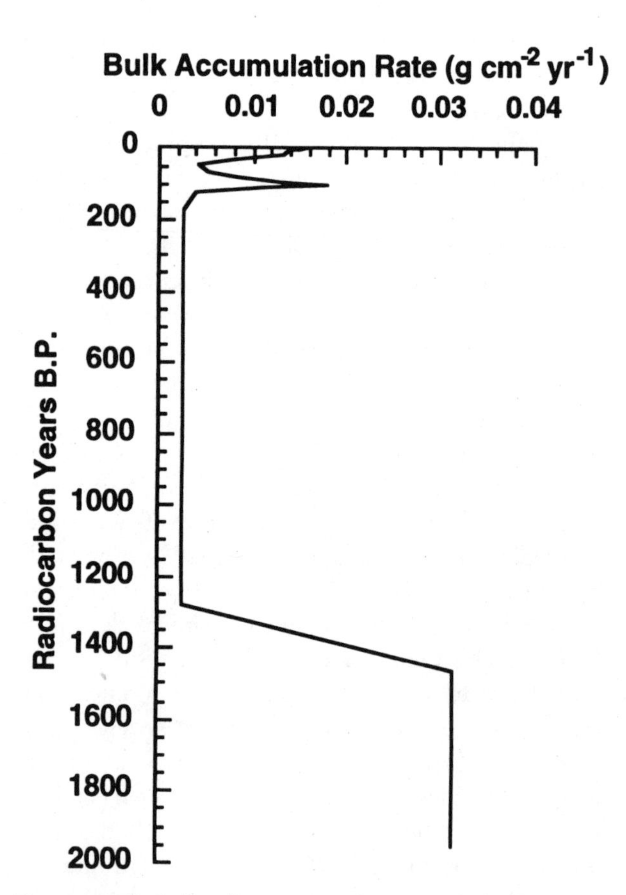


**Figure 4.6.** The bulk sediment accumulation rate for Lukurmata core 22-VIII-86-1. The two zones with an apparently constant accumulation rate are the result of only two radiocarbon dates (at 40–44 centimeters and 90–98 centimeters) and a $^{210}$Pb date at 19–20 cm. The mass accumulation rate was assumed to be constant among the three dates.

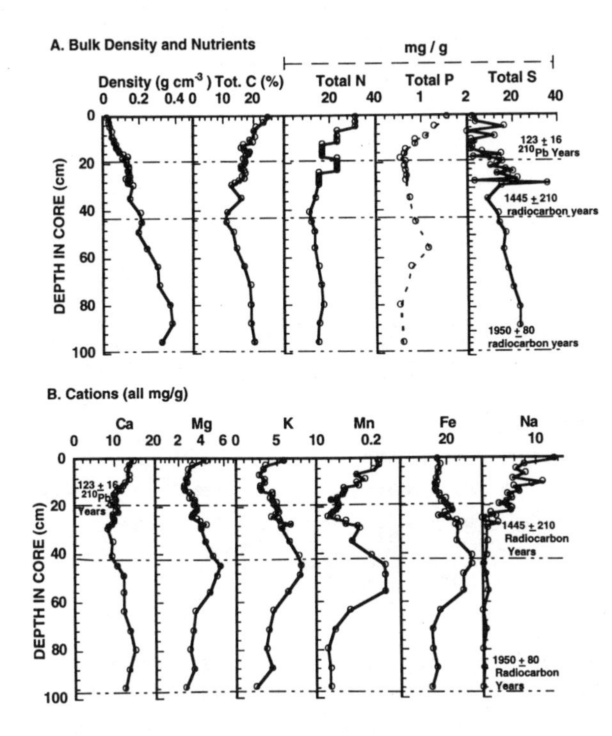


**Figure 4.7.** Histograms showing (*a*) bulk density and (*b*) element concentrations in the Lukurmata sediment-water interface core 22-VIII-86-1 (after Binford, Brenner, and Engstrom 1992).

century that were a consequence of land-distribution programs and the break-up of haciendas (Binford, Brenner, and Engstrom 1992).

## Sediment Geochemistry

### BULK DENSITY AND ELEMENT CONCENTRATIONS

Concentrations of elements in the Lukurmata sediment-water interface core are presented in figure 4.7. Table 4.2 presents a matrix that shows all significant correlations between elemental concentrations. Detailed geochemical results and interpretations for this core have been published elsewhere (Binford and Brenner 1989; Binford, Brenner, and Engstrom 1992). We summarize the relevant data here.

Bulk density of the sediment (g dry cm$^3$ wet) increases with greater depth in the core, primarily as a consequence of compaction. Total carbon content is highest in the surface deposits and declines rather steadily to about 44 centimeters before rising again toward the bottom of the profile. Total carbon in surface sediments is about twice that measured in the middle of the core. The low values were measured in a section of light gray, clayey material, and the presence of this material suggests an increase in inorganic deposition relative to organic sedimentation. Clay-rich strata are frequently encountered in lakes whose watersheds have supported human settlement. The fine-grained sediments constitute eroded material that was delivered during periods of intense disturbance (Binford et al. 1987).

Total carbon concentrations and Loss on Ignition at 550° C (LOI) are significantly correlated ($r = 0.96$, $n = 35$, $p < .01$). Total carbon is 49.6 ± 6.4 percent of LOI throughout the core. LOI is not shown in figure 4.7 because of its nearly perfect correspondence to total carbon. Inorganic carbon concentration was below detectable limits, so effectively all the carbon in the sediments is contained within the organic fraction.

Total nitrogen concentration remains relatively constant throughout the section except for a nearly threefold increase toward the uppermost 25 centimeters (fig. 4.7). Sediments above 30 centimeters had low density and required combining material from three contiguous levels to provide sufficient sediment for analysis. This accounts for the appearance of constant nitrogen concentrations at some levels in the top part of the core.

Total phosphorus concentrations remain less than 1.0 milligram per gram, except for the sample at 54–58 centimeters taken from the gray, clayey sediment (fig. 4.7). If organic carbon and nitrogen are low in the gray clays while phosphorus content remains high, it may suggest that phosphorus is associated primarily with inorganic matter. The recent increase in phosphorus content of the sediments may reflect enrichment from erosion of phosphorus-rich mineral matter in the drainage basin.

Total sulfur concentration is highly variable but tends to decrease in more recent deposits (fig. 4.7). Sulfur content in the sediments is correlated with dry density ($r = 0.62$, $p < .05$). Total sulfur is negatively correlated with sodium ($r = -0.64$, $p < .05$) but is uncorrelated with all other elements. Low sulfur measurements are approximations because concentrations in digestate were near analytical detection limits.

The cations magnesium, potassium, iron, and manganese are highly correlated with one another (table 4.2). Their similarly shaped concentration profiles suggest that all are probably bound in the same sediment fraction, probably the clastic component (Engstrom and Wright 1984). Not surprisingly, these

Table 4.2. **Matrix of Significant Correlations between Element Concentrations ($p < .05$)**

| | Total C | Total N | Total P | Total S | Ca | Mg | Fe | K |
|---|---|---|---|---|---|---|---|---|
| Total C | | | | | | | | |
| Total N | 0.698 | | | | | | | |
| Total P | 0.452 | 0.518 | | | | | | |
| Total S | | | | | | | | |
| Ca | 0.664 | | 0.568 | | | | | |
| Mg | −0.595 | | | | | | | |
| Fe | −0.789 | −0.410 | | | −0.530 | 0.879 | | |
| K | −0.668 | −0.402 | | | −0.405 | 0.967 | 0.895 | |
| Mn | | | 0.832 | | | 0.547 | 0.457 | 0.433 |
| Na | 0.577 | 0.716 | 0.551 | −0.636 | | | −0.427 | −0.414 |

elements display their highest concentrations in the middle of the core, where organic matter was diluted by the rapid influx of inorganic material, especially eroded clays.

Calcium content in the sediments is negatively correlated with iron and potassium concentrations (table 4.2), and sodium content is negatively correlated with sulfur, iron, and potassium. Calcium is positively correlated with total carbon ($r = 0.66$, $p < .05$) and phosphorus ($r = 0.57$, $p < .05$), which is expected in sediments containing little calcium carbonate (Engstrom and Wright 1984). Sodium is positively correlated with carbon, nitrogen, and phosphorus but is difficult to interpret stratigraphically because of its high solubility. Dissolved sodium may remain in place in the lake muds but is also capable of diffusing through the sediment column.

## ELEMENT RATIOS

Elemental ratios in cores from the lake bottom can be used to identify sediment source material if the ratios in watershed soils and other possible sediment sources are known. Stratigraphic shifts in nutrient ratios in the Lukurmata sediment profile indicate that the input of inorganic matter increased relative to the input of terrestrial organic matter during the period of raised-field development. Variation of carbon-nitrogen (C:N) ratios indicates changing relative contributions of organic matter from terrestrial (high C:N) to aquatic (low C:N) sources (fig. 4.8). Note that the ratios are expressed in the illustration as atoms:atoms and not as mass:mass. Terrestrial organics are rich in structural carbohydrates and have higher C:N (greater than 15) and carbon-phosphorus (C:P) ratios (greater than 200) than organic matter produced in aquatic environments (ca. 6–12 and less than 150, respectively) (Bowen 1979; Reiners 1986). Organic C:N in upland and canal soils at Lukurmata ranges from 9.7 to 24.2 (mean = 16.6 ± 3.1 s.d.; only 2 of 18 samples were less than 14: see fig. 4.9), and sediment C:N varies between 5.7 and 11.8 (mean = 8.2 ± 1.56 s.d.) (fig. 4.8).

The C:P ratio in sediments (mean 90 ± 26 s.d.; fig. 4.8) is higher than in upland soils (26.42 ± 11.69; fig. 4.9) but lower than in canal muck (191.4 ± 60.4), although phosphorus concentrations (fig. 4.9) are similar (0.7–3.1 milligrams per gram dry mass in soils, 0.5–1.6 mg per gram in sediments, 2.1–2.6 mg per gram in canal muck). Differences in C:P between soils and sediments are attributed to high production of organic material by lake biota or to loss of soil carbon to oxidation and decomposition of organic material, leading to low C:P ratios.

Sedimentary phosphorus is associated mostly with allochthonous inorganic materials (Binford, Brenner, and Engstrom 1992), and carbon and nitrogen are bound nearly completely in the organic fraction. Therefore, high sedimentary C:N indicates periods of high accumulation rates of terrestrial organic material relative to all other sediment constituents, a consequence of high soil erosion rates. High sedimentary C:P indicates that deposition of organic material (both terrestrial and aquatic) is relatively greater than deposition of inorganic material. If both ratios are high, as they are at levels in the core that correspond to early agriculture, then terrestrial organics were deposited predominantly, indicating that early agricultural practices exacerbated losses of soil organic matter. If both ratios are low, as they are at core levels corresponding to major raised-field activity, then aquatic sources dominate organic sedimentation. Inorganic clastics, however, are an important part of total sediment, because raised-field agriculture still generated some transport of inorganic material to the lake. Low C:N and high C:P, which occurred between 330 and 100 years ago, indicates that aquatic organics dominate input to sediments, and erosion sources are minor. Periods of high C:N and low C:P did not occur. These observations suggest that raised fields retained a greater proportion of organic material than did unmodified fields or undisturbed nearshore landscapes. As a consequence of the sequestering of organic material within the raised-field system, fertility and crop yields may have been enhanced. In chapter 9 we describe the results of experimental work in rehabilitated raised-field complexes in our research area that substantiate this conclusion.

The nitrogen-phosphorus (N:P) ratio declines at the onset of raised-field agriculture about 1800–1600 B.P., then rises slowly until peaking between 200 and 400 years ago (fig. 4.8). Soil N:P is higher in canal mucks (range 6.3–16.6) than in upland soils (0.5–3.2; fig. 4.9). The N:P ratio in lake sediments (range 5.3–19.4; fig. 4.8) is similar to that in canal mucks. The assayed nitrogen is nearly all organic and is subject to loss through organic matter decomposition. In addition, although the canal muck environment is most likely conducive to denitrification, we suspect that the nitrogen-fixing bacterium *Anabaena azollae*, associated with the abundant aquatic fern *Azolla*, produces large amounts of biologically available nitrogen. Preliminary bioassay studies have demonstrated the rapid uptake of biologically available nitrogen in canal waters by algae and macrophytes (see chapter 7). Thus nitrogen is retained in the canals and fields primarily by assimilation into organic material, but some loss may be due to denitrification in the anaerobic sediments.

Alkali and alkaline-earth metals are weathered and transported by surface water in both dissolved and particulate forms. Dissolved sodium, potassium, and magnesium are conservative and not normally sedimented by chemical precipitation or biological uptake, whereas calcium combines with organic ligands and is deposited in the sediment (Engstrom and Wright 1984). As a result, sedimentary calcium and sodium concentrations normally decrease relative to other elements during periods when more soil is transported to the lake, because they are diluted by eroded silicates and clay minerals (Mackereth 1966). In this case the organic fraction is disproportionately reduced, reducing calcium accumulation rate and calcium ratios.

When used in conjunction with the radiocarbon dates, ratios of calcium to other cations indicate the timing of changes in erosion rates. This index suggests that the long-term decrease of material flow to the lake, and consequent sediment accumulation, began about 1,750 radiocarbon years ago and was at its historic low by 1,450 years ago (fig. 4.8). Thus, the onset of the decline in sediment accumulation rates was coincident with the initiation of raised-field agriculture about 1800 B.P., and the period of lowest sediment accumulation was coincident with the peak of raised-field construction activity in the research area.

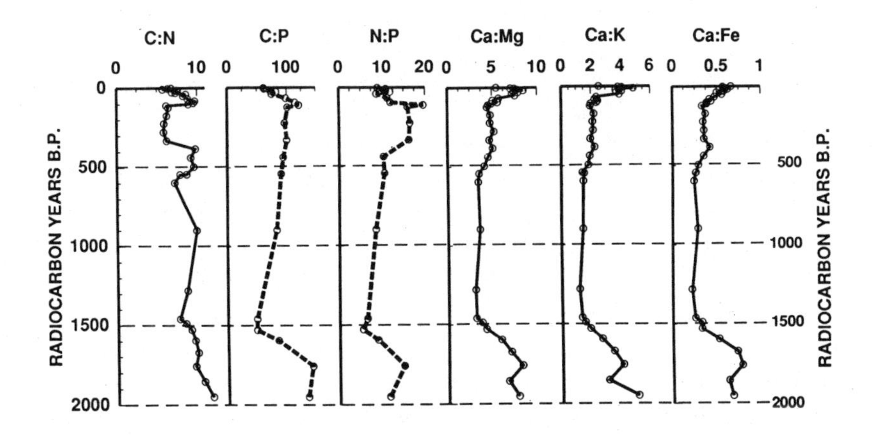


**Figure 4.8.** Stratigraphy of atomic ratios of important elements in the Lukurmata core 22-VIII-86-1.

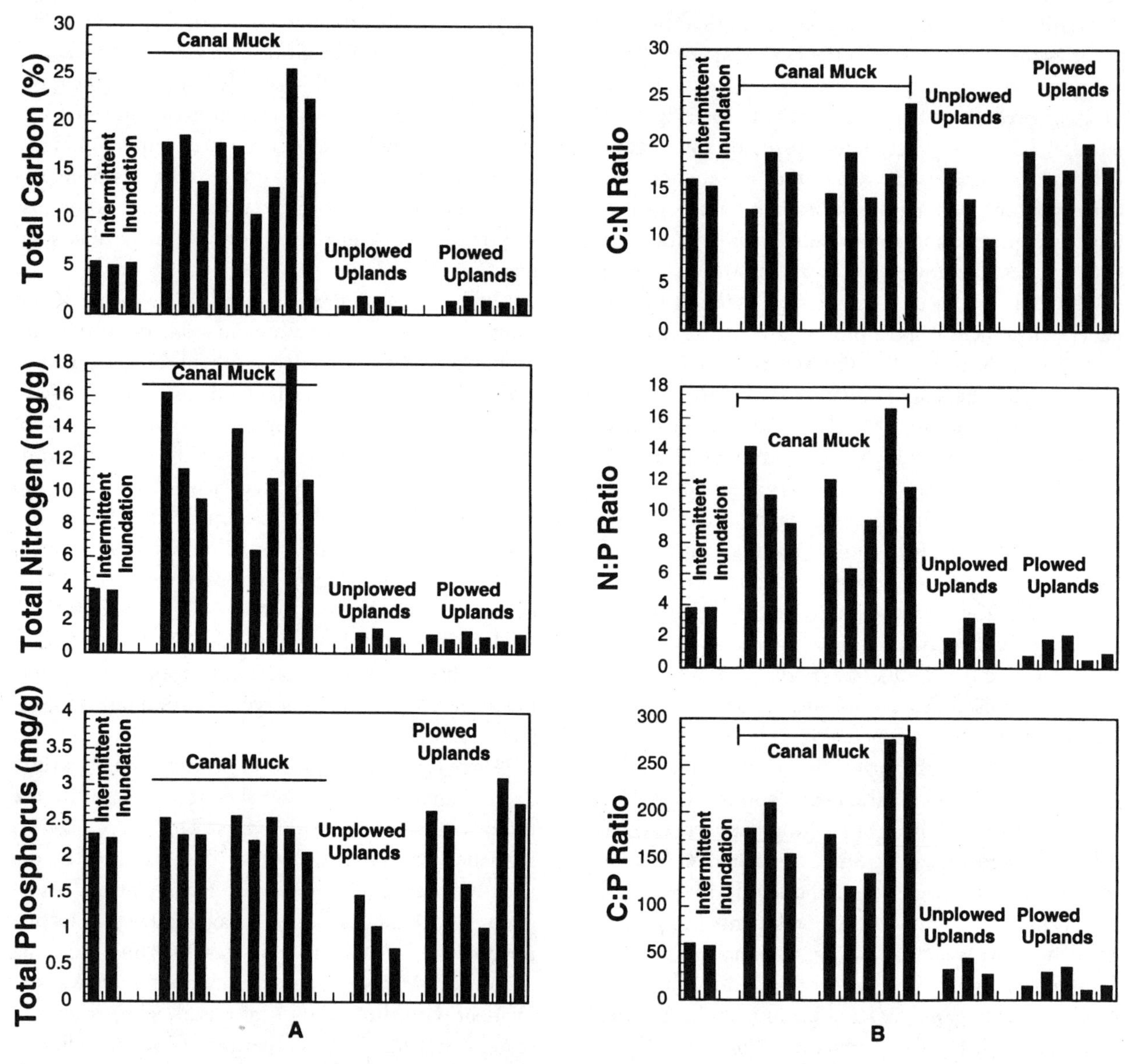


Figure 4.9. *a*, Histograms of nutrient content of soils at Lukurmata. Intermittent inundation means that the soil was under water in 1986 but dry in 1987. *b*, Histograms of nutrient ratios of soils at Lukurmata.

## Soil Geochemistry

Geochemical analyses of drainage basin soils can shed light on the source of lake sediments because transported soils often constitute a major fraction of the sediment matrix (Mackereth 1965, 1966). Carbon, nitrogen, and phosphorus concentrations in soils from the Lukurmata drainage basin (fig. 4.9) vary dramatically despite having been collected within an area of about 1 square kilometer. The soil collection sites were assigned to four categories at the time of sampling: unplowed uplands, plowed uplands, canals, and intermittently inundated soils. Upland soils have generally low concentrations of carbon and nitrogen, but canal mucks are rich in these nutrient elements (fig. 4.9). Intermittently inundated soils possess intermediate carbon and nitrogen concentrations. Phosphorus concentrations are roughly equivalent in all soil samples.

When nutrient concentrations and ratios in soils are compared with values from the sediment core, some interesting relationships emerge (compare figs. 4.7 and 4.9). Total carbon content in canal mucks (17.38 ± 6.79 percent) is similar to concentrations measured in the lake mud (17.37 ± 2.97 percent), but carbon in dry soils is much lower, constituting less than 3 percent of the dry mass. Core sediments average 18.9 milligrams of nitrogen per gram and are richer in nitrogen than are any of the soil types, including nitrogen-rich muck soils, with an average of 12.1 ± 3.32 milligrams per gram. Other soil types all contain less than 4 milligrams of nitrogen per gram. Phosphorus differs from carbon and nitrogen in that the mean phosphorus concentration in all soil samples (2.12 ± 0.64 mg per gram) is greater than the mean for the sediment core (0.82 ± 0.06 mg per gram). Only in the upper part of the core (fig. 4.7) are sedimentary phosphorus concentrations comparable to the lowest soil phosphorus values, those in the unplowed upland soils.

C:N ratios are similar among all soil types (fig. 4.9) and are generally higher than ratios measured in lake sediments (fig. 4.8). Other aspects of C:N ratios have already been discussed.

N:P ratios in the various soil types are all statistically significantly different from one another at $p < .05$ (multiple t-tests). Canal mucks display the highest N:P ratios, followed by intermittently inundated soils, unplowed uplands, and plowed uplands. Because phosphorus content across all soil types is relatively constant, the high N:P ratio in muck soils reflects their relatively high nitrogen content. The mean N:P ratio in even the most nitrogen-rich canal mucks (5.1 ± 1.4) is considerably less than that in lake sediments (mean 11.4 ± 3.7).

We collected lake water and spring water samples from springs that flow into the lake and determined conductivity and concentrations of selected elements. Specific conductance, a measure of dissolved ion content in water, ranges between 10 and 75 milliSiemens per meter among the different spring waters. Groundwaters are thus chemically heterogeneous over relatively short distances. Conductivity in Lake Wiñaymarka is typically between 100 and 140 milliSiemens per meter, indicating that all the springs are less saline (i.e., fresher) than lake waters.

Major cation concentrations (calcium, sodium, magnesium, and potassium) in water from selected springs, along with values for lake water derived from the literature, explain the chemical basis for the differences (table 4.3). Two of the springs (samples 249 and 252) have calcium and potassium concentrations similar to those of lake water, but the other two springs are much more dilute in these elements. Sodium and chloride concentrations are always five to ten times higher in the lake than in the springs. Magnesium in spring water ranges from one-tenth to one-half of concentrations in the lake. Thus, the major

**Table 4.3. Chemistry Analysis of Lukurmata Spring and Stream Water**

| | Element | | | | | | | |
|---|---|---|---|---|---|---|---|---|
| Field Sample No. | $Ca^{2+}$ | $K^+$ | $Na^+$ | $Mg^{2+}$ (mg/g) | $HCO_{3-}$/$CO_{3-}$ | $SO_{4-}$ | $Cl^-$ | Conductance mS/m |
| **Spring water** | | | | | | | | |
| 249a | 68.5 | 26.6 | 19.9 | 16.5 | | | 53.3 | 43.8 |
| 249b | 71.2 | 26.9 | 19.8 | 17.0 | | | 48.6 | |
| 250a | 13.1 | 1.9 | 5.2 | 2.9 | | | 3.3 | 10.0 |
| 250b | 13.2 | 1.7 | 5.0 | 3.0 | | | 2.0 | |
| 251a | 14.2 | 2.7 | 5.7 | 3.1 | | | 4.5 | 11.3 |
| 251b | 14.6 | 2.8 | 5.9 | 3.2 | | | 4.7 | |
| 252a | 68.4 | 10.1 | 24.1 | 15.1 | | | 4.3 | 39.5 |
| 252b | 69.5 | 10.1 | 24.6 | 15.3 | | | 25.2 | |
| Lake water | | | | | | | | |
| Outlet | 61.3 | 17.6 | 193.2 | 36.5 | 114.0 | 254.4 | 281.8 | |
| Mid-lake | 63.3 | 15.2 | 174.3 | 33.0 | 123.0 | 233.3 | 254.9 | 112.5[a] |

Source: Lake water data are from Carmouze, Arce, and Quintanilla 1992: tables V and X).

Note: Lowercase letters following sample numbers indicate replicates.

[a]Conductance was measured by the authors on 26 August 1988 at the site of the Huatajata core.

chemical difference between spring water and lake water consists of the elevated sodium and chlorine in the lake, with a minor contribution by calcium.

## Palynology of Surficial Sediments

The deposition of pollen is not necessarily uniform across a lake basin. Water depth and distance from shore can affect pollen deposition in surficial sediments, while productivity in the water column above influences the algal representation. Certain conditions may also produce an overrepresentation of local vegetation relative to the regional pollen signal. Pollen analysis of surficial lake sediments thus provides a basis for interpreting past limnetic conditions represented in the core sediments.

Three transects of surficial lake sediments (A, B, and C in figure 4.1) were examined for pollen. Total pollen concentrations, including aquatic taxa, are low (800–16,000 grains per cubic centimeter). The greatest concentrations of aquatic pollen are in the shallowest water and nearest to shore. Conversely, terrestrial pollen is twice as abundant in the deep-water Huatajata transect (averaging 1,880 grains per cubic centimeter) as in the two shallow-water transects. The pollen composition of the three transects is distinctive with respect to the limnetic variables (figs. 4.10, 4.11). The pollen of terrestrial taxa predominates in sediments from water deeper than about 5 meters (the Huatajata transect) or on steep slopes, whereas pollen of aquatic taxa predominates in the two shallow-water transects. The averaged percentages for terrestrial pollen types are similar among the three transects, although individual samples were sometimes influenced by localized sources. Therefore, terrestrial pollen in Wiñaymarka basin sediments primarily reflects the regional vegetation.

Pollen percentages of aquatic taxa vary in accordance with the present relationship between water depth and species distributions at the sampling location (especially for *Potamogeton*) (fig. 4.10). Percentages of algae to total terrestrial pollen are related to water depth. Average percentages for *Botryococcus* and *Pediastrum* in the Huatajata transect are 77 percent and 25.16 percent, respectively. Both algae are rare in the two Pajchiri transects. These results compare well with measurements of phytoplankton productivity, which is greatest in the deeper portions of the lake (Lazzaro 1981). Photoinhibition of photosynthesis in the upper water column may partially ex-

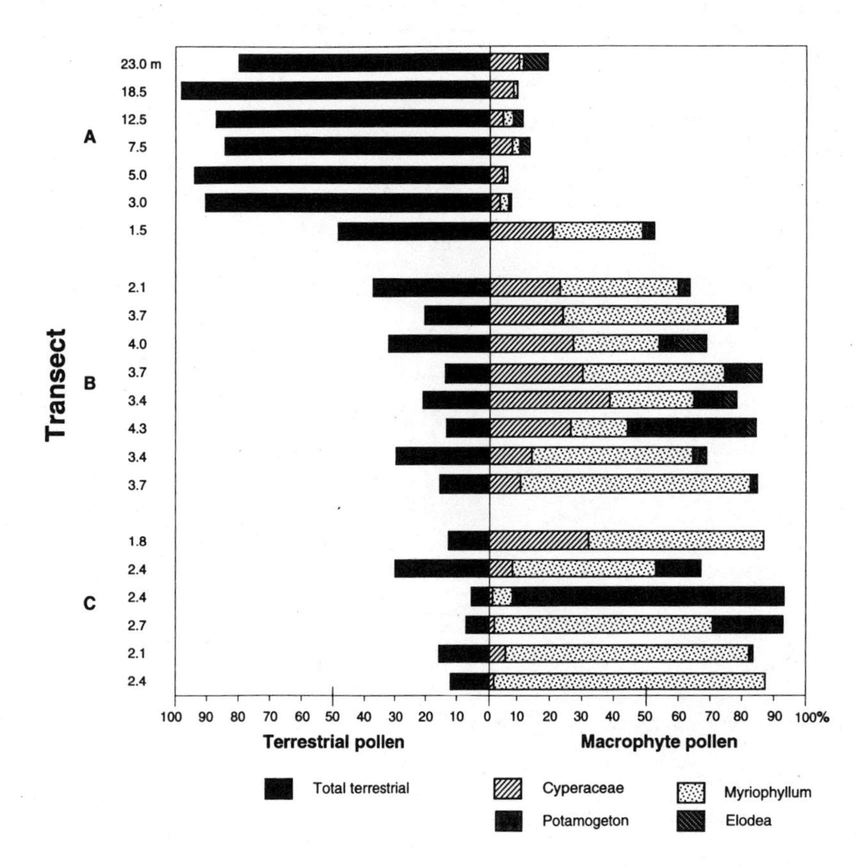


**Figure 4.10.** Pollen percentages in three surface-sediment transects from (*a*) Huatajata, (*b*) North Pajchiri, and (*c*) South Pajchiri, with macrophyte pollen included in the sum, contrasting terrestrial and aquatic representation.

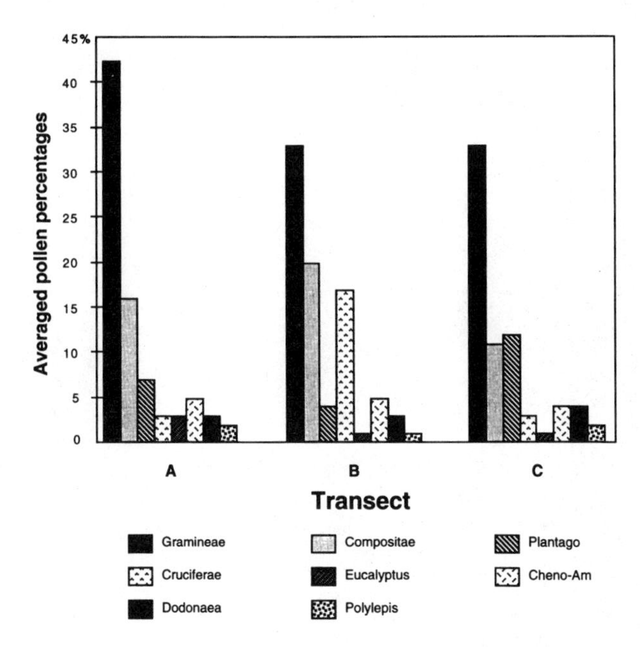


**Figure 4.11.** Averaged pollen percentages in three surface-sediment transects from (*a*) Huatajata, (*b*) North Pajchiri, and (*c*) South Pajchiri, with macrophyte pollen excluded from the sum.

plain the differences in productivity, which is maximal at 3 to 5 meters (Lazzaro 1981).

## Palynology of Cores

The ability to distinguish the pollen of cultivars is critical for testing hypotheses about the Tiwanaku ecosystem. Unfortunately, two of the major cultivars and much of the natural vegetation are within the families Chenopodiaceae and Amaranthaceae, which in most instances are impossible to distinguish with light microscopy. On the altiplano, both *Amaranthus* (*A. caudatus*) and *Chenopodium* (*C. quinoa* and *C. pallidicaule*) have been cultivated as grains for millennia, and weed species within both genera are common.

Scanning electron microscopy (SEM) provides a means of distinguishing the pollen of Amaranthaceae from that of Chenopodiaceae. Scanning electron micrographs of pollen taken from the Lukurmata short core (22-VIII-86-1) at 98 centimeters (1950 B.P.) and at 44 centimeters (1450 B.P.) suggest that the fossil grains are *Chenopodium*, based on the number of spinules (fig. 4.12). The number of spinules on the grains differs between the two levels, perhaps indicating different species. One differentiating characteristic of the pollen is the minute pores reported by Tsukada (1967). Our SEM resolved the pores, and distinct differences between pollen grains at different levels are clearly seen.

#### THE LUKURMATA CORE

Charcoal is abundant in the pollen preparations from the Lukurmata short core, except in the top 25 centimeters, where it is essentially absent (Leyden 1987). The cheno-am pollen follows the same pattern. Charred particles are also present in the field soil samples. The abundance of charcoal clearly indicates human disturbance, and the magnitude of the influx should reflect the intensity of human activities. The precise nature of those activities remains to be determined. Ellenberg (1979:411) states that in the 1970s, pasture lands adjacent to fields were burned annually and that the topsoil was black with charred plant materials. Fields for crops were not burned, and weeds were left to prevent erosion. Raised fields may have been managed in the same manner prehistorically. Charcoal presence may be related to the burning of plant matter and dung for fuel, and charcoal accumulation rates may be related to the density of local settlements.

Pollen concentrations are low in the upper portions of the Lukurmata core, averaging 19,000 grains per cubic centimeter above 43 centimeters below the sediment-water interface (fig. 4.13). Below 43 centimeters the concentration increases to an average of 66,000 grains per cubic centimeter. Between 1,600 and 1,440 radiocarbon years B.P., there is a major change in the pollen percentages, representing a shift in the local macrophyte assemblage and algal productivity. There is no correspondence with percentages from the modern transect data, which lack such high values for *Elodea*. The *Elodea* percentages, higher values for Gramineae and *Pediastrum*, and lower values for Cyperaceae all suggest deeper water around 1,400 years ago that lasted for several hundred years.

#### THE HUATAJATA CORE

Pollen analyses of 12 widely spaced samples from the Huatajata core 27-VIII-88 are presented in figure 4.14. Total pollen concentrations are low, ranging from 684 grains per cubic centimeter in the basal sample to a maximum of 16,775 grains per cubic centimeter at 3 meters. Based on the interpretation of the transect data, the Huatajata coring site appears always to have been covered by a minimum water depth of 5 meters. At a core depth of 3 meters, there is a peak of *Elodea* (one of the major components of "other aquatics" in fig. 4.14), which is concurrent at about 1,400 radiocarbon years B.P. with the increased

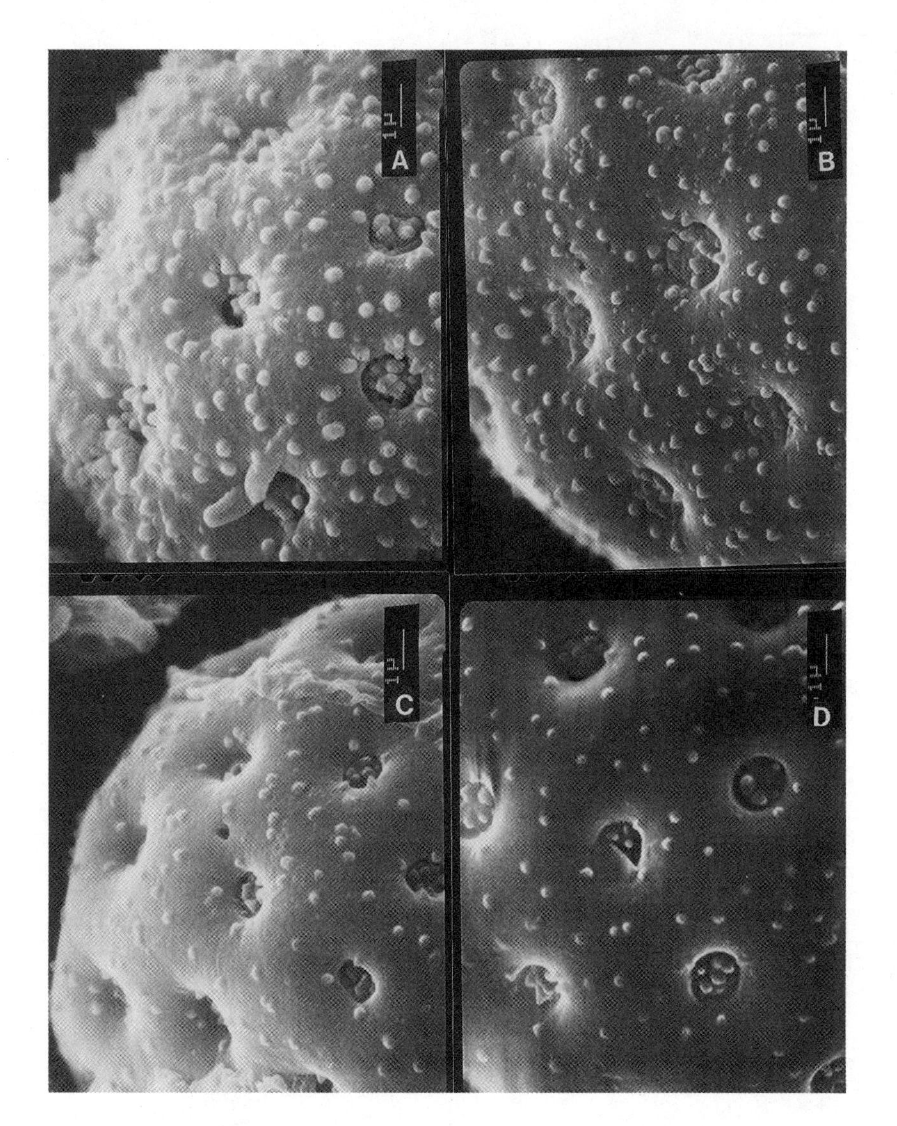


**Figure 4.12.** Fossil Chenopodiaceae-Amaranthaceae pollen grains taken from the Lukurmata short core (22-VIII-86-1). A and B are from a depth of 44 centimeters (radiocarbon date 1450 B.P.), and C and D are from 98 centimeters (1950 B.P.). All grains appear to be *Chenopodium,* perhaps a different species at each level. All lack minute holes in the exine. A and B have an average of 8.6 spinules per square micron, while C and D have an average of 5.4 spinules per square micron. Magnification is 10,000X.

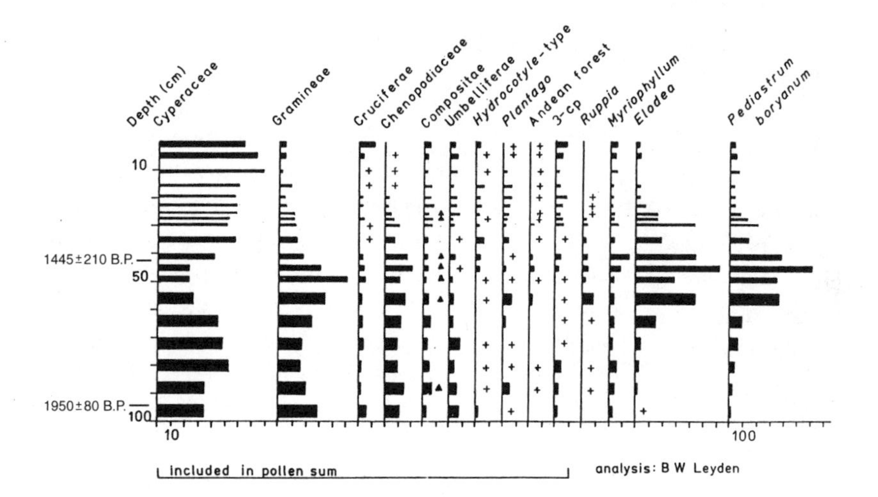


**Figure 4.13.** Pollen percentage diagram for Lukurmata core 22-VIII-86-1. Pluses represent percentages less than 2. Triangles indicate levels in which *Ambrosia* is present. Aquatic taxa are excluded from the pollen sum. All profiles are drawn to the same scale except for that of *Pediastrum boryanum,* which is displayed at a 1:10 scale.

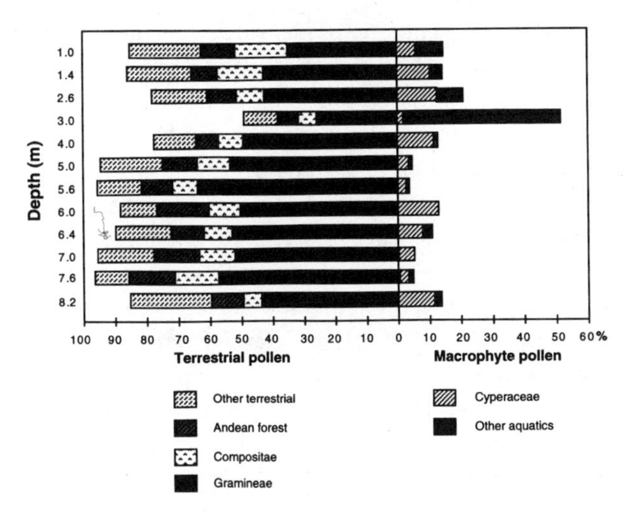


**Figure 4.14.** Coarse palynology of Huatajata core 27-VIII-88. Aquatic macrophyte pollen is included to contrast with terrestrial and aquatic representation.

*Elodea* representation observed in the Lukurmata sediments. Thus, the two cores record a nearshore and deeper-water record of the same basinwide event, which was a deepening of the lake above present levels.

The terrestrial pollen displays some variation. The basal marly clays are older than 3,400 radiocarbon years B.P., predating large-scale agricultural activities, and contain almost no Chenopodiaceae. Pollen of *Plantago, Podocarpus, Alnus,* and *Hedyosmum* is more abundant in these basal clays than elsewhere in the core. The last three are representatives of the Andean forest zone incorporated through long-distance transport, while the *Plantago* probably represents a local bog plant. Thus, the climate may have been warmer and somewhat drier.

## Palynology of Archaeological Samples

Five soil samples associated with ancient raised fields and one hearth sample were also examined for pollen. The pollen is sparse, averaging fewer than 11 grains per sample, and consists primarily of Gramineae, Chenopodiaceae, Compositae, and Cyperaceae. In these small samples, Chenopodiaceae was relatively abundant (17–50 percent) compared with all nonarchaeological samples. As previously discussed, SEM analysis will be required to determine whether the grains are from one of the two chenopods used as cereals.

# Reconstructing Tiwanaku Ecosystems

We describe in this section the structure and function of the Wiñaymarka basin ecosystem as it has changed over the past 6,000 years in response to climate change and to human activities. In essence, our interpretations based on lake-level changes are attributed to climate, whereas those based on changing sediment accumulation rates are attributed to humans. Lake-level fluctuations are the result of changes in the balance between evaporation and precipitation, that is, climate. We believe, however, that changes in the rate of deposition of sediment constituents on the lake bottom were anthropogenically driven. Lake-level changes can also affect sediment accumulation rates when shorelines (i.e., areas of eroding soils) move closer to or farther from the core site. Although lake-level variation has an effect on accumulation rate, we argue that the effects of human activities are much more significant. Further studies will be necessary to differentiate between the two causes with confidence.

Our interpretations are organized temporally. We present a description of ecosystem conditions and their changes for each time period that can be established within the limitations of the dating procedures. These interpretations should be considered hypotheses based on strong inferences rather than a final, definitive narrative. Each statement made with confidence is supported by at least two lines of evidence that we have generated in field studies. When a proposition is not supported by a minimum of two lines of evidence, we consider it more speculative. These more speculative propositions, however, are themselves supported by logical reasoning or literature citations. At the end of this section, we describe a set of testable hypotheses that will be the focus of future studies.

## Tiwanaku Ecosystems: Structure and Function

"Structure" is the physical state of the ecosystem—for example, hydrology (net precipitation, lake level, availability of water for agriculture), composition of terrestrial and aquatic plant communities, and size and activities of human populations (including agriculture, urbanization, hydraulic engineering, and the like). Our interpretations of past ecosystem structure in the Lake Titicaca basin are grounded largely on (1) analysis of sedimentary algae and pollen that are informative about past phytoplankton and higher plant communities; (2) lake-level changes inferred from sediment cores, hydrologic and climatic modeling, and comparisons with paleoclimate data derived from the Quelccaya glacier; and (3) correlation of lake sediment properties with pre-Hispanic human activities as drawn from the archaeological record.

The ecosystem functions on which we focus include biogeochemical fluxes and erosion and deposition processes. Measured rates of accumulation of bulk sediments and nutrients (carbon, nitrogen, phosphorus) on the lake bottom are assumed to be proportional to rates of delivery to the lake, and thus proportional to removal rates from the riparian landscape. Nitrogen dynamics in the study area are especially interesting because weathering of local bedrock yields large amounts of phosphorus, potassium, and other nutrients but very little nitrogen (Argollo and Ticlla 1991; Brenner, unpublished data; Wurtsbaugh et al. 1984, 1985). Plant growth in both terrestrial and aquatic ecosystems on the altiplano is limited by the availability of nitrogen, and nitrogen-fixation plays an essential role in biological production, including agriculture (Carney 1984; Vincent et al. 1984, 1985; Wurtsbaugh et al. 1984, 1985).

#### 15,000–3400 B.P.

Paleoenvironmental inferences for the period prior to 3400 B.P. rely solely on the sediment section from Lukurmata. At depths in the core older than 6,000 years, there are terrestrial deposits that indicate fluctuations in water level. These major lacunae in the historical record make it impossible to compute reliable estimates of sediment or nutrient accumulation. At the Lukurmata coring site, currently in 2 meters of water, sediment accumulation appears to have been uninterrupted for the past 6,000 years. The implication is that water at this coring site has been high enough to inundate the site continuously for six millennia. Paleolimnological evidence of lake-level fluctuation prior to 3400 B.P. from other coring sites, however, is contradictory. At deep-water (8.8-meter) coring sites near Huatajata and Guaqui, lacustrine deposition began only 3,400 to 3,000 years ago. The evidence from these two cores indicates a decline in lake stand of at least 9 meters and therefore a significantly drier climate before 3400 B.P. Complete desiccation of the Wiñaymarka basin requires only a 20 percent reduction in mean, long-term net precipitation. This magnitude of rainfall deficit is well within the range of recent interannual variations (Hastenrath and Kutzbach 1985; and see chapter 2).

The inferred dry episode that ended with a rise in lake level about 3400 B.P. is supported by the data of Wirrmann and Oliveira Almeida (1987), who show a dramatic increase in water level beginning a little more than 3,000 years ago. It is no coincidence that agriculture was not widespread in the altiplano before 3400 B.P.: there may simply have been too little available moisture to support extensive farming. Only with an increase in long-term net precipitation, beginning about 3400–3000 B.P., was there sufficient moisture to support effective agriculture in the altiplano. The archaeological record documents the inception of small-scale subsistence farming at that time (Kolata 1993a).

Two basal pollen samples from the Huatajata core predate 3400 B.P. They differ from younger samples in having greater percentages of *Plantago* and Andean forest elements. Local vegetation may have been sparse because of a warmer and drier climate, which would explain the greater proportion of pollen deposited from long-distance transport. Graf (1981a) studied pollen profiles from nearby bogs and determined that Holocene climate varied only slightly but was warmest between 7500 and 5500 B.P. and drier than today. Chenopodiaceae is essentially absent. This implies that much of the Chenopodiaceae in later sediments represents domesticated varieties resulting from agricultural activities.

#### 3400–2000 B.P.

After 3400 B.P., climate on the altiplano became moister and was probably in a relatively steady state, at least on a time scale indexed in century-long increments. There is some evidence that the climate was even moister, or perhaps more seasonal, than today. Thin laminations are present in older deposits of the Guaqui and Huatajata cores. The preservation of laminations suggests formation in deep water, where they were protected from wind-driven mixing and bioturbation. Laminations are not being formed in sediments currently being deposited at the Huatajata and Guaqui sites.

The pollen percentages change above the contact with the marly clay in the Huatajata core. Chenopodiaceae and *Polylepis* types are now present in the regional vegetation, while Moraceae becomes the dominant representative of the Andean forest transported long-distance by wind currents. These changes may indicate a commencement of wetter conditions, which then change little throughout the rest of this period.

Human populations began to grow in the research area about 3000 B.P., and their increase was accompanied by the diffusion of agricultural practices, particularly in the nearshore zones of the Lake Titicaca basin. As more land was put into cultivation, there was an increase in material flux from the land to the lake. Soil organic matter was transferred to the lakeshore at increasingly greater rates.

We speculate that the nitrogen-phosphorus ratio in lake waters was sufficiently low (less than 30) to maintain dominance of the phytoplankton by blue-green algae (bacteria). Blue-greens dominate the phytoplankton of the larger lake basin (Titicaca) today, but not those of the Wiñaymarka basin (Lazzaro 1981).

### 2000–1400 B.P.

During the period from 2000 to 1400 B.P., riparian human populations approached their maximum densities and raised fields were developed and employed on a broad spatial scale. It is during this time frame that altiplano ecosystems sustained their greatest anthropogenic impacts. Direct archaeological evidence indicates that raised-field technology arose in the research area about 2000 B.P., although there is circumstantial evidence for somewhat earlier origins between 2000 and 3000 B.P. (Kolata 1993a). Initial construction of raised fields is correlated temporally with rising lake levels, and we infer that the new agricultural practice constituted an effort to raise planting surfaces above the zone of saturated soils. Lake level may have been 1 to 2 meters higher than at present (mean twentieth-century level) because of slightly greater net precipitation. Paleoclimatological data from the nearby Quelccaya ice cap also indicate relatively greater precipitation throughout the period, supporting the inference for a high lake stand (Ortloff and Kolata 1993; Thompson et al. 1985).

The pollen record shows that terrestrial vegetation was not altered at the family or genus level, despite the fact that agriculture was becoming widely practiced in the basin. But this pattern is not particularly problematic for ecosystem interpretation. Both the native and the principal domesticated plants belong to the same genera, and they cannot be distinguished in the palynological record. Proportional representation of both aquatic plant pollen and algae increased during this period, providing additional evidence of increased water depth at the coring site and greater moisture availability.

Raised fields were advantageous to local farmers for several reasons. Field platforms elevated planting surfaces and thereby removed the zone of root development from the stratum of completely saturated soil. Continuous flow of low-salinity groundwater from local springs provided a reliable source of irrigation water and probably prevented, or at least mitigated, soil salinization. The constant presence of water in canals between fields afforded crops protection against freezing temperatures. Raised fields also altered local biogeochemical cycles by retarding soil loss. The fields, characterized by sinuous trough-and-platform shapes, served as effective retention basins that slowed the movement of both dissolved and particulate materials from the land to the lake (see chapters 5–8 for detailed discussions of raised-field function and performance). This last conclusion is supported by the reduction in sediment accumulation rate that accompanied raised-field construction. Although it is reasonable to assume that earth-moving activities involved in raised-field construction might have accelerated erosion, we find no evidence for a pulse of soil delivery to the lake. We hypothesize that fields were first built adjacent to the lake in saturated soils. Wet soils in flat terrain would not have been prone to transport, even when disturbed. Subsequent field construction may have caused short-term soil loss, but effects were mitigated by interception and deposition of transported soils in the earlier-constructed, nearshore raised-field systems.

Canals between raised fields also functioned as aquatic habitats for nitrogen-fixing organisms, a conclusion that is supported by observations and measurements in modern, rehabilitated raised-field systems (see chapter 9). The aquatic fern *Azolla* is common in rehabilitated fields and is host to the nitrogen-fixing cyanobacterium *Anabaena azollae* (Sprent 1987). Other, free-living blue-green algae (bacteria) such as *Nostoc* are also abundant in canals between raised fields and in slack-water channels.

Nitrogen can be lost from the raised-field system via several pathways. Denitrification in anaerobic sediments may recycle nitrogen to the overlying waters, where it will be utilized again by nitrogen-fixing cyanobacteria or lost to the atmosphere. Organically bound nitrogen may settle and be buried on the canal bottom. Nevertheless, nitrogen in the canal sediments is not permanently lost and can enter the agricultural food chain when cultivators recycle the nitrogen-rich canal deposits on raised fields. We hypothesize that nitrogen fixation dominated the nitrogen cycle in raised fields and that there was a long-term net yield of biologically incorporated nitrogen that was used as fertilizer and enabled sustainable crop production (see chapter 7 for a further discussion of this proposition).

Nitrogen fixation in raised fields may have indirectly enhanced fish production in the Wiñaymarka basin. Excessive nitrogen produced in raised-field canals may have flowed into the lake in dissolved form, thereby raising the nitrogen-phosphorus ratio of the lake waters. Under conditions in which ample nitrogen is available for primary production, green algae (chlorophytes) and golden-brown algae (chrysophytes) are favored. Fishery management techniques often include manipulation of nutrient ratios to alter the aquatic environment in favor of green algae or other useful primary producers (Boyd 1982). If raised fields drove a shift from cyanobacteria to chlorophytes and chrysophytes, and the result was a change in fish population structure and densities, then Tiwanaku raised fields may have enhanced another aspect of natural resource yield, indirectly stimulating a major protein source for human consumers. Fisheries remain a significant element of the local economy today (Laba 1979; Ponce Sanginés 1989).

#### 1400–1000 B.P.

The paleoecological and paleolimnological records are less informative about the period after the peak in raised-field agriculture. These fields were then the dominant features on the floors of the valleys and acted as effective nutrient and sediment traps. The long period of low sediment accumulation rate following this period indicates that abandoned fields continued to retain materials. The sinuous, corrugated structure of the original fields is well preserved in many parts of the research area, so this sustained retention capacity is not surprising.

Lake level declined significantly at the end of this period (Leyden 1989), indicating a long-term (400-year) drought that was verified by Ortloff and Kolata (1993; and see chapter 8). Regional-scale raised-field systems were abandoned around this time. Ortloff and Kolata argue that the proximate cause for the political fragmentation of Tiwanaku after 1000 B.P. was the collapse and widespread abandonment of raised-field technology induced by chronic drought conditions. Natural vegetation may have recolonized the valley, but the paleoecological record is uninformative on this point because, as noted earlier, the different taxa are indistinguishable palynologically.

## Conclusions

Despite our qualification that these interpretations are hypotheses subject to further testing, ecosystem structure and function in the Wiñaymarka basin clearly were influenced substantially by human activities, particularly during the hegemony of the Tiwanaku state, but also in the nearly 1,000 years since its decline. To varying degrees, most human activities consume and degrade natural resources. Contrary to this normal expectation, our research suggests raised-field cultivation techniques actually enhanced the natural system of the lake by decreasing the rate of nutrient delivery and increasing the nitrogen-phosphorus ratio in inflowing water. We predict that rehabilitating and constructing new raised fields (projects that are increasing in tempo and spatial scope) will not have deleterious effects on either the lake fishery or the trophic state of the lake. Nevertheless, we caution that the tenets of scientific method demand additional tests of these hypotheses and their resulting predictions in order to verify them, or at least to increase the strength of our inferences. Moreover, from the pragmatic, applied perspective, effective management of rehabilitated raised fields depends on a comprehensive understanding of the hydrologic, biogeochemical, and ecological mechanisms that stimulate them to produce such bountiful harvests.

# 5

# Tiwanaku Raised-Field Agriculture in the Lake Titicaca Basin of Bolivia

ALAN L. KOLATA AND
CHARLES R. ORTLOFF

This chapter summarizes a large body of empirical data and interpretations concerning the spatial and temporal distribution, physical characteristics, and functions of raised-field agriculture in Tiwanaku's near hinterland. Most of these data have been generated by Proyecto Wila Jawira since 1986, although some relevant information stems from research conducted as early as 1979. New data and interpretations derived from ongoing research will add to and most likely alter the perspective presented here, particularly with respect to the origins and early organization of raised-field agriculture in our research area. Nevertheless, the material we present in this chapter represents the most comprehensive analysis of raised-field agriculture in Tiwanaku's hinterland currently possible.

Our approach to investigating the space-time systematics of raised-field agriculture is framed in terms of a general distributional model that consists of the following propositions: (1) raised-field agriculture was initiated in the wetlands of Lake Titicaca's near-shore environment no earlier then 3500 B.P (see Erickson 1988a for a hypothesis regarding initiation of raised-field agriculture on the Peruvian side of the lake that is consistent with the spatial, although not with the chronological, implications of this proposition); (2) in the period from about 1600 to 1000 B.P., raised-field agriculture in the study area was integrated into a regional system of intensive production B.P. that entailed development of a substantial hydraulic infrastructure under the aegis of the Tiwanaku state; and (3) raised-field agriculture collapsed as an integrated, regional system of production between about 900 and 1000 B.P.

The evidence supporting these three propositions is derived from both paleoecological and archaeological research. As indicated in chapters 2 and 4, we have evidence that each of these major transitions in land use induced environmental changes that are recorded with various degrees of clarity in sediment cores from Lake Titicaca (see also Binford 1989; Binford, Brenner, and Engstrom 1992; Leyden 1989). Paleoenvironmental evidence is particularly implicated in substantiating the first and third propositions outlined here.

We are currently focusing our investigations on the paleoecological and social context of the origins of intensive raised-field agriculture. As noted in chapter 4, agriculture was not widespread in the Bolivian altiplano before 3500 B.P. because there was too little available moisture to support extensive farming. Only with an increase in long-term net precipitation beginning about 3400–3000 B.P. was there sufficient moisture to support intensive agriculture in the region. Although we have substantial paleoenvironmental evidence to support this proposition about the timing of the origins of raised-field agriculture in the altiplano, additional archaeological and paleoecological research will be required to verify the hypothesis.

At the other end of the historical spectrum, we believe a long-term deterioration of climatic conditions after 1000 B.P. was directly and causally related to the ultimate abandonment of Tiwanaku's regional-scale raised-field systems. We further contend that this environmentally driven abandonment of a productive agricultural landscape was the proximate cause of Tiwanaku's political fragmentation around this time. A complete deurbanization of altiplano society and significant dispersion of human populations after about A.D. 1000 was one significant product of this agricultural collapse (Kolata 1993a; Ortloff and Kolata 1993). The evidentiary details of this collapse hypothesis are discussed in chapter 8.

The chronological focus of this chapter, then, is the period between 1600 and 1000 B.P., when raised fields in the study area were integrated into a regional system of intensive agricultural production. This period correlates with the emergence of Tiwanaku as the preeminent city of the Andean high plateau and with the coalescence and expansion of Tiwanaku political authority in the south-central Andes as a whole. The geographical focus of this chapter is the area we refer to as the metropolitan district of the Tiwanaku heartland (see fig. 1.2). This area formed the immediate sustaining hinterland of the Tiwanaku state and consisted of a series of interlinked, nucleated, urban settlements—Tiwanaku, Lukurmata, Pajchiri, and Khonko Wankané, among others—set in a constellation of smaller, dispersed rural settlements. Tiwanaku's metropolitan district lies in a series of three valleys hemmed in on the east by the Cordillera Oriental and bounded on the west by a long north-south trending mountain chain of volcanic origin that delimits the modern frontier between Bolivia and Chile. Each of these valleys, defined geologically as separate hydrological units referred to as the Catari, Tiwanaku, and Machaca basins (or sub-basins when considered from a larger geographic frame of reference), borders on the shores of Lake Titicaca.

The casual observer might perceive the Bolivian altiplano as a uniform, featureless plateau. This image distorts ecological reality. The three valleys of the altiplano that became the setting for the emergence of Tiwanaku as an urban civilization are morphologically complex and highly variegated in terms of topography, soils, vegetation, and sources of water. They are a patchwork of physical forms and textures. Each presents a complicated landscape of mountains and plains, rivers and streams, quebradas, and lake terraces. Ancient mountain slopes deeply incised by flowing surface water carry enormous charges of sediment to the land below. Extensive alluvial fans and plains were formed in the past 15,000 years from clay, sand, and gravel erosional products originating in these surrounding mountain chains. The broad littoral and nearshore zone of Lake Titicaca presents an entirely different environmental aspect. Muddy organic soils, marshes, and stony beaches form a rich wetlands teeming with wildlife and aquatic plants. High, arid pockets of pastureland exist at elevations higher than 4,100 meters above sea level.

The local economy of Tiwanaku's metropolitan district revolved around three principal, interrelated systems of production: intensive agriculture, extensive llama and alpaca pastoralism, and exploitation of Lake Titicaca. Each was associated with a particular environmental zone, and each involved distinct forms of human activities and organization. Each system of production also entailed different intensities of labor investment and management (Kolata 1993a). Arguably the most important of these three basic modes of economic production, and the one that manifests the most intense degree of state involvement in planning and mobilization of human labor, was Tiwanaku's extensive system of raised-field agriculture, together with a supporting infrastructure of hydraulic technology: dikes, aqueducts, causeways, and canals.

The history of the reclamation of natural wetlands for intensive agricultural production by the Tiwanaku state is, in a sense, emblematic of the larger social history of the people of Tiwanaku. The emergence, florescence, and ultimate collapse of intensive raised-field agriculture in the circum-Titicaca region virtually recapitulates the trajectory of Tiwanaku state expansion and decline. We can perceive a general relationship between the capacity to create and sustain a substantial surplus of agricultural production and the institutionalization of political power in the hands of the Tiwanaku elite. The fundamental basis of power for the Tiwanaku elites was control over a secure, sustainable fund of agricultural products which was then employed to finance other local and foreign ventures: construction of monumental temples and palaces, subsidies for artisan retainers, wars of conquest and territorial expansion, and reinvestment in the agricultural landscape. In the world of Tiwanaku, agriculture was power. The elites of that world were supremely sensitive to this equation.

The first step toward understanding the political economy of Tiwanaku society, then, is to capture the complex relationships that underwrote the technology and organization of agricultural production on the broad littoral and alluvial plains of Tiwanaku's sustaining hinterland. The spatial distribution, physical characteristics, and agroecological functions of raised-field systems are the subjects of this chapter, with emphasis on their technological dimensions. Subsequent chapters, particularly the conclusion to this volume, will explore the organizational dimensions of intensive, raised-field production.

## The Distribution of Raised Fields in Tiwanaku's Hinterland

Excavations and distributional analyses of raised fields in the near hinterland of Tiwanaku were inaugurated between 1979 and 1982 with a pilot program conducted under the aegis of the Instituto Nacional de Arqueología de Bolivia. This pilot program of research focused on large-scale raised-field systems in the Pampa Koani zone of the Catari River basin (figs. 5.1, 5.2). We now designate the Catari River basin as the northern component of the Tiwanaku sustaining area (Kolata 1987a:188, 1991, 1993a). Subsequently, we expanded our systematic investigation of raised-field systems to include the Tiwanaku Valley. This chapter describes raised-field distribution, morphology, and functions in both the Catari and Tiwanaku river valleys, with only passing reference to preliminary research undertaken in the Machaca-

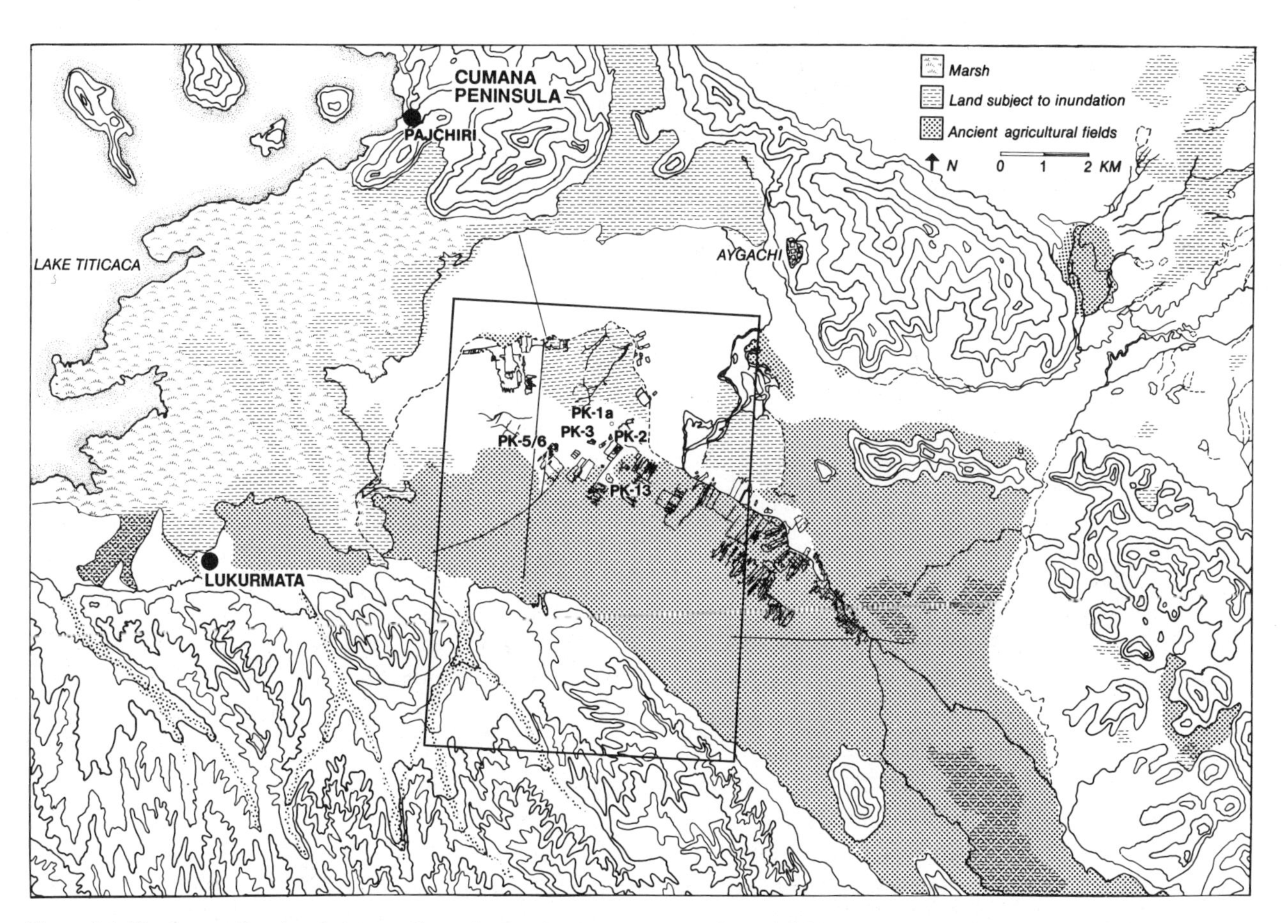


**Figure 5.1.** The Pampa Koani and vicinity. Shown here is the extensive zone of raised fields in the nearshore environment of Lake Titicaca, together with a system of causeways that linked local administrative, ritual, and residential sites with the regional urban centers of Lukurmata and Pajchiri. The box outlines the area mapped in detail in figure 5.2.

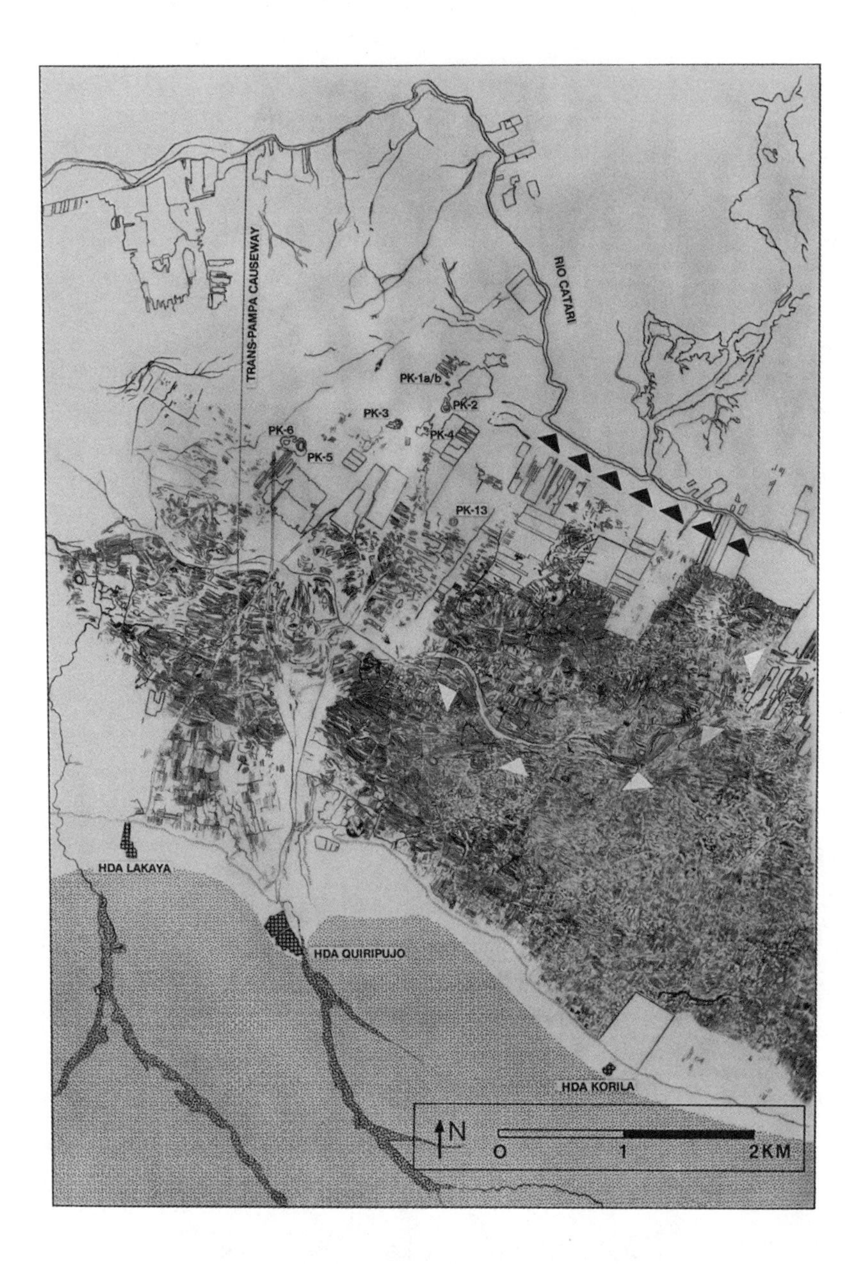


**Figure 5.2.** Detailed map of a portion of the Pampa Koani, showing networks of ancient raised fields and principal archaeological sites. Mound structures are designated PK-1, PK-2, and so forth. White arrows point to the course of an old river meander. Black arrows point to the artificially canalized course of the Catari River.

Desaguadero region, the southern component of Tiwanku's immediate sustaining area, located in the modern Bolivian province of Pacajes. Future research will examine the Machaca-Desaguadero systems in greater detail.

The three central valleys that were the setting for Tiwanaku's heartland of cities contain approximately 190 square kilometers of fossil raised fields, or some 19,000 hectares (Catari basin: 7,000 hectares; Tiwanaku Valley: 6,000 hectares; Machaca-Desaguadero: 6,000 hectares). There are substantial differences in the published and unpublished literature with respect to the areal extent of raised fields on the Bolivian side of Lake Titicaca. Smith, Denevan, and Hamilton (1968:355) published a figure of 30 square kilometers (3,014 hectares) for the Catari basin and a total for the entire Bolivian side of 39 square kilometers (3,938 hectares). They calculated an additional 65 square kilometers (6,501 hectares) for the Desaguadero region on the Peruvian border with Bolivia. This last figure corresponds well to the 60 square kilometers that we project for the southern component of Tiwanaku's sustaining area, which, in our definition, includes an area straddling the Peru-Bolivia border. Our estimate of 60 square kilometers for the Machaca-Desaguadero region is based on analysis of aerial photographs and unsystematic survey. This region has not yet been analyzed as intensively as the Catari and Tiwanaku basins, and therefore this estimate is in part conjectural.

Graffam (1990) revised the figure for the Catari basin upward to 44 square kilometers but did not address the extent of raised fields outside of the Catari region. Both Graffam's and Smith, Denevan, and Hamilton's estimates are based on calculations drawn from aerial photographs. Previously, one of us (Kolata 1986) suggested that the maximum extent of raised fields in the Catari basin was 70 square kilometers, and here we estimate that the total for the three-valley Tiwanaku hinterland approaches 190 square kilometers. The estimate of 70 square kilometers for the Catari basin is based on the analysis of aerial photographs, pedestrian survey, and soil coring and not simply on surface expression of raised fields. Graffam's (1990:311) distribution map does not include raised fields northwest of the Catari River, southeast of the village of Aygachi, or east and northeast of the community of Catavi. Because of differential preservation, many of these relic fields do not appear on the available aerial photographs. They are evident in ground survey, however, sometimes as subtle differences in surface vegetation, or they appear in subsurface soil cores.

The estimate of 60 square kilometers for the Tiwanaku Valley is based on analysis of aerial photographs and on the results of systematic pedestrian survey in the lower and middle sections of the valley, a portion of which is reported in Albarracín-Jordan and Mathews (1990). As in the case of the Machaca-Desaguadero region, our work on relic agricultural landscapes in the Tiwanaku Valley is not as complete or detailed as that in the Catari basin. Therefore the estimate of 6,000 hectares of raised fields in the Tiwanaku Valley is not as secure as our calculations for the Catari basin. This estimate may be excessive and should be considered with reservation. Furthermore, it must be noted that all of these estimates represent the *absolute maximum* extent of raised-field complexes, irrespective of time. That is, they do not take into account simultaneity of field use. At any given time in the history of Tiwanaku agriculture, a substantially smaller area of raised fields was in production than the maximum extent of 190 square kilometers that we have calculated.

Our estimate of raised-field distribution in the sustaining hinterland of Tiwanaku reflects those fields that have been identified from aerial photographs, surface investigation, and a coring program undertaken in the Pampa Koani region between 1979 and 1981. In the three valleys, huge areas of wetlands intricately crisscrossed by rivers and small streams fed by perennial springs show no evidence of raised fields on the surface. Yet soil coring and excavations in such wetlands in the Pampa Koani revealed buried raised-field systems as well as rich organic sediments that may represent agricultural soils deposited under clay, gravel, and sand up to 2 meters thick. The active river systems of these wetlands carry enormous quantities of sediments eroded from surrounding uplands. During the altiplano rainy season, these rivers often breach the natural levees that contain them, redepositing their sediment loads across the adjacent floodplain. As a result of this inexorable geomorphological process, many raised fields lie undetected, buried deeply beneath the modern surface of the pampa.

Other fields on the surface have been effaced through erosion triggered by wind and rain and by rivers that meander across the floodplain, cutting and reshaping the unconsolidated sediments of alluvium. Cultural processes have also contributed to the physical disappearance of ancient field systems. Centuries of cattle herding across the broad plains that once were the setting for intensive cultivation, along with the introduction of metal plows and mechanized farming, have obliterated the traces of abandoned raised fields. Despite the evident loss of some ancient raised fields, the 19,000 hectares that are documented in the Tiwanaku sustaining area most likely represent a substantial proportion of the fields that existed in Tiwanaku times.

## Raised Fields in the Catari River Drainage Basin

The Catari River drainage basin contains the largest expanse of raised fields with clear surface expression in the Tiwanaku hinterland (figs. 5.1, 5.2). These fields occupy a broad and gently but complexly sloping floodplain. They were fed by four distinct sources of freshwater supply: springs, rivers, groundwater, and seasonal rainfall. The last two sources are spatially generalized phenomena and, in the case of rainfall, aleatory as well. Springs and rivers, on the other hand, are discrete, predictable point sources of water accumulation and as such are more amenable to human manipulation by means of artificial hydraulic structures such as dams, reservoirs, dikes, and irrigation canals. Figure 5.3 illustrates a reticulated system of artificial canals that fed spring and river water to Tiwanaku raised-field complexes in the western por-

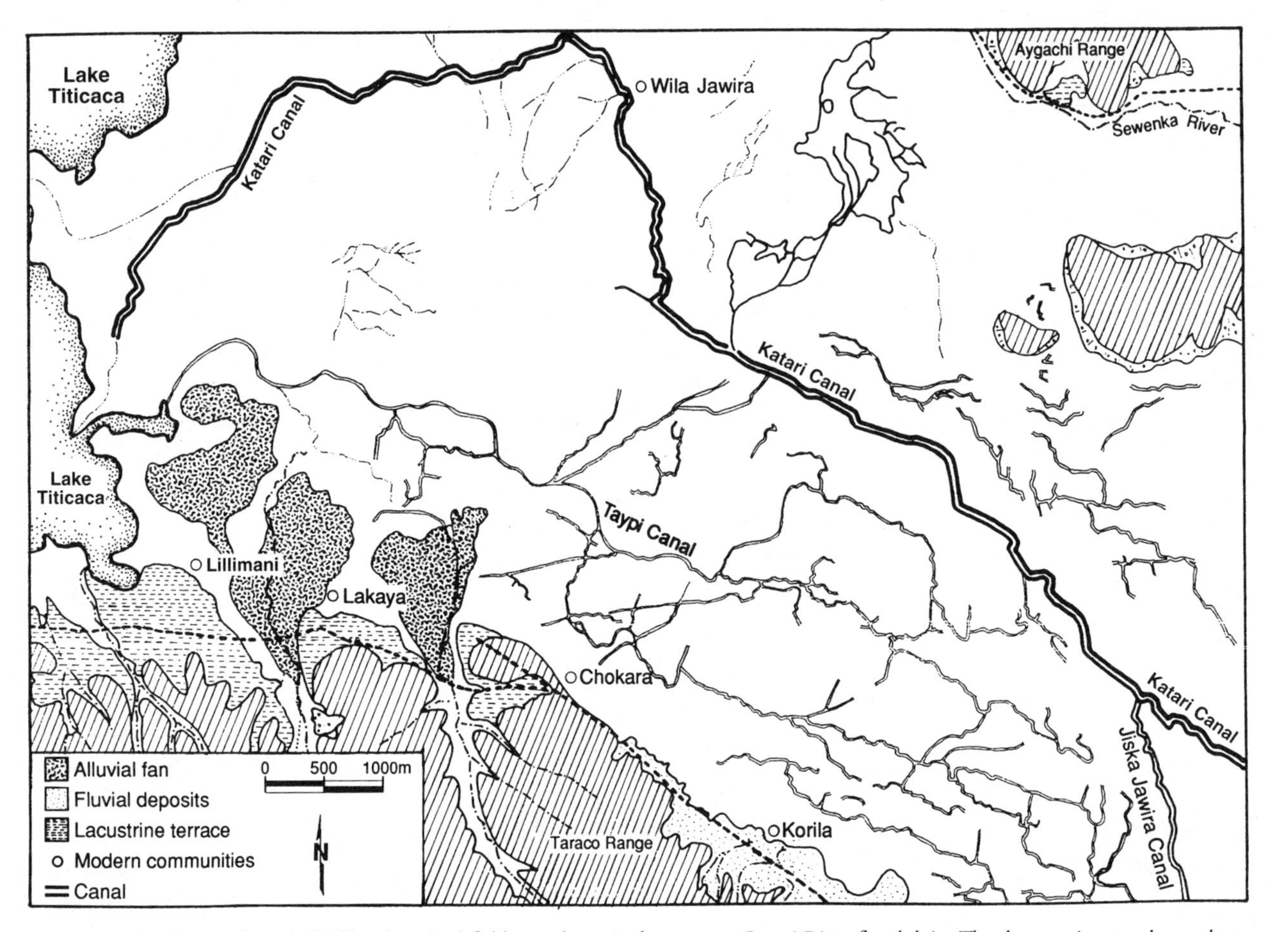


Figure 5.3. The system of canals feeding the raised-field complexes in the western Catari River floodplain. The three major canals are the Katari, the Taypi, and the Jiska Jawira.

tions of the Catari River floodplain. This canal network has several notable features.

The system consists of a hierarchical, latticelike arrangement of several major, east-to-west–trending, longitudinal canals articulated by a series of smaller, orthogonal canals. These smaller canals distributed irrigation water to raised-field complexes while the larger, longitudinal canals served principally as conduits to extract and drain excess water from the agricultural landscape. The principal longitudinal canal in this system was the Catari River itself, which in this section of the basin was canalized and stabilized in its bed by construction of massive earthen levees. More than 15 kilometers of the river's bed were artificially canalized, and we designate this section of the river the Katari Canal to distinguish it from the natural course of the river. The modified riverbed has an average width of 20 meters. The lateral levee walls average 2.5 meters in height and take the form of a trapezoidal escarpment built with sod blocks (locally called *tepes* or *tepes de champa*) cut from the dense, heavy soils of the alluvial plain. Upstream (eastward) from the raised-field complexes in the western Catari basin, the Katari Canal is joined by a second major channel, the Jiska Jawira Canal, flowing from the southeast.

Although we discuss the functions of these river canalizations in greater detail later, it is worth emphasizing that the hydraulic modifications were designed primarily to facilitate reclamation of natural wetlands for intensive agricultural production. That is, their principal function was to ensure adequate, permanent drainage of a perennially inundated landscape. However, as is clear from the canal network illustrated in figure 5.3, the Katari Canal also served the function of feeding secondary and tertiary canals that in turn irrigated discrete raised-field complexes. In short, the large, canalized rivers served a dual function: drainage and distribution.

A third major east-to-west–trending canal, the Taypi Canal, bisects the raised-field complexes in the Catari basin (fig. 5.3). Unlike the Katari and Jiska Jawira canals, the Taypi is not a modified natural river course but rather an artificial structure. It generally parallels the course of the Katari Canal. We hypothesize that, like the Katari and Jiska Jawira canals, the Taypi channel primarily served a drainage, or water extraction, function. We favor this hypothesis because (1) the pampas on either side (north and south) of this canal tend to gently slope down toward it, and (2) apart from the Katari Canal itself, this is the only watercourse running across the middle of the pampa that debouches directly into Lake Titicaca.

The secondary canals in this hierarchical network have spatially distinct sources of water supply on the north and south sides of the Taypi Canal. On the south side of the basin, these secondary canals are linked directly to two sources. One is the multiple natural and modified quebradas cut into the Taraco Range. These quebradas support substantial seasonal water flow, particularly from December to April. They were exploited opportunistically by the building of canals designed to capture this seasonal flow and conduct it to raised-field systems in the lower-lying pampas zones. The second water source for canals on the south side of the pampa was naturally occurring springs that emerge along the base of the Taraco Range. Each of the modern human communities along this range is situated adjacent to a significant zone of freshwater springs (fig. 5.3). Because the Taraco Formation sustains an enormous aquifer (see chapters 2 and 3), many of these springs maintain constant flows, even during episodes of serious drought such as occurred in the region during 1982–83. Several of the south-side canals illustrated in figure 5.3, particularly near the contemporary communities of Chokara, Lakaya, and Lillimani, extract water directly from such springs. Particularly lush wetlands form around these perennial springs, and it is not surprising that humans selected these zones in which to locate their settlements. In fact, each of these modern communities sits astride not only the springs themselves but also significant archaeological sites ranging from the Formative period to the Colonial, suggesting that this pattern of preferential settlement in the springs zones is of great historical depth. In contrast, on the north side of the Taypi Canal, the secondary canals are fewer in number and are not articulated with multiple water sources. Rather, they draw their water directly from the canalized section of the Catari River.

Although it is evident that the secondary canals on both the north and south sides of the pampa were used for irrigation purposes—to maintain constant water levels in and flow through raised fields—it is equally clear that these canals, like their larger counterparts, were also designed to promote drainage of the agricultural landscape. In effect, the hierarchical canal system in the Catari basin enabled Tiwanaku farmers to regulate groundwater levels across an enormous expanse of natural wetlands, and in the process to transform these wetlands into an agriculturally productive landscape (see chapter 6 for in-depth analyses of Tiwanaku groundwater manipulation technologies). Tiwanaku's manipulation of land and water resources in the western Catari basin was so extensive that it is not inappropriate to consider this entire region an anthropogenic landscape.

This transformation of the natural environment on a regional scale was both intentional and the product of unintended consequences. The latticework of canals described here was clearly a consciously designed element of a hydraulic infrastructure intended to reclaim wetlands for the benefit of human populations. The successful implementation of these major drainage features materially altered the hydrological regime of the basin. At the same time, the construction of integrated, regional-scale canal and raised-field systems resulted in significant changes in terrestrial and aquatic environments that can be termed collateral, unanticipated, or perhaps even accidental. Differential retention of sediments and nutrients in raised-field complexes and reduction in water turbidity in raised-field canals (Carney et al. 1993) are instances of presumably unintended environmental changes induced by human intervention. The environmental impact of raised-field agricultural intensification is considered in greater detail in chapter 7.

## Raised Fields in the Tiwanaku Valley

Raised fields in the Tiwanaku Valley have a spatial distribution rather different from that in the Catari basin. Moreover, as we describe later, there were differences in the techniques employed to manipulate these two distinct hydrological regimes, as well as substantial variability in the morphology of individual field complexes. In the Catari basin, raised-field complexes occur in a virtually continuous distribution from the edge of Lake Titicaca to areas some 12–15 kilometers inland (fig. 5.4). In contrast, in the Tiwanaku Valley, raised fields visible on the surface are distributed principally along the north side of the valley (fig. 5.4) and in smaller, discontinuous pockets in the vicinity of significant Tiwanaku settlements.

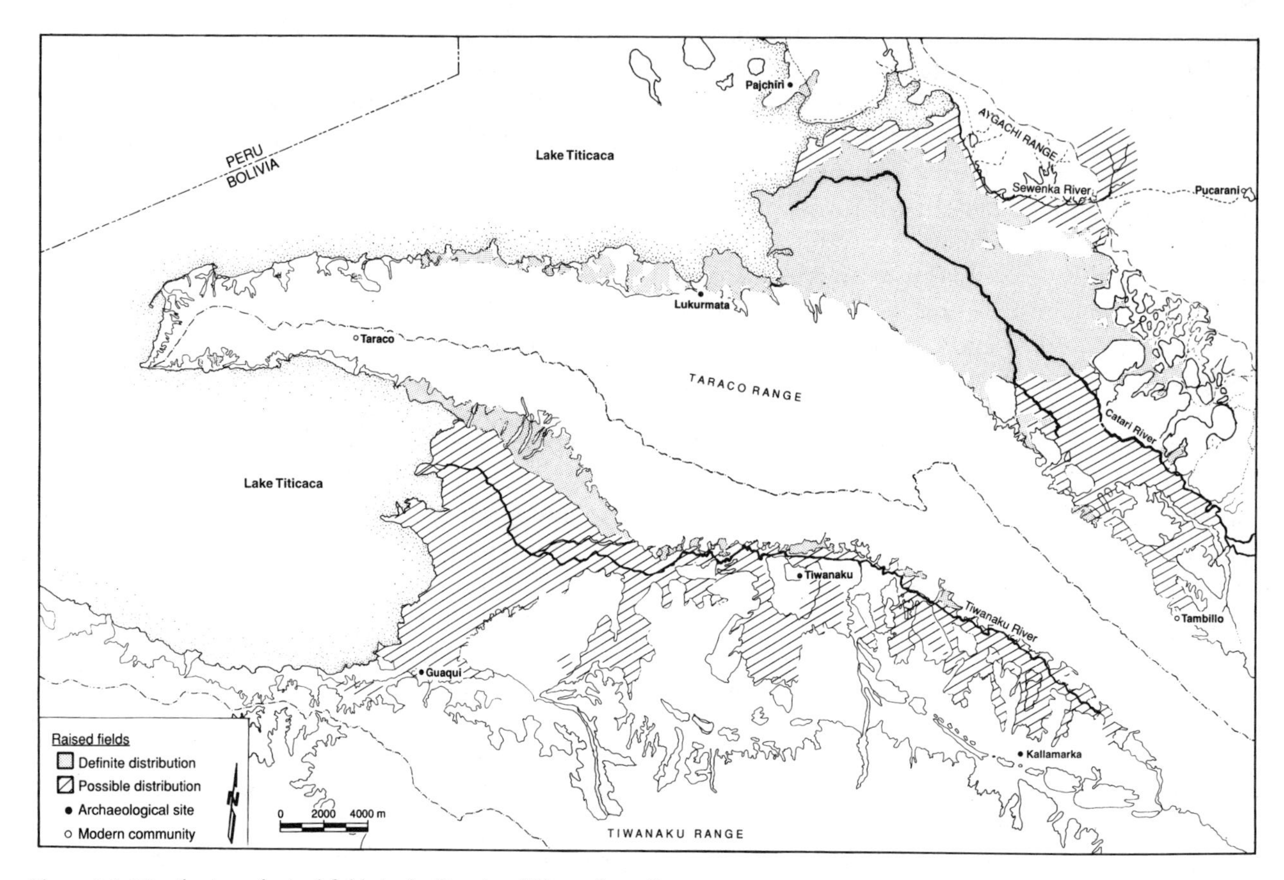


Figure 5.4. Distribution of raised fields in the Catari and Tiwanaku valleys.

On the south side of the valley are large areas that may have contained raised fields. But if such fields existed, they are now deeply buried under extensive alluvial fans and sheet wash deposits.

The explanation for this skewed distribution is not immediately obvious, although there is a strong possibility that it was related to differences in hydrological regime between the north and south sides of the valley. As noted earlier, the Taraco mountain range sustains an enormous aquifer, and its heavily eroded southern flanks form the northern border of the Tiwanaku Valley. Most of the visible raised-field complexes in the valley occur immediately adjacent to the piedmont region of this mountain range, which is characterized by massive colluvial, alluvial, and in some locales lacustrine terraces, alluvial fans, and deeply incised quebradas that support heavy seasonal flows. As on the northern flanks of the Taraco Range, numerous perennial springs emerge in this piedmont.

Two additional geomorphological features of the valley contribute to the peculiar character of its north-side hydrological regime. First, the Tiwanaku River itself flows along the northern edge of the valley (fig. 5.4), contributing substantial inputs to the local groundwater table through deep infiltration. Second, because of local topography, groundwater as a whole flows from the south side of the valley toward the Tiwanaku River on the north side, constantly charging the near-surface aquifer of the valley floor. The product of these various hydrological conditions is that the groundwater table on the north side of the valley frequently intersects with the surface, particularly during the altiplano rainy season, when water inputs peak. At this time, immense, standing pools of water form all along the valley floor. During the dry season, the water table remains relatively close to the surface, and springs on the north side of the valley rarely disappear entirely, even though water flow can be reduced. In essence, the north side of the valley presents an aspect of seasonal wetlands. Although the Tiwanaku Range on the southern side of the valley receives substantial rainfall and its piedmont region is relatively lush, on the pampas of the valley floor away from the immediate piedmont zone, the groundwater table is deeper than on the north side of the valley. In effect, the southern pampas are generally higher, drier, and, as a result, less amenable to raised-field cultivation than their counterparts on the north side.

Despite the relatively well-watered aspect of the Tiwanaku Valley's north side, this region does not sustain extensive, permanent wetlands as is the case in the Catari basin. Apart from some localized zones with permanent springs, most of the wetlands in the Tiwanaku Valley are seasonal phenomena. Moreover, in aggregate terms, over 35 percent of the western Catari basin is currently classified as wetlands, in contrast with only 12 percent of the Tiwanaku Valley. Not surprisingly, then, the strategies and technologies for manipulating surface and, most particularly, groundwater in raised-field complexes in the Tiwanaku Valley are strikingly different from those developed for the Catari basin.

The hydraulic infrastructure developed by Tiwanaku to support intensive raised-field agriculture in the Catari basin turned particularly on ensuring adequate drainage of natural wetlands. This strategy can best be viewed as one of extraction, eliminating excess water that could induce chronic supersaturation of soils deleterious to sustained agricultural production. Although, as we will describe later (see also Kolata 1991, 1993a), we have evidence for artificial modifications of the Tiwanaku River associated with the construction of a massive canal immediately west of the city of Tiwanaku—the Waña Jawira system—this major channel (5.0 to 9.3 meters wide at different points) is closely articulated with smaller secondary and tertiary canals that directly feed discrete blocks of raised fields (fig. 5.5). The Waña Jawira Canal draws water from the Tiwanaku River and eventually loops back and empties into the river. Like the Katari Canal, the Waña Jawira system could function both to extract and to distribute water. But unlike the Katari Canal, the Waña Jawira system appears to have been constructed so as to maximize its capacity to accumulate and distribute river water. In other words, the architecture of the Waña Jawira system reflects a predominant concern with the conservation and distribution of water on the agricultural landscape rather than with its extraction. Nevertheless, the system design retained the capacity to serve as a drainage conduit of regional scope (see chapter 6 for detailed hydraulic analyses of the Waña Jawira and Katari canals).

That the architects of Tiwanaku's raised fields in the Tiwanaku Valley were intensely concerned with impounding, conserving, and distributing water to field complexes is even more clearly expressed in the system of dikes that were developed along the north side of the valley. The spatial arrangement of these dikes, which generally parallel the colluvio-fluvial terraces of the piedmont region, directly implicates a strategy of water impoundment and conservation. These Tiwanaku Valley systems were organized through large-scale planning of agricultural space which included continuous, linear dikes to impound water linked to secondary irrigation canals that distributed water both within and between individual raised-field complexes. For instance, the section of the Tiwanaku agricultural landscape located between the contemporary community of Yanarico and the archaeological site of Iwawe is delimited by a main dike approximately 7 kilometers long and averaging 6 meters wide (fig. 5.6). Minor transverse dikes run through the colluvio-fluvial and fluvio-lacustrine deposits in the area of Yanarico. Similarly, a representative segment of the ancient agricultural landscape near the communities of Achuta Grande and Pillapi illustrates a complicated network of impoundment dikes, principal and secondary distribution canals, and blocks of raised fields (fig. 5.7). Like most of the agricultural fields on this side of the valley, these were irrigated with a combination of spring water emerging in the piedmont zone and surface runoff from seasonal precipitation. Some agricultural fields, such as those in the Chambi Chico and Achuta Grande zone, were also irrigated with Tiwanaku river water by means of artificial canals.

This analysis of agricultural land-use planning drives home an essential point. The architects of Tiwanaku's raised-field systems fully appreciated the environmental differences between the Catari basin and the northern Tiwanaku Valley. They responded to these differences by developing alternative strategies of land and water exploitation that are reflected materially in the functionally distinct hydraulic infrastructures of these two regions. Yet despite differences in the strategies and technologies of natural resource exploitation, the *regional* scope of the solutions to problems of intensive agricultural production in these two critical parts of Tiwanaku's sustaining hinterland remains evident.

Having canvassed the overall distribution of Tiwanaku raised fields and introduced some of the features of raised-field hydraulics, the remaining sections of

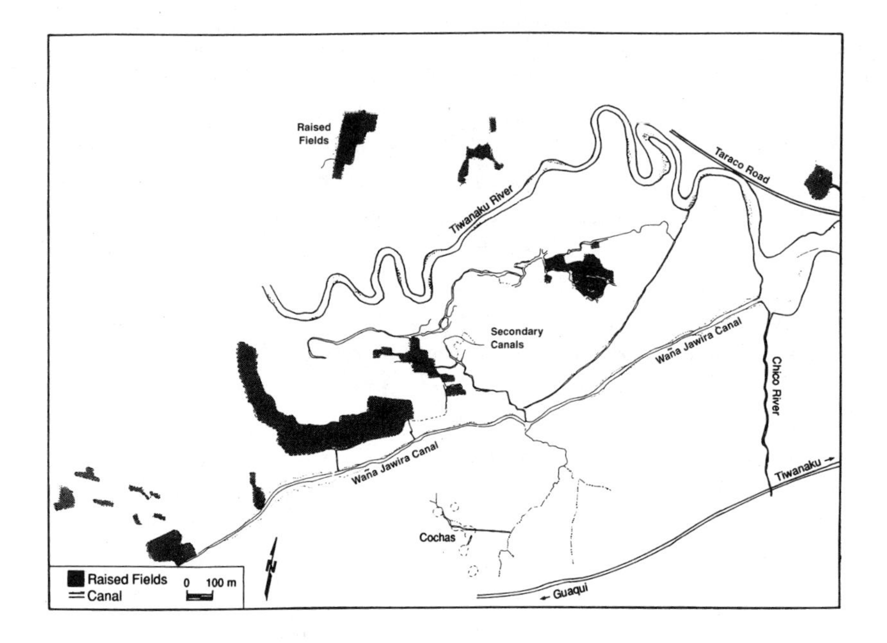


Figure 5.5. Investigated portions of the Waña Jawira Canal in the Tiwanaku Valley. Its intake is near the current bed of the Tiwanaku River, and it articulates with secondary irrigation canals (indicated by solid lines) and raised fields.

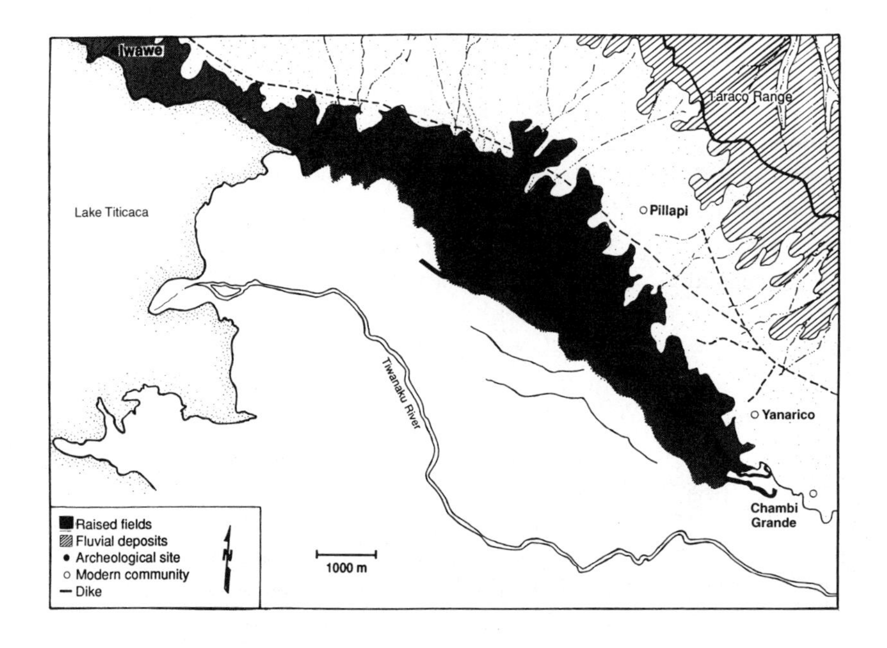


Figure 5.6. A major dike, approximately 7 kilometers long, near the archaeological site of Iwawe in the Tiwanaku Valley. Dashed lines indicate location of the principal modern road on the north side of the Tiwanaku Valley.

this chapter will describe the morphology of raised fields themselves, present a model of raised-field functions in the Lake Titicaca basin, and analyze in detail specific elements of Tiwanaku's hydraulic infrastructure.

## The Morphology of Raised Fields in Tiwanaku's Hinterland

The raised fields of the Titicaca basin are essentially elevated planting platforms ranging from around 2 to 10 meters wide and up to 200 meters long. Within a given segment of a raised-field system, approximately 30 to 60 percent of the area of the segment is given over to the planting surface itself (fig. 5.8). The remaining portion is occupied by intervening canals that derive their water from local fluvial networks, natural springs, percolating groundwater, or seasonal rainfall (Kolata and Ortloff 1989). As noted earlier, the flow of water from natural sources that fed Tiwanaku raised-field systems was frequently enhanced and regulated by artificial hydraulic structures such as dikes, aqueducts, primary canals, and canalized springs, quebradas, and rivers (Ortloff and Kolata 1989).

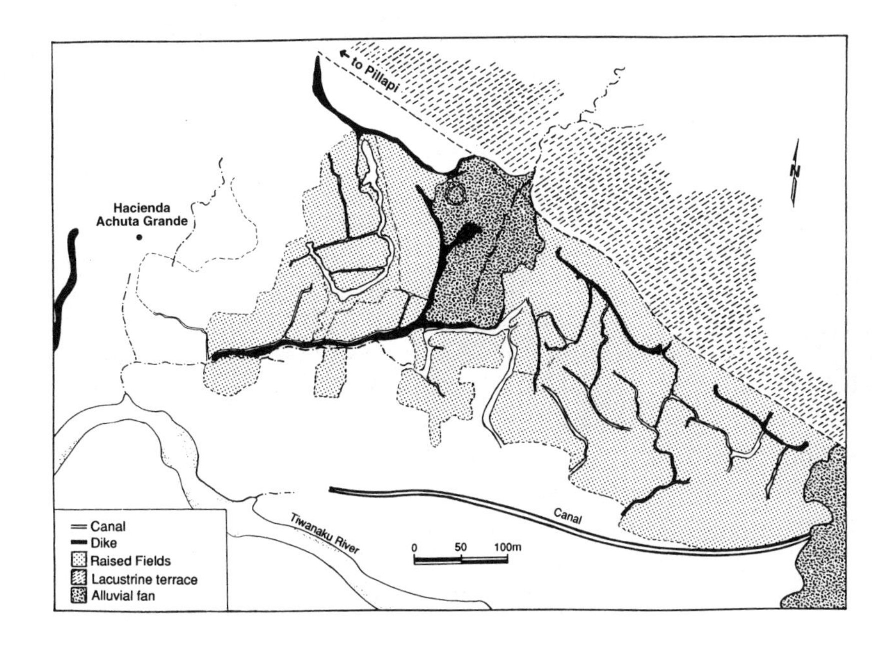


**Figure 5.7.** A portion of the ancient agricultural landscape near Achuta Grande and Pillapi, showing the arrangement of impoundment dikes, canals, and blocks of raised fields.

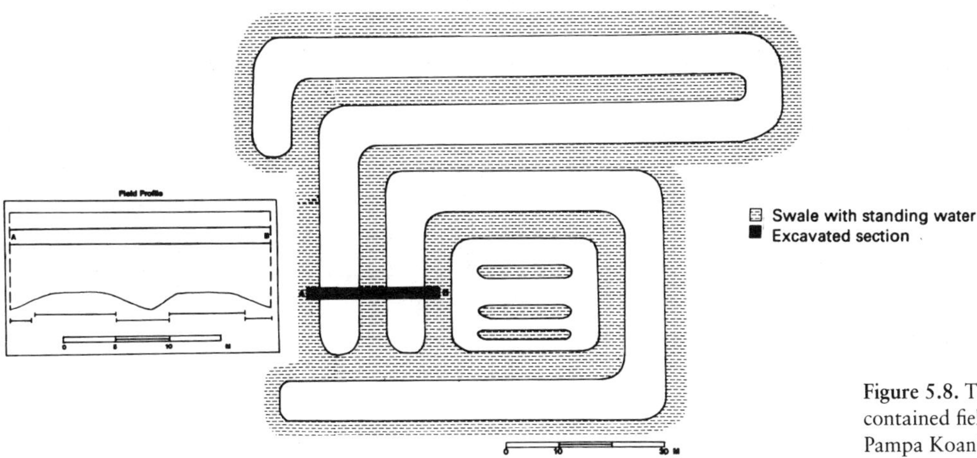


**Figure 5.8.** The form and profile of a self-contained field segment in the western Pampa Koani.

Essential properties of the Lake Titicaca raised-field systems stabilized and enhanced their productivity and sustainability. Recent experimental work in restored Tiwanaku raised fields indicated that the canals adjacent to the elevated planting surfaces were rapidly colonized by a diverse range of aquatic macrophytes, such as *Azolla, Myriophyllum,* and *Elodea.* These plants trap suspended, waterborne particulates and thereby sequester nutrients in the agricultural environment (Binford, Hill, and Janosky 1990; Carney et al. 1993). Plants were probably harvested directly from the surface of the water and incorporated into the planting bed immediately before sowing, or their decayed products were dredged from the muddy sediments of the canals and redistributed over the surface of the field. The high nutrient content of decomposed aquatic plants would have greatly ameliorated the nitrogen deficit that characterizes most altiplano soils (Unzueta 1975; Winterhalder, Larson, and Thomas 1974:99). Excavations in the agricultural sector at the site of Lukurmata provided direct archaeological evidence that Tiwanaku farmers periodically cleaned the sediments from canals between raised fields. These nitrogen-rich sediments were then used to resurface and revitalize the planting platforms of the raised-field system.

Comprehensive descriptions of Titicaca basin raised-field morphology and structure can be found in Erickson (1988a) and Lennon (1982, 1983). Within the Tiwanaku hinterland there is substantial morphological variability among contemporaneous raised-field complexes both within individual regions, such as the Catari basin, and between regions. Tiwanaku Valley raised fields, for instance, can be quite distinct from those in the Catari basin, frequently possessing significantly shorter wavelengths. The wavelength of a raised field is defined here as the distance between the centers of the two canals adjacent to an individual raised-field platform. This is a usage consistent with the terminology employed by other investigators in the region (e.g., Erickson 1988a:66). Similarly, within regions there is significant variability between lake-edge fields and fields located farther inland.

A few examples illustrate the range of morphological variability present in the Tiwanaku hinterland. In the Catari basin, raised-field complexes in the community of Lakaya tend to have an east-west orientation. The widths of individual raised-field platforms range from 3.4 to 7 meters, and the widths of the adjacent canals range from 2.3 to 3.2 meters. Farther east in the basin, raised-field platforms in the community of Korila take on a predominantly north-south orientation and range from 2 to 6 meters in width, whereas the adjacent canals vary from 1 to as much as 4 meters.

In contrast to the Catari basin field systems, individual raised-field complexes in the Tiwanaku Valley tend to be smaller and less massive. For instance, raised-field platforms in the community of Achuta Grande vary from 1.6 to 2.8 meters, while the canals vary from 1.1 to 1.6 meters. In the community of Sequeri, the range of variation is much smaller. Platform width varies only from 1.7 to 2.0 meters, and the canals are almost uniformly 1.5 meters wide, with a few individual canals reaching 2 meters in width. In the community of Yanarico, raised-field platforms, but not the corresponding canals, are significantly larger than those of Sequeri and Achuta Grande. In Yanarico the platforms average around 3.6 meters in width. Canals in Yanarico average 1.6 meters wide, consistent with the higher end of canal variability in the Achuta Grande and Sequeri field systems. Much of this variability in contemporaneous raised-field complexes may be explained by local differences in hydrological regime. However, differences in local topography, in subsurface sediments, in the availability and stability of water supply, and in individual cultivator preferences may also play a role in accounting for this variability.

Diachronic variability in the morphology of raised fields also occurs. Interestingly, diachronic variability in raised-field wavelength occurs in a consistent pattern: buried raised-field systems in the Tiwanaku hinterland possess a shorter wavelength than preserved, surface configurations. Erickson (1988a) has documented an identical pattern of surface raised-field complexes with long wavelengths superimposed on earlier, buried raised-field complexes with shorter wavelengths in the Department of Puno on the Peruvian side of Lake Titicaca.

The explanation for this consistent diachronic variation in field morphology throughout the Lake Titicaca basin is not immediately apparent. Potentially, the general pattern could be a response to changing environmental factors common to the entire lake basin. Specifically, long-term transformations in the basin's hydrological regime could be implicated. At present, however, we cannot discount alternative social factors that might account for this variability. For example, smaller wavelength fields might be the product of social formations of local rather than regional scope; if so, their occurrence in the Titicaca basin could be explained as an outcome of earlier pre-state social formations that did not mobilize labor on a regional scale. Similarly, changes in conceptions of land tenure or even technological innovation might account for this variation. Accounting for diachronic variation in raised-field morphology remains an important problem in Lake Titicaca basin archeology and agroecology.

## Results of Raised-Field Excavations at Lukurmata

The morphological and functional properties of high-altitude raised-field systems that are modeled later in this chapter are based in great part on data from our investigations at the Tiwanaku urban center of Lukurmata. Although we now realize that the raised fields in the immediate vicinity of Lukurmata are atypical of the majority of such field systems in the Catari basin, principally because of their greater internal structural complexity, our excavations in these fields are currently the most detailed and thoroughly analyzed. Moreover, continuing work demonstrates that the general structural principles we infer from the Lukurmata field excavations apply to such systems elsewhere.

The raised fields incorporated within the site boundaries of Lukurmata were built in a broad, crescent-shaped strip of land that lies between the civic-ceremonial district of the site (the acropolis) and the steep hill slopes that constitute the site's southern

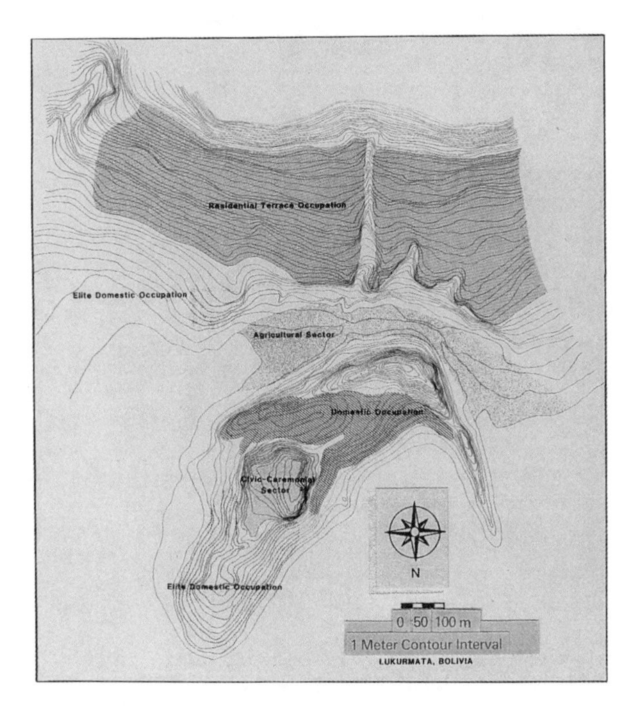


**Figure 5.9.** The civic-ceremonial, residential, and agricultural sectors at Lukurmata. Raised fields lie in the crescent-shaped strip of land between the civic-ceremonial district and the steep slopes of the residential terraces to the south.

boundary (fig. 5.9). This location was particularly appropriate for exploiting drainage from a quebrada cutting into the southern hill slopes of the settlement. This quebrada was artificially canalized in the Tiwanaku IV period through construction of stone revetment walls. We return to an analysis of this and other, similar hydrological features later in this chapter. These hill slopes are sources of fresh spring water that flows as groundwater northward into a topographic low on which the raised fields of Lukurmata were constructed. The groundwater ultimately discharges into Lake Titicaca itself.

The agricultural sector at Lukurmata is drained by an artificial canal that encircles the acropolis escarpment. Apart from its drainage function, this canal also acts as a moat cutting off easy access to the civic-ceremonial architecture that surmounts the escarpment (Kolata and Ponce 1992; Kolata 1993a). Water in the canal flows in two directions: to the east and to the west around the acropolis, which juts like a peninsula into Lake Titicaca. This unusual bifurcated drainage results from local topographic conditions in combination with directional flow from the canalized quebrada to the south of the canal. Flow from the quebrada was directed into a trapezoidal-shaped aqueduct constructed of earth, cobbles, and gravel fill faced by stone retaining walls. The linked canalized quebrada–aqueduct system discharged water into the surrounding canal in an easterly direction.

The strip of land dedicated to agricultural constructions encompassed approximately 65,000 square meters, or 6.5 hectares, of the site, representing approximately 3 percent of the total estimated settlement surface. This relatively small agricultural sector could not have supplied the entire subsistence requirements of a settlement as large as Lukurmata. The bulk of the population at Lukurmata must have derived its sustenance from fields outside of the site boundaries. The massive field systems in the adjoining Pampa Koani zone are the logical candidates for the source of this nonlocal production.

The raised-field system preserved on the surface at Lukurmata consists of two distinct hydrological units demarcated by the breakpoint, or point of bifurcation, in the flow of water into the canal, which defines the northernmost extension of the agricultural sector at the site. The surface fields and adjoining swales that constitute these two hydrological units are large, curvilinear constructions of soil, gravel, and clay that arc around the base of the acropolis for a distance of approximately 800 meters. The surface fields themselves are exceptionally large, forming cultivation platforms that average approximately 10 meters in width.

The adjacent swales are smaller, ranging from 3 to 5 meters in width. Two test trenches (operations 1 and 2) that were cut into these surface field constructions encountered distinct sets of stratigraphically separate (that is, vertically superimposed) buried raised or ridged fields representing repeated episodes of field construction. This superimposition confirmed that the area had formed part of an ancient landscape of long-term agricultural reclamation. These buried fields took several different forms. A summary of the internal structural characteristics of this raised-field system is essential to understanding the variables relating to field function that have been factored into our general model of raised-field functions in the Lake Titicaca basin.

## Test Trench 1: N2633–N2636 E2948

Buried raised-field surfaces were encountered in this trench at a depth of 60 centimeters below the local datum. There the soil changed from a dark brown fine sand to a dark grayish brown loamy clay. This darker, more organic material was mounded to form several

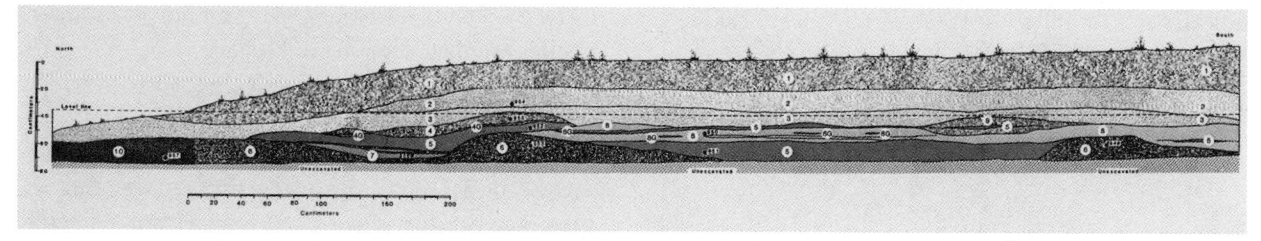

**Figure 5.10.** Stratigraphic profile of a Tiwanaku raised-field segment at Lukurmata (N2633 E2948 to N2636 E2948, after Kolata and Ortloff 1989:fig. 6). Strata key:

1. 10yr 3/3 dark brown loamy clay with some gravel; sticky when wet, friable when moist, and very hard when dry. Contains infrequent carbon fragments larger than flecks. This is the modern plow zone.
2. 10yr 4/3 brown loamy clay with some gravel and frequent white salt inclusions. Sticky when wet, friable when moist, and hard when dry. Contains infrequent carbon fragments.
3. 10yr 4/3 brown sandy clay with some gravel and frequent white salt inclusions. Sticky when wet and friable when moist. It appears to be quite similar to stratum 2, although it retains moisture in profile. Contains occasional carbon.
4. 10yr 4/4 dark yellowish brown medium sand with very little gravel. Not sticky when wet and not friable when moist. Seen at the north end of the trench only, it overlies raised fields and associated surfaces.
5. 10yr 4/4 dark yellowish brown loamy clay, which contains lighter secretions. Very sticky when wet and very friable when moist.
6. 10yr 4/2 dark grayish brown loamy clay with very little gravel. Very sticky when wet and very friable when moist. Contains carbon. This is an agricultural soil.
7. 10yr 3/3 dark brown clay with no gravel. Very sticky when wet and very friable when moist. Contains flecks of carbon.
8. 10yr 4/4 dark yellowish brown fine sand. Not sticky when wet, not friable when moist; contains some gravel.
9. 10yr 4/4 dark-yellowish brown sandy clay (very fine sand grains).
10. 10yr 3/2 very dark grayish brown loamy clay. Sticky when wet and friable when moist. This is a swale soil that is somewhat uniform but also shows some mottling.

agricultural beds (fig. 5.10, stratum 6). These beds were oriented in the same east-west direction as their counterparts on the surface, although they were substantially smaller in wavelength, approaching 4.5 meters when measured from adjacent centers-of-canals. The wavelengths of the surface fields taken from the same center-of-field points of reference ranged between 12 and 15 meters, or approximately three times that of the buried fields. The overall length of the buried field system was not determined, but as noted previously, the surface field constructions both at Lukurmata and on the adjacent Pampa Koani run for several hundred meters.

No diagnostic artifacts were encountered directly within this set of buried fields. However, diagnostic Tiwanaku IV and V ceramics were recovered from overlying soil contexts, indicating that these buried fields date minimally to that period. They may, of course, relate to an earlier phase. The conspicuous absence of post-Tiwanaku and Inca ceramics in these strata, and in the agricultural sector of the site as a whole, strengthens this hypothetical chronology. Furthermore, a minimal Tiwanaku IV–V date for these fields is consistent with the similar relative dating of the adjacent Pampa Koani field systems (Kolata 1986:754–55).

Two distinct buried field surfaces appeared in cross section in the trench profile (fig. 5.10), each roughly 20 centimeters in height from top of field surface to base of adjacent swale. This measurement, however, may not reflect the original height of the fields when they were in production, given the probability that processes of swale infilling and surface erosion were active throughout the life of the field system. The homogeneity of the soil matrix forming the agricultural beds indicates that they were the product of a single episode of field construction. The actual planting surface of the buried fields consisted of a loamy clay in which no microstratigraphy was apparent. The agricultural beds presented the appearance of a mixed matrix that was repeatedly disturbed, churned, and homogenized, perhaps through extensive use of a *chaquitaclla*-like implement, the characteristic Andean digging stick (see fig. 9.2, the tool identified by the Aymara term *huyso*), during episodes of field preparation and planting.

Microstratigraphy in the adjoining swales (fig. 5.10, strata 4G, 5, and 7) implies that this set of buried fields was in production for several years and that periodic maintenance in the form of field resurfacing and partial reconstruction was necessary. A layer of sand and gravel overlies these fields, indicating that an episode of flooding occurred soon after, or at the time of, field abandonment (fig. 5.10, strata 8 and 8G). Thin bands of microstratigraphy appeared clearly in this stratum in the form of water-sorted sands and fine gravel, with coarser material deposited at the bottom of the lens. This coarser material was more extensively deposited close to the edge of the adjacent swale, indicating that flooding in the channel with subsequent flow over adjoining field surfaces caused this characteristic pattern of waterborne sand and gravel deposition.

Abnormally high rainfall, possibly combined with an elevated lake level, may explain this depositional event. Such stratigraphic evidence of ancient flooding, if confirmed by collateral data drawn from the project's ongoing program of lake coring and from future field excavations, may provide essential insights into understanding the processes of localized raised-field burial and abandonment in the Lake Titicaca basin (see chapter 8 for an analysis of final abandonment processes).

## Test Trench 2: N2638 E2882

Two distinct types of buried fields were uncovered in this trench. The first type was similar to that encountered in test trench 1: noncomplex, homogeneous mounds of dark loamy clay forming agricultural beds (fig. 5.11, stratum 2). However, the soil forming these beds differed from that of trench 1 in color and texture: this loamy clay was yellowish brown and contained a greater admixture of fine sand. We believe these differences relate to minor variations in the distribution of soils in the agricultural sector at Lukurmata and that the general similarity between these two sets of buried fields in morphology, context, and structure indicates contemporaneity. Moreover, ceramic associations with this first type of buried field in test trench 2 support a conclusion of contemporaneity with the set of buried fields in trench 1.

### TYPE 1 BURIED FIELDS

This first type of buried field was uncovered in the southern end of test trench 2: units N2635 E2882 and N2638 E2882 on the Lukurmata grid map. The buried field was first encountered at 80 centimeters below local datum. Several Tiwanaku IV sherds were found in the base of the field itself, as well as in overlying strata. In particular, one fragment of a decorated, banded vessel bearing the distinctive, polished, deep red and black color scheme of the Tiwanaku IV period (ca. A.D. 400–800) was recovered from the base of the field. These ceramic associations suggest that the field structure dates to this period, although an earlier date cannot be discounted. No post-Tiwanaku or Inca sherds were encountered in this excavation or in the surrounding surface areas. Unfortunately, there was insufficient organic material in this field construction suitable for a radiocarbon assay.

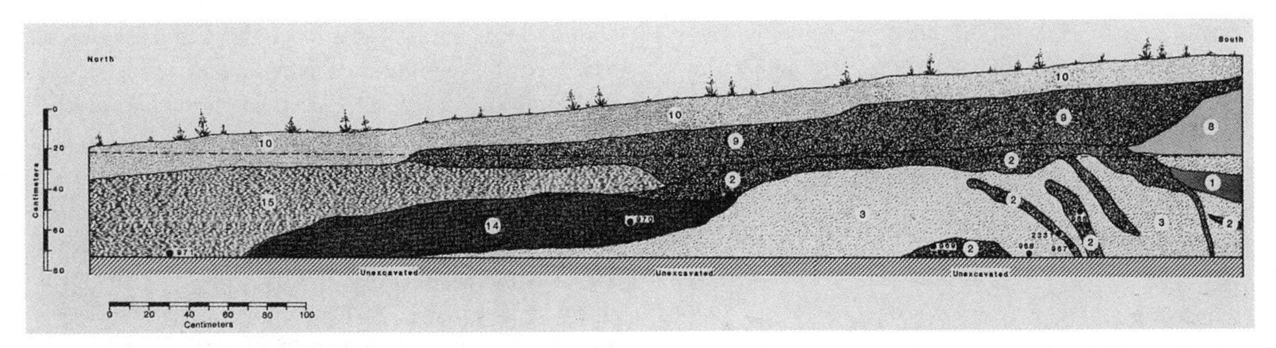


**Figure 5.11.** Stratigraphic profile of a Tiwanaku raised-field segment at Lukurmata (N2638 E2882, after Kolata and Ortloff 1989:fig. 7). This profile illustrates buried agricultural features including sequential field resurfacing (stratum 2). Strata key:

1. 10yr 3/3 dark brown loamy clay; sticky when wet, friable when moist.
2. 10yr 3/4 dark yellowish brown loamy clay; sticky when wet and friable when moist. Occasional carbon flecks.
3. 10yr 4/6 dark yellowish brown loamy clay; sticky when wet and friable when moist.
8. 10yr 4/6 dark yellowish brown sand with much gravel, many pebbles, and an occasional cobble; not sticky when wet, not friable when moist.
9. Same as stratum 2, with gravel and occasional small pebbles; also white (salt) concretions.
10. 10yr 3/3 dark brown loamy clay with gravel and occasional small pebbles; sticky when wet, friable when moist.
14. 10yr 3/6 dark yellowish brown fine sand with a mixture of clay, gravel, pebbles, and small cobbles.
15. 10yr 3/3 dark loamy clay with gravel inclusions.

This buried field was a simple mound of soil approximately 15–45 centimeters wide, oriented parallel to the modern drainage pattern in the same east-west direction as the surface raised fields. In profile, the field appeared roughly symmetrical in shape but with a steeper declination along its southern border (fig. 5.11). Several resurfacings of the original field occur in the profile, appearing as arcs of loamy clay that curve over the southern border of the field contour (fig. 5.11, stratum 2). Each of these arcs was separated from the previous one by a stratum of yellowish brown loamy clay identical to the field base (fig. 5.11, strata 2 and 3). The soil constituting the features that we interpret as sequential field resurfacings was darker in color, bearing a larger organic content, as might be expected from its intended function as planting surfaces rejuvenated by the recycling of nutrient-rich sediments.

At least five of these resurfacing features were identified in the profile, each capping the other. However, some of the arcs of organic soil were ephemeral and difficult to distinguish in the highly complex stratigraphy that characterizes these buried agricultural constructions. Accordingly, we cannot state with certainty that these five represent the entire sequence of resurfacing. Each of these features was approximately 5 centimeters thick, and each represents an eroded planting surface. Together they indicate that the field had multiple seasons of use with regular periods of maintenance and resurfacing.

It is difficult to estimate the intervals between successive resurfacings of the field, but the relatively substantial soil deposition between these features suggests that resurfacing was not an annual event. However, distinct periods of field resurfacing with presumptive replacement of organically rich nutrients from adjacent swales establish quite clearly that these fields were maintained and in production for a substantial period of time.

### TYPE 2 BURIED FIELDS

A second, strikingly different type of buried field was also encountered in test trench 2. This field was morphologically similar to the raised fields on the surface: both are characterized by massive planting platforms with a wavelength exceeding 10 meters. But the second type of buried field in trench 2 possessed a remarkably sophisticated, composite internal structure that was not found elsewhere in the agricultural sector at Lukurmata.

This second type of raised field was first encountered in the southern end of the trench in units N2635 E2882 and N2638 E2882 (fig. 5.11 ). It extended south and west, forming a more massive structure than any other we have yet described. Further excavations to the west in units N2635 E2878.5, N2635 E2877, and N2638 E2880.5 uncovered larger segments of this construction. Excavation of the field revealed a complex, precisely layered sequence of cobbles, clay, sorted gravels, and topsoil (fig. 5.12). The bottom stratum consisted of a packed, level layer of rounded cobbles that functioned as ballast, forming a massive, stable pediment or foundation for the field base. These cobbles apparently were transported to the construction site from the quebrada that cuts through the southern hill slopes of Lukurmata. The function of the pediment seems clear. Because the raised fields in the agricultural sector of Lukurmata were constructed in a topographic low, they would have required some form of stable foundation providing superior drainage properties to counteract the excessively marshy conditions of this area.

The architects of this field construction then laid down over the cobble pediment a layer of pure, dense clay of apparent lacustrine origin approximately 5 to 8 centimeters thick (fig. 5.12, stratum 13). The presumptive function of this clay stratum, which to our knowledge has never been described for any other raised-field construction in the New World, is of special interest. We hypothesize that it served to inhibit the percolation of slightly saline water from Lake Titicaca into the main body of the field structure. That is, the impermeable clay cap over the cobble pediment impeded the migration of salts upward into the crucial zone of root development in the field. Alternatively (or perhaps simultaneously), the clay stratum may have served as a microaquifer maintaining a thin, evenly distributed lens of freshwater at a stable level into which the root systems of the food crops could tap. The principal sources of freshwater in this vicinity lie in a series of permanent springs and seasonal streams originating in the mountain slopes to the south of Lukurmata. In effect, both seasonally flowing surface water and permanent groundwater percolating down from the heads of the mountain springs would have charged the microaquifer formed by the clay layer of the fields year round.

The clay stratum of the Lukurmata fields is unique; it does not occur in any other raised-field complexes that we have investigated in the Pampa Koani or Tiwanaku basins. It is unlikely that this feature was a

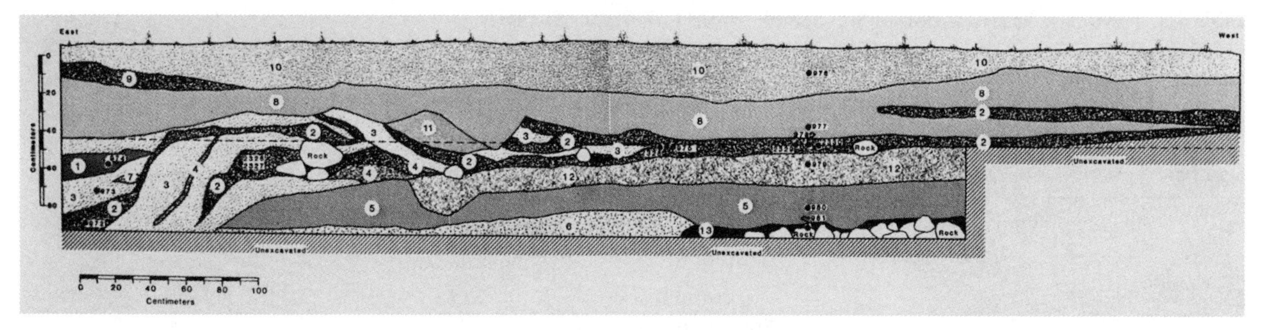


Figure 5.12. Stratigraphic profile of a Tiwanaku raised-field segment at Lukurmata (N2635 E2882 to N2635 E2877, after Kolata and Ortloff 1989:fig. 8). Strata key:

1. 10yr 3/3 dark brown loamy clay; sticky when wet, friable when moist.
2. 10yr 3/4 dark yellowish brown loamy clay; sticky when wet, friable when moist. Occasional carbon flecks. Stratum 2′ is the same as stratum 2 with mottling from stratum 3.
3. 10yr 4/6 dark yellowish brown loamy clay; sticky when wet, friable when moist.
4. 10yr 4/6 dark yellowish brown fine sand; not sticky when wet and not friable when moist.
5. 10yr 3/6 dark yellowish medium sand with gravel, pebbles, and occasional small cobbles; not sticky when wet, not friable when moist.
6. 10yr 3/4 dark yellowish brown (mottled) coarse sand with large gravel, pebbles, and cobbles; not sticky when wet, not friable when moist.
7. Gravel.
8. 10yr 4/6 dark yellowish brown sand with much gravel, pebbles, and occasional cobbles; not sticky when wet, not friable when moist.
9. Same as stratum 2, with gravel and occasional small pebbles; also white (salt) concretions.
10. 10yr 3/3 dark brown loamy clay with gravel and occasional small pebbles; sticky when wet, friable when moist.
11. 10yr 4/4 dark yellowish brown clay with a mixture of sand and gravel; slightly sticky when wet, friable when moist.
12. 10yr 4/6 dark yellowish brown sandy loam with pockets of sandy clay, coarse gravel, and occasional pebbles; stickiness and friability are variable.
13. 10yr 4/2 dark grayish brown clay with carbon flecks; very sticky when wet, very friable when moist.

common element of raised-field construction in the region. The urban setting of the Lukurmata raised fields suggests that the elaborate features they exhibit relate more to their special spatial and symbolic associations (Kolata and Ponce 1992:327–30; Kolata 1993a) than to their structural and functional roles.

Surmounting the clay stratum of this buried field were two layers of sorted gravels and sands and a final layer of topsoil that capped the entire field surface. The first layer of gravel immediately covering the clay stratum (fig. 5.12, stratum 5) was characterized by a mix of medium- to coarse-grained sands with relatively large pebble inclusions (ca. 1.0–1.5 centimeters in diameter). The second layer of gravel consisted of fine-grained sands and small pebble inclusions (less than 0.5 centimeter in diameter) with an admixture of sandy clay (fig. 5.12, stratum 12). These layers of carefully sorted sands and gravel, transported at the cost of substantial labor investment, clearly functioned to enhance drainage in the body of the field structure, thereby preventing supersaturation and subsequent crop damage.

The final stratum in this structure was the agricultural topsoil, which originally covered the entire domed surface contour of the buried field (fig. 5.11, stratum 2). This topsoil consisted of composite layers of loamy clay of a dark gray color reflecting a composition higher in organic matter than the deeper, structural strata of the field. We may reasonably infer that the immediate source of this topsoil was the rich, organic mud deposits extracted from adjacent swales. As might be expected, this original topsoil showed evidence of erosion, particularly toward the field borders that sloped down toward the adjacent swales. We assume that when this now-buried field was in production, the layer of agricultural topsoil was considerably thicker than its current average of approximately 10 centimeters.

Evidence for agricultural resurfacing of this buried field was also detected in cross section (fig. 5.12, strata 2 and 4). Multiple planting surfaces were documented in the western portion of the field and along its eastern periphery as it slopes down toward an adjacent swale. These soil layers—dark, yellowish brown loamy clays—were similar in color and texture to the resurfacing layers observed in other contexts already described. The resurfacing layers were also similar in thickness, roughly 8 centimeters, and were

Table 5.1. Phosphate Fractionation of Soil Samples from Lukurmata Fields

| Sample Number | Unit | Profile | Depth below Datum (cm) | Context and Stratum | P in ppm: Fractionation No. Ia | Ib | II | III | Total | Percent P Ia + Ib |
|---|---|---|---|---|---|---|---|---|---|---|
| 949 | N2633 E2948 | East | 73 | Agricultural soil Stratum 6 | 6.5 | 199.6 | 122.2 | 689.6 | 1017.9 | 20 |
| 953 | N2636 E2948 | East | 73 | Agricultural soil Stratum 6 | 9.9 | 113.0 | 94.6 | 451.2 | 668.7 | 18 |
| 954 | N2636 E2948 | East | 42 | Above field surface Stratum 2 | 2.6 | 69.1 | 142.9 | 355.6 | 570.2 | 13 |
| 956 | N2636 E2948 | East | 78 | Swale Stratum 7 | 5.5 | 77.9 | 164.7 | 388.0 | 636.1 | 13 |
| 957 | N2636 E2948 | East | 83 | Swale Stratum 10 | 8.1 | 84.7 | 115.1 | 391.2 | 599.9 | 16 |
| 966 | N2635 E2882 | East | 77 | Agricultural soil Stratum 2 | 4.9 | 180.1 | 124.6 | 459.7 | 769.3 | 24 |
| 967 | N2635 E2882 | East | 94 | Agricultural soil Stratum 2 | 4.4 | 182.3 | 188.6 | 482.1 | 857.4 | 22 |
| 969 | N2635 E2882 | East | 94 | Agricultural soil Stratum 2 | 3.5 | 208.6 | 162.8 | 461.1 | 836.0 | 25 |
| 975 | N2635 E2878.5 | South | 52 | Agricultural soil Stratum 2 | 6.4 | 35.2 | 72.5 | 321.6 | 435.7 | 10 |
| 978 | N2635 E2878.5 | South | 49 | Agricultural soil Stratum 2 | 3.9 | 204.4 | 251.9 | 605.4 | 1065.6 | 20 |

separated by a loamy clay of a lighter color. The exceptionally complex stratigraphy evident near the adjacent swale suggests that it was the source of material for the multiple resurfacings (fig. 5.12). Microstrata formed arclike patterns near the swale, but the tortuous intercalation of soil deposits at this point prevented us from following these arcing patterns out over the adjoining field surface. Still, the general implication of this stratigraphy is clear: soils from swales were periodically dug up and redistributed over field surfaces to provide a new, richly organic planting surface.

Chemical analysis of soil samples drawn from different contexts in the excavated raised fields, such as from swales, agricultural topsoils, and field construction fill, supports the interpretation that these sediments represent anthrosols, or human-altered soils (Eidt 1977). In particular, phosphate fractionations of selected soil samples from the Lukurmata fields exhibit high total phosphate values indicative of anthropogenic sediments (table 5.1). According to Eidt (personal communication 1987), these values are comparable to results of samples extracted from buried raised fields in Colombia that suggest a land-use pattern of long-term mixed residential and associated agricultural activities. Such a conclusion is consonant with the archaeological evidence for Tiwanaku IV–V settlement activities at Lukurmata.

Ceramics were found incorporated in the various layers of structured fill in this buried field (approximately 250 per square meter in a given level). The bulk of these sherds derived from undecorated utilitarian vessels. Roughly 10 percent, however, represented fragments from decorated ceramics, particularly *keros,* a high-status drinking vessel characteristic of Tiwanaku occupations. Preliminary analysis of these sherds indicates that the vessels had a red or orange-red slip and were painted in Tiwanaku IV color schemes and motifs. Of particular note was the modeled foot of a classic Tiwanaku IV puma *incensario,* or incense burner. This ceramic material indicates that the fill of the field structure was scraped up from surfaces bearing cultural deposits and artificially transported to the construction site. Furthermore, the diagnostic ceramics suggest a chronological association with the Tiwanaku IV period, although a later Tiwanaku V association cannot be discounted.

At some point in the history of agricultural reclamation at Lukurmata, the swales of this complex field structure were filled in and the old field surfaces covered over to provide the base for the overlying, surface raised-field system (fig. 5.12, strata 8 and 10). No natural deposits like the fine, water-sorted sands overlying the buried fields in test trench 1 were uncovered here. The lack of such natural waterborne or aeolian deposits on the surface of the type 2 buried fields in trench 2 indicates that (1) relatively little time elapsed between the cessation of production on this buried field and the period of reconstruction represented by development of the surface fields; (2) the episode of flooding that clearly affected the buried field system uncovered in trench 1 did not play a role in the history of this field system; and (3) therefore there is a high probability that the two types of buried fields uncovered in the test trenches represent temporally distinct phases of agricultural reclamation in the agricultural sector of Lukurmata.

During the pilot program of research that preceded Proyecto Wila Jawira, several test trenches were excavated across raised-field segments in the Lakaya sector of the Pampa Koani zone in order to determine their chronological context and cultural affiliation and to examine their technology of construction, modification, and use. Portions of this early research were summarized in Kolata (1986, 1991, 1993a). Diagnostic ceramics in the context of these agricultural structures were extremely rare. However, direct structural association between field segments and habitation mounds containing such diagnostics indicated chronological and cultural affiliations principally with the Tiwanaku IV and V periods (ca. A.D. 400–1100). The possibility of earlier Tiwanaku III (ca. A.D. 100–400) utilization of habitation mounds and raised-field segments was also raised by the initial work of the pilot program, but in the absence of clear, unambiguous ceramic associations this inference remains tentative (Kolata 1986:table 1). In general, the results of the initial work in Lakaya and our subsequent more detailed research at Lukurmata are consistent and present the opportunity to construct a general model of raised-field morphology and functions in the Lake Titicaca basin.

## Modeling Raised-Field Function[1]

The representative field systems excavated in the Lukurmata and Lakaya areas reveal significant diversity in terms of platform/swale geometry, orientation, and stratigraphy. Despite this diversity, typical patterns can be discerned and analyzed that relate field morphology and internal structure to specific function in the demanding environment of the Andean altiplano. To gauge the types of analysis that need to be performed and to understand the workings and efficiencies of raised-field systems, a number of factors need to be considered. These include (1) *salinization* by incursion of saline Lake Titicaca waters (either the lake level [temporarily] exceeds the local fresh water table height or the water table recedes because of drought conditions, leading to saline water intrusion); (2) *drainage* of (freshwater) saturated soils into raised-field swales when the lake level is below the local water table height; (3) *agricultural land area,* which depends upon the lake level (since the ground slope of lakeside land is low, a rise in lake level can reduce this area considerable); (4) *heat storage capability* of a raised-field system, and (5) *soil fertility* (which may decrease continually due to nutrient leaching, monocropping, and lack of replenishment of organic matter).

All of these parameters depend on the variability of the water level in Lake Titicaca. This level undergoes episodic and long-term fluctuations that are not cur-

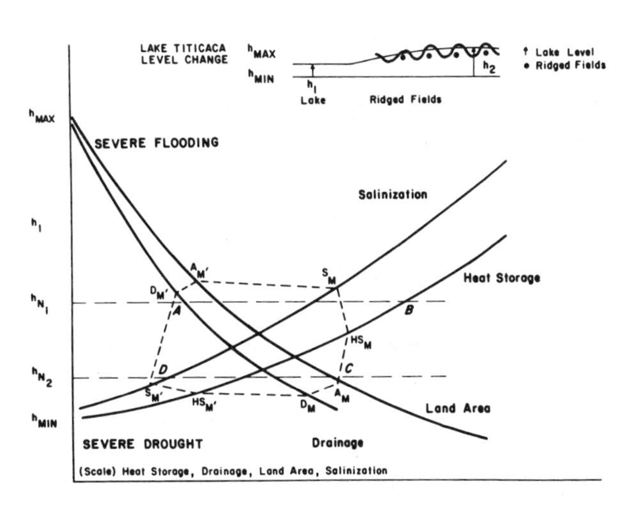


Figure 5.13. Theoretical survivability polygon for raised-field agricultural systems. The polygon represents a "normal operating range" for nearshore raised fields under the constraint of four physical parameters—heat storage, drainage, land area, and salinization—as they vary qualitatively with changes in lake level.

rently well understood, although they are potentially associated with global changes in climatic and precipitation patterns. The relationship between four of these five parameters—salinization, drainage, land area, and heat storage capability—and lake level, or $h_1$ measured from a given reference plane, is shown schematically in figure 5.13. In this figure, $h_{MIN} < h_1 < h_{MAX}$, where $h_{MIN}$ and $h_{MAX}$ represent maximum and minimum possible Lake Titicaca levels. The quantity $h_{MIN}$ represents the extended drought-period lake level, while $h_{MAX}$ represents the flood-condition lake level. The "normal" lake level fluctuation range is defined as $h_{N2} < h_{N1} < h_1$, where $h_{N2}$ and $h_{N1}$ represent the normal seasonal lake-level variation.

Other lake-level fluctuations may occur due to long- or short-term climate cycles involving varying amounts of rainfall to the altiplano drainage or watershed zone that channels groundwater and runoff into the lake. As lake level increases, salinization, which is a function of $(h_2 - h_1)^{-1}$, also increases (the quantity $h_2$ is defined as the average height of groundwater above a reference plane; fig. 5.13). This relationship reflects that fact that saturation by other than (fresh) groundwater is increasing as $(h_2 - h_1)$ decreases. Similarly, drainage of groundwater varies with $(h_2 - h_1)$: that is, the higher the groundwater level with respect to lake level, the greater the drainage capability of the raised field.

This factor greatly affects the start and finish times for the growing season. The arrival of maximum groundwater flow to field systems near the lake edge occurs past the peak of the rainy season because of the generally low flow velocities of groundwater deposited at remote locations in the collection basin of the lake. The (local) low ground permeability constants and flow pressure gradients are then the cause of the continuous arrival of groundwater to the lake edge, including significant groundwater flows during the dry season. Thus the swales can serve as channels to help drain platforms in dry (as well as wet) months provided $h_2 > h_1$. The swales present alternate drainage paths for saturated soils in the ridges. Water may flow either into the swales and then to the lake (provided $h_2 > h_1$) or through the aquifer to the lake. The residence time for water particles for the latter path is much greater than for the swale path, so the swale paths are more efficient drainage routes to the lake.

The land area available for agriculture is also dependent upon lake height. In cases in which the field platforms protrude above the lake level (for near-shoreline agriculture) and $h_1$ is approximately equal to $h_2$, then artificial mounding and/or buried impervious clay layers, such as that found in the field system at Lukurmata, may be used to regulate the relationship between platform surface and water table height to protect crop root systems from waterlogging.

The heat storage capability of field systems depends upon the saturation state of the raised-field soils. Heat storage from solar flux heat input plays the role of modulating diurnal ground temperature. As soil saturation increases as a function of groundwater height with respect to the field-system surface, the heat storage capability of the soil expands. Expansion of heat storage capacity enhances the survival of root crops during cold altiplano nights and determines an effective "end of growing season" because such effects limit ground freezing and concomitant destruction of root crops.

The degree to which these parameters are effective in determining the success of the agricultural system depends additionally on soil fertility. As soil fertility declines, we expect that crop tolerance for salinization, waterlogging, or decreased heat storage capacity will similarly decline. As the range of tolerance of crops to these conditions contracts, a new set of constraints affecting the type, sequence, and fallow periods of crops grown in given field segments will be established with a probable correlative reduction in plant productivity.

Based on the general effects of these five main parameters and their qualitative variation with lake level, a "normal operating range" of lakeside raised-field agriculture can be determined. If the normal height fluctuation of the lake is $h_{N2} < h_{N1} < h_1$, then a polygonal area A-B-C-D bounds the normal operating ranges of the four parameters shown in figure 5.13. Operation of the raised-field system within the values defined by A-B-C-D then ensures stable agricultural production. If the lake level $h_1$ approaches a high (maximum) level, then high salinization, low land area, and poor drainage considerations apply. Although high heat storage in field systems can result under these conditions, the waterlogging of the fields leads to shallow root systems for any crop. This effect occurs because root systems do not penetrate the water table but rather spread out above it. Waterlogging of shallow root systems creates biological conditions unfavorable to crop maturation and under these conditions will lead to decreases in crop yields. At low lake levels, low heat storage prevails while good drainage and low salinization accompany agriculture on a large, exposed land area.

To a certain degree, salinization (or incursion of lakeborne concentrants), heat storage, and distance from roots to water table surface can be regulated by artificial mounding and elevation of planting surfaces. Such control can be exercised if fill is available for transport or can be obtained from further swale dredging. Observations of field plots in the Pajchiri area indicate clearly that this strategy was applied, perhaps for selected crop types.

Further limits in land area may exist because of topographic constraints. The A-B-C-D "normal operating range" polygon may then effectively be replaced by a somewhat different polygon figure ($D_{M'}$, $A_{M'}$, $S_M$, $HS_M$, $A_M$, $D_M$, $HS_{M'}$, $S_{M'}$, $D_{M'}$) to delimit more realistic operating limits for successful agricultural production. The M subscript denotes the maximum tolerable operating limit of a particular parameter, and the M′ subscript denotes the minimum tolerable limit. As soil fertility decreases, $S_M$, $S_{M'}$, $HS_M$, and $HS_{M'}$ will contract inward along the given salinization and heat storage curves, respectively, and produce a "distorted" normal operating zone for successful raised-field agriculture. This "distorted" polygon may considerably limit crop types and growing season duration. More field-system area may have to be created to maintain the same total yield from less productive field systems as soil fertility decreases. Outside of the stability polygon, agricultural production is severely compromised.

## Heat Storage in High-Altitude Raised-Field Systems

One of the important parameters delimiting the successful operation of raised-field systems is heat storage capability. In order to analyze the effect of heat retention on crop survival under seasonal temperature variations, we developed a model to illustrate the physical phenomena involved (Kolata and Ortloff 1989).

With reference to figure 5.14, consider a one-dimensional unsteady heat conduction problem governed by the parabolic heat conduction equation. Variables and parameters are defined below the governing equation in figure 5.14. The solution to the partial differential equation can be written in analytic form in terms of the error function (erf) of argument $x/2\sqrt{Kt}$, where t is time, K is the thermal diffusivity, and $\times$ is the depth into a medium from its surface plane.

Suppose that the initial-boundary value problem to be solved is one of a medium initially at a temperature $T_o$ at $t = 0$ for $0 < X < \infty$; at $t > 0$, the $x = 0$ boundary is maintained at $T = 0$. The solution to the heat conduction problem then gives the ensuing $T(x, t)$ temperature distribution in the medium for $t \geq 0$, $0 < x < \infty$.

From standard tables of the error function (Abramowitz and Stegun 1964), $T = T_o/2$ at $x/2\sqrt{Kt} = 0.477$; the temperature in the medium has therefore dropped to half its initial temperature at a depth $x = x_1$ from the $x = 0$ top plane at a time equal to $t = K^{-1}(x_1/2[0.477])^2$. The mechanism for the temperature drop is the continuous heat flow from the interior of the medium to the constant low-temperature ($T = 0$) boundary at $x = 0$. From this solution, the time for a temperature reduction to $T_o/2$ at $x = x_1$ depends inversely on the thermal diffusivity, K. From the table of K values for different media given in figure 5.14, it can be seen that if the medium of heat conduction is air, then cooling at a depth of $x_1$ to $T_o/2$ takes place rapidly; that is, the thermal diffusivity for air is a large number, so the time to cool to $T_o/2$ is a small value. If the medium for heat conduction is wet sandy soil, the time to cool (at $x_1$) is considerably larger. If the medium is water, then time to cool to $T_o/2$ is about 133 times greater than if the medium is air. The thermal diffusivity thus regulates the heat storage and transfer capability of a given medium. The lower the thermal diffusivity value, the more heat storage effect occurs in a given medium.

Based upon these observations, given a soil medium (such as that found in raised-field systems), if heat can

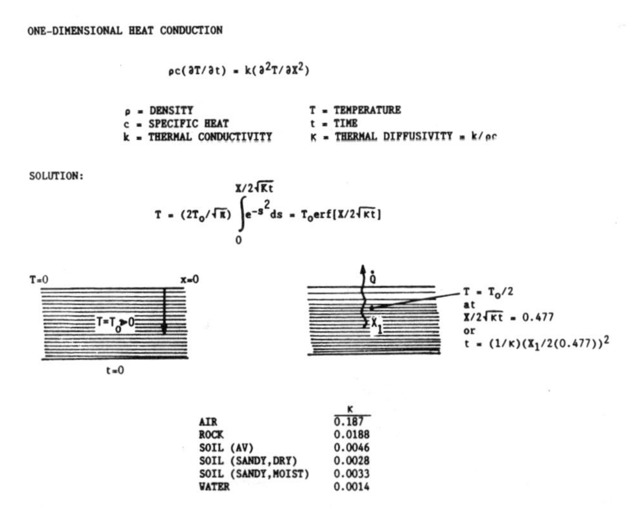


**Figure 5.14.** Heat conduction equation and solution with a table of thermal diffusivity values for raised-field systems (after Kolata and Ortloff 1989:fig. 10).

be absorbed internally by means of daily solar flux input, then the possibility for heat retention during cold nights is high. In other words, the time required for wet heated soil to cool is long, because its thermal diffusivity value is small. The heat retention capability of soils then acts as a protective enhancement to preserve root crops against cold (subfreezing) altiplano night temperatures that would ordinarily destroy crops. The presence of water in the swales of the raised-field systems further enhances the heat storage capability of the system. Because the thermal diffusivity of water is low, it will retain its heat for long periods and thus serve as a heat source for the adjacent field ridges during cold nights. By means of these heat transfer mechanisms, an extension of the growing season may be achieved, creating the possibility of double cropping of certain types of products or at least survival of the existing crops to further levels of maturity.

In order to study this heat retention effect in greater detail, the heat transfer model was increased in sophistication to more closely model actual Pampa Koani and Lukurmata raised-field systems. To this end, a finite element model (fig. 5.15) of an excavated raised-field profile (fig. 5.8) was constructed with matching geometry. Water was assumed to exist in the swales to a given height.

The finite element method is a numerical method used to solve more complex transient temperature distribution problems in a multiproperty medium (Gallagher 1975; Sagerlind 1976; Swanson and DeSalvo 1985; Zienkiewicz 1971). Effects of conduction, convection, and radiation are also included. In the model, a number of types of media are used. The raised-field depth profile (considered as a two-dimensional medium) is divided into saturated soils (below the height of the water in the swales) and soils above the swale water level, which are in the phreatic and vadose zones; that is, these soils have a lower water content than saturated soils. These phreatic- and vadose-region soils obtain their moisture through capillary action from subsurface groundwater. The air above the raised-field system, as well as a stone layer in the internal structure of the field, is also included in the model. This sort of stone construction has been found in some excavated profiles. Heat input is through solar flux into the soil and water surfaces. Heat loss from the soil and water surfaces occurs by means of radiation and free convection. Heat conduction occurs throughout the various soil types, the ambient air, and the water contained in the swales. The scale lengths used in figure 5.8 are the same as those in the finite element model (fig. 5.15) for consistency.

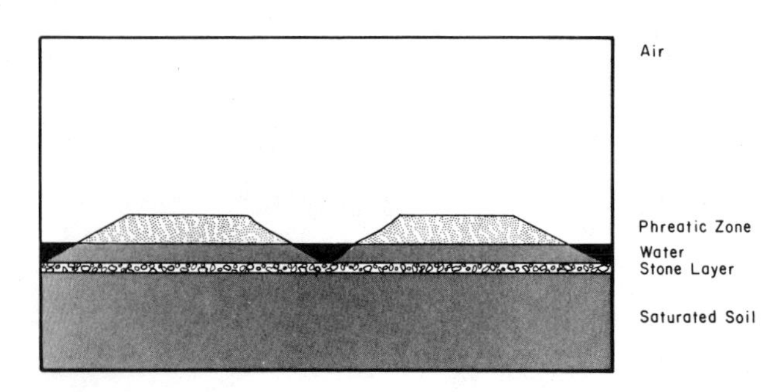


**Figure 5.15.** ANSYS finite element model based on empirically determined raised-field geometrics (after Kolata and Ortloff 1989:fig. 13).

We use the ANSYS finite element code (Swanson and DeSalvo 1985) to analyze the resulting heat flow problem in order to obtain transient soil temperature distributions. Time-averaged solar flux values as a function of month in the Bolivian altiplano are obtained from Duffie and Beckman (1974:34–37). Surface heat transfer coefficients for free convection as well as radiation and reradiation emissivities and related constants are estimated from Duffie and Beckman (1974), Kreith (1973), and Swanson and DeSalvo (1985). Because solar flux (BTU/sec-area) varies on an hourly basis in a 24-hour cycle, an ANSYS cosine distribution model of the input flux (fig. 5.16) was made to represent the diurnal solar flux variation. Similarly, the air temperature changes continuously on a 24-hour cycle. The input temperature values (in degrees Rankine) are represented in figure 5.17 and are used as input to the heat transfer problem. These temperature values are estimated from observations taken on a 24-hour basis in a typical altiplano winter month.

The finite element method for heat transfer problem solution starts with the Poisson equation with temperature as the dependent variable. This equation, in matrix form, is

$$[c]\{\dot{T}\} + [k]\{T\} = \{Q\}$$

where $[c]$ = specific heat matrix (including the appropriate mass effects), $[k]$ = thermal conductivity matrix (including equivalent face convection terms), $\{T\}$ = nodal temperature vector, and $\{Q\}$ = heat flow rate vector (including the applied heat flow, internal heat generation, and convection).

This equation is solved by an implicit direct integration scheme based on a modified Houbolt method (Swanson and DeSalvo 1985) and uses a quadratic

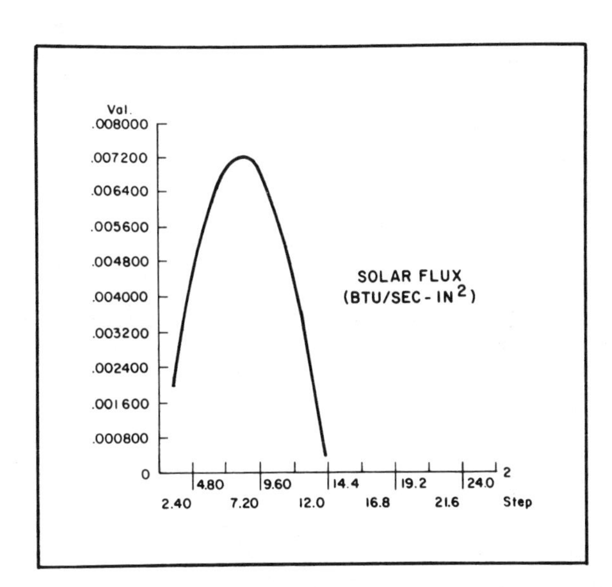


**Figure 5.16.** Graphic input for the solar heat flux diurnal cycle in the Pampa Koani zone (after Kolata and Ortloff 1989:fig. 11).

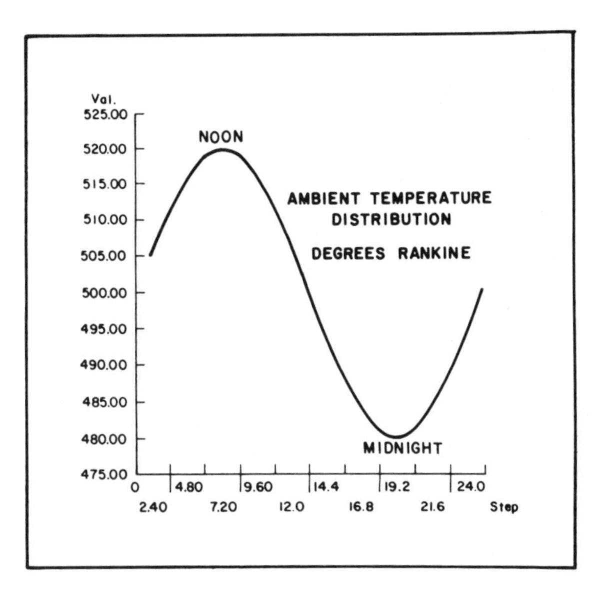


**Figure 5.17.** Diurnal air temperature variation in the Pampa Koani raised-field zone (after Kolata and Ortloff 1989:fig. 12).

temperature function $T_t = a + bt + ct^2$. This function is substituted into the governing equation to yield an equation in three (spatial) unknowns: a, b, and c. If $\Delta t$ is the step between iterations, a set of three equations may be defined at t, $t - \Delta t$, and $t - 2\Delta t$ and solved simultaneously to give the integration equation

$$(c_1/\Delta t[c] + [k])\{T_t\} = \{Q_t\} + f([c], \{T_{t-\Delta t}\}, \{T_{t-2\Delta t}\})$$

which may be solved for $T_t$ since solutions at previous times are known. For the present problem, the deep groundwater temperature is fixed at a given value on the lower boundary (fig. 5.15). A value of 50° F, determined by test measurements in the field, was utilized. The diurnal air temperature variations are prescribed as previously discussed.

Initially, typical raised-field material constants are set (density, specific heat, and conductivity) for the four material types. Additional constants are set for convection and radiation heat transfer loss terms at the raised-field and swale water surfaces. Time-dependent solar flux and air temperature are input and the heat transfer problem solved for $t > 0$. Results are in the form of temperature profile contours in the raised-field model at various times during the diurnal cycle.

Shown in figures 5.18 and 5.19 are typical temperature profiles in the raised-field system on the Pampa Koani at times during the day and night. Contour letters in the plots can be identified with the RHS temperature values. At a time corresponding to noon-to-early-afternoon, when solar flux and air temperature peak, the soil temperature exhibits maxima on the soil surface (fig. 5.18). As solar flux and air temperature decrease toward late afternoon and early evening, surface soil temperature decreases while internal soil temperatures remain high, owing to the low thermal diffusivity of the soil and water compared to the adjacent air elements.

Toward evening and night (fig. 5.19), the temperature maximum is clearly internal—in the soil platforms—while the outer soil layers experience temperature minima. The presence of groundwater at a near-uniform temperature above that of the ambient air effectively serves to direct heat flows upward at night, decreasing slightly the heat storage effect of the high-thermal-diffusivity soils.

During the day, the low groundwater temperature ensures a thermal gradient, thereby improving the input heat transfer. Although the groundwater temperature is low, it is still higher than ambient air temperature at night. This thermal differential leads to an upward heat flow. The presence of the swale water is also effective in maintaining higher-than-ambient-air temperatures in the interiors of the field platforms. The zone of interest for root crops is that between soil surface and water height in the swales (one or two finite element heights from the ridgetop surface). Observation of the temperatures below the surface then indicates the diurnal temperature variation of the soil containing the root crops.

Clearly, the heat storage effect efficiently maintains

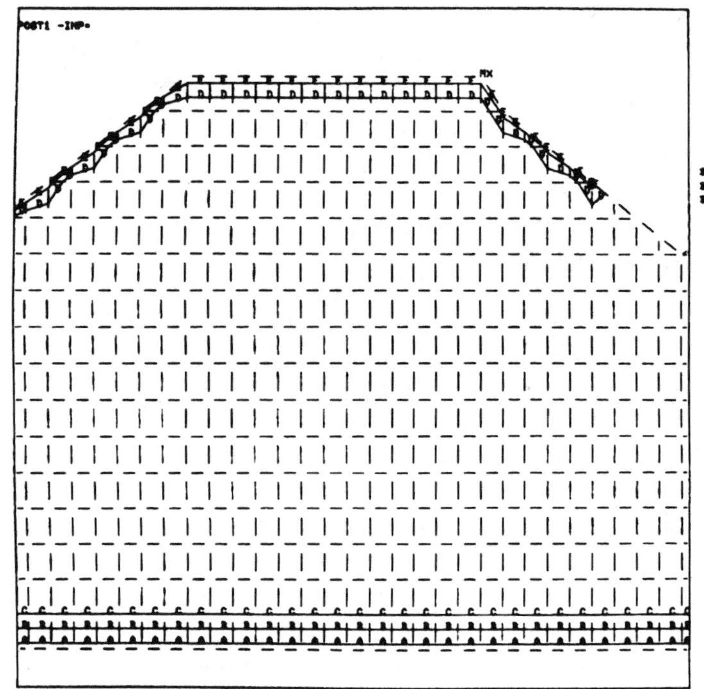


**Figure 5.18.** Raised-field soil temperature profile modeled in the late morning (after Kolata and Ortloff 1989:fig. 14). MX denotes maximum values; MN denotes minimum values.

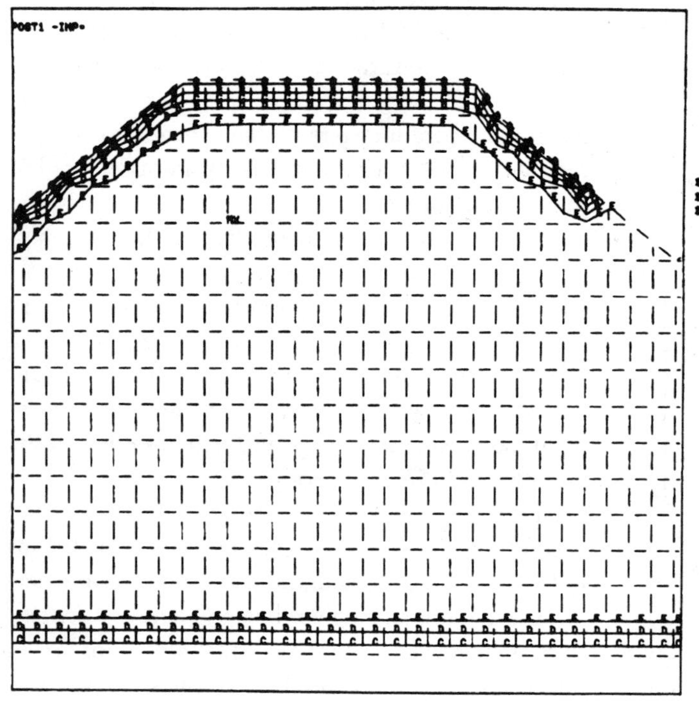


**Figure 5.19.** Raised-field soil temperature profile modeled in the late evening (after Kolata and Ortloff 1989:fig. 15). MX denotes maximum values; MN denotes minimum values.

internal soil temperatures warmer than air temperature, with the consequence of preventing or ameliorating root damage during subfreezing altiplano nights. Although only a few degrees Rankine separate internal from external temperatures during the night, this difference is instrumental in keeping the internal ground temperature above the freezing limit at depths where root systems exist. Because freezing temperatures are encountered in the interiors of the raised fields, a certain amount of time is required to extract the latent heat of solidification from the soils (and root crops) before total freezing destroys the crop.

The presence of this auxiliary heat storage capability is therefore important to root crop survival. The freezing of plant parts at the soil surface level is likewise delayed by the heat absorption effect, which helps keep these temperatures slightly higher than ambient air temperature. It should also be noted that native aquatic macrophytes such as *Myriophyllum-Elodea, Potamogeton, Ruppia,* and *Schoenoplectus totora* were most likely dredged from the swales between field platforms and used as green manure to replenish macronutrients (nitrogen, phosphorus, potassium) in the soil (see chapter 7). The decomposition of this plant material, if mixed into the soil, may have generated a further source of heat during the planting season.

The calculations presented here are for typical air temperatures, solar fluxes, and soil material constant values as found in the Pampa Koani area for given field geometrical patterns. Although these field-system patterns change locally on the pampa with respect to the sun's path (and exhibit different orientations and thus different received flux values), the results presented here are nonetheless typical of qualitative trends in heat storage capability of raised-field systems. Soil temperature values may change in time with different soil types, ground cover, solar flux, and air temperature levels, as well as with diurnal wind speed changes over the fields. The qualitative trends discussed here, however, are expected to apply in a general sense.

Field measurements were made for air, swale water, and ground temperature at various times during the diurnal cycle to check the qualitative predictions of the theory. Generally, the heat storage effect was confirmed. The model assumed that absorption, reflection, and transmittance radiation properties were those of clear water. However, the presence of darker organic material in the swales provided a further solar radiation trap that yielded higher swale water temperatures than predicted by the model. It was observed, for example, that actual swale water temperature could exceed ambient air temperature by as much as 15–20° F during peak solar flux times. The presence of this augmented thermal effect through higher (than predicted) swale water temperatures clearly enhances the heat storage capability of raised-field agricultural systems. In combination with higher vadose-zone ground temperatures, this effect provides an additional source of heat storage for raised-field agricultural systems in high altitude environments.

The intensification of agricultural production through reclamation of seasonally or periodically inundated land in the Titicaca basin represented a prime economic strategy of the Tiwanaku state. The technology of land reclamation entailed construction of massive raised-field systems in the nearshore environment of Lake Titicaca. These raised fields were linked to sources of freshwater by near-surface groundwater flow and by spring-fed, open-channel aqueduct and canalized quebrada delivery networks. ANSYS finite element modeling of the thermal properties of excavated Tiwanaku raised fields, utilizing empirically established field geometries, internal structure, and hydrological conditions, indicates that heat conservation was an essential design element of these agricultural features.

Although the general hypothesis of frost mitigation in high-altitude (Brookfield 1961; Denevan 1970; Erickson 1985; Wadell 1972) and middle-latitude (Riley and Freimuth 1979; Riley, Moffat, and Friemuth 1980) raised-field systems has been suggested previously, the ANSYS finite element model presented here represents the first formal consideration of specific heat storage pathways and potentials in these systems.

Striking experimental confirmation of the heat conservation effects described here was obtained during the 1987–88 growing season in the Lakaya sector of the Pampa Koani. A 1.5-hectare plot of land with well-preserved Tiwanaku raised fields was reconstructed by local Aymara communities between August and September 1987 and planted in a variety of indigenous crops (principally potatoes) and introduced crops. No commercial fertilizers were applied to the experimentally rehabilitated fields, and cultivation and weeding proceeded in a traditional manner. On the nights of February 28 and 29, 1988, the Bolivian altiplano in the Pampa Koani region suffered a killing frost, with temperatures in the Lakaya sector dropping to –5° C in some areas. Substantial zones of potato and quinoa cultivation on plains and hill slopes along the southern rim of Lake Titicaca were severely damaged by this heavy frost. Many traditional potato fields within a few hundred meters of the experimental plots experienced crop losses as high as 70–90 percent. In contrast, losses in the experimental raised field of Lakaya I were limited to superficial frost lesions on the leaves of potato plants. Barley, broad beans, quinoa, *kañiwa,* onions, and lettuce were equally unaffected. Only 10 experimentally placed maize plants were lost in this hard freeze.

We attribute this differential in plant survival to the heat storage benefits of the saturated raised fields. Subsequently, several 100-square-meter test plots of potatoes in the reconstructed raised fields in Lakaya were harvested, with average yields ranging from 18 to 33 metric tons per hectare. This yield contrasts with an average potato harvest of 3 to 8 metric tons per hectare obtained from traditional, shallow-furrow dry farming techniques practiced in the area (MACA 1985). Although this differential between traditional and experimental raised-field systems may be attributed partly to the fact that the experimental fields were reconstructed in areas not intensively cultivated for over 800 years, where one might expect higher-than-average yields, the radically different impact of subfreezing air temperatures on these two forms of cultivation must play a significant explanatory role (see chapter 9 for an extended consideration of yields on experimentally rehabilitated raised fields).

Empirical evidence supporting the heat conservation hypothesis continues to emerge on rehabilitated raised fields in our study area. Frosts have significantly affected crop production in the area, at both highly localized and regional scales, in every agricultural cycle since 1987. Major frosts in 1990 and 1991 resulted in a similar experience of differential crop survival on raised fields versus control plots on hill slopes, cultivated by shallow-furrow dry farming. Experiments explicitly directed toward testing the thermal properties of ridged fields in middle-latitude, temperate geographical zones in the United States (central Illinois) by Riley and colleagues (Riley and Freimuth 1979; Riley, Moffat, and Freimuth 1980) tend to confirm this hypothesis, even though the suggested pathways of frost mitigation in their experiment differ from those proposed here. Long-term experimental research in reconstructed raised-field systems at high altitudes will be required for confirmation and more highly resolved quantification of the heat storage capacity of these systems. We anticipate that our continuing experimental crop production and environmental analyses on the rehabilitated fields in the southern Lake Titicaca basin will contribute to verification and quantitative refinement of the model of the thermal properties of these systems presented here.

## Hydraulic Infrastructures of Tiwanaku Raised-Field Systems[2]

During the 1987–91 field seasons, a series of hydraulic structures associated with Tiwanaku raised-field systems became a major focus of analysis. Among these hydraulic features were aqueducts, artificial riverbed diversions and canalizations, river shunts, articulated networks of drainage canals, and water impoundment and retention structures such as dikes, causeways, and qochas. Six aqueducts were documented in Tiwanaku urban environments during the 1987 season—four at Pajchiri and two at Lukurmata. Since that time, additional aqueducts have been recognized at the site of Chiripa during its Tiwanaku phases (Graffam 1990), as well as aqueduct/dikes associated with several rural settlements in the valley of Tiwanaku (Albarracín-Jordan 1992; Mathews 1992).

The aqueducts at Lukurmata and Pajchiri, the first surface-water transport structures to be definitely associated with Tiwanaku urban sites, are linked to adjacent raised-field complexes. Therefore, our initial hypothesis regarding their function was that they were designed to irrigate agricultural field systems in the urban environment. However, detailed analyses of local hydrological conditions and of aqueduct design suggested a second hypothesis: the hydraulic structures were intended primarily to reduce the infiltration of surface water into the groundwater reservoir and to mitigate the impact of landscape erosion and mass sediment transport on the urban environment. These two hypotheses, one reflecting a distributive function and the other an extractive function for the aqueducts, are not necessarily mutually exclusive.

In addition to the aqueducts, we identified a number of other hydraulic control features in the Tiwanaku hinterland related directly to the management and optimization of raised-field systems. Artificial riverbed diversions and canalizations, river shunts, articulated networks of drainage canals used in both irrigation and extraction strategies, and water impoundment and retention structures such as dikes and causeways were all important elements in the repertoire of Tiwanaku agricultural engineering. Furthermore, qochas (or *kkotas/kkotanas,* as they are known in Aymara) were an important system of water management that may have represented an alternative, or a complement, to intensive raised-field cultivation in the Tiwanaku state. Qochas, which are still constructed and maintained today, are essentially artificial wetlands created by excavating surface sediments to the water table or by diverting freshwater spring flows to natural or artificially created depressions (Flores Ochoa 1983). We will consider each of these elements of Tiwanaku's hydraulic infrastructure in turn. Some of them have been studied more intensively than others, and the following analyses are necessarily uneven in scope and detail. Nevertheless, these analyses do afford a comprehensive overview of the nature and function of agricultural infrastructures in the Tiwanaku hinterland.

Local hydrological conditions in the Catari sub-basin heavily influence contemporary land use and have important implications for the interpretation of the pre-Hispanic agricultural landscape. The elevated local water table characteristic of the marshy pampas zone in the Catari sub-basin results from the interaction of several geological and climatic features. There are two principal aquifers in this sub-basin: one confined in the Tertiary sandstones of the mountainous Taraco Formation, and a second one beneath the Quaternary sediments of the pampas zone. The Tertiary aquifer is recharged by seasonal precipitation. The Quaternary aquifer has several sources of recharge: (1) direct seasonal precipitation; (2) permanent subterranean groundwater seepage from the higher Tertiary aquifer; (3) permanent surface flow from the springs in the adjacent mountain slopes, particularly from the Tertiary Taraco Formation to the south; (4) torrential surface flow driven by rainy-season downpours on the relatively impermeable adjacent mountain slopes; and (5) deep seepage from surface rivers and streams that cross the pampas. Remnants of ancient lake-bed terraces and multiple meander scars from rivers and streams are distinguishing geomorphological features of the Catari pampas zone. Large alluvial fans spread out from the distal ends of numerous quebradas that punctuate the mountain ranges on both the north and south sides of the Catari drainage. Seasonal water flow in these quebradas, driven by sustained downpours during the altiplano rainy season (December–March), transports enormous quantities of heterogeneous erosional products ranging from fine-grained sediments and small clasts to cobbles and boulders of substantial size.

Given the five significant vectors of freshwater recharge just described, along with the geological characteristics of the Catari sub-basin and the climatic cycle with its marked alternation between dry and wet seasons, it is not surprising that the pampas zone is perennially marshy and subject to seasonal inundation. Throughout the year, the merging of low-gradient aquifer and ground surfaces creates pools of standing water. These pools gradually diminish through evapotranspiration during the height of the dry season (June–September), leaving behind thick alkaline crusts.

In this context of perennial high groundwater conditions, without constructed drainage systems the environment is profoundly debilitating for agricultural production. Waterlogging of plant root systems is predictably coupled with surface deposition of soluble salts induced by high evapotranspiration rates of standing water. Efficient intensive agricultural production in this environment requires artificial drainage that will maintain a locally regulated groundwater table (see Darch 1983 for a summary of research on drained-field agriculture in the Americas). We have hypothesized elsewhere that raised fields were built originally to raise the critical rooting zone of cultivars out of saturated soils (Kolata and Ortloff 1989). Raised fields, by elevating planting surfaces, represent one technological response to the problem of drainage and the regulation of relative groundwater level. Aqueducts and major drainage canals that reduce the input of subterranean and surface water into local aquifers by directing flows away from the reclamation zones represent a second technique for maintaining appropriate groundwater levels.

The two aqueducts definitely identified at Lukurmata share important structural and design characteristics. Their key construction features can be appreciated through the detailed archaeological analysis of one of them (figs. 5.20–5.24). The entire drainage system entailed construction or modification of two linked, spatially contiguous components: an upper channel formed by an artificially modified natural quebrada, and a lower channel consisting of a constructed, elevated aqueduct that provided passage for water over an open field for eventual discharge into the moat encircling the base of the civic-ceremonial precinct at Lukurmata (fig. 5.20). The upper channel was stabilized by modifying the irregular natural sides of the quebrada through a cut-and-fill operation and then re-facing the new vertical channel walls with roughly cut stone revetments (fig. 5.21). As might be expected, only the walls of the channel were artificially stabilized; the quebrada floor was left unmodified. It is important to note that major residential terraces at Lukurmata are built up to the edge of the modified quebrada and that subsidiary drainage canals from these domestic areas discharged excess water into it (see fig. 5.9). However, the principal source of water flowing into the modified quebrada was seasonal precipitation that accumulated in a collection basin of at least 1 square kilometer to the southwest of Lukurmata proper (fig. 5.20).

The modified quebrada articulated with the completely artificial lower channel (the aqueduct itself) at

Figure 5.20. Aerial photograph of Lukurmata with the canalized quebrada indicated.

a point near the modern road that bisects the site. A good portion of this critical articulation point is obscured by the fill of the modern roadbed, and excavation to clarify the structural features of this articulation is not feasible. The aqueduct is trapezoidal in shape, consisting of parallel external walls made of river cobbles laid without mortar that were designed to retain an internal unconsolidated structural fill of river cobbles, earth, gravel, and sand (figs. 5.22, 5.23, 5.24). Tiwanaku ceramics incorporated in this construction fill suggests a general chronological placement of the structure in the Tiwanaku IV–V phases (ca. A.D. 400–1100), a date consistent with that of an associated, structurally compatible raised-field complex for which we have one calibrated AMS radiocarbon date of A.D. 950 ± 100 (ETH-3178).

The external walls of the aqueduct are cobble-lined throughout its entire length, but only the east wall,

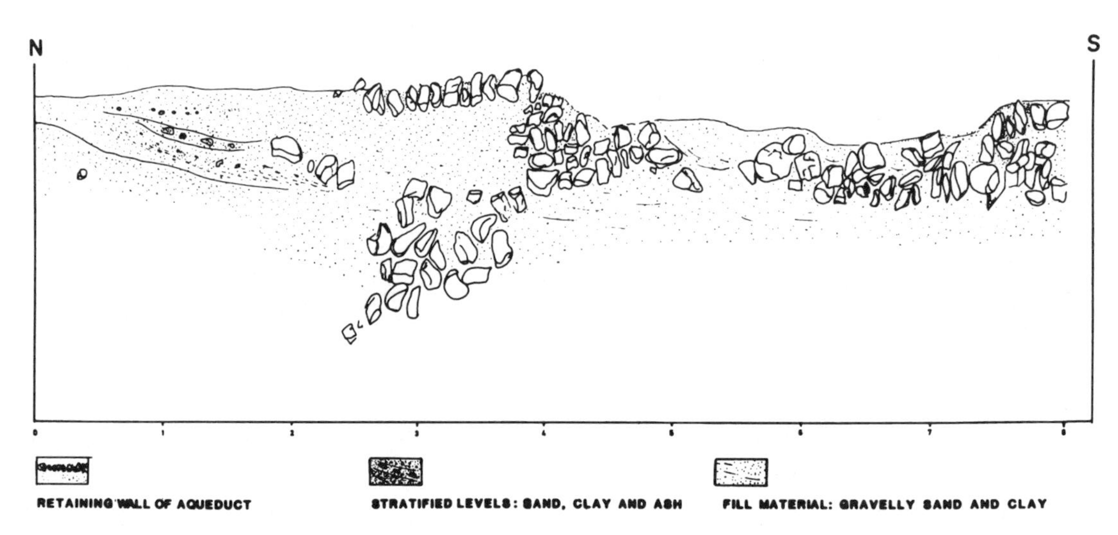


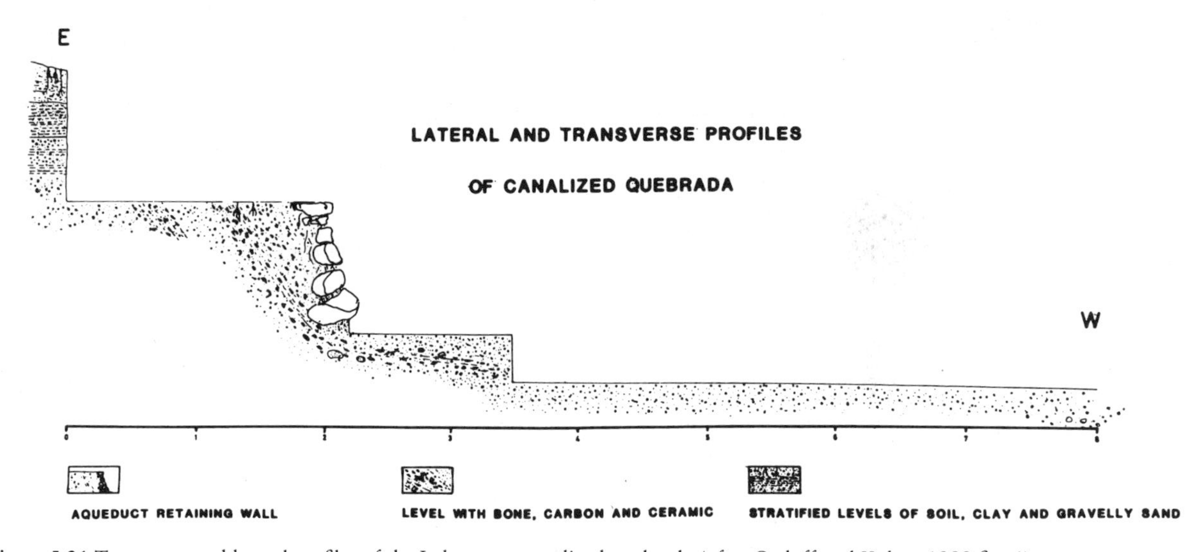


Figure 5.21 Transverse and lateral profiles of the Lukurmata canalized quebrada (after Ortloff and Kolata 1989:fig. 4).

**Figure 5.22.** Aerial view of the east wall of the Lukurmata aqueduct.

with a bonded corner that structurally joins the aqueduct orthogonally with a massive terrace retaining wall, remains in a good state of preservation (fig. 5.24). Excavations on the west edge of the aqueduct revealed fragments of the foundation stones for the parallel retaining wall, but the remaining portions of this wall were apparently destroyed by repeated erosional events. This distal end of the aqueduct curves toward the northeast to discharge into a large drainage canal (the Lukurmata moat illustrated in fig. 5.25) that in turn flows into Lake Titicaca.

Because the flow rate of water through the aqueduct/canalized quebrada system depended upon fluctuating intensity of rainfall runoff, the engineers of this ancient aqueduct did not construct a standard, internally lined channel of a given shape and cross-sectional area. Instead, precipitation runoff was apparently directed onto the surface of the fill and permitted to cut a natural erosional channel. If the channel was carved out during an event of near-maximum flow rate, it would be sufficient to contain the current of all lesser flows. Although this technique of channel creation is unusual, it nevertheless represents a viable method for accommodating input flows that varied considerably in magnitude and duration. In theory, the eroded shape will be a stable, minimum-resistance profile for a given flow rate and specific energy. An excavated cross section of the aqueduct illustrates a sequence of such eroded, minimum-resistance channels in the construction fill (fig. 5.26). The reconstructed hydraulic characteristics of these internal aqueduct channels are analyzed in the next section.

## Hydraulic Analysis of the Lukurmata Aqueduct

Throughout the following discussion, which draws on a formal analysis of the Lukurmata aqueduct, we utilize concepts and analytical techniques developed in

**Figure 5.23.** Detail of the basal construction of the Lukurmata aqueduct.

**Figure 5.24.** The cobblestone exterior retaining wall of the Lukurmata aqueduct.

**Figure 5.25.** A view of the civic-ceremonial sector at Lukurmata on the shores of Lake Titicaca. The Lukurmata aqueduct discharges into the moat, which in turn flows into Lake Titicaca.

association with the modern theory of hydraulics of open channel flows. It should be noted, however, that many of the same results can be obtained by observation and documentation of empirical results from multiple controlled tests. Indeed, many complex contemporary problems in open channel flow are amenable to treatment only by controlled tests because analytical solution techniques are not yet available. In this respect, hydraulics from ancient to modern times have much in common.

BASIC HYDRAULIC CONCEPTS AND DEFINITIONS

Several parameters govern flow through a canal: bed slope ($\Theta_b$), channel wall slopes ($\Theta_r$, $\Theta_l$), base width (B), and channel wall roughness (n, the Manning roughness coefficient). In addition, there are three flow classifications. *Critical* flow is the velocity at which a fluid flows through a given conduit exhibiting streamwise free surface excursion instabilities. *Subcritical* flow is the case in which flow through the conduit creates generalized upstream influence on flow characteristics, and *supercritical* flow is the case in which flow through the conduit has no observable upstream influence. A localized instability zone in a conduit such as the Lukurmata aqueduct indicates a point of transition between supercritical and subcritical flow. This zone of transition, characterized by a downstream increase in flow depth and a decrease in flow velocity, is termed a hydraulic jump. Changes in

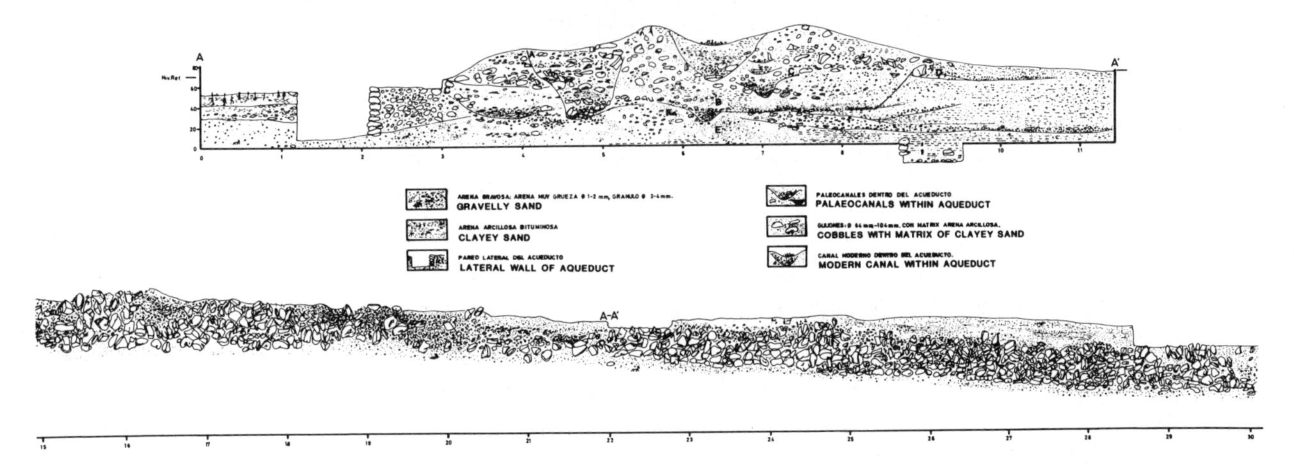


**Figure 5.26.** Lateral and transverse profiles of a 15-meter section of the Lukurmata aqueduct (after Ortloff and Kolata 1989:fig. 8).

the cross-sectional area of a conduit that create a choked supercritical flow may generate a hydraulic jump.

To determine whether subcritical or supercritical flow exists in a channel, one must compute the theoretical normal depth ($D_N$) and the critical depth ($D_C$) based on channel cross-sectional geometry (Henderson 1966). The theoretical normal depth is defined as the hydraulic depth at which uniform flow exists in a channel and is obtained by solution of the Manning equation for depth given a known flow rate, incorporating the bed slope for the head loss term. If $D_N > D_C$, then subcritical flow exists on moderate slopes; if $D_N < D_C$, then supercritical flow exists on steep slopes. In the case of subcritical flow, the Froude number, F, is less than 1 where $F = V/(gD)^{1/2}$. In this equation, V represents mean water velocity, *g*, the gravitational constant, and D, the hydraulic depth. In cases of supercritical flow, $F > 1$. Finally, for the special case in which $D_N = D_C$, denoted as *critical flow,* $F = 1$. Maintaining the Froude number close to unity, or theoretical normal depth close to critical depth, results in a maximum flow rate for a given intake-to-outlet height difference for a fixed channel area (Henderson 1966).

#### FORMAL HYDRAULIC ANALYSIS

For purposes of analysis, the Lukurmata aqueduct/canalized quebrada may be idealized into a series of trapezoidal cross sections along the streamwise length. In this idealized geometry, it is assumed that smooth transitions join successive trapezoids and that average section properties are used in flow computations. For each local section characterized by such a trapezoid, a bottom width B, sidewall slopes $\Theta_r$ and $\Theta_l$, and a bed slope $\Theta_b$ can be measured, together with the streamwise distance between measurement stations, $\Delta S$. Results of these measurements for the Lukurmata systems are given in table 5.2. The first measure, for station Q′, was taken at a point in the upper reaches of the channel in the canalized quebrada; subsequent stations were measured in the downstream direction.

The principal and secondary eroded channel profiles in the aqueduct can be seen in the excavated cross section of the aqueduct in figure 5.26 and in abstracted form in the upper right corner of figure 5.27. These profiles are slightly asymmetrical due to fluid rotation induced by channel sinuosity upstream of the entrance region of the aqueduct. The rotation direction of the fluid is illustrated facing upstream. Stratigraphically, the profile segment designated A-B in figure 5.26 is reasonably distinct, while the segment from B to D represents the remnants of an earlier channel that has been in-filled. A small pocket of gravel, E, probably represents an erosional sub-cut induced by a later low flow rate passing through the D-E-C channel.

The aqueduct fill material is composed of gravels, clays, and mixtures of cobbles of various dimensions, as is indicated in figure 5.26. The Manning roughness coefficient (n) is estimated to be 0.030 for aqueduct internal channel walls and 0.025 for modified quebrada walls of the upper channel (Chow 1959). Assuming noncohesive, unconsolidated fill material and erosive behavior over the entire wetted perimeter of the channel, existing theories of hydraulics can be em-

Table 5.2. Structural and Hydraulic Characteristics of the Lukurmata Aqueduct

| Station | B (m) | $\Theta_r$ | $\Theta_l$ | $\Theta_b$ | $\Delta S$ (m) | $D_N$ (m) | $D_C$ (m) | F | Profile Type | h (m) |
|---|---|---|---|---|---|---|---|---|---|---|
| Q′ | 5.0 | 15°11′ | 30°15′ | 4°48′ | 9.42 | 0.19 | 0.35 | 1.0 | S-2 | 0.19 |
| P | 4.7 | 17°32′ | 18°10′ | 4°12′ | 23.0 | 0.18 | 0.37 | 2.5 | S-2 | 0.18 |
| O | 4.7 | 17°32′ | 18°10′ | 4°10′ | 29.8 | 0.18 | 0.37 | 2.5 | S-2 | 0.18 |
| M | 4.7 | 17°32′ | 18°10′ | 4°46′ | 29.7 | 0.17 | 0.37 | 2.7 | S-2 | 0.17 |
| N | 7.6 | 11°30′ | 9°49′ | 4°46′ | 29.7 | 0.13 | 0.27 | 2.8 | S-2 | 0.13 |
| M′ | 4.0 | 18°50′ | 8°54′ | 3°03′ | 14.0 | 0.18 | 0.44 | 2.7 | S-3 | 0.18 |
| L | 4.3 | 10°35′ | 9°13′ | 5°20′ | 30.0 | 0.17 | 0.43 | 2.8 | S-2 | 0.17 |
| K | 8.3 | 17°07′ | 31°36′ | 4°02′ | 21.0 | 0.13 | 0.24 | 2.4 | S-2 | 0.13 |
| J | 8.3 | 17°07′ | 31°36′ | 5°37′ | 3.8 | 0.12 | 0.24 | 2.4 | S-2 | 0.13 |
| I | 7.2 | 15°47′ | 19°52′ | 5°37′ | 30.0 | 0.13 | 0.27 | 3.0 | S-3 | 0.12 |
| H | 16.0 | 13°16′ | 9°18′ | 5°03′ | 16.0 | 0.08 | 0.16 | 3.7 | S-2 | 0.12 |
| G | 5.5 | 9°56′ | 5°24′ | 3°36′ | 30.0 | 0.16 | 0.37 | 2.6 | S-3 | 0.15 |
| F | 13.7 | 17°03′ | 7°54′ | 5°40′ | 30.0 | 0.09 | 0.50 | 2.6 | S-2 | 0.09 |
| E | 1.8 | 9°56′ | 4°20′ | 5°37′ | 30.0 | 0.22 | 0.95 | 6.0 | S-3 | 0.12 |
| D | 1.8 | 9°56′ | 4°20′ | 5°37′ | 5.0 | 0.22 | 0.95 | 2.9 | S-3 | 0.22 |
| D′ | | | | 4°17′ | 40.8 | | | | | 1.01 |
| B | 4.06 | 10° | 80° | 2°24′ | 6.0 | 1.05 | 2.16 | | S-2 | 0.87 |

Note: B = Base width (m), $\Theta_r$, $\Theta_l$ = right and left channel sidewall slopes, $\Theta_b$ = bed slope, $\Delta S$ = streamwise distance (m), $D_N$ = normal depth (m), $D_C$ = critical depth (m), F = Froude number, h = water height at the end of the section (m).

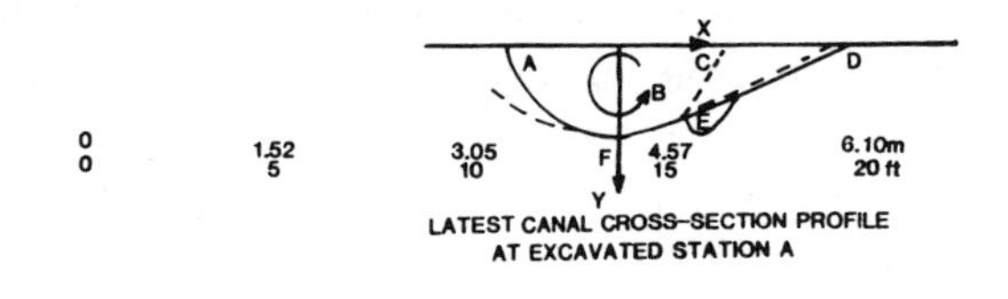


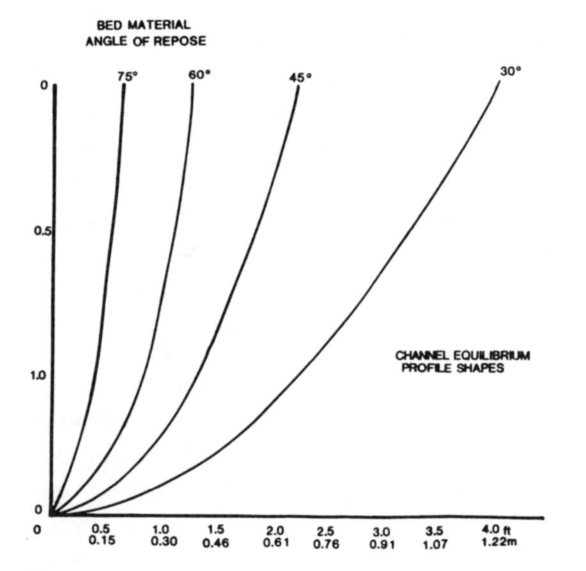


Figure 5.27. Upper right: Schematic cross-sectional profile of the Lukurmata aqueduct. Lower left: Channel equilibrium profile shapes of the Lukurmata aqueduct. (After Ortloff and Kolata 1989:fig. 9.)

ployed to predict the shape of the erodible section and to compare this prediction to the observed geometries. It should be noted that the erodible channel section, for a given angle of repose of fill material and a given discharge, yields a channel of minimum water area, minimum top width, maximum mean water velocity, and minimum excavation.

From assumptions stated in Chow (1959), then, the differential flow equation

$$(dy/dx)^2 + (y/y_0)^2 \tan^2\Theta = \tan^2\Theta \qquad (1)$$

is derived for the erodible cross-sectional shape where $y = y_0$ at $x = 0$ (the channel center; fig. 5.27), $\Theta$ is the angle of repose for fill material, and the $y = f(x)$ solution represents the stable channel shape. A solution of equation (1) yields equation (2),

$$y = y_0 \cos\left[(\tan\Theta/y_0)(x)\right] \qquad (2)$$

which is plotted in figure 5.27 for various repose angles. Observing a repose angle of about 30–40° for excavated wet fill, the computed erodible profile is comparable in channel shape to the Lukurmata aqueduct segment A-F in figure 5.27.

Of course, larger flow rates would carve out larger

channels, and several remnant earlier channels of greater size can be observed below the latest one illustrated in figures 5.26 and 5.27. This sequence of eroded channel profiles of varying geometries suggests the possibility of a sequence of heavy precipitation episodes in the past. For cases of large flow rate events, given stone-packed lower bedding, sidewall erosion leads naturally to wide, flat-bottomed profiles similar to those observed below the A-F-C channel in figure 5.27 (compare also the actual profile in fig. 5.26). The erosion profile sequence of the observed aqueduct channels is discussed in more detail later.

In order to gain insight into the design purpose of the Lukurmata aqueduct, hydraulic calculations were made to assess the functioning of the system. Starting from point Q′ at the uppermost reach of the drainage channel, a critical flow point is assumed together with a typical estimated flow rate of 108.5 cubic feet per second. This value is arrived at from estimates of flow at the base of the drainage channel observed during the height of an average rainy season. Independent of the critical flow assumption at Q′, the flow will soon accelerate to a supercritical flow regime due to the steep slopes ($\Theta_b$ generally $> 4°$) of the drainage channel (table 5.4). Normal and critical flow heights are calculated for each measurement station listed in table 5.2 (Chow 1959; Henderson 1966; Morris and Wiggert 1972; Pashkov and Dolgachev 1977).

For skewed trapezoidal-shaped approximations of the channel cross sections in table 5.2, channel area (A), wetted perimeter (P), hydraulic radius ($R_h$), hydraulic depth (D), and section factor (Z′) are given by the following equations:

$$A = By + (y^2/2)(Z_R + Z_L) \quad (3)$$
$$P = B + y[(1 + Z^2_R)^{1/2} + (1 + Z^2_L)^{1/2}] \quad (4)$$
$$R_h = A/P \quad (5)$$
$$D = [By + (y^2/2)(Z_R + Z_L)]/[B + y(Z_R + Z_L)] \quad (6)$$
$$Z' = [By + (y^2/2)(Z_R + Z_L)]^{3/2}/[B + y(Z_R + Z_L)]^{1/2} \quad (7)$$

where $Z_R = \text{ctn}\,\Theta_R$, $Z_L = \text{ctn}\,\Theta_L$, and y is the water height from the base of the trapezoid. Critical depth is determined from a solution for $D_C$ from

$$Q = \sqrt{g}Z' \quad (8)$$

while normal depth $D_N$ is determined from the Manning equation for a given flow rate (Q) and local bed slope (Chow 1959; Henderson 1966; Morris and Wiggert 1972; Pashkov and Dolgachev 1977). Because the flow is supercritical throughout, calculations can be performed in a downstream stepwise manner starting from the critical section. The Manning equation, in English units, is given by

$$Q = (1.49/n)(R_h^{2/3})AS^{1/2}$$

where Q = VA and V is the average velocity in a cross section. From Morris and Wiggert (1972),

$$\Delta R = \int_{h_i}^{h_j} \frac{(1 - Q^2B/gA^3_m)dD}{i_b - (nQ/1.49R_{h,m}{}^{2/3}A_m)^2} \quad (9)$$

where integration is over y from substitution of equations (3)–(6) in (9). Here, dD = (dD/dy)dy. Integration is performed numerically for ΔR, the stream length increment.

In the equation, Q is the channel flow rate and $i_b$ the local bed slope. The i, j subscripts on h denote a y height increment over which the integration is carried out to produce a streamwise length increment, ΔR. The quantity *g* represents the gravitational constant of 32.2 feet per second squared. For rectangular cross-section canals, D = Y. The m subscript represents a mean value of parameters between integration limits.

Calculations produce details of the flow profile and velocity in the drainage canals. Results from the measured stations on the Lukurmata drainage system summarized in table 5.2 indicate that the flow height of a given station approaches the local value of normal depth $D_N$ for each adjacent station. As is typical for supercritical flows on steep slopes, the normal depth asymptote is approached rapidly at each measurement station. As is indicated in table 5.2, the local Froude number ranges between 2.5 and 3.7 in the upper channel, while the Froude number at station D, the entrance region to the aqueduct, is 2.9. Flow depth at D is equal to the normal depth (0.73 feet) at the aqueduct entrance region. Thus, the channel flow upstream of the aqueduct makes smooth transitions in depth between stations, close to the local normal depth and locally uniform throughout its length. The upper drainage channel, then, efficiently transports water such that locally the fluid surface is parallel to the channel bottom. A check of the Vedernikov number (Chow 1959) produces values less than unity, indicating flow stability on the steeply sloped upper channel.

The purpose of these computations is to determine typical flow conditions at the entrance region to the lower aqueduct. The design of this hydraulic structure offers the deepest insights into the expertise of Tiwanaku engineers and the nature of the problems they perceived in attempting to contain seasonal flows in the drainage channels of the Lukurmata environment. Since the aqueduct channel is erodible, the first calculations are designed to determine whether the flow in the lower aqueduct is still uniform and supercritical for the parabolic channel sections shown in figure 5.27. To this end, the foregoing equations are employed, and the result is given in table 5.2.

The principal problem with respect to the hydraulic characteristics of the lower aqueduct is to determine whether the geometry and structural features of this channel generate a hydraulic jump or support a smooth transitional supercritical flow. If a hydraulic jump developed at the juncture of the upper and lower channels, then severe erosion would have (periodically) destroyed the aqueduct fill. To answer this question, figures 5.28–5.31 were constructed utilizing modern hydraulic theory (Chow 1959).

On plots of flow rate versus lower aqueduct slope, the critical slope line demarcates the presence of critical flow. Assuming a rectangular canal cross section, a channel with a slope of 0.015 supporting a flow rate of 26 cubic feet per second with a flow depth of Y = 1 foot would then be subcritical for a bottom channel width of B = 5 feet. A slope greater than 0.020 would support a supercritical flow. For a subcritical flow on the lower aqueduct, a hydraulic jump *must* occur to

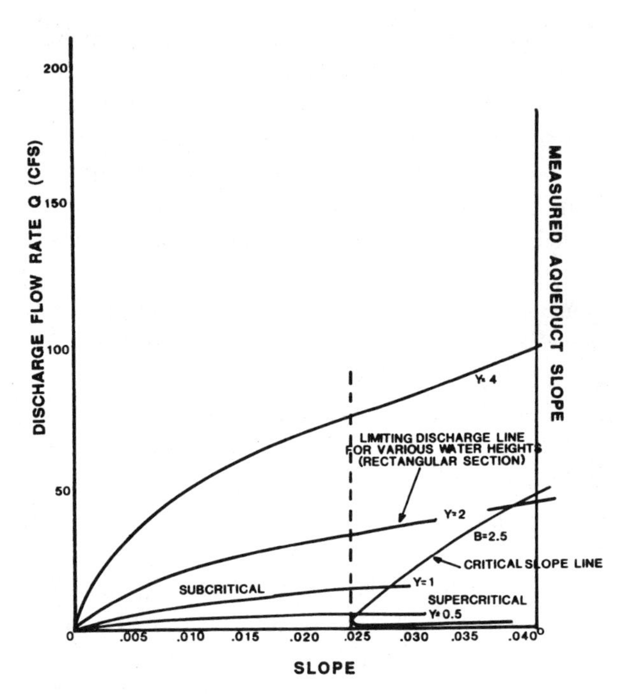


**Figure 5.29.** Critical slope line for a channel width (B) of 2.5 feet and varying flow depths (Y) for the Tiwanaku-period aqueduct at Lukurmata. Note that flow depth and channel width are measured in English units rather than in metric units here and in figures 5.30 and 5.31.

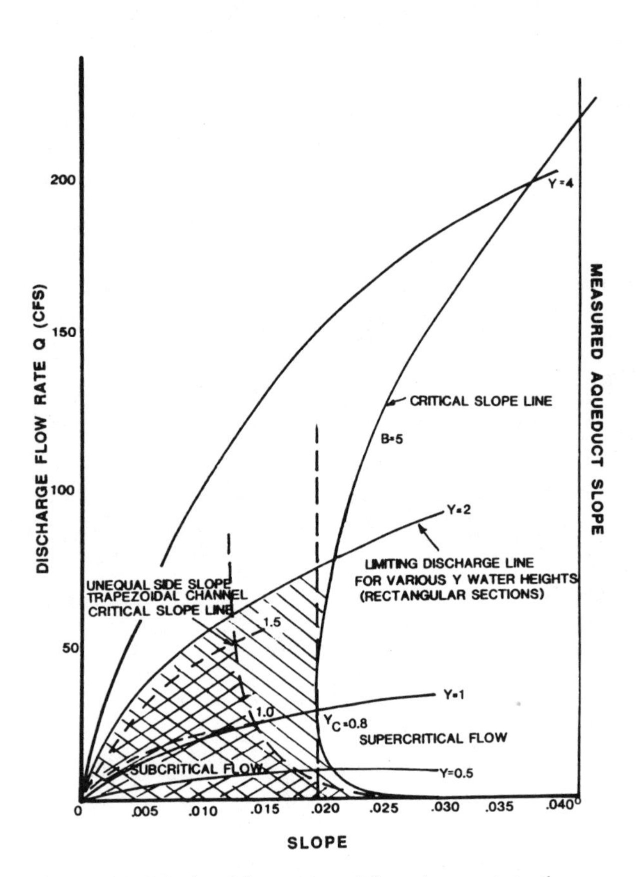


**Figure 5.28.** Calculated flow rates and flow characteristics for various channel slopes for the Lukurmata aqueduct (after Ortloff and Kolata 1989:fig. 10).

shift the upper channel supercritical flow to subcritical flow. Since the measured aqueduct slope is 0.043, it can be concluded that the lower aqueduct supports a supercritical flow for the class of channel widths B = 5 feet. Continuation of the search for possible subcritical flows among the classes of eroded profiles characterized by a bottom width of B = 2.5 feet (fig. 5.29), B = 10 feet (fig. 5.30), and B = 15 feet (fig. 5.31) for a range of possible Y flow depths that the aqueduct could support reveals that subcritical flow does not exist on the lower aqueduct at the measured slope of 0.043.

A calculation made for a nonrectangular channel cross section (fig. 5.28) reveals that the rectangular cross-section calculations are conservative with respect to slopes at which the critical flowline exists. Therefore, over a variety of eroded channel bottom widths, flow depths, and flow rates, the lower aqueduct *always* supported a supercritical flow. Accordingly, for a wide class of eroded profile shapes, there exists a smooth supercritical transition from the exit normal depth on the upper channel to a higher normal depth on the lower aqueduct. The value of this depth can be obtained by solving the Manning equation for given Q, n, and B' for any eroded profile shown in figure 5.27.

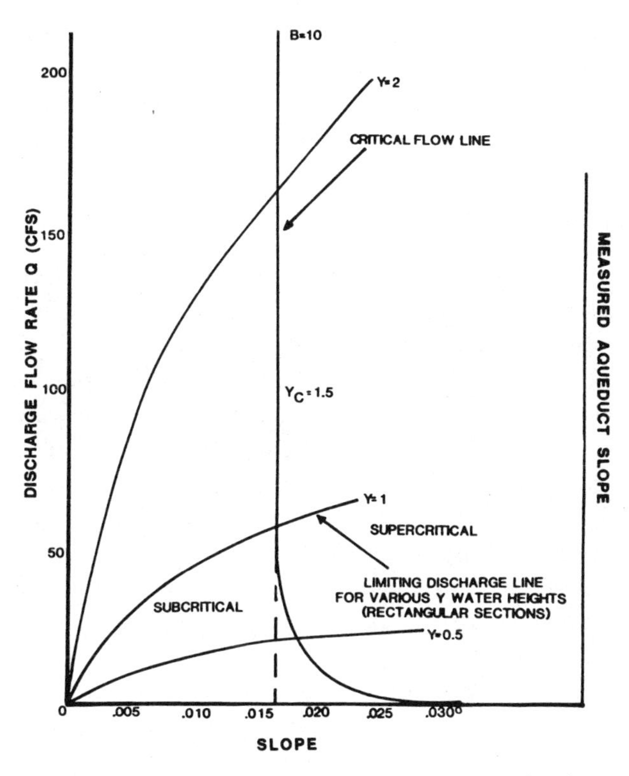


**Figure 5.30.** Critical slope line for a channel width (B) of 10 feet and varying flow depths (Y) for the Tiwanaku-period aqueduct at Lukurmata.

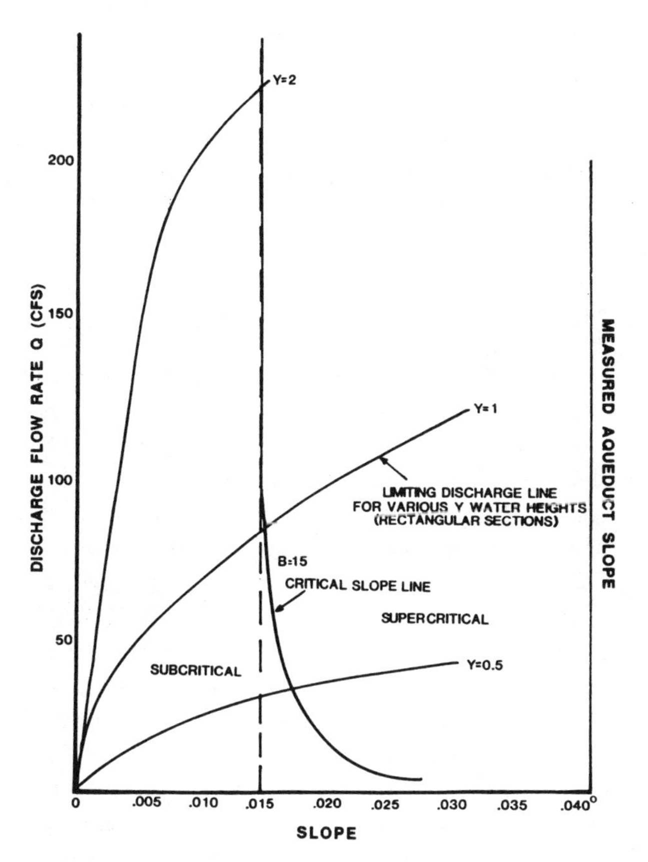


**Figure 5.31.** Critical slope line for a channel width (B) of 15 feet and varying flow depths (Y) for the Tiwanaku-period aqueduct at Lukurmata.

Past station A, the aqueduct curves smoothly to the northeast while maintaining its full structural width. By characteristic methods, the supercritical turning of the flow and height change can be determined (Chow 1959; Henderson 1966; Morris and Wiggert 1972). However, the key problem here is the effect of the backwater height on aqueduct flow. This height is essentially the current lake level, which is known to vary considerably in historical times. The lake level has fluctuated as much as 5 meters within a two-year period (Carmouze and Aquize Jaen 1981). For the case in which lake level is high and intersects the supercritical aqueduct flow, serious erosion problems potentially destructive to the structural integrity of the aqueduct could be generated by the development of a highly turbulent hydraulic jump.

Referring to table 5.2 and figures 5.28 and 5.32a, the supercritical flow on the aqueduct approaches the normal depth line $D_N$ on an S-2 profile (see Chow 1959 for a discussion of these profiles). If the backwater height is below $D_N$, then no upstream effect is induced in the supercritical flow. If the backwater level is high (b‴), however, then a hydraulic jump (HJ) will occur on the aqueduct, leading to erosion of the unconsolidated, unlined canal fill in the vicinity of the jump's water height increase. For instance, for the reconstructed hydraulic characteristics of the lower portions of the aqueduct in which F = 2 and the bed slope of the channel = 0.043, the hydraulic jump height can approach three times that of the pre-jump height. As the backwater height increases, the hydraulic jump can migrate up the aqueduct, causing additional damage to the structure through turbulent fluid action in the erodible channel fill. Moreover, in this situation of high backwater levels, we would expect that the already unconsolidated structural fill would

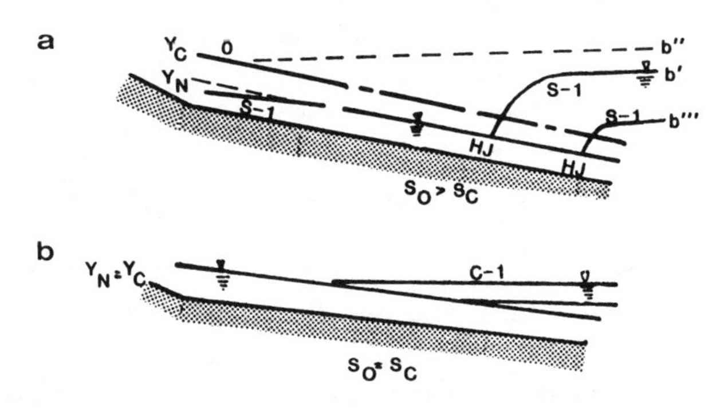


**Figure 5.32.** *a,* Lower aqueduct supercritical flow at Lukurmata with varying backwater heights. *b,* Neutralizing reach. $Y_N$ = normal depth; $Y_C$ = critical depth; S = slope; HJ = hydraulic jump; $S_C$ = critical slope; $S_O$ = actual slope. (After Ortloff and Kolata 1989:fig. 11.)

be further compromised by the wetting action of the intersecting lake level. The merging of aqueduct flow and lake backwater will destroy the local fill region by the action of unsteady, turbulent mixing within the hydraulic jump.

As the backwater height further increases (fig. 5.32a), the theoretical limit 0-b″ on an S1 curve (Chow 1959) is reached, and the aqueduct is submerged. The geometry of the curved, distal portion of the Lukurmata aqueduct raises the height of the flow slightly over the normal depth through Froude wave interaction, while slightly decreasing the supercritical velocity. Here the effect of backwater height change is to produce an intermediate step-up in fluid height before the hydraulic jump adjustment to the backwater height described previously. This effect limits the erosional potential of the hydraulic jump on the lower reaches of the aqueduct and suggests that the Tiwanaku engineers may have incorporated this curved section of the aqueduct into their design to mitigate structural deterioration.

Another solution to the problem of potentially destructive hydraulic jumps on the lower reaches of an aqueduct is to construct a neutralizing reach (Bakhmeteff 1932; Chow 1959). This entails establishing the aqueduct bed slope equal to the critical slope, thereby causing backwater levels to approximate horizontal lines (C-1 profiles) that intersect the surface of the flow without causing turbulence (fig. 5.32b). This solution is equivalent to a hydraulic jump of zero height. The curve for the trapezoidal section critical slope ($S_c$) is found from selection of Y values in equation (8) to produce Q (or discharge rate of flow) values. The Q and Y values are then substituted into the Manning equation to determine $S_c$ values. This method is used to determine $S_c$ curves in figures 5.29–31.

For the A-F-D channel (fig. 5.27), the intersection of the critical slope line with a flow height of Y = 2 feet occurs at a critical slope of approximately 0.02 (fig. 5.28). This critical slope is well below the measured aqueduct bed slope of 0.043, and therefore no neutralizing reach was possible for the A-F-D parabolic channel as a preventive measure against canal erosion during conditions of high rainfall and high lake levels intersecting the lower reaches of the aqueduct.

Incomplete remains of earlier erosional channels appear below the A-F-D channel (see the cross section illustrated in fig. 5.26). Many of these channel remnants are partially destroyed by later erosional and filling events. Consequently, no secure time sequence of channel configurations can be readily discerned. It is clear, however, that a sequence of wide-base, parabolic channels characterized by high rates of flow are intercalated with low-flow-rate incised channels.

Calculations based on rectangular canal sections have been made for a variety of base widths (B = 2.5 feet, 5 feet, 10 feet, and 15 feet) in figures 5.29–5.31 that show the critical slope line for different possible water depths in the channel. For all cases in which B > 5 feet, a neutralizing reach is impossible for the assumed flow rate. The limiting discharge line is calculated from the Manning equation using $S_c$ and a given depth. The flow is still supercritical for these cases, and hydraulic jump phenomena can still be expected to have occurred in the lower reaches of the aqueduct channel under conditions in which elevated backwater height intersected the lower reaches of the aqueduct.

Interestingly, for hypothesized massive channel flow rates generated by torrential rainfall events, there are some possibilities of neutralizing reach conditions for channels in which B < 5 feet, if this base width can be maintained. For example, for B = 2.5 feet and Y = 2 feet (fig. 5.29), the point of intersection of the two curves lies close to the measured aqueduct bed slope of 0.043. This indicates that the channel can function as a neutralizing reach for this set of flow rate, base width, and water depth conditions, thereby eliminating an on-aqueduct hydraulic jump for any backwater depth.

The basic problem encountered in the aqueduct design is that the input flow rate, which depends fundamentally on precipitation intensity and duration, varies radically from event to event. Therefore, a single, standard-design channel cannot be built to perform transport tasks efficiently for a wide range of input flow rates. In this hydrological context, the erodible channel technique evident in the Lukurmata aqueduct serves design purposes well because it carves out the "necessary" channel to support a given flow rate, maintains a nearly uniform flow throughout, and, under inundation conditions when the lake level is high, can function as a neutralizing reach to eliminate on-aqueduct hydraulic jumps near the exit region of the aqueduct. The presence of several deep, flat-bottomed channel profiles with base widths in the range of 5–10 feet in the Lukurmata aqueduct suggests massive rainfall events in the early history of this hydraulic structure. The lower flow rate events are more likely to produce "permissible" velocities (Henderson 1966) and achieve the equilibrium parabolic profiles illustrated in fig. 5.27.

## Hydraulic Analysis of the Pajchiri Aqueduct

To gain further insight into the design of Tiwanaku hydraulic structures, we analyzed one segment of an aqueduct system at the site of Pajchiri. Like the aqueduct at Lukurmata, three of the four aqueducts constituting the Pajchiri hydraulic system are characterized by two components: an upper channel consisting of an artificially canalized quebrada, and a lower channel that conducted water over an open plain on an elevated structure built of parallel stone retaining walls infilled with earth, stone, and gravel. As at Lukurmata, the modified quebrada channels of these aqueducts reach into high montane catchment basins where they were charged by precipitation runoff and by permanent springs and subterranean seeps. The fourth aqueduct was not structurally associated with an artificially modified quebrada. Rather, it consisted of an elevated, stand-alone hydraulic structure linked by a surface canal to an artificial spring-charged reservoir adjacent to the principal civic-ceremonial precinct of Pajchiri (fig. 5.33).

**Figure 5.33.** One of the four aqueducts at the site of Pajchiri.

The hydraulic structures at Pajchiri are much larger than the Lukurmata aqueduct just analyzed, running over a kilometer in length and achieving maximum structural heights of between 4 and 7 meters. They were carefully built with retaining walls of large, cut stones rather than with the simple river cobbles that characterize the structure at Lukurmata. In addition, unlike the Lukurmata aqueduct, those at Pajchiri have well-constructed stone drop structures linked to smaller feeder canals that were apparently intended to distribute freshwater to local raised-field systems arrayed between the aqueducts themselves. The Pajchiri aqueducts exhibit fine structural detailing and a massive investment of labor.

Fieldwork on the Pajchiri aqueduct chosen for analysis entailed surface measurements of preserved channel widths, lateral shapes, and canal bed slopes in a mid-structure segment approximately 90 meters long. Measurements were taken at 3-meter intervals over this segment, commencing at a point approximately 300 meters from the spring-reservoir water intakes. The results are shown in table 5.3. As observed from the base width (B) column, the canal shape profile of this aqueduct exhibits an expansion-contraction design. Upstream and downstream from the analyzed section, the channel width is relatively uniform. The question presents itself: does this design feature—a channel width that expands and contracts—perform a hydraulic function, or was it simply the product of unstandardized construction techniques?

Table 5.3 lists the normal ($D_N$) and critical ($D_C$) depths for assumed typical flow rates in the range of 1 cubic meter per second and 0.5 meter per second from the spring/reservoir water sources. For both flow rates, $D_C > D_N$, indicating the presence of a supercritical flow. In most cases, the difference between $D_N$ and $D_C$ is on the order of 20–30 percent. The flow depth is therefore close to the local value of the normal depth. Because the critical depth is not excessively divergent from the normal depth and the slope is not excessively greater than the critical slope, the flow rate will be close to the maximum possible for the given slope, channel area, and initial specific energy. The calculated flow on this aqueduct is in the supercritical region, with a Froude number ranging from 1.5 to 2.5.

Table 5.3. Structural and Hydraulic Characteristics of the Pajchiri Aqueduct

| | | | | | $Q = 1$ m s³ | | $Q = 0.5$ m s³ | |
|---|---|---|---|---|---|---|---|---|
| Station (m) | B (m) | $S_b$ | $Z_L = \text{ctn}\ \Theta_L$ | $Z_R = \text{ctn}\ \Theta_R$ | $D_C$ (m) | $D_N$ (m) | $D_C$ (m) | $D_N$ (m) |
| 0 | 1.05 | 0.37 | 1 | 1 | 0.41 | 0.28 | 0.26 | 0.19 |
| 3 | 3.00 | | 1 | 1 | 0.22 | 0.15 | 0.14 | 0.10 |
| 6 | 3.25 | | 1 | 1 | 0.21 | 0.15 | 0.13 | 0.10 |
| 9 | 3.00 | | 1 | 1 | 0.22 | 0.15 | 0.14 | 0.10 |
| 12 | 3.30 | | 1 | 1 | 0.21 | 0.14 | 0.13 | 0.09 |
| 15 | 3.00 | | 1 | 1 | 0.22 | 0.15 | 0.14 | 0.10 |
| 18 | 3.00 | | 0 | 0 | 0.20 | 0.16 | 0.14 | 0.10 |
| 21 | 3.10 | | 0 | 0 | 0.21 | 0.16 | 0.14 | 0.10 |
| 24 | 3.20 | | 0 | 0 | 0.20 | 0.15 | 0.13 | 0.10 |
| 27 | 2.70 | | 1 | 0.58 | 0.23 | 0.16 | 0.15 | 0.10 |
| 30 | 2.30 | | 1 | 0.58 | 0.20 | 0.18 | 0.17 | 0.12 |
| 33 | 3.10 | | 1 | 0.58 | 0.22 | 0.15 | 0.14 | 0.10 |
| 36 | 3.20 | | 0 | 1 | 0.21 | 0.15 | 0.13 | 0.10 |
| 39 | 2.80 | | 0 | 1 | 0.23 | 0.16 | 0.15 | 0.11 |
| 42 | 2.65 | | 0 | 1 | 0.23 | 0.17 | 0.15 | 0.11 |
| 45 | 2.65 | | 1 | 1 | 0.24 | 0.16 | 0.15 | 0.11 |
| 48 | 2.65 | | 1 | 1 | 0.24 | 0.16 | 0.15 | 0.11 |
| 51 | 2.65 | | 1 | 1 | 0.24 | 0.16 | 0.15 | 0.11 |
| 54 | 2.26 | | 0 | 0.58 | 0.25 | 0.19 | 0.16 | 0.12 |
| 57 | 2.26 | | 0 | 0.58 | 0.25 | 0.19 | 0.16 | 0.12 |
| 60 | 1.90 | | 0 | 0.58 | 0.28 | 0.21 | 0.18 | 0.14 |
| 63 | 1.90 | | 0.58 | 1.19 | 0.29 | 0.20 | 0.19 | 0.13 |
| 66 | 2.02 | 0.033 | 0.58 | 1.19 | 0.28 | 0.20 | 0.18 | 0.13 |
| 69 | 2.38 | | 0.58 | 1.19 | 0.25 | 0.18 | 0.16 | 0.12 |
| 72 | 1.72 | | 0 | 0 | 0.28 | 0.24 | 0.19 | 0.16 |
| 75 | 1.61 | | 0 | 0 | 0.28 | 0.26 | 0.19 | 0.16 |
| 78 | 1.42 | | 0 | 0 | 0.31 | 0.28 | 0.20 | 0.18 |
| 81 | 1.40 | | 0 | 0 | 0.31 | 0.29 | 0.21 | 0.18 |
| 84 | 2.26 | | 0 | 0 | 0.25 | 0.20 | 0.21 | 0.13 |
| 87 | 2.30 | 0.041 | | | | | | |

The lower normal water depths in the vicinity of the analyzed expanded channel section, compared to upstream and downstream water depths, enhanced the function of the drop structures and smaller feeder canals with low intake heights constructed perpendicular to the main channel in this region. The flow velocity is small into the drop structures when the water height is only slightly above the intake height. This may aid in irrigation strategies that required slow water input over long periods rather than rapid flow over a short time with large volume flow rates. The lower intake heights of the drop structures, made possible by the locally lower water height in the expansion region of the channel, permitted easy manipulation of the secondary water distribution system. Simple sluice-gate structures of small stones could be used to block the intakes periodically and thereby regulate water supplies to the feeder canals.

Despite the presence of occasional well-elaborated drop structures and secondary feeder canals, it appears that the principal function of the Pajchiri aqueducts was to transport excess water from surrounding spring and quebrada systems to the lake basin. Each of the four aqueducts running through the field systems at Pajchiri appears to channel water from a specific local drainage basin and spring system. The presence of near-critical-slope canals reinforces the transport rather than the distribution model of canal function. In this respect, it is important to note that several segments of raised fields at Pajchiri were cut on laboriously constructed terraces between the aqueducts. This is a clear indication of design response to high groundwater conditions and supersaturation of soils that would have been potentially deleterious to agricultural production.

The aqueducts at Pajchiri, then, can be best interpreted as hydraulic structures that supported continuously functioning drainage canals designed to remove excess water from areas of field reclamation, thus maintaining a stabilized water table at a point below that of crop root systems. The occasional drop structures and feeder canals along the aqueducts may have been incorporated into the structures to address the problem of periodic drought that afflicted the Andean altiplano or, somewhat more speculatively, to mitigate the problem of hypersalinization of field systems by providing a direct method of suffusing them with freshwater, thereby cleansing them of soluble salts. In either case, it is clear that the various features of the Pajchiri hydraulic structures represent a case of designed multifunctionality responsive to the severe inundation-drought cycles characteristic of the Andean altiplano climatic regime.

The two aqueduct systems at Lukurmata and Pajchiri employed supercritical open channel flows and served as drainage systems to prevent excess surface water from entering the groundwater reservoir. For the Lukurmata aqueduct, an erodible channel system was constructed to collect runoff from a large, local basin and divert it directly into Lake Titicaca. This aqueduct may have features related to a neutralizing reach concept, which would have eliminated on-aqueduct hydraulic jumps under flood conditions and/or elevated lake levels. The aqueduct supports a flow at local normal depth values under typical usage conditions, implying a flow of constant velocity and constant area parallel to the canal bed on the aqueduct. Under flood conditions, the lower channel of the aqueduct/canalized quebrada system may have supported critical flow, enhancing rapid drainage.

The Pajchiri aqueduct analyzed here also exhibits a design intended to divert excess surface water to Lake Titicaca to reduce the problem of supersaturated soils. Because the aqueduct slopes were constructed near the critical slope, maximum flow rates from spring and drainage basins to the lake could be achieved. This slope configuration, along with the otherwise puzzling presence of four long, parallel aqueducts within 100 meters of each other, indicates that the major hydrological concern of the Tiwanaku engineers at Pajchiri was water diversion and drainage rather than distribution to agricultural fields or to residential populations.

The evidence from both Lukurmata and Pajchiri therefore implicates a design related principally to a strategy of transport and drainage, rather than one of redistribution. The rationale behind this strategy can be associated directly with climatological, hydrological, and topographical circumstances that induced elevated local groundwater conditions in and around these Tiwanaku cities. The hydraulic engineers of Tiwanaku apparently responded to problems generated by seasonal inundation of urban and agricultural landscapes by building appropriate aqueduct systems linked to modified natural quebrada channels. These systems effectively served to reduce the infiltration of surface water into the groundwater reservoir, thereby lowering the local water table with respect to the ground surface. This regulation of water table height was essential to ensure the long-term sustainability of agricultural fields within the boundaries of these cities, as well as in their immediate hinterlands.

The canalized quebrada/aqueduct systems simultaneously prevented, or at least mitigated the impact of, massive erosion and sediment transportation in residential zones of Lukurmata and Pajchiri. A substantial proportion of the populations in these two urban settlements resided on artificially constructed terraces carved into hillsides with slopes approaching 20° (Kolata 1989). Today, unprotected slopes in the region of these sites exhibit substantial local erosion and, at times, mass wasting induced by seasonal torrential downpours. By canalizing this heavy seasonal flow and diverting it to the lake basin, Tiwanaku hydraulic engineers were, in effect, conserving the inhabitability of the urban environment. Monumental subterranean sandstone drains, or, more aptly, sewer systems, recently excavated at the capital city of Tiwanaku dramatically emphasize the state's preoccupation with efficient, large-scale drainage in the urban landscape (Kolata 1993a).

## River Shunts, Dikes, Causeways, and Primary Canals in the Tiwanaku Hinterland

In addition to the aqueduct/canalized quebrada systems, Tiwanaku hydraulic engineers developed other sophisticated structures to manage water flow in their artificial agricultural landscapes. The repertoire of water control devices included, but was not restricted to, major river canalizations, artificial river shunts, dikes, and articulated networks of primary drainage canals. Figure 5.34 illustrates two kinds of public construction projects on the Pampa Koani that served functions related to the operation of raised fields, not as bounded, independent bundles of field plots but as an interdependent *regional* system of production.

The first of these public constructions is a network of elevated causeways and dikes. The principal route of the largest elevated roadbed, the trans-pampa causeway, together with that of its major branch, connected the marshy, low-lying zone of raised fields in the western end of the Pampa Koani with roads running along mountain terraces forming the northern and southern boundaries of the pampa, respectively. These contour roads running along the base of the mountain slopes led directly to the important regional Tiwanaku urban settlements of Lukurmata and Pajchiri, as well as to the smaller towns of Yayes and Lakaya. The trans-pampa causeway itself was walled and possibly paved with cut stone in its southern extremity as it approached Lakaya. Several smaller elevated roadbeds radiate out laterally from the trans-pampa causeway to articulate field segments with the larger platform mounds in the central ritual and administrative settlement cluster. The formal causeways on the Pampa Koani were designed to facilitate travel and presumably the transportation of agricultural goods from the production zone to consuming and processing centers of population. Transport of bulk produce along the causeway and road network was most likely facilitated by organized pack trains of llamas.

The north-south trending trans-pampa causeway may have served another function besides that of

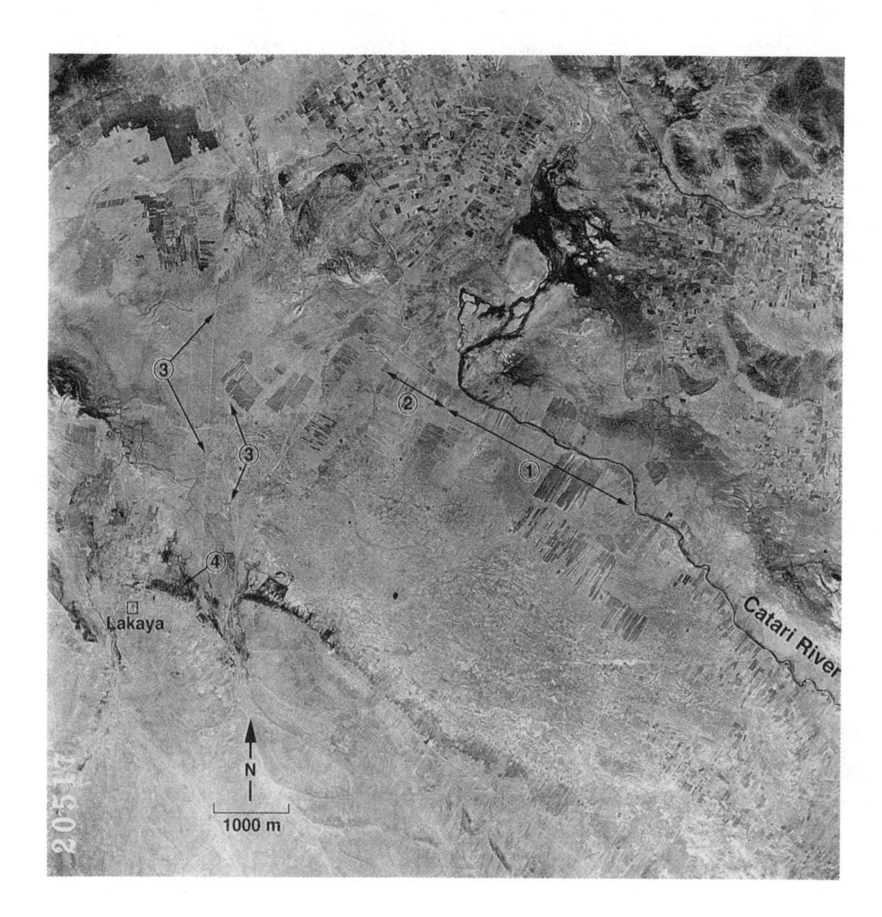


Figure 5.34. Aerial view of the southern portions of the Pampa Koani raised-field study area. 1, Artificially canalized section of the Catari River; 2, intake of the river by-pass system, or "shunt"; 3, causeway on the west side, which may have served as a dike as well as an elevated roadbed; 4, Lakaya rehabilitated raised fields. (Instituto Geográfico Militar, Bolivia, sheet 20517, 10 August 1955).

transport. Its elevated bed runs astride the maximum elevation contour in the western end of the Pampa Koani. To the west, the land slopes gradually down from this maximum elevation (3,824 meters above sea level) to the shores of Lake Titicaca. East of the causeway, the land slopes downward so gently that 11 kilometers inland from the shore, absolute elevation is only 3,820 meters above sea level. During the catastrophic flood that affected the Andean altiplano between September 1985 and April 1986, this ancient causeway acted as an effective dike, impounding the rising waters of Lake Titicaca for a time. Once the lake had risen over 2.75 meters, however, the entire stretch of the pampa to the east of the causeway was rapidly inundated with brackish waters to a depth of nearly 1 meter, which destroyed houses, pastures, and potato fields. When the floodwaters finally receded by late 1988, salt deposits that still depress local crop yields were left behind in thick, patchy crusts. Tiwanaku engineers may well have been aware of this natural elevation feature and sited the trans-pampa causeway along it to enhance its capacity to impound water. The causeway/dike, in short, may have been a disaster control device that prevented destruction of the raised fields in the eastern reaches of the Koani plain during years when rainfall did not reach the proportions of the unusual 1985–86 event.

The second Tiwanaku construction project on the Koani plain, illustrated in figure 5.34, was definitely a regional hydraulic control device. At some point in the history of land reclamation on the Pampa Koani, a long segment of the Catari River, the principal watercourse bisecting the pampa, was artificially canalized (the Katari Canal). This canalization was accomplished by diverting the natural course of the flow at a point approximately 20 kilometers inland from the lakeshore into a new bed furnished with massive earthen levees. The diversion and canalization of the natural river achieved two important goals for the efficient operation of a regional agricultural system: it opened up huge stretches of land to raised-field reclamation in the southern portions of the Pampa Koani, and it permitted some measure of human control over potentially disastrous flooding of the reclaimed landscape.

A previously unrecognized facet of the Catari River canalization was discovered during the 1990 field season. Excessive rainy-season flow can result rapidly in bed erosion, river excursions, and potentially disastrous inundation of adjacent land. In order to augment the canal's capacity to handle periodic flooding, Tiwanaku hydraulic engineers constructed a canal by-pass system paralleling the banks of the canalized sections of the Catari River to shunt excess flow away from critical reclaimed lands toward Lake Titicaca. The southern bank of the canal by-pass (the side facing the bulk of the raised fields in the Pampa Koani region) was reinforced by an earthen levee averaging about 2.5 meters high and 3 to 5 meters wide (fig. 5.35). This river shunt effectively extracted substantial quantities of seasonal flow and redirected it away from areas critical to agriculture.

The canalization of the Catari River and subsequent construction of a river shunt system are not unique in the annals of Tiwanaku hydraulic engineering. Indeed, river and stream canalization is a dis-

**Figure 5.35.** The remains of a massive earthen levee along the Catari River, part of a canal by-pass system.

tinct and rather audacious strategy of water control common in Tiwanaku's rural and urban landscapes. A similar shunt system was identified as a crucial feature of the recently recognized Waña Jawira Canal that bisects the middle and lower Tiwanaku Valley (see fig. 5.5). The artificial canal serves as a shunt for excess flow in the Tiwanaku River, in addition to irrigating raised-field complexes downstream. As in the Catari River system, this canal has substantial, reinforced earthen levees to stabilize extracted river flow.

Like the Pajchiri aqueducts, the Waña Jawira Canal illustrates a sophisticated principle of Tiwanaku's regional hydraulic engineering: designed multifunctionality. The canal, together with its shunt system, was capable of implementing either a water distribution or a water extraction strategy. That is, in the dry season or in times of drought, the canal could carry river water from its intake on the Tiwanaku River to secondary canals downstream for distribution to adjacent raised-field complexes (see fig. 5.5). During the rainy season or a flood, the intakes of the secondary distribution canals could have been blocked with some sort of formal or informal sluice gate, and excess river flow could have been redirected away from the agricultural landscape. In the case of the Waña Jawira system, the principal canal rejoins the Tiwanaku River some 7 kilometers downstream from its intake. There appears to be evidence from aerial photographs of a second loop to the Waña Jawira system that takes off from the Tiwanaku River immediately west of the point at which the first section of the canal rejoins the river; this segment of the canal eventually terminates at the shoreline of Lake Titicaca. This presumed second loop is inadequately investigated, and we cannot yet confirm that it is an artificial feature rather than, for instance, an ancient river meander. In any case, designed multifunctionality of hydraulic structures integrated into a regional regime of water control was clearly a key principle in the organization of Tiwanaku agricultural production, and not an aberrant or unique occurrence.

In the volatile environment of the Andean high plateau, agricultural disaster lurks in many disguises. One of them—potentially as catastrophic as drought—is torrential rainfall and inundation (the 1985–86 event being the most recent instance). Inundation can have an exceptionally long-term deleterious impact on crop growth by generating high groundwater conditions and supersaturation of soils. The principal purpose of Tiwanaku's hydraulic infrastructure in its hinterland was to support continuously functioning drainage canals designed to remove excess water from areas of field reclamation and so reduce the incidence of dangerously high groundwater conditions. By diverting excess water from the raised fields, such structures may have helped stabilize the water table at a point below that of the critical zone of crop root development. The river canalizations and shunt systems in the Catari and Tiwanaku basins, as well as the aqueducts of Pajchiri and Lukurmata, can be interpreted as technologically sophisticated examples of designed multifunctionality responsive to the severe inundation-drought cycles that characterize the altiplano. The river canalizations, quebrada modifications, aqueducts, dikes, and causeways functionally integrated Tiwanaku's sustaining hinterlands into a regional landscape of water management and intensive agricultural production.

Human populations in Tiwanaku's sustaining area were not distributed uniformly or broadly across the landscape. Rather, we have documented a pattern of nodal population clustering in large urban centers such as Lukurmata and Pajchiri and in intermediate-scale settlements such as Chiripa, Chojasivi, Lakaya, and Yayes, arrayed along the combined geological and human-altered terraces that define the northern and southern borders of the Koani plain, as well as in the Tiwanaku Valley itself (Albarracín-Jordan 1992; Mathews 1992). The regionally integrated agricultural field systems in these same zones were constructed and maintained during the Tiwanaku III through Tiwanaku V phases (ca. A.D. 300–1000). During Tiwanaku phases IV and V, these field systems achieved their maximum spatial reach. The most technologically advanced manipulation of the reclaimed landscape of raised fields in this area, represented by the construction of interconnected spring, reservoir, and aqueduct water delivery systems, was associated with these same two periods of Tiwanaku's internal development (Kolata 1993a).

We can best understand the Tiwanaku hinterland, by about A.D. 500, as a constructed landscape of state production. The labor invested in shaping that landscape was drawn from taxation of both local and nonlocal groups headed by political leaders who acted as intermediaries and surrogates for the Tiwanaku political elite. But the autonomy of these local *kurakas* was constrained by the needs and prerogatives of the more highly ranked nonlocal elites who resided in the network of urban centers in the greater Tiwanaku metropolitan zone. This hierarchized system of intensive agricultural production was to persist for some five centuries until the collapse and political fragmentation of the Tiwanaku state in the period after A.D. 1000.

## Notes

1. A version of this section was published in "Thermal Analysis of Tiwanaku Raised Field Systems in the Lake Titicaca Basin of Bolivia," by A. L. Kolata and C. R. Ortloff, *Journal of Archaeological Science* 16 (1989): 233–63.

2. A version of this section was originally published in "Hydraulic Analysis of Tiwanaku Aqueduct Structures at Lukurmata and Pajchiri, Bolivia," by C. R. Ortloff and A. L. Kolata, *Journal of Archaeological Science* 16 (1989): 513–35.

# 6

# Engineering Aspects of Tiwanaku Groundwater-Controlled Agriculture

CHARLES R. ORTLOFF

Tiwanaku raised-field agriculture was characterized by massive and sophisticated manipulation of groundwater inputs. Chapter 5 provided an overview of the spatial distribution, morphology, and function of raised fields in the Tiwanaku hinterland, including an initial discussion of groundwater control devices and strategies. This chapter provides a more detailed analysis of this essential aspect of raised-field design and function as expressed in Tiwanaku agricultural landscapes dating between about A.D. 400 and 1000, that is, during the florescence of the Tiwanaku state.

Upwards of 70 square kilometers of abandoned agricultural fields adjacent to the southern edge of Lake Titicaca in the Catari River basin constitute the largest continuous raised-field system in the Tiwanaku hinterland. Other, comparatively small zones of raised fields exist in the vicinity of the Tiwanaku satellite city of Pajchiri and in the Pukarani region northeast of the Catari basin (see fig. 5.1). Although surface preservation is poorer in the Tiwanaku Valley than in the Catari basin, ground survey indicates a large zone of raised fields adjacent to Lake Titicaca within the Tiwanaku Valley, estimated to approach some 20 square kilometers. Additional inland extensions of raised fields occur along the northern margin of the Tiwanaku Valley.

Unlike the virtually continuous fields of the Catari basin, raised-field systems in the Tiwanaku Valley appear to occur in distinct spatial clusters in association with major human settlements. For example, large-system clusters appear immediately to the north, east, and west of the city of Tiwanaku itself. This pattern of raised-field clusters adjacent to significant settlements appears throughout the middle and lower Tiwanaku Valley (chapter 5; Albarricín-Jordan and Mathews 1990). We expect that this same "agro-settlement" association is expressed in the upper Tiwanaku Valley as well, but confirmation of this assumption awaits the completion of full-coverage archaeological survey in this sector of the valley. The totality of these raised-field systems formed the agricultural foundations for Tiwanaku civilization, particularly during the Tiwanaku IV and V periods that are of principal concern here.

## Tiwanaku Groundwater-Controlled Agriculture

All Tiwanaku raised-field systems are constructed so that the excavated canals intersect the water table. In essence, the water in the raised-field canals is the piezometric surface of the aquifer. Capillary action causes further upward moisture penetration into the mounded platforms of the planting surface, thereby generating capillary and vadose moisture zones. The height of the mounded earth above the water table surface then establishes the moisture content of the root zone. Groundwater level is controlled by a number of factors: the rainfall infiltration rate into the collection basin area and the concomitant contribution to groundwater flow directed toward Lake Titicaca; the current lake level compared with the height of the water table (triggering gravity-driven transient groundwater flows); and the intrusion of collected and channeled springwater conducted into the canal network, possibly in part for purposes of altering the salinity and pH of water in near-lake raised-field canals. Surface canals linked to springs supplied supplemental water for irrigation (particularly during drought episodes that lowered water table levels) and potentially for field flushing purposes.

All water entering the lake directly or by groundwater flow and surface runoff is more or less equally balanced by lake evaporation and, to a minor degree, lake outflow through the Desaguadero River on the southernmost margin of Lake Titicaca. In periods of excessive rainfall, lake level can change rapidly, with seasonal fluctuations of $\pm$ 1 meter. Exceptional 2- to 5-meter lake-level excursions have been recorded in recent lake history (see chapter 2). For example, between September 1985 and April 1986, a 3-meter lake rise was recorded, the result of exceptionally heavy seasonal rainfall. Raised fields within 12 kilometers of the lake edge flooded and/or became saturated to the point of being inoperable for agricultural use. During this episode, a minimum of 75 percent of the ancient raised-field zone in the Catari basin was flooded. The return from this elevated lake level to previous preflood levels required on the order of three to four years. We assume that current hydrological patterns are generally indicative of events occurring in the past. Therefore, in the absence of suitable regional hydraulic infrastructure, a comparable flood experienced by Tiwanaku farmers would have rendered much of the agricultural landscape inoperable.

## The Groundwater Model

In order to understand the impact of groundwater changes on Tiwanaku raised-field agriculture, we construct a model that approximates the sequence of conditions and processes occurring during a significant lake-level excursion (a rise-fall oscillation). We develop the model by analyzing the events depicted in figure 6.1. This schematic represents the groundwater effects resulting from lake-level oscillations on the nearshore terrestrial environment without additions from remote groundwater sources. (In this and subsequent schematics—which result from computer calculations of groundwater flow patterns that are detailed in later sections—the arrows in the individual frames denote the direction of groundwater flow.) Initially (fig. 6.1A), for lake level at $h_{AL}$ and for an initially higher groundwater level $h_A$, groundwater flow is directed into the lake by gravity. The lake and groundwater levels are always equal at the lake-terrestrial boundary. As the lake rises to $h_{BL}$, groundwater achieves height $h_B$ (fig. 6.1B). As the lake continues to rise to $h_{CL}$, the direction of groundwater flow is reversed (fig. 6.1C). A further rise in lake height to $h_{DL}$ (fig. 6.1D) increases the groundwater flow rate away from the lake. In fig. 6.1E, for a lake-level decrease to $h_{EL}$, groundwater flow is away from the point of maximum height, and groundwater flow may become bidirectional, that is, induced in opposite directions. Under conditions of continuing lake-level decrease (fig. 6.1F) to the original lake level, $h_{FL} = h_{AL}$, the cycle returns to its starting configuration.

In order to approximate real-world conditions more accurately, we must make the model more complex by taking into account the effects of remote groundwater sources. As discussed in earlier chapters, the local environment of the Tiwanaku hinterland is characterized by multiple, remote sources of groundwater input, all of which play a role in regulating the hydrological regime. Tiwanaku's agricultural landscape was tied directly to this regime. The presence of remote groundwater sources flowing toward the lake is illustrated schematically in figures 6.2 and 6.3. Figure 6.2 considers the effects of lake-level oscillations on groundwater flows *without* raised-field networks in the nearshore environment, and figure 6.3 represents the case in which such networks are present. Note that the modified groundwater height profile in these figures is represented by the dashed line, in contrast with the solid line representing events previously shown in figure 6.1 (the case in which remote groundwater-source effects are not considered).

The strength of groundwater flow from remote sources is related to the infiltration rate over the entire collection zone, which is large in comparison with the lake area. This relationship implies a continuous influx of groundwater toward the lake throughout the

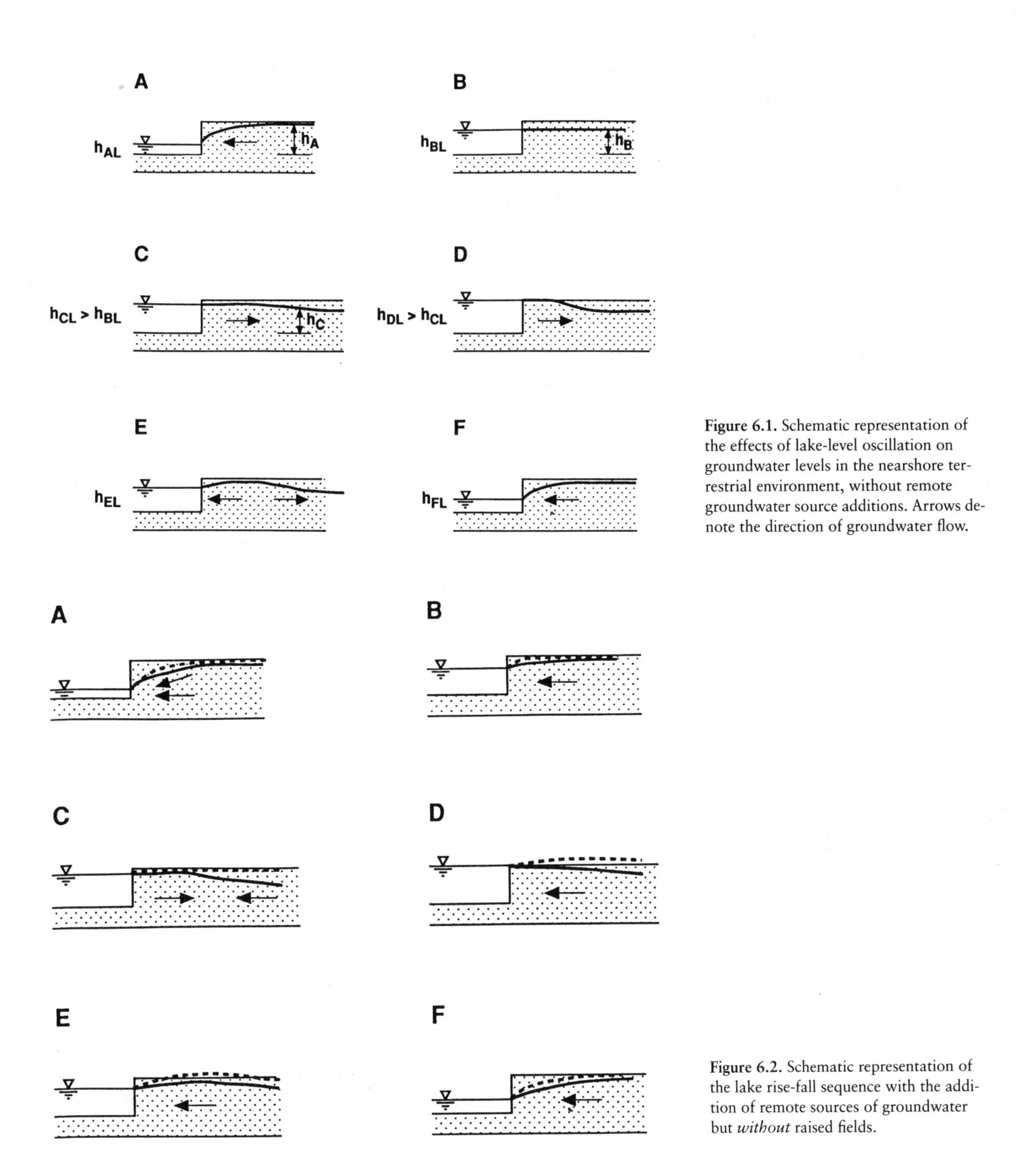


**Figure 6.1.** Schematic representation of the effects of lake-level oscillation on groundwater levels in the nearshore terrestrial environment, without remote groundwater source additions. Arrows denote the direction of groundwater flow.

**Figure 6.2.** Schematic representation of the lake rise-fall sequence with the addition of remote sources of groundwater but *without* raised fields.

year as rainfall captured in remote catchment basins arrives slowly but continuously to the lake through the aquifer. The presence of the additional input flow and its effect on the groundwater level is shown in frame A of figure 6.2 as a slight increase in height over the result shown in figure 6.1A. Frame B of figure 6.2 indicates surface saturation. The input flow arrives continuously and raises the groundwater level above the lake level. As the lake rises further (fig. 6.2, frame C), the groundwater outflow from the lake, combined with the incoming source flow, begins to distort the groundwater profile upward into a "bulgelike" effect until saturation and runoff are achieved at locations distant from the lake. For the maximum lake-rise condition (fig. 6.2, frame D), ground saturation is achieved, with the possibility of surface runoff toward

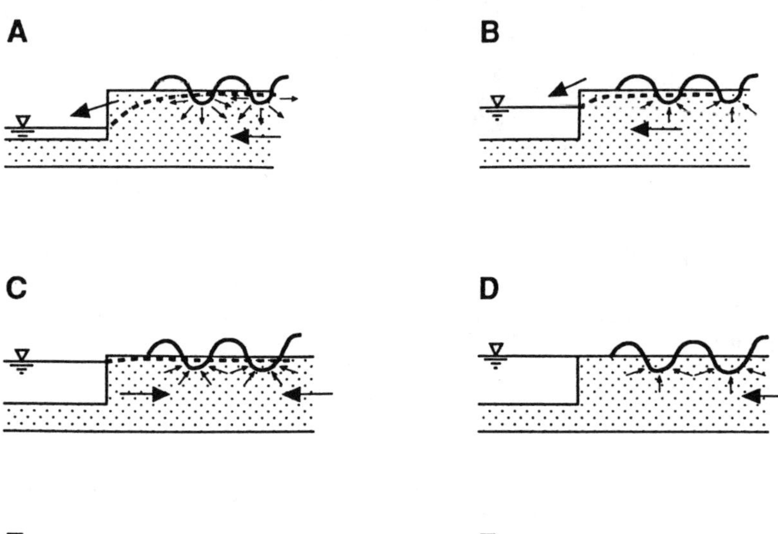


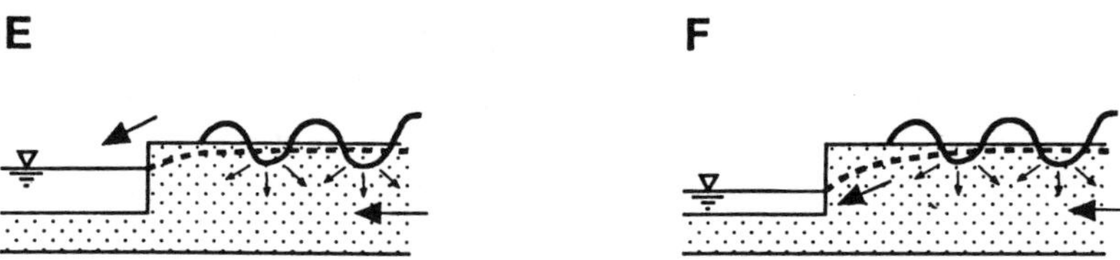


**Figure 6.3.** Schematic representation of the lake rise-fall sequence with the addition of remote sources of groundwater and *with* raised fields draining the landscape. Raised-field platforms and canals are represented by undulating lines. Small arrows denote inflow and outflow to canals.

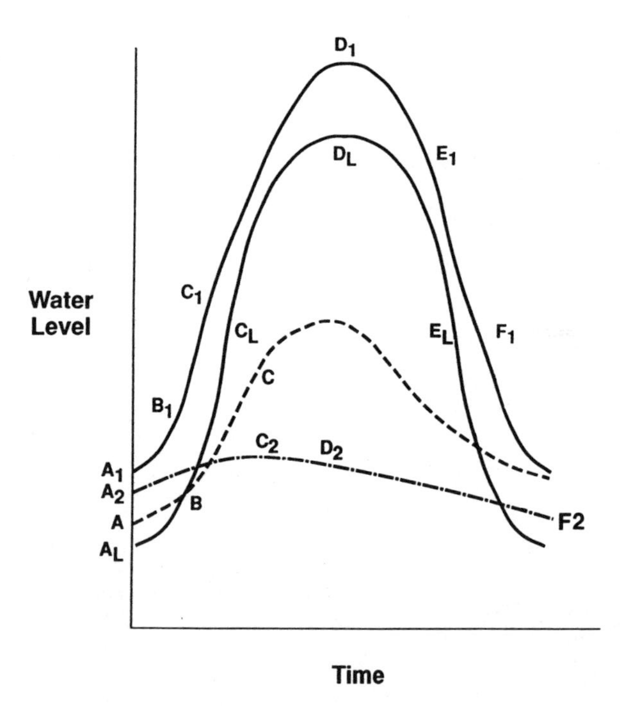


**Figure 6.4.** Hydrograph showing the effects of lake-level oscillation on groundwater levels in the nearshore environment.

the lake. As the lake level subsides (fig. 6.2, frame E), the groundwater "bulge" persists, producing flow toward the lake (consisting of surface and groundwater flow), with continuing groundwater flow toward the bulge from the collection zone. Finally, with further lake-level subsidence, frame F completes the cycle, returning the system to the initial conditions. The hydrograph for these events is illustrated in figure 6.4.

Figure 6.3 shows the effects on water table height when field drainage systems are active in the presence of lake height fluctuations and ground water arrival from a remote source. The dashed line represents the groundwater profile corresponding to figure 6.1. As the lake level rises (fig. 6.3A–D), the groundwater level is reduced by active drainage through canals leading to the lake. Drainage commences when the water table height exceeds the maximum canal depth. This depth regulation system can be actively controlled by weirs placed in drainage canals that permit flow when water depth exceeds the weir height (fig. 6.3C–D). (This design concept is actively employed in the Catari River canal, for example.) Figure 6.3E–F indicates that the water table height may be controlled by restricting outflow when canal water height is less that weir height (drainage canals may be blocked by temporary artificial barriers.) The presence of the drainage canals may therefore act as regulators of water height either to maintain or to lower water height as required.

The hydrograph plot, figure 6.4, summarizes these results. For the lake height excursion history (curve $A_L$-$D_L$) the groundwater height transient response is shown for the three cases. Groundwater is defined to be the mean height between a lake bottom reference plane and a remote field location (fig. 6.1). Figure 6.1

shows the gradual rise of the mean groundwater height with rising lake level but a more rapid decline as lake level peaks. The bi-directional groundwater flow (fig. 6.1E) tends to maintain groundwater height even as lake level decreases. For the addition of a remote groundwater source in the model, curve $A_1$-$F_1$ in figure 6.4 applies. The additional remote-source water contribution causes mean groundwater height to follow the lake height history closely. Note that high groundwater zones resulting from remote-source water arrival can exist far from the lake to support agriculture in the presence of drought-driven lake height decrease. Figure 6.3 shows the effect of lake height excursions on mean groundwater height in the presence of raised fields connected to the lake by drainage canal nteworks. Curve $A_2$-$F_2$ in figure 6.4 indicates that mean ground water height can be regulated by means of drainage networks that preserve canal water height at fixed levels throughout lake height excursions. This design feature of the integrated raised-field systems permits continued agriculture despite moderate lake-level fluctuations caused by climate variations.

In general, the addition of remote-source groundwater flow raises the water table surface throughout the lake rise-fall cycle, temporarily inducing a saturated zone away from the lake edge. Farming on a landscape subject to such lake rise-fall cycles requires adequate drainage of saturated zones to lower the locally high water table levels. The raised-field system of interconnected canals and primary drainage networks provides one such mechanism (fig. 6.3, and refer to fig. 6.4). Because the flow paths through perimeter boundaries of raised fields are relatively short, water table equalization can occur locally in canals that are not interconnected. The interconnected canals play a further role of mitigating local groundwater height excursions by providing drainage paths to the lake with relatively rapid outflow when compared with normal ground seepage alone.

Moreover, as described in chapter 5 and considered in detail later, major canals and artificially canalized rivers serviced substantial areas of raised fields in both the Catari and Tiwanaku River basins. These canals provided high-volume drainage capacity over large portions of the agricultural landscape. With this hydraulic infrastructure in place, Tiwanaku agriculturalists were able to shunt excess water from seasonal rainfall or periodic flooding away from the reclamation zones and into Lake Titicaca. The presence of raised fields with their adjacent canals thus acts to provide surface drainage paths to the lake, helping to regulate groundwater height excursions caused by normal lake-level oscillations and by periods of excessive rainfall, runoff, and infiltration. This interconnected hydraulic infrastructure, constructed and operated on a regional scale, effectively stabilized field system design and aided in achieving optimum production.

Because of these system-wide drainage features, groundwater height excursions from either a rising lake level or remote-source infiltration were not necessarily deleterious to agricultural production. Water transport between canals and into arterial drainage networks that ultimately emptied into Lake Titicaca promoted a nearly constant water table height in locally connected segments of raised-field systems. Of course, the schematics in figure 6.3 are indicative only of a hypothetical lake rise-fall cycle in which lake-level excursions occur at a regular frequency and the groundwater response lags because of nonlinear, flow-through-porous-media effects (Bear 1988; Collins 1961). In reality, the lake-level rise effect is caused by a superposition of rainfall, surface runoff, and groundwater flows in seasonal and aperiodic cycles. The decline in lake level is caused mainly by evaporation from the lake surface, and to a lesser degree by outbound groundwater flow when lake level exceeds mean groundwater level.

In order to observe groundwater flow patterns in greater detail, a computer model based on the Flow-3D Fluid Mechanics code was constructed to model lake-groundwater interaction (Sicilian and Hirt 1989). The flow solutions shown result from numerical solution of Navier-Stokes equations with a Darcy Law to relate pressure-velocity conditions in flow through an unsaturated porous medium. The interaction analyzed represents transient groundwater responses characterized by a sudden, large flux of water delivered into a lake (by rainfall) and by a proportional (infiltrated) amount delivered from a remote groundwater source. Such conditions have occurred historically in the Lake Titicaca basin, most recently during the 1985–86 flood that inundated several linear kilometers of the littoral zone and devastated thousands of hectares of agricultural fields. During this event, the level of Lake Titicaca rose nearly 3 meters in six months.

Figure 6.5A shows the computer model employed for the analysis of the near-lake interaction zone. The ground surface is represented by line A-B. Initially, the lake level is at the height of A-B. We assume that

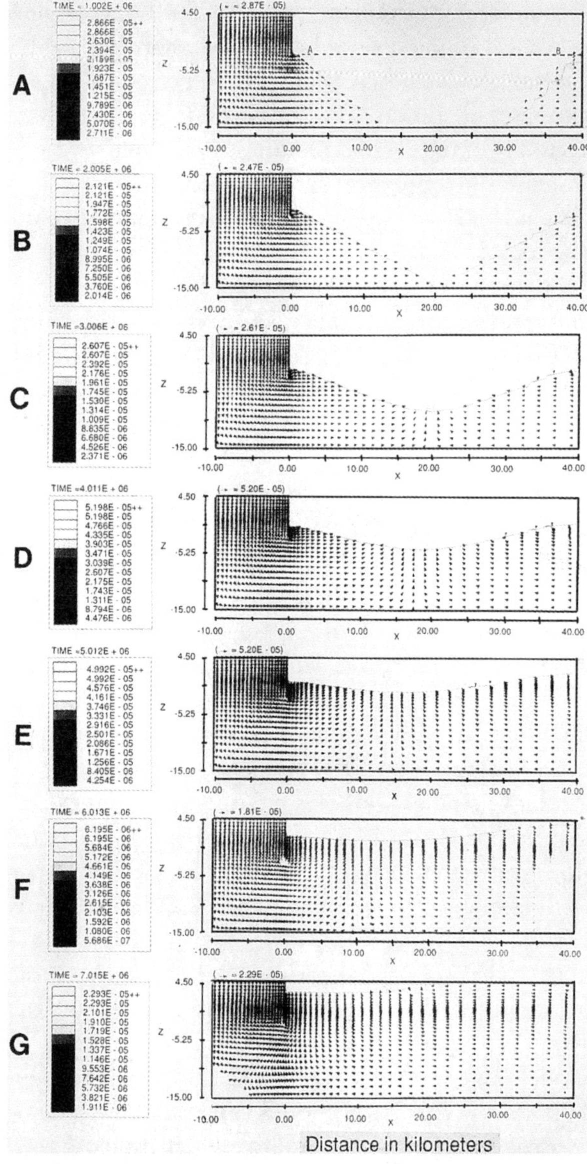


**Figure 6.5.** A computer model based on Flow–3D Fluid Mechanics code, constructed to model lake-groundwater interaction. The interaction analyzed here represents conditions characterized by a sudden flux of water delivered into a lake and a proportional amount delivered to a remote groundwater source.

the clay-rich soil void fraction is typically 2 percent and that the ground is originally unsaturated. A sudden change in lake level is represented by a change in hydrostatic pressure on the boundary region $Z = 4.50$, $X < 0.0$. The lake level is effectively given by following the vertical progress of point A through time (frames A–G). On the right side of figure 6.5A, a left-flowing groundwater is initiated by infiltration from a rainfall event over a remote collection zone. The computed sequence of events then mimics the time evolution of the interaction of the two converging flows and the resulting groundwater profile. The time interval between each frame (A–G) in figure 6.5 is about 15 days. Velocity is given in meters per second, and distances are in meters (mks units applied). Note that groundwater velocities are on the order of $10^{-5}$ to $10^{-6}$ meters per second.

In the sequence illustrated in figure 6.5, the groundwater flow below ground surface A-B is initiated, and the two groundwater fronts then approach, join, and form a rising concave surface. The heights of both the lake and the infiltrated remote-source flow rise as the rainfall input adds mass to both zones. After three months (the interval represented by frames a–g), a dry zone remains near the lake edge, but this zone is rapidly infilling from advancing groundwater source flow and lake-to-land seepage. The later stages of this sequence of events are indicated by frames A and B in figure 6.2.

The actual shapes of the profiles and reaction times will depend upon local parameters of ground permeability, soil void fraction, and the rise time of the lake relative to the magnitude of the groundwater input mass (or to the height of the remote groundwater source). Therefore, the events modeled here are qualitative in nature. Because precipitation in the Lake Titicaca basin exhibits substantial seasonal variation as well as occasional extraordinary excursions from the mean over longer periods of time, the results of the Flow–3D computations shown here indicate only one of many possible combinations of events and outcomes. The model is meant to illustrate both lake-level/groundwater lag time effects and groundwater arrival effects.

With these qualifications in mind, it is clear from these results that bands of relatively unsaturated land surface may exist temporarily around, but back from, the lake edge during the (rise-fall) cycle of lake-level excursion. The location, extent, and temporal persistence of these zones of unsaturated land will depend upon the local soil and groundwater parameters noted previously. This effect of shifting, temporary bands of unsaturated land may explain the apparent overabundance of Tiwanaku raised fields in the Catari and Tiwanaku basins relative to the food production requirements of local populations in this region (Kolata 1991). In essence, because of lake-driven water table height excursions and varying amounts of remote groundwater source flow, only some fraction of the total raised-field reclamation zones may have been suitable for production at any one time. We must emphasize, however, that Tiwanaku farmers were capable of constructing spring- or river-driven canals to irrigate these bands of unsaturated land.

To summarize the groundwater model to this point, the effect of the raised-field canal systems is to transfer water through open channel paths (if canals are interconnected) or by groundwater flow through field platform bases (if the canals are not interconnected) so that a nearly constant groundwater surface height is achieved in locally connected areas of the field systems, similar to the A–F sequence illustrated in figure 6.3. This effect—maintaining a stable water table height—is due to the communication between canals through open channels or by short groundwater flow paths through field platform bases. The nearly level water table over the entire field system creates the need for slightly different raised-field platform heights between inland and near-lake field locations. We expect that this property explains some portion of the variability in raised-field morphology described in chapter 5.

From field observation it appears that most, but not all, raised-field segments are arrayed in units that have access to the lake for drainage through primary canals (see chapter 5 for maps of the regional drainage networks and water impoundment devices in the Catari and Tiwanaku basins). This connectivity implies that groundwater height with respect to the field platform surface can be controlled by selectively altering access routes to the primary drainage canals. This may be accomplished by installing simple sluice gates and dams in field systems or by more massive undertakings such as constructing large-scale impoundment structures (dikes and causeways). Groundwater height within field systems could also be manipulated by regulating the quantity of irrigation water flowing into the raised-field canals from point sources of supply (springs and rivers). For those raised-field areas where canals are interconnected and lead to the lake, the drainage path to the lake is much shorter. Therefore, drainage flow is more rapid than it would be if incremental groundwater seepage alone were the sole source of field drainage. Recall that whereas groundwater flow velocities are on the order of $10^{-5}$ to $10^{-6}$ meters per second, open channel flow velocity (at typical Catari ground slopes) can be 0.1 to 1 meter per second, resulting in more rapid field drainage.

A key question with respect to the impact of extraordinary lake-level excursions is that of recovery time of agricultural land after a major inundation. The first phase of the inundation is simply lake water overlying the land surface. The time needed for evaporative effects to lower the lake level in the presence of groundwater arriving from a remote source determines the recovery time. During the 1985–86 inundation, the lake rose approximately 3 meters from its prior level in a period of approximately six months, and agricultural fields as much as 9 kilometers inland from the lake were covered with 1 meter of standing water. Subsequently, after four years of "normal" rainfall (that is, closer to the mean of recorded precipitation over the past century), the net effects of evaporation gradually resulted in a return to the postinundation lake level and to the uncovering of the flooded field systems. But it is critical to note that even after a lake recedes to its prior level, additional time is required for subsidence of elevated groundwater trapped in raised-field platforms. Until a sufficient difference is achieved between the ground surface and groundwater height, agricultural production cannot resume. Of course, artificial techniques to promote lowering of the water table are available. For instance, existing access channels to the lake could be interconnected by simple excavation to allow direct drainage to the lake. This process, however, is slowed by the long seepage time from field platforms to canals. After this phase, drainage is relatively immediate from the open channels to the lake.

To examine this process in greater detail, we analyze results of the decay of the phreatic surface, assumed initially to correspond to the contour of the field platform (fig. 6.6). Under Dupuit flow assumptions of material homogeneity and no rainfall infiltration, a closed form solution exists for the time of deflation of the phreatic surface to the depth of the canals (Bear 1988; Collins 1961). This model problem assumes (1) that the phreatic surface is surrounded by parallel drains (in this instance the pairs of adjacent raised-field canals or canals), and (2) that the time to drain the raised-field platforms to canal bottoms is key to restoring the appropriate moisture balance within field systems, thereby enabling them to resume production. This scenario also assumes interconnectedness of the field blocks to the lake by secondary and primary channels. (In chapter 5, we demonstrate that most of the raised-field systems in the Catari basin fit this assumption, having been linked into a hierarchical series of drainage channels.) The alternative to this scenario is incremental seepage through subsurface paths to return water to the lake. In the presence of arriving groundwater, this process is extremely slow and prevents fields from being reused until much later than in the case of the drained

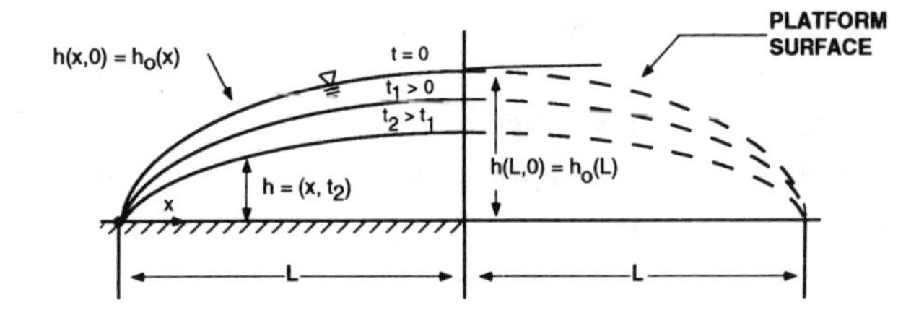


**Figure 6.6.** Graphic representation of the decay of the phreatic surface over time. The $t = 0$ surface corresponds to the mound cross-sectional profile. L is the mound half-width, $h(x,t)$ is the groundwater surface profile at time t, and $h_o(x)$ is the initial profile at $t = 0$.

field scenario. Therefore, the model proposed is the most viable strategy for agriculturalists motivated to return fields quickly to production after a major inundation.

In order to obtain an estimate of field platform drainage time, some solutions to Boussineq's equation are given, utilizing typical morphological profiles derived from raised fields excavated in the Pampa Koani (Kolata and Ortloff 1989; and see chapter 5). From Bear (1988), the solution for the groundwater height $h(x, t)$ is

$$\frac{h(x, t)}{h_o(x)} = \frac{1}{1+\beta K h_o(L)t/n_e L^2}$$

where geometric data are given in figure 6.6 and $\beta = 1.12$, $K$ = hydraulic conductivity (cm/second), $t$ = time (seconds), $n_e$ = effective porosity (= interconnected pore volume/total volume of medium) = drainable porosity/total volume, $L$ = mound half width, $h_o(L)$ = groundwater height at mid-mound position at $t = 0$, and $h_o(x)$ = initial groundwater top surface shape at $t = 0$.

For a typical raised field, $2L = 15$ meters and $h_o(L) = 2$ meters. For loosely consolidated raised-field soil that contains a base layer of gravel or cobbles, $n_e = 0.50$ and $K = 10^{-3}$ to $10^{-2}$ centimeters per second (table 6.1). In order to achieve a decline of the centerline phreatic height to 0.6 of its initial height, a solution to Boussineq's equation yields times of $t = 1.06$ to 0.11 year. If the material in raised-field platforms were densely packed without aerated soils or large cobble inclusions, then typically $n_e = 0.20$ and $K = 10^{-4}$ to $10^{-5}$. In this case, drainage times are 4.25 to 100 years. We may conclude that loosely aggregated soils significantly accelerate the rate of drainage necessary for a resumption of agricultural production. The upper, dried layers of soil, however, have low thermal conductivity and retard evaporative processes. Therefore, mound drainage may effectively take up to a year to restore the correct moisture level for resumption of agriculture under the assumptions of this model.

Accretion to the field systems by subsequent (that is, postflood) seasonal rainfall extends the time to agricultural recovery, whereas evaporation/evapotranspiration reduces time to system recovery. For this case, evaporation/evapotranspiration processes are a function of the depth of the water table below ground surface and the characteristics of the emergent plant cover as field surfaces drain. Solutions to the accretion and reduction cases are given in Bear (1988). Because of local variability and lack of precise information about precipitation levels, aquifer properties, and evapotranspiration constants (which depend on climate variations and plant surface density and types), the present calculations indicate only qualitative trends and orders of magnitude of postulated recovery times. Additional questions relating to the extent of the capillary fringe zone and depth of the water table with respect to the soil surface for various crop types also enter into the recovery time for reemergent field systems.

Based on the observed 1985–86 inundation event in which approximately 75 percent of the (abandoned) raised-field system in the Catari basin was flooded to depths of 1 meter while the remaining 25 percent of the field area was saturated, we may conclude that a 3-meter rise in lake level requires a minimum four-year recovery time for agricultural reuse in

**Table 6.1. Standard Values for Porosity and Hydraulic Conductivity**

| Material | Porosity Value (%) $n_e$ | Hydraulic Conductivity (K) (cm/second) |
|---|---|---|
| Soils | 50–60 | $10^{-1}$–$10^{-3}$ |
| Clay | 45–55 | $10^{-4}$–$10^{-6}$ |
| Silt | 40–50 | $10^{-3}$–$10^{-5}$ |
| Medium-to-coarse sand | 35–40 | 1–$10^{-3}$ |
| Uniform sand | 30–40 | 1–$10^{-2}$ |
| Gravel | 30–40 | $10^{2}$–1 |
| Shale | 1–10 | $10^{-7}$–$10^{-10}$ |
| Disaggregated soils | 10–30 | $10^{-2}$–$10^{-4}$ |

Source: Bear (1988).

the absence of human intervention to open drainage channels to the lake. In this instance, observed time to recovery entailed three years for complete recession of surface floodwater to approximate preflood levels and one to two years for subsequent groundwater reduction (as calculated with the present model) within field complexes to restore appropriate moisture balances and render fields viable for agriculture once again.

Figure 6.7 generalizes from this empirically observed case. With reference to figure 6.7, if the evaporation loss rate is constant, then curve E-F-A-0 represents a linear rate of decline in the lake level. The parallel slope D-C evaporation line is followed until the point of 100 percent field area coverage is reached. Then the combination of evaporation, evapotranspiration, and aquifer drainage occurs at a slower rate along line C-B to restore fields to 80 percent area coverage, which is the start of productive use. Finally, as the lake level declines further, drainage proceeds along slope B-0 to restore all field systems fully to agricultural production. Therefore, for a 6-meter rise in the lake level, approximately seven years are required to restore agricultural production in the Catari basin. For cases of extremely high porosity (well-aerated soils), line D-C-B-0 approaches E-F-A-0 because drainage is exceptionally rapid and evaporation is the key pathway to water removal and subsequent agricultural recovery. The width of the area circumscribed by points 0, A, F, C, and B is thus directly related to ground porosity.

In summary, an advantage of well-aerated raised-field structure is rapid drainage potential. In a major inundation event, nothing can be done to accelerate drainage until the fields are uncovered by normal evaporation effects. At that point, however, drainage of stored raised-field platform groundwater is aided by the presence of aerated soils and open channels to the lake edge. Aerated soils are effectively produced by mixing organic matter into field platform soil, which encourages mineral particles to form granules, thus forcing water storage to occur in pore spaces. Incorporation of organic matter also increases microbial action in the soil. As microbes break down organic material, they produce polysaccharides that stabilize soil by binding particles into aggregates. These aggregates are less vulnerable to wind and water erosion. However, soil organisms also break down polysaccharides, so organic material must be added continuously to maintain the supply of these stabilizing substances (see chapter 7). The positive benefits

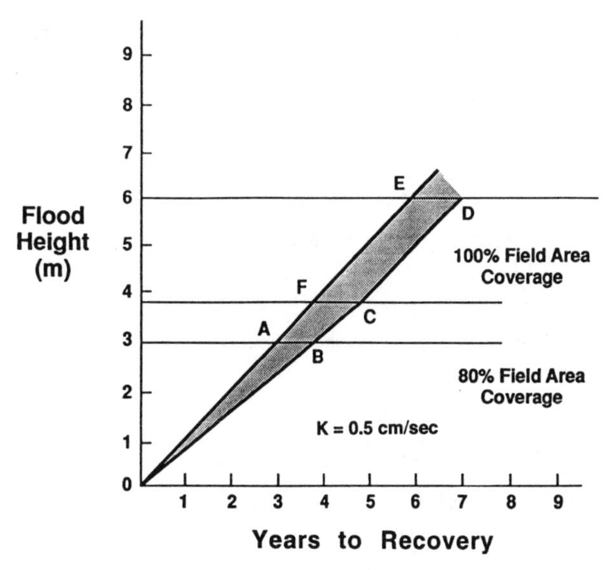


**Figure 6.7.** Projected time to restoration of agricultural production for different flood heights. Curve E-A-0 represents evaporation only; curve D-C-0 represents evaporation with field drainage and seepage effects.

of fixing nitrogen in soils by adding organic material are resistance to erosion by aggregate formation, soil moisture retention capability, increased drainage capability due to increased porosity, increased heat retention capabilities, and increased cation exchange capacity (related to the soil's ability to store nutrients). In the rigorous environment of the Andean high plateau, subject to substantial seasonal and periodic climate variations, these features are essential for sustained agricultural productivity. Tiwanaku's raised fields were then operated as organized regional systems of production, designed to reduce the risk of climate variation (particularly periodic flood-drought cycles) by sophisticated manipulation of groundwater sources and field architecture.

Apart from supersaturation of agricultural soils, a significant rise in lake level induced by sustained rainfall will increase groundwater volume and infiltrated flow from remote sources. This increase in groundwater, along with rising lake water, will in turn transport soluble salts into the planting surfaces of the raised fields. During inundation events, a doubly deleterious condition develops in which agricultural soils become both waterlogged and infused with crop-damaging salts. Even normal annual fluctuations of the lake and seasonal rainfall will induce these two environmental problems, particularly in field systems close to the lake. The hydraulic infrastructure developed by Tiwanaku offered at least a partial solution to the problem of hypersalinization of the raised fields, particularly along the south side of the Catari basin and the north side of the Tiwanaku basin. There, a series of irrigation channels drew freshwater from emergent springs fed by the aquifer within the Taraco Formation (see chapters 2, 3, and 5). These channels flowed into adjacent raised-field complexes and suffused the field canals with freshwater, in effect flushing salts from the fields. Soluble salts were ultimately transported to the lake via the interconnected field and primary canal drainage network or returned to deeper groundwater after lake subsidence.

## Hydraulic Analysis of the Waña Jawira Canal

Tiwanaku's regional hydraulic infrastructure includes massive irrigation and drainage canals, several of which are described in detail in chapter 5. These major canals were essential for manipulating regional groundwater conditions in Tiwanaku's principal zones of agricultural reclamation. In the rest of this chapter we analyze the hydraulic characteristics of two of the largest of these canals, the Waña Jawira and the Katari.

The Waña Jawira Canal originally extracted river water from an intake on the Tiwanaku River to irrigate a zone of raised fields immediately west of the city of Tiwanaku itself (see fig. 5.5). The original intake configuration of the canal has been lost to erosion induced by the river's meandering. The base of the present canal inlet stands about 2.5 meters above the current dry-season river height, indicating that the Tiwanaku River has downcut substantially since the canal was abandoned during the Tiwanaku V period. The canal itself is composed of a relatively shallow channel excavated into the alluvial sediments of the valley floor, flanked by large earthen levees built over the existing ground surface that served to contain extracted flow (fig. 6.8). The result was a contour canal of extraordinary character.

We surveyed the canal 1,000 meters downstream from its present intake to ascertain key design parameters. Table 6.2 lists these parameters. Canal wall slopes are $\Theta_L$ and $\Theta_R$, canal base width is B, and canal bed slope is $\Theta_b$. The $D_n$ and $D_c$ parameters are the normal and critical depths, respectively (Morris and Wiggert 1972). These depths are calculated for an assumed flow rate of 2 cubic meters per second. Note that for $D_n > D_c$, the flow is subcritical (the Froude number is less than unity). For flow depth D with $D > D_n > D_c$, the flow depth will tend asymptotically toward horizontal. For $D_n > D > D_c$, the flow depth will approach $D_c$ asymptotically from above. For $D_n > D_c > D$, the flow depth will approach $D_c$ asymptotically from below. The channel gradually varies in cross-section, for which local $D_n$, $D_c$ values are given (table 6.2); therefore, local depths will tend to the appropriate asymptotic limits in each canal section.

The canal drop distance is only 0.68 meter over a distance of 700 meters, indicating an almost level canal with a mean slope over this segment of –0.0014 (0.080°). This implies a sophisticated level of survey-

Figure 6.8. The remains of a massive earthen levee along the Waña Jawira Canal. This canal was recently reactivated to water rehabilitated raised fields in the Tiwanaku mid-valley region (see chapter 9).

Table 6.2. Parameters of the Waña Jawira Canal

| Station | Distance from Intake (m) | $\Theta_b$ (degrees) | $\Theta_L$ (degrees) | $\Theta_R$ (degrees) | B (m) | Drop Height (m) | $D_n$ (m) | $D_c$ (m) |
|---|---|---|---|---|---|---|---|---|
| 2 | 0 | −0.111 | 78.3 | 77.9 | 7.90 | 0.00 | 0.32 | 0.18 |
| 10 | 100 | −0.250 | 78.3 | 77.9 | 7.90 | −0.19 | 0.25 | 0.18 |
| 20 | 200 | −0.081 | 72.7 | 73.0 | 9.22 | −0.33 | 0.32 | 0.17 |
| 30 | 300 | −0.340 | 78.6 | 84.8 | 8.30 | −0.47 | 0.44 | 0.18 |
| 40 | 400 | −0.007 | 80.5 | 77.9 | 5.30 | −0.53 | −0.59 | 0.23 |
| 50 | 500 | −0.028 | 43.4 | 39.5 | 9.27 | −0.55 | 0.43 | 0.17 |
| 60 | 600 | −0.047 | 43.4 | 39.5 | 9.27 | −0.60 | 0.46 | 0.17 |
| 69 | 700 | — | 72.6 | 72.3 | 7.30 | −0.68 | 0.43 | 0.17 |

ing accuracy. Flow in this canal segment is subcritical, with mean velocities in the range of a few centimeters per second. Canals with this mean slope cannot successfully contain flow over the existing land contours without artificially built levees over much of its length. The width of the canal at the intake (7.9 meters; table 6.2) is such that the *entire flow* of the Tiwanaku River could have been diverted to adjacent Tiwanaku raised-field systems.

Because the channel is subcritical and the streamwise cross-section variation gradual, Manning's equation may be used to analyze flow at normal depth throughout its length (Morris and Wiggert 1972). This equation, expressed in English units, is

$$Q = \frac{1.49}{n}(R_h)^{2/3}A(S_b)^{1/2}$$

where n = Manning roughness factor (0.025 assumed), $R_h$ = hydraulic radius = (canal area/perimeter), A = canal cross-sectional area, and $S_b$ = bed slope. Table 6.3 characterizes the system function for different contained flow heights.

Under the assumption that ancient and modern flow rates are approximately equivalent, we estimate from the current flow rate of the Tiwanaku River during the dry season that the flow height in the canal was on the order of 0.5 meters. At this height, the canal levees (sidewalls) as presently preserved could easily contain the estimated flow.

The Waña Jawira Canal appears to have been elevated above low groundwater level during its period of function, resulting in continuous loss from seepage and evaporation over its 7-kilometer path. (As was noted in chapter 5, the Waña Jawira system may have a second loop from the Tiwanaku River to Lake Titicaca, which would mean that the entire channel covers approximately 17 linear kilometers from the site of Tiwanaku to the lakeshore; of course, the actual length of the canal is greater because it follows local landscape contours.) Seepage and evaporative loss on this canal was substantial because of the large exposed surface area of the water. Transverse excavations across the canal did not reveal any stone or clay lining of the bed, but profiles in the sidewalls clearly indicate multiple cleaning episodes. The choice of a wide, shallow channel profile was made largely to obtain maximum intake elevation in order to sustain a negative slope sufficient to reach field systems toward the distal end of the canal. Given that bed slopes were very small because of the nature of the terrain traversed by the canal (table 6.2), a shallow but wide cross-section was required to obtain sufficient flow rates to compensate for high evaporative and seepage losses en route to the field systems. Because flow velocity is slow (table 6.3), bed and sidewall erosion is

Table 6.3. Approximate Waña Jawira Canal Flow Parameters (B = 9 m, $\Theta_L = \Theta_R = 80°$)

| Flow Height (m) | Flow Rate ($m^3$/second) | Velocity (m/second) | Froude Number | Hydraulic Radius (m) |
|---|---|---|---|---|
| 0.91 | 8.69 | 1.05 | 0.35 | 8.17 |
| 0.61 | 4.60 | 0.84 | 0.34 | 5.77 |
| 0.30 | 1.51 | 0.55 | 0.32 | 3.08 |
| 0.15 | 0.49 | 0.18 | 0.15 | 1.57 |

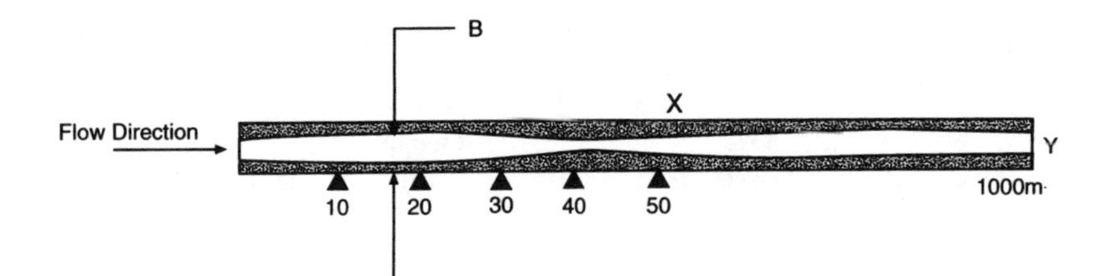


Figure 6.9. A linear top-view of the first 1,000-meter section of the Waña Jawira Canal, illustrating its substantial variations in channel width.

minimal and the capability of the channel to transport suspended load is correspondingly small, resulting in silt deposition. Under these flow conditions, it is not surprising that our excavations revealed multiple episodes of canal cleaning along the Waña Jawira system: by necessity, this was a maintenance-intensive design.

Figure 6.9 shows a linear top-view of channel widths along the first 1,000-meter section of the Waña Jawira Canal. This figure illustrates substantial variations in channel width, with a particularly prominent constriction at station 40, approximately 400 meters west of the current intake. Several measured cross-sectional profiles of the channel along this section of the canal are shown in figure 6.10. These profiles correspond to survey stations 10, 20, 30, 40, and 50 along the canal. The locations and relevant channel parameters of these stations are compiled in table 6.2. In figure 6.10, calculated water height corresponds to $D_n$; $D_c$ is also plotted on these figures. The Flow-3D code was used to compute free surface profiles and was checked against normal depth estimates for consistency. The graphic output confirms the presence of a smooth, transitional flow through the channel constriction at station 40, typical of low Froude number conditions. This constricted segment occurs in the area of lowest slope (table 6.2) and raises local water velocity relative to adjoining channel segments with wider base widths. Because the flow is subcritical, flow height will increase slightly through the contraction segment. The flow that the canal intake will accept depends upon the resistance of the total system as a unit; in practice, because the flow is close to normal depth throughout, local flow characteristics can be closely estimated by use of the Manning equation. Flow velocity is characteristically low, confirming the subcritical nature of the flow and the tendency to siltation with use.

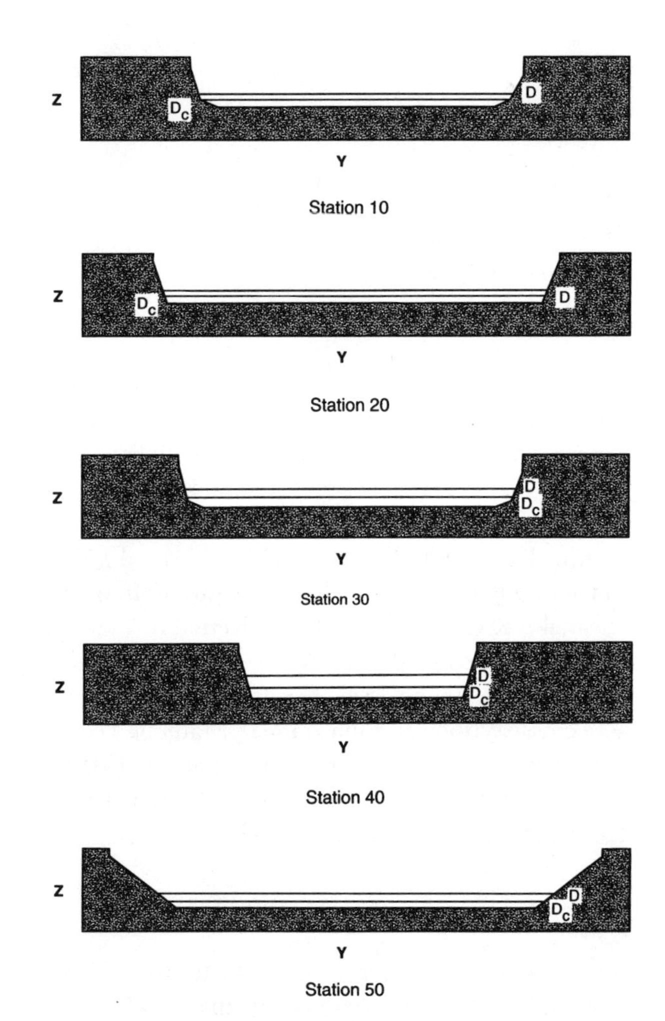


Figure 6.10. A series of five measured cross-sectional profiles of the Waña Jawira Canal. Calculated water height corresponds to $D \cong D_n$; $D_c$ is the critical depth. Flow–3D was used to compute free surface profiles. Stations lie at 100-meter intervals from the intake.

The intake of the Waña Jawira Canal was originally cut just west of the city of Tiwanaku. This position is optimum for a variety of pragmatic reasons. If the intake were farther downstream to the west, an even wider channel would have been required to generate flow sufficient to supply raised fields at the distal end of the canal. Wider channel beds would suffer correspondingly higher evaporative and seepage losses, requiring extraction of larger volumes of river water to deliver the required volume of water to the field systems. If the intake had been placed east of the city, the canal would have been much longer with a significantly steeper slope that would have caused sidewall erosion from the contained supercritical flow. Also, because such a canal would traverse northern portions of the city, seepage from the canal would have contributed to near-surface saturated soils within the urban environment, flooding the ancient city's underground drainage system and rendering it inoperative. Moreover, there would have been a constant threat of flooding of city precincts if the canal levees were breached during a sustained rainy season. The degree of ancient surveying accuracy and indigenous understanding of open channel hydraulics reflected in the design of the Waña Jawira system is comparable to, if not greater than, that achieved in any pre-Columbian society previously studied (Ortloff 1995).

## The Katari Canal System

As described in chapter 5, the state of Tiwanaku constructed a hierarchical system of artificial canals that fed spring and river water to raised-field complexes in the western portions of the Catari River floodplain (see fig. 5.3). The system consists of a latticelike arrangement of several major, east-west trending, longitudinal canals articulated by a series of smaller secondary canals. The larger longitudinal canals served principally as conduits to drain excess water from the agricultural landscape. The principal longitudinal canal in this system was the Catari River itself, which in this section of the basin was canalized and stabilized by construction of earthen levees (fig. 6.8). The river was artificially canalized by diverting the natural drainage course at a point approximately 20 kilometers inland from the lakeshore into a new bed delineated by earthen levees. The diversion and canalization of the natural river opened up immense areas of land to raised-field reclamation in the southern portions of the Catari basin. As noted in chapter 5, we refer to the canalized portion of the Catari River as the Katari Canal. Here we provide a brief analysis of the essential hydraulic characteristics of the Katari Canal system.

As in the Waña Jawira system in the Tiwanaku Valley, water in the Katari Canal is contained by artificial levees. These levees were constructed with large base widths—on the order of 5 meters—to limit the rate of lateral seepage relative to the rate of open channel flow. Channel base width is typically 10 meters, with 45° sloping interior and exterior banks (fig. 6.8). An estimate of lateral seepage from the Katari Canal can be calculated by recourse to Flow-3D calculations for a sudden influx of water through a banked canal into adjacent porous soils. The sequential frames in figure 6.11 model the subsurface progress of lateral seepage. Each frame represents an interval of about 12 days, with frame 6.11D representing conditions at about one and a half months after initial flow.

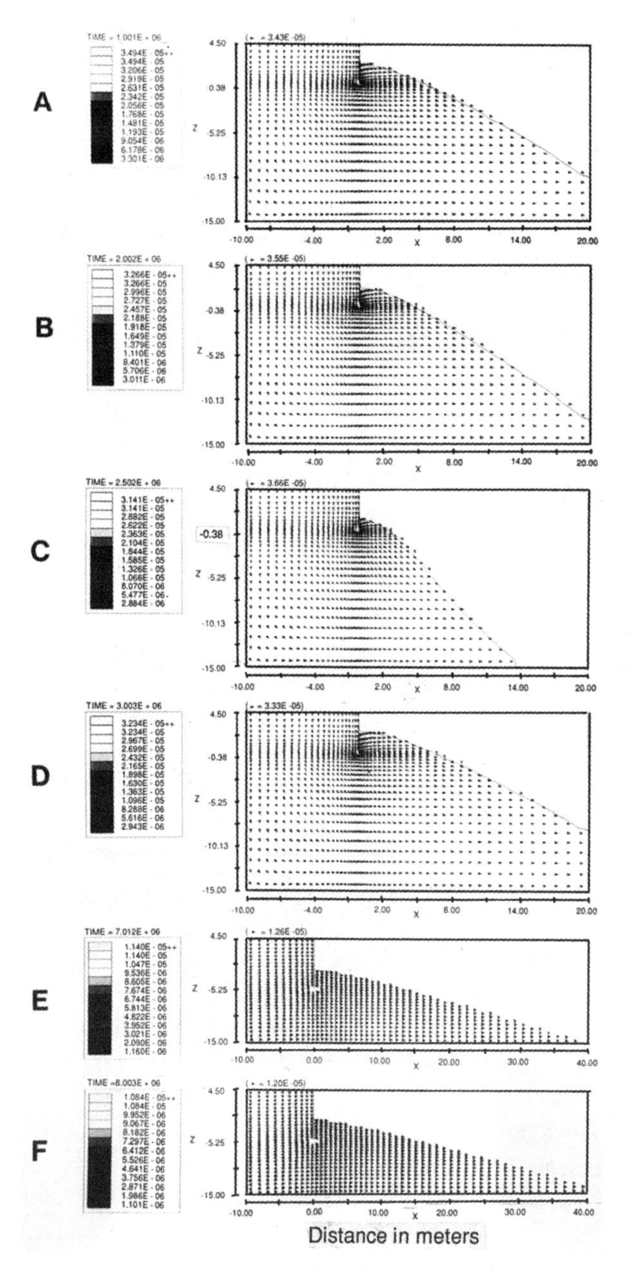


**Figure 6.11.** A computer model of the subsurface progress of transient lateral seepage along the Katari Canal under constant flow conditions at a single typical station. Each frame represents about a 12-day interval; frame D represents conditions at about 90 days past initial flow.

For these calculations, average soil porosity is taken to be 0.03, which is typical of clay-rich soils. In these frames, time is scaled as $Kt/n_e$; that is, if K is doubled, then the legend time is halved for the fluid interface to arrive at a given location. (Recall that K = hydraulic conductivity [cm/second]; t = time [seconds]; and $n_e$ = effective soil porosity.) For the present results, if $n_e = 0.40$ and $K = 10^{-2}$ (typical values for disaggregated soils; see table 6.1) while $n_e = 0.03$ and $K = 10^{-3}$ for the computer calculations, then time scales are approximately the same, so that the frames in figure 6.11 model actual field conditions closely. For the present calculation set, seepage from the canal appears to progress laterally a distance of about 15 meters in one month's time. The worst case scenario of accelerated seepage is for an impervious layer bounding the aquifer from below, as shown in the computer model (–15.0 meters depth). These calculations indicate that for even a month or two of continuous flow in the Katari Canal at a depth of 5 meters (the maximum theoretical capacity), less than 30 meters of adjacent ground is saturated by lateral seepage from the canal. Because this canal skirts the main part of the enormous raised-field system in the Catari River basin, this saturation level would affect only a small proportion of the total area of raised fields situated along the fringe of the Katari Canal itself. Therefore, although some seepage occurs from the canal, water is deposited into a zone restricted to the northern boundary of the main field-system complex.

Clearly, the Katari Canal is extremely effective in limiting lateral seepage from channel flow into the adjacent raised-field system aquifer. The large canal width and canal bed slope (generally between 0.10° and 1°) ensures low channel depths and high flow rates (high Froude number) of the contained runoff water derived from the remote collection zone in the eastern Catari basin. The efficient shunting of rainy season runoff directly to the lake by the Katari Canal largely removes its entry into groundwater reservoirs. Because the ratio of the velocity of open-channel surface transport to the velocity of groundwater seepage is on the order of $10^6$, only a small fraction of the intercepted runoff is returned to groundwater. In the absence of artificial surface drainage systems such as the Katari Canal, groundwater flow alone requires orders of magnitude longer (on the order of several years) to reach the lake from the canal intake zone, thereby inducing ground saturation for extended periods of time.

From this analysis we may conclude that without the regional network of canals described in chapter 5 and illustrated in figure 5.3, sustained, intensive agricultural production over much of the potential arable land in the Catari basin would have been difficult at best, and perhaps impossible. Periodic episodes of drought and inundation in the altiplano would have rendered the agricultural landscape unmanageable, with oscillating groundwater levels causing either excessive soil aridity or supersaturation. Tiwanaku's agriculturalists resolved this chronic, long-term environmental problem by designing a hydraulic infrastructure that could mitigate climate-driven changes in transient groundwater levels on which intensive raised-field production depended.

Although the Katari Canal functioned principally to capture and transport seasonal surface runoff and near-surface groundwater, the canal did not intercept deeper groundwater flows, which entered unimpeded into the raised-field production zones. The Katari Canal, like the Waña Jawira system in the Tiwanaku Valley, is constructed with a shallow channel depth in which the base reaches only slightly below the ground surface. Therefore the canal does not substantially affect deeper groundwater flows. This design artifice permits dry season groundwater to pass underground from the eastern parts of the Catari basin unintercepted toward the Pampa Koani raised-field systems. In the wet season, runoff is both intercepted and shunted rapidly toward the lake, with only a minor canal-to-groundwater contribution.

Our research has demonstrated that hierarchically organized drainage networks embedded in Tiwanaku agricultural landscapes, in both the Catari and the Tiwanaku basins, played a central role in sustaining intensive raised-field production. This interconnected drainage network extended from the level of individual field design to regional canal systems. As a total, regional system, this network promoted recovery of the agricultural landscape after major flooding events, which are endemic to the long-term altiplano climatic regime. The formal analyses presented here enabled us to model the time to recovery of the Tiwanaku hinterland's zones of agricultural reclamation in the context of a rise-fall cycle in the level of Lake Titicaca. We showed that major features of Tiwanaku's regional hydraulic infrastructure, such as the Waña Jawira and Katari canals, exhibit sophisticated elements of design intended to regulate groundwater levels under challenging climatic conditions. This infrastructure was capable of mitigating the agroecological consequences of excessive rainfall or drought by either extracting or conserving surplus water in the zones of reclamation as the prevailing climatic conditions required.

We believe that, when considered as a totality, the

evidence for technical design sophistication, contingency planning, and geographical scope of the manipulation of natural resources indicates an integrated, state-coordinated effort to derive maximum, sustained agricultural output from the Tiwanaku hinterland. In some sense, what we witness in the Tiwanaku hinterland are the efforts of a state to promote agricultural development on a regional scale for the benefit of its rural and urban populations. The organizational implications of our interpretations of the physical design and function of Tiwanaku's agricultural landscape are the subject of the concluding chapter to this volume.

# 7

# Nutrient Fluxes and Retention in Andean Raised-Field Agriculture

## *Implications for Long-Term Sustainability*

HEATH J. CARNEY,
MICHAEL W. BINFORD, AND
ALAN L. KOLATA

As one component of our investigations into the agroecological characteristics of rehabilitated raised fields in the Lake Titicaca basin of Bolivia, we studied major landscape patterns of water, nutrient, and sediment fluxes in a variety of ecotone transects (fig. 7.1). A major conclusion of this aspect of our research is that raised-field systems in this environmental context promote enhanced retention and recycling of major nutrients in comparison with conventional methods of cultivation. Versions of this nutrient retention/recycling hypothesis are implicit in much of the descriptive work on rehabilitated raised fields in the Andes (Erickson 1988b, 1992). Indeed, the proposition has gained nearly axiomatic status, despite a lack of experimental tests to verify and quantify these physical processes.

This chapter provides the first experimentally derived evidence to substantiate this hypothesis. We demonstrate that the anthropogenic landscape of raised-field networks differentially retains mineral nutrients (nitrate and soluble reactive phosphorus) and sediments (measured as turbidity) as water circulates through the fields en route to the lake. Experimental nutrient-limitation bioassays indicate that although nitrogen is generally the most important limiting nutrient in raised-field canals, there is important spatial variability, and phosphorus can also be a limiting factor. We integrate these results with broader considerations of agricultural and regional sustainability. This chapter expands upon conclusions that have been partially published elsewhere (see especially Carney et al. 1993) and provides an experimentally derived (partial) explanation for the high crop yields on rehabilitated raised fields described in chapter 9.

Nutrient availability, consumption, and cycling are critical aspects of agricultural land use. In turn, different agricultural technologies and methods can have a profound impact on essential nutrient dynamics. Inappropriate tillage will induce soil depletion and erosion. In time, chronic application of chemical fertilizers, pesticides, and other synthetic inputs will contaminate downstream watersheds and incur social and environmental costs. But human-induced environmental degradation is not a phenomenon limited to the industrialized societies of the twentieth century. Although the degree of environmental degradation intensified enormously with the advent of industrial activities, negative human impact on local environments has been proposed as a contributing factor in the collapse of several preindustrial societies—the Sumerians, Akkadians, Greeks, Romans, and Mayas, among

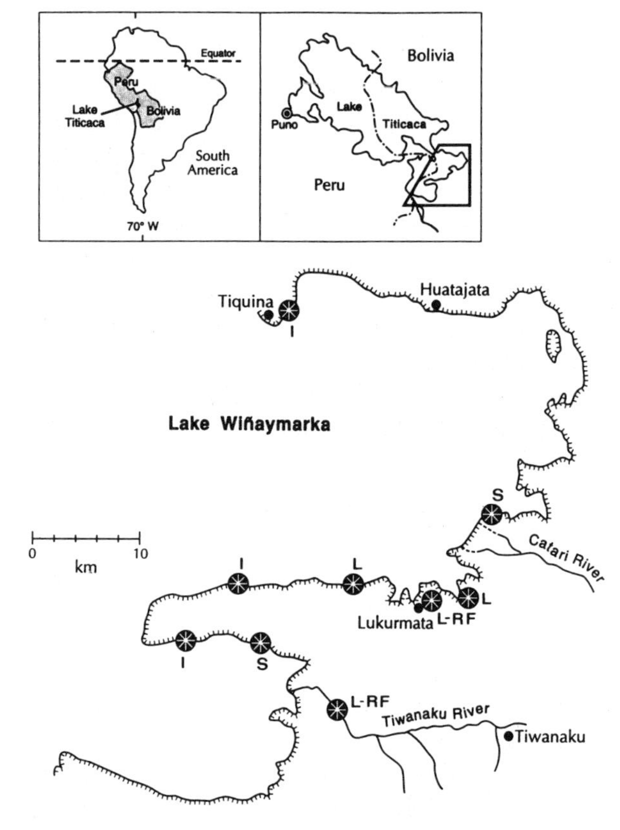


Figure 7.1. The locations of ecotone sampling transects in the study region, as indicated by stars. The two raised-field sites (labeled RF) are at Lukurmata and along the Tiwanaku River. Letters indicate ecotonal transect length: S = short, I = intermediate, L = long.

others (Deevey et al. 1979; Hyams 1952). Cost-effective, environmentally sustainable food production methods with the capacity to support complex societies are rare. The search to discover, develop, implement, and promote such methods has become the focus of the new fields of agroecology and sustainable agriculture (Altieri 1987; Gliessman 1990; Harwood 1990).

In much of the Andean highlands, agricultural soils are low in essential nutrients and organic matter (Godoy 1984). These environmental conditions contribute to poor yields and reduced incomes for indigenous farmers of the region. The inexorable trajectory in these rural zones has been toward declining nutritional and health status, chronic poverty, and, for many, permanent migration to cities. As a result, vast tracts of once-productive agricultural lands have been abandoned throughout the Andean highlands. Clearly, one key to sustainable development there will be the improvement of nutrient conditions and consequently of agricultural productivity. In this chapter we describe important aspects of water use and nutrient dynamics in raised-field agriculture in the Lake Titicaca basin. We identify and discuss specific agroecological processes and practices that can enhance sustainability in this vital Andean environment. Our results have implications both for a historical understanding of the productivity and management of intensive agriculture in the Tiwanaku state and for the design and optimization of contemporary rehabilitated raised-field systems.

## General Nutrient Cycling in Raised-Field Systems

Major nutrient dynamic processes fall within the broad categories of net inputs, internal cycling, and net outputs. We focus here on perhaps the most important and complex element, nitrogen (fig. 7.2), but many of these processes are also relevant to the analysis of the other major and trace nutrients. A major net input of nutrients to raised fields derives from the inflow of water from ground and surface sources to the canals. For nitrogen, this input can include very high concentrations of the major dissolved forms: nitrate ($NO_3^-$), ammonium ($NH_4^+$), and nitrite ($NO_2^{2-}$). Groundwater springs in the piedmont region of our research area immediately adjacent to and upstream from raised-field systems are a particularly significant source of these dissolved forms of nitrogen. Although not quantified to date, nitrogen fixation in raised-field canals may be a second significant source of nitrogen in the system. The aquatic fern *Azolla* frequently grows on the surface of canal water in great profusion, and endosymbiotic blue-green bacteria colonizing the underside of leaves may fix substantial amounts of atmospheric nitrogen. This nitrogen then becomes biologically available to other organisms. Free-living blue-green bacteria (e.g., *Nostoc*) also colonize some of the canals between raised beds and may also fix atmospheric $N_2$.

Management techniques on contemporary rehabilitated raised fields in our research area do not include the introduction of processed chemical fertilizers or pesticides. Thus, commercial forms of nitrogen are not a factor in terms of net nutrient input. However, as noted in chapter 9, small quantities of organic fertilizer, principally dried cattle and sheep manure, are routinely incorporated into the fields prior to seeding. It is likely that pre-Hispanic raised fields were treated with similar soil amendments derived from the waste products of camelid herds, and possibly with addi-

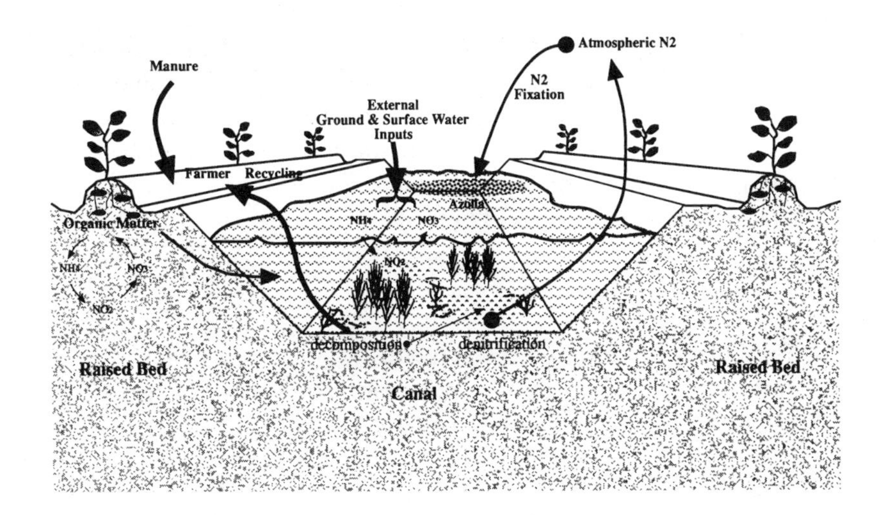


Figure 7.2. Nitrogen fluxes and transformations in raised-field and canal systems. Arrows indicate the pathways of major processes, and arrow thickness indicates the probable relative magnitude of the process.

tional fertilizers from fish by-products. Excavations in buried field segments in the Pampa Koani zone near Lukurmata revealed substantial quantities of fish bones and scales mixed in with the agricultural topsoil. Spanish chroniclers of the sixteenth century such as Cieza de León and Cristóbal de Molina reported that heads of fishes or small, whole fish such as anchovies were frequently planted alongside maize seeds by indigenous farmers on the coast of Peru. This was certainly a pattern that extended back into the period of Inca domination. The use of fish rich in natural oils as fertilizer was apparently a common practice in the pre-Hispanic Andean world wherever sufficient quantities were available. Communities of small, gregarious fish quickly colonize the canals of Tiwanaku raised fields that we have rehabilitated adjacent to Lake Titicaca. Along with the archaeological evidence for fish remains in agricultural topsoils, the proximity and ready availability of small fish in the field canals strongly imply that ancient farmers exploited this rich source of natural fertilizer to maintain and enhance the fertility of their raised fields.

A major process of internal cycling of nutrients that distinguishes raised-field agriculture from other practices is the transfer of organic plant matter by farmers from the adjacent canals to the raised-field platforms. The communities in our research area that are engaged in field rehabilitation practice two principal methods of recycling organic matter. First, live aquatic plant material (algae and macrophytes) are drawn from the water-filled canals, spread over fallow fields, and then worked into the soil. Second, the canals are drained of water during the winter dry season, and the highly organic basal sediments are excavated and redistributed over the surface of the raised-field platforms. This management practice transfers fine, highly organic sediment and detritus as well as decaying plant material. In addition, these procedures serve to maintain both the flow of water in the canals and the structure of the raised beds themselves.

Balancing these organic transfer and decay processes is the uptake of dissolved and available essential nutrients. The two most significant forms of nitrogenous nutrients are nitrate and ammonium. These are major nutrients for both the aquatic plants that colonize the canals and the crops on raised beds. Since both the canal water and raised-field soils are oxygenated, there is likely substantial oxidation of ammonium and nitrite to nitrate. The rates of these processes and the relative uptake of the major nutrients are still unknown, but quantification is a principal goal of our continuing studies into the nutrient dynamics of raised-field agriculture.

The most obvious and easily quantified output of nutrients is the harvesting of crops by farmers. Additional clearing or grazing by animals may also account for significant exports. Within the canals, denitrification may be significant in anoxic areas such as the sediment-water interface. Because there is substantial uptake of dissolved inorganic nutrients in the canals and their concentrations are low at outflows (as we will discuss later), we infer that the output of nutrients is primarily in organic form in the surface and groundwater flows that exit the system. This organic material ranges in size from microscopic colloidal material to suspended detritus (which contributes to turbidity) and larger macroscopic plant materials.

# Materials and Methods

## Transect Sampling

Our sampling strategy entailed establishing a series of nine transects which allowed us to determine (1) the effects of watershed ecotone type (short and simpler versus long and complex), and (2) the effects of land-use type (conventional versus raised field) on the dynamics of nutrient cycling in this system. The horizontal distance from the start of surface water flow to the lakeshore was used to place transects in one of three categories: less than 1.5 kilometers (short), 1.5–3.5 kilometers (intermediate), and greater than 3.5 kilometers (long). With increasing length of transect there is greater diversity and structural complexity in soil type, land use, topography, and vegetation cover through which water flows and can be altered. These transects cut across various kinds of surface water throughout the land–inland water ecotones: small streams derived from emergent springs that feed the raised fields; canals between rehabilitated raised fields or swales in fossil (unrehabilitated) fields; streams and marshes leading to the lake; the several components of the littoral; and finally, open water. Four long ecotone transects, two in raised-field systems and two in areas of conventional land use, are of particular interest here because they were subjected to the most intense scrutiny. At least three points along each transect (near agricultural fields, in the central segment of the respective ecotone, and in the nearshore zone) were chosen for measurement of nutrient and sediment loads. These points included the inflow and outflow points of raised-field systems and comparable locations at other sites.

We collected replicate samples for nitrogen and phosphorus in various forms, other minor nutrients, and suspended sediments along transects crossing all components of the land-water ecotone at monthly (wet season) to bimonthly (dry season) intervals. Samples were preserved, filtered, and prepared in the field for later analyses. Filtration was accomplished with either hand pumps or an electrical pump powered by a generator or battery. We filtered at pressures less than 12 psi (300 millimeters mercury) to prevent rupture of cells and subsequent leakage of nutrients into the filtrate. Analyses were completed in the laboratory in Bolivia or in the United States at the University of California at Davis.

We also sampled for aquatic vegetation (macrophytes and algae) at the same transect points as for nutrients. Qualitative samples of the most abundant taxa (generally two to five) were placed in small plastic containers and preserved with acid Lugol's. Samples were then taken to the laboratories in La Paz and the United States for identification and additional processing.

## Analyses

Chemistry analyses focused on the major forms of the two most important nutrient elements: nitrogen and phosphorus. We analyzed for the two major available dissolved forms of nitrogen ($NO_3^-$ and $NH_4^+$): total dissolved nitrogen and total nitrogen. The following methods were used: modified blue indophenol for ammonium (Liddicoat, Tibbits, and Butler 1975; Solorzano 1969); cadmium reduction for nitrate (Strickland and Parsons 1972); and digestion (APHA 1985) for total Kjeldahl N (TKN). The three major forms of phosphorus were measured with the ascorbic acid–molybdenum blue method (Goldman 1974; Strickland and Parsons 1972). They are distinguished by filtration and acid hydrolysis. The forms are total (hydrolyzable) phosphorus (acid hydrolysis of unfiltered samples), total soluble phosphorus (acid hydrolysis of filtered samples), and soluble reactive phosphorus (orthophosphate; filtered sample, no acid hydrolysis).

Aquatic vegetation was analyzed as follows. The material sampled at a given site was placed in a Petri dish and identified. Macrophytes were identified with the naked eye or a dissecting scope, and algae were identified with a dissecting scope and/or light microscope. Standard identification manuals were used, and voucher specimens were left in the National Herbarium at the Institute of Ecology, Universidad Mayor de San Andrés, La Paz, Bolivia. Taxa in each sample were scored as dominant (abundant), subdominant, or present. The data for dominant and subdominant taxa were then combined with the nutrient data to determine how nutrient concentrations were related to the occurrence of these taxa.

## Bioassays

Nutrient bioassay experiments were performed to determine which nutrients most limited the growth of algae and macrophytes. Fifteen-day nutrient-enrichment bioassay experiments were started with water from raised fields, adjacent streams and rivers, and the littoral region of the lake. Water was filtered through 140-$\mu$m Nitex netting to remove grazing invertebrates and other large particulates and then carefully transported to the La Paz laboratory in 10-liter containers. The filtered water was placed into 500-milliliter sterilized polycarbonate flasks in the laboratory at La Paz. Experimental conditions approximated ambient light and temperature. Treatments included enrichments of nitrogen (700 μg N per liter per day as $NO_3^-$ or $NH_4^+$), phosphorus (100 μg P per liter per day as $PO_4^{2-}$), N + P, silicate, trace elements, and controls (all in triplicate). The following chemical and biological responses were monitored and analyzed every three days: nutrient chemistry, phytoplankton and other algae for enumeration and wet weights, and chlorophyll-*a* fluorescence (Carney 1984). The nutrient additions that significantly enhanced biomass (wet weight or chlorophyll fluorescence) over controls were considered to be limiting under field conditions.

### Statistical Analyses

Data were entered into an Excel spreadsheet program, and additional statistical analyses were completed with a Statview package for the Macintosh computer. Descriptive statistics were calculated for nutrients and species. The different types of transects were compared with paired t-tests and multiple-comparison tests. For the bioassays, one-factor ANOVAs and two-tailed paired t-tests were used to evaluate the effects of nutrient enrichments. Each nutrient addition was compared with the control to determine the statistical significance of treatment effects.

## Results and Discussion

### Nutrient and Sediment Retention

We have found experimental evidence for retention of nutrients and sediments within rehabilitated raised-field systems that are potentially beneficial for agricultural practice. Nitrate is of special interest because it is a major nutrient and can indicate land-use changes with important consequences for water quality (e.g., Addiscott 1988; Hearne and Howard-Williams 1988). Nitrate moves readily through soil and can accumulate in groundwater. As detailed in chapters 5 and 6, groundwater was perhaps the most significant source of water supplying Tiwanaku-period raised fields, and it represents a significant input to the fields that have been rehabilitated in contemporary communities in our research area (see chapter 9).

In the Lukurmata raised-field transect (fig. 7.1), nitrate values were generally higher (mean 4,195 μg per liter N at the inflow to raised fields, number of samples = 6) than in comparable sites of most other transects. Nitrate concentrations then decreased dramatically (mean 57 μg per liter N) as water flowed through the raised-field canals filled with algae and macrophytes (fig. 7.3). The percent concentration in the outflow divided by inflow was substantially lower in this transect (1.4 percent) than in other transects. This double-order-of-magnitude decline in nitrate concentrations in the Lukurmata transect most likely reflects biological uptake in the raised-field canals in these complex ecotones. Experimental nutrient bioassays demonstrated that growth of the aquatic vegetation in the canals was limited by both nitrogen and phosphorous and that this growth lowered concentrations of these nutrients in the canals.

This decline in nitrate concentrations, however, might also indicate denitrification processes in anaerobic canal sediments or a combination of biological uptake and denitrification. Although denitrification has not been measured, it is probably significant at the sediment-water interface in canals where organic carbon levels are high and oxygen is low (Gersberg, Elkins, and Goldman 1984). In many locations, especially in northern temperate regions, denitrification is used to reduce nitrate pollution (Brix and Schierup 1989). This may be the best strategy when the water also has high concentrations of toxins and other waste materials. However, potentially recyclable nitrogen is lost to the atmosphere during this process. Thus, in the environmental context of raised fields in the Lake Titicaca basin, minimizing rather than maximizing denitrification in canals may be a more appropriate management strategy. The most severe problems here are nutrient, particularly nitrogen, deficits, and not toxicity or contamination of the watershed. With low losses of nitrogen, nitrate taken up by aquatic vegetation is ultimately recycled to raised-bed soils.

In comparison with the Lukurmata transect, at the Tiwanaku Valley raised-field site, inflowing nitrate levels were relatively low (83 μg per liter N) because the primary source of water for the fields was the Tiwanaku River and not groundwater as is the case at the Lukurmata site. Photosynthetic algae upstream in the river absorbed and depleted this nutrient. Nitrate was reduced still further in this raised-field system to outflow levels (43 μg per liter N) that were below, but not significantly different from, the Lukurmata out-

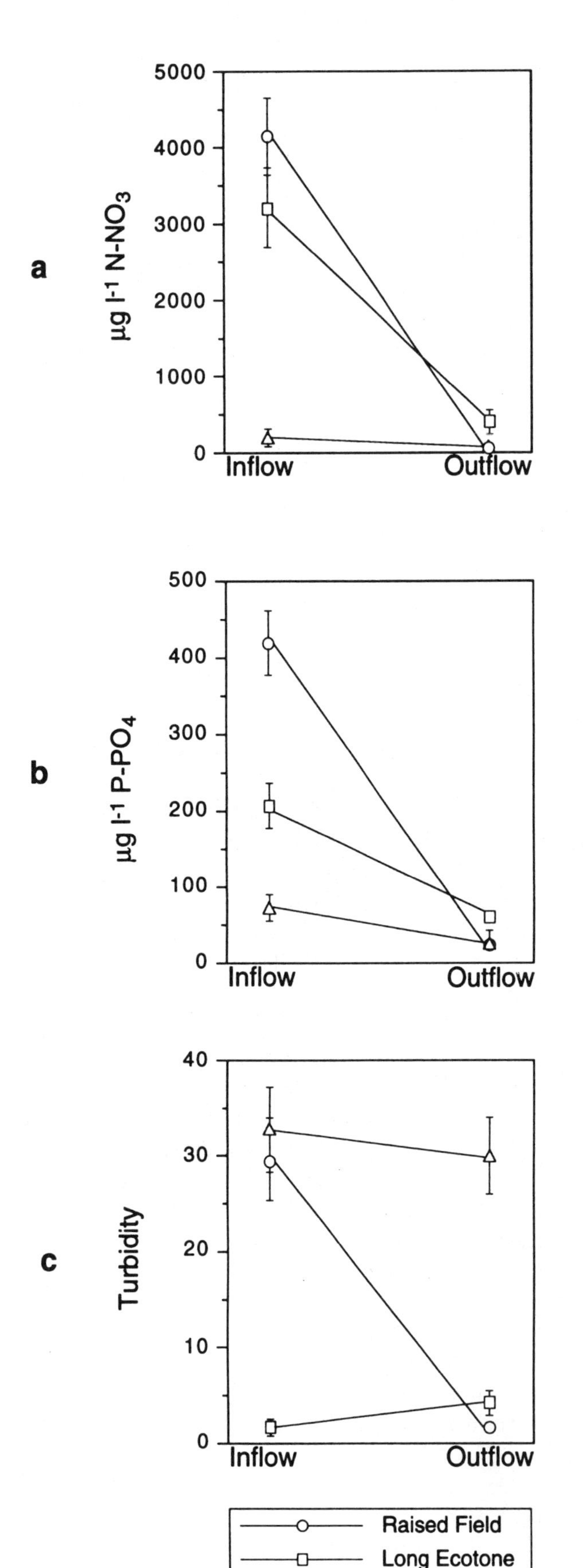


flow values. In the two transects with conventional land use, nitrate levels also declined substantially from inflow to outflow stations. Mean outflow levels (464 and 413 μg per liter N, respectively), however, remained an order of magnitude higher than those at the two raised-field sites (see fig. 7.4).

As in the case of dissolved nitrogen, soluble reactive phosphorus (SRP) also declined dramatically as water passed through the raised fields. This nutrient can adsorb to sediment and soil particles. The inflow concentration in the Lukurmata transect averaged 425 μg per liter P, while the outflow concentrations declined to a mean of 34 μg per liter P ($n = 6$) (fig. 7.3). This was remarkably close to the mean outflow level of 35 μg per liter P in the Tiwanaku Valley transect.

In long, complex ecotone transects transiting conventional land-use areas, nutrient concentrations also decreased, but not as much as in the raised-field sites (Conventional 1: inflow 3,230 μg per liter N-$NO_3^-$ and 209 μg per liter P-SRP to outflow 464 μg per liter N-$NO_3^-$ and 64 μg per liter P-SRP; Conventional 2: inflow 3,338 μg per liter N-$NO_3^-$ and 234 μg per liter P-SRP to outflow 413 μg per liter N-$NO_3^-$ and 69 μg per liter P-SRP). Multiple-comparison tests showed that declines in soluble reactive phosphorous concentrations were significantly greater in the Lukurmata raised-field transect ($p < .05$) than in the adjacent, conventionally farmed long ecotones (fig. 7.3). These results are generally comparable to those for nitrate. In transects cutting across simpler ecotones, nutrient concentrations never decline as much as they do in the complex ecotones en route to the lake. Instead, nutrient concentrations are relatively constant or may even increase as water flows to the lake. If we add nitrate to TKN for total nitrogen (TN), we find that TN:TP ratios were much higher on average in raised-field transects (mean 14.19, $n = 2$) than in other transects not containing raised fields (mean 7.25, $n = 4$).

The transect near the Tiwanaku River also demonstrates that raised fields filter out and settle suspended sediments, thereby dramatically increasing water clarity (fig. 7.3). Many raised fields, such as the Lukurmata site complex, are fed by small streams and springs with clear inflowing water. Fields in the Tiwa-

Figure 7.3. Mean outflows of major nutrients and suspended sediments for raised fields and conventional land use in long ecotones: *a*, nitrate concentration; *b*, soluble reactive phosphorus concentration; *c*, turbidity. Error bars are 95-percent confidence limits.

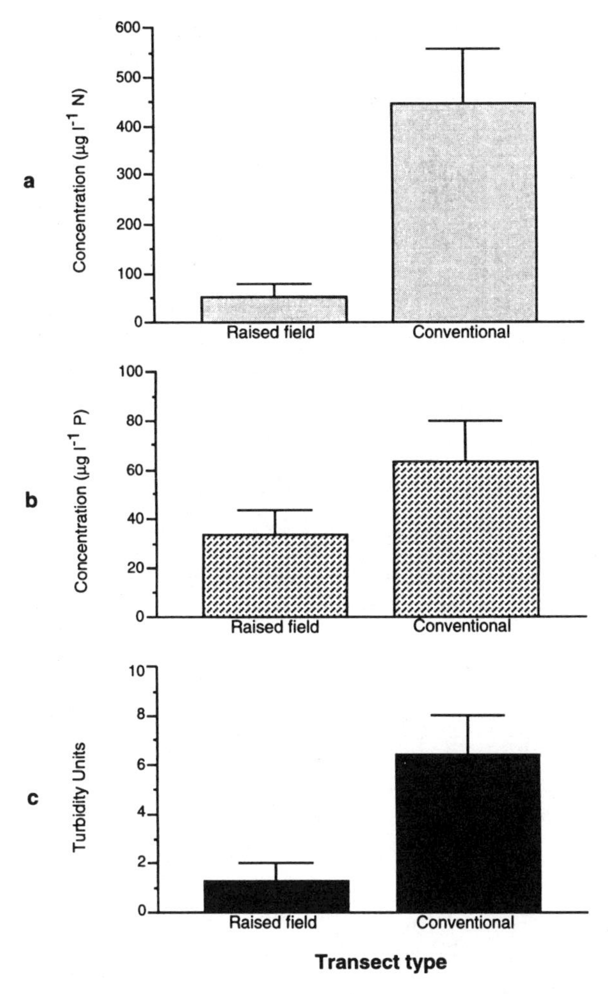


Figure 7.4. Outflow concentrations of nutrients and sediments in two types of transects: *a*, nitrate; *b*, phosphate; *c*, suspended sediments.

naku transect, however, are fed by extremely turbid water diverted from the Tiwanaku River. This turbidity is due to high suspended sediment load in the river. At the inflow to these fields we noted high suspended sediment concentrations (29.5 turbidity units; turbidity was measured as absorbance spectrophotometrically). In the raised fields, in contrast, these concentrations declined substantially to 5 turbidity units as water flow rate declined and particles settled. At the outflow to the lake, sediment concentrations fell to 1.7 turbidity units. At the Lukurmata raised-field transect, water turbidity at outflow was even lower (0.9 units), but there, inflow was derived from clear spring water and so initial turbidity was also low (2 turbidity units). We have not observed such dramatic reductions in turbidity in any other transects. In fact, in the conventionally farmed long ecotones, turbidity *increased* significantly to a mean value of 6.5 turbidity units (fig. 7.3). We conclude that except for the special case of raised-field transects, turbidity is relatively constant within a transect or may even increase as water flows from the hills toward the lake.

Concentrations of nutrients and sediments flowing into the raised-field systems varied substantially according to water source—surface versus groundwater. Therefore, in order to evaluate the retention capacity of raised-field systems, we compared differences in outflow concentrations between pooled raised-field transects and pooled conventional long ecotone transects (fig. 7.4). We found strikingly lower outflow concentrations in raised-field transects for both major nutrients and for turbidity. This pattern of reduction in outflow concentrations of nutrients and sediments reflects enhanced and consistent retention of these materials within raised-field systems. The differences between raised fields and conventionally farmed ecotones were greatest for nitrate (fig. 7.4a). The mean outflow at raised-field sites, 53 µg per liter N, was approximately one order of magnitude lower than the mean at other long, complex ecotones, 441 µg per liter N. Mean outflow concentrations of phosphate and suspended sediments were also significantly lower ($p < .05$) at raised-field sites.

These data suggest that there are certain environmental features of raised-field agriculture that contribute to sustained high crop yields. Major nutrients are sequestered within the agricultural system because they are taken up in dissolved form by aquatic vegetation or are otherwise retained in the canals. In addition, the colonization of raised-field canals by the water fern *Azolla* and its nitrogen-fixing endosymbionts contributes to the production and retention of nutrients in the system. The retention of nutrients and sediments in raised-field systems mitigates problems of landscape erosion and reduces the downstream, near-lakeshore sedimentation and nutrient contamination observed in other parts of Lake Titicaca (Addiscott 1988; Vitousek et al. 1979). As discussed in more detail later, these results have important implications for contemporary management and development plans in the Lake Titicaca watershed.

## Nutrient Limitation

Nutrient limitation in raised-field cultivation systems was determined by whether experimental additions of nutrients increased algal biomass in field samples in relation to controls without nutrient additions. The nutrient(s) that significantly increased biomass over controls were considered limiting at that time. In raised-field canals, phosphorus limitation generally became stronger during the rainy season (December to April) and the beginning of the dry season (fig. 7.5). The strong shift from nitrogen limitation in February to greater phosphorus limitation later in the assay period is compelling. This shift may have been due to increased nitrate inflows and/or nitrogen fixation by blue-green endosymbionts of the aquatic fern *Azolla*.

Bioassay experiments were also completed with samples from adjacent streams and the nearshore zone of Lake Titicaca. There was both temporal and spatial variability between raised-field canals, streams, and the nearshore lake zone. During the assay period, the wet season began in late December and gradually diminished during April and May. During this time, nitrogen limitation decreased in the lake and raised-field canals but increased in streams. Some spatial variability may be attributed to the different organisms assayed in the lake versus the canals and stream.

Our nutrient-enrichment bioassays indicated that nitrogen was generally more limiting than phosphorus for both lake phytoplankton and benthic, filamentous algae of inflowing waters. Ammonium generally enhanced growth more than nitrate when both additions were included. A mixture of trace elements (Cu, Mn, Mo, Zn, and EDTA) did not stimulate algal growth, although this experiment was implemented only once. Addition of both nitrogen and phosphorus enhanced growth substantially more than any of the other treatments. This indicates that the plant community was close to the threshold of nitrogen and phosphorus limitation, and the two nutrients individually also enhanced growth. Occasionally, such as in raised-field canals in July and in streams in March, one element (N or P) was clearly most stimulatory to growth, and the addition of both N and P enhanced growth about the same because the second nutrient had little effect.

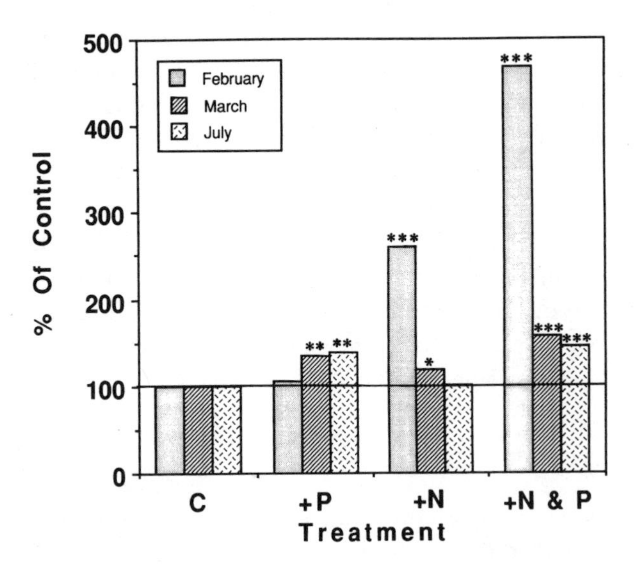


Figure 7.5. Nutrient-enrichment bioassay results for Lukurmata raised-field canals during 1991. Asterisks represent how significantly different the treatment is from the control: * = $p < .10$; ** = $p < .05$; *** = $p < .01$.

## Agricultural and Landscape Sustainability

Although our results are preliminary, we believe they hold important implications for the development of sustainable agriculture in our research area and, more generally, throughout the Andean highlands and other, similar environmental contexts. Sustainable agriculture has been defined by Harwood (1990) as "an agriculture that can evolve indefinitely toward greater human utility, greater efficiency of resource use, and a balance with the environment that is favorable both to humans and to most other species." More specifically, Brady (1990) lists three elements which the United States Agency for International Development considers critical for agricultural sustainability: income generation, especially among the poor; expanded food availability through increased production and improved marketing; and conservation and enhancement of natural resources. Although there are alternative definitions of sustainable agriculture and development, these two examples demonstrate the general overarching themes.

The agricultural productivity of raised fields is reviewed in chapter 9 and elsewhere (Erickson 1988a, 1988b, 1992; Erickson and Candler 1989). The focus in this chapter is on natural resource use, biodiversity, and other important environmental factors. In considering these environmental factors, two interacting spatial scales are particularly important: agricultural fields and canals, and the larger regional landscape. We consider these in turn.

### Agricultural Sustainability

A number of environmental factors significantly constrain agricultural productivity and sustainability in the Lake Titicaca region. Therefore, the problems of environmental degradation and retarded economic development are strongly coupled and should be addressed together. Several production-limiting factors operating at the level of the agricultural fields quickly become clear even to casual observers. First, as noted previously, soils are low in essential nutrients and organic matter (Godoy 1984). Some soils in the region are naturally poor in relative terms. Inappropriate land-use practices can also degrade soils. Since the arrival of Europeans en masse in the mid-sixteenth century, cultivation has intensified in piedmont zones while declining in the lacustrine and riverine pampas (Erickson and Candler 1989). In addition, sectoral fallowing systems that allow soil restoration have broken down with agricultural intensification, population increase, and commercialization in the Lake Titicaca basin (Erickson and Candler 1989; Godoy 1991) and other parts of the central Andes (Orlove and Godoy 1986). These trends exacerbate the loss of topsoil, enhance the tempo of erosion, and contribute to very high sediment loads in streams and rivers that pass through these regions (Carney et al. 1993).

As we have demonstrated empirically, raised fields possess a number of features that improve nutrient capture and recycling. Moreover, two techniques are used regularly to fertilize raised fields (at least among the communities with which we work): harvesting live vegetation and incorporating this organic matter into raised-field bed soils, and recycling the highly organic and nutrient-rich canal sediments. Our work thus far indicates that the processes of nitrogen uptake and denitrification, in particular, need more careful study and comparisons. Such information could help provide the basis for determining optimal management practices. For example, the relative rates of nitrogen uptake and denitrification can be changed by altering the mix of groundwater and surface water flow through raised-field swales, the concomitant dissolved oxygen levels (especially at high altitude), and the amount of aquatic plant cover. The type of aquatic vegetation grown and harvested, as well as the amount and timing of recycling to fields, can have important implications for both soil fertility and water quality.

Although many maintenance techniques on raised fields appear to be both environmentally and economically beneficial, careful study and evaluation are needed to determine the best combination of cultivation practices. One key dimension of systematic evaluation is to regularly monitor raised-field soils in rehabilitated complexes, as well as the water that circulates through them. To date, the high potato yields from recently constructed raised fields may be attributed in great part to the nutrient-rich, long-uncultivated soils of the pampas (Kolata 1991). Initial soil conditions for rehabilitated fields are excellent because fossil fields have been dormant for centuries. It is now essential to monitor major nutrient levels, organic content, salinity, and other physical characteristics of rehabilitated raised-field complexes to determine how they are maintained with present practices.

## Landscape Sustainability

Forman (1991) has emphasized that the landscape is a most critical spatial scale for sustainable development. This is evident for both land use and water quality in the Lake Titicaca basin. Generally, the Lake Titicaca landscape includes the following salient elements: (1) mountain escarpments, hills, and piedmont zones with relatively poor soils, sparse vegetation (grasses, some shrubs, and very few trees), and dry-farmed agricultural fields of low productivity; (2) the lakeside plain, with richer soils and grasses appropriate for grazing livestock and small-scale agricultural activity in better drained areas; (3) the lake itself, together with extensive, adjacent permanent and seasonal wetlands; and (4) a broad range of inflowing waters, from small, seasonally flowing streams to large rivers that flow year-round and transport significant quantities of materials.

With respect to water flow and nutrient flux, an important objective from the perspective of effective human land use of the region is retention of nutrients and other materials before they are removed from the terrestrial landscape into the lake. Currently, there are several important nonpoint sources of materials transported from the land to the lake. Erosion and sheet wash from slopes are accelerated by indiscriminate grazing and agricultural activities. The dissolution of sectoral fallow systems and lack of contour plowing, in particular, contribute to erosion in the piedmont zones. Humans and all major livestock (cattle, sheep, pigs, and llamas) use inflowing streams and rivers heavily. Major human and animal activities involving these inland waterways are travel along the edges, grazing, bathing, drinking, and deposition of wastes. Materials from these activities in the form of nutrients, sediments, and organic matter are transported downstream, particularly at the beginning of the wet season. Largely because of these activities, there is little or no riparian vegetation that can reduce these material fluxes. Mitigating the impacts of these human and animal activities and improving the riparian vegetation corridors are essential for enhancing agricultural productivity.

A second priority in altering and enhancing current land-use practices is to determine the optimal location for raised fields within the Titicaca basin. Several major factors that must be considered in this regard are efficient nutrient and water use for increased productivity, environmental impacts on basinwide hydrology, and integration of high-efficiency raised-field cultivation with other resource use activities. At present, most rehabilitated raised-field sites are situated on broad alluvial plains in proximity to both lakeshore wetlands and nearby hills and piedmont zones (see chapters 2 and 5). Raised-field systems seem ideally located at the base of, or in close proximity to, the piedmont zones in pampas characterized by relatively rich lacustrine, alluvial, and colluvio-fluvial deposits. These locations are favorable for sustained agricultural production because they are close to sources of freshwater, particularly emergent springs; because they possess soils with relatively higher indices of organic matter; and because they intercept nutrients from nonpoint sources of material flux. As described previously, these transported materials can be recycled within the field systems in order to enhance and sustain productivity.

Currently, apart from a few areas with active copper and other mineral mines, most human activities upstream are of low technology and near subsistence level. Consequently, the principal materials flowing into streams and eventually raised-field canals are nutrients, sediments, and organic matter. Therefore, if raised-field agriculture is promoted on a regional scale along with the recycling of sediments from canals, infection from fecal bacteria and other waterborne diseases may become a serious health concern. This problem is already developing in the Catari River drainage basin. The source of the Catari River extends eastward into the metropolitan areas of El Alto, a vast, rapidly growing urban annex of La Paz. The burgeoning population of El Alto, most of whom are recent immigrants from rural mining and farming communities, is grossly underserved by basic services such as sanitary water supplies and sewage systems. New sewage lines have been installed in parts of the El Alto metropolitan region, but effluents are not treated before they flow into the Catari River and its tributaries. The inevitable result has been increasing downstream contamination of the Catari, which traverses some of the most potentially productive raised-field zones. In fact, according to our local informants, the river water is now contaminated to the point at which it cannot be used safely for irrigation purposes or for watering livestock. Even more environmental stress will be introduced into the system if local farmers make greater use of synthetic fertilizers and pesticides, as is the current trend when agricultural credits are made available to them. If these practices continue or increase, the recycling of canal sediments in rehabilitated raised-field systems will have to be reevaluated.

The importance of regional hydrology and climate change for agricultural sustainability is clear (Kolata and Ortloff 1989; Ortloff and Kolata 1993; and see chapters 5, 6, and 8). Hydrological manipulations should be considered carefully. Mean annual rainfall is fairly high in this region (758 millimeters), but so is evaporation. This fact should be taken into account when contemplating plans for water diversion, especially from the lake. Lake Titicaca is already slightly saline (about 1 part per thousand, compared to 35 parts per thousand for seawater). Lake water has a slight yet distinct salty taste, and freshwater organisms are osmotically sensitive at this level. Long-term salinity trends are still uncertain because the relevant hydrological and paleosalinity data are still inadequate. Richerson, Widmer, and Kittel (1977) calculated an increase in chloride concentration from 247 milligrams per liter in 1937 to 260 milligrams per liter in 1973. This analysis needs further verification, but it is clear that lake evaporation is a major factor in water loss that must be compensated for by sufficient freshwater inflows if salinity is to remain relatively low. Economically crucial activities such as fishing and macrophyte harvesting may be dramatically affected by salinity changes. Potential impacts on these activities must be considered in any strategies for the diversion of lake water for terrestrial uses. The littoral and nearshore wetlands also harbor a substantial and unique biodiversity of algae, higher plants, invertebrates, fish, and other animals. Species richness is higher in these zones than in any other part of the basin.

To design a long-term, sustainable plan for human land use in the Lake Titicaca basin, raised-field rehabilitation must be integrated with other major resource uses. Grazing has been the predominant activity on the agriculturally optimal pampas lands. Extensive livestock herding and intensive raised-field cultivation are incompatible during the principal growing season from September through April. This inherent incompatibility has presented us with the greatest number of problems in our attempts to promote raised-field cultivation among the rural communities in our research area. One way to resolve this conflict is to determine the best spatial and temporal combination of these activities within the pampa. For example, raised-field agriculture may be most efficient and productive near zones of high groundwater and surface water flows; herding might then be pursued in the interstices between high groundwater zones. Spatial segregation of herding and raised-field cultivation in zones of optimal productivity for each of them may represent one solution to this problem. Of course, landholding patterns, usufruct rights to land and water, and other such local social arrangements may render this solution untenable.

Another option may be to increase production on raised fields to produce two crops in a single agricultural season, with one cycle of production invested in subsistence and cash crops and the other in high-quality forage, such as alfalfa. We have successfully experimented with double cropping in several communities in our research area. However, instituting a double-cropping regime represents a significant change in social behavior for the Aymara and entails resolving collateral problems of establishing alternative pasture and holding areas for livestock distant from the traditional grazing lands on the pampas. Whatever the solutions devised for specific problems, a guiding principle in integrating raised-field agriculture into total land-use patterns should be to maximize the environmental benefits of wetlands while also providing economic benefits. This principle corresponds to the more general agroecological principle of creating agricultural systems that are functional analogs of natural systems and thus mitigate environmental degradation (Altieri 1987; Gliessman 1990).

## Conclusions

Among the principal results of our research is the observation that there is substantial variation in the flux of nutrients and sediments in the basin of Lake Titicaca related to both ecotone complexity and type of agricultural and other land use. Nutrient and sediment transport to the lake can be reduced in complex ecotones relative to the simpler systems. This reduction may be accentuated where rehabilitated raised fields occur in flat pampas between the lake and surrounding piedmont regions. On the other hand, perennially flowing rivers such as the Tiwanaku and the Catari, which pass through large, complex watersheds and flow into the lake, can accumulate high concentrations of these materials. Nitrogen is the most important limiting nutrient, although phosphorus can also be limiting. In raised-field canals, seasonal shifts to phosphorus limitation may be associated with increased inputs of nitrogen to the system. Rehabilitation of raised fields can have ecological advantages (reduction of nutrient and sediment losses to the lake) as well as economic advantages (increased yields and protection against drought and frost; see chapters 5, 6, and 9). Sustainable development in the Lake Titicaca basin will require continued environmental analysis and monitoring of nutrient fluxes in the complex, lake-edge landscape that is the principal situs of most economically viable human activities, including raised-field rehabilitation.

# 8

# Agroecological Perspectives on the Decline of the Tiwanaku State

ALAN L. KOLATA AND
CHARLES R. ORTLOFF

There is an undeniable material basis to the political integrity of states, archaic or modern, and a large part of any explanation of state collapse resides in the vicissitudes of the production and distribution of wealth. In the preindustrial state, economic well-being was synonymous with agriculture: wealth was generated primarily by intensive farming and not by industry or commerce. This essential truth holds with even greater rigor for the pre-Columbian Andean world, where markets and mercantile activities were, on the whole, nonexistent or at least severely restricted in geographic and economic scope. Not surprisingly, some of the greatest public works of Andean civilization are its monumental agricultural and hydraulic structures, which reshaped entire deserts, mountains, and high plateaus into economically productive landscapes. When we look for the causes of large-scale political collapse in the Andes, then, we might profit from a close analysis of agricultural history.

This chapter examines the collapse of the Tiwanaku state through the lens of its agricultural history. We argue that the direct cause of Tiwanaku's decline as a politically integrated, expansive state society was the deterioration and ultimate abandonment of its regional-scale agricultural systems. We present evidence that the collapse of Tiwanaku intensive agriculture was triggered by regional change in climatic conditions. The full implications of this agroecological-climatological collapse model reach well beyond an explanation for the decline of Tiwanaku alone.

## The Prelude to Tiwanaku Collapse

After approximately 700 years of growth and colonial expansion, the Tiwanaku state disintegrated as a regional political force in the south-central Andes between A.D. 1000 and 1100.[1] Through progressively complex statecraft and apparent economic opportunism, Tiwanaku expanded from its core territory in the Lake Titicaca basin to establish a dispersed network of cultural and economic centers in diverse ecological settings (Kolata 1993b). Tiwanaku cultural, political, and economic presence took different forms in different geographical zones both inside and outside its heartland on the high plateau.

In the Lake Titicaca basin, we can isolate the full panoply of Tiwanaku state action: an integrated network of densely populated, internally differentiated settlements distributed strategically across the landscape, with the capacity to exploit a variety of production zones. In the lower yungas zones lying both east and west of the altiplano, Tiwanaku appears in the form of large-scale colonizing populations which, to judge by their scope and persistence of occupation, were clearly established in permanent residences. The case of the Moquegua Valley of south coastal Peru is a particularly clear example of intense altiplano colonization of a yungas environment for the purpose of directly controlling lower-altitude arable land (Goldstein 1989). This territorial expansion and control of lower-altitude zones, which began late in the Tiwanaku IV phase (ca. A.D. 400–750), qualifies the mature Tiwanaku state as a true imperial system. In the more distant, southerly reaches of Tiwanaku's sphere of influence, such as the high Atacama Oasis of Chile, its physical presence appears most prominently in elite mortuary and domestic contexts, imparting a more specialized, fluid, and transactional quality to the relationship between the altiplano state and its local counterparts.

Although Tiwanaku colonies exploited yungas zones to produce a number of products otherwise unavailable at high altitudes, the economic key to the functioning of the state was the integrated agricultural core area in the Lake Titicaca basin, which operated by means of regional manipulation of land, labor, and, especially, water resources (Kolata 1991, 1993a). Secondary state centers and their immediate rural hinterlands in close proximity to Tiwanaku (for example, Lukurmata, Khonko Wankané, and Pajchiri) appear to have possessed both agricultural self-sufficiency and substantial potential for the production of surpluses that were funneled into redistributive networks incorporating other colonial and administrative centers of empire (Kolata 1993b).

Technical expertise stemming from centuries of empirical observation and experimentation is evident in the planning, engineering, construction, and maintenance of these state agricultural systems. Earlier in this volume, we concluded that the hydraulic control devices essential to the long-term functioning of these systems were sophisticated examples of "designed multifunctionality" responsive to the severe inundation-drought cycles characteristic of the altiplano climatic regime. Consistent with the degree of organizational complexity evidenced in the archaeological record, the administrative resources necessary to coordinate this state-level agricultural system, as well as to implement agricultural innovations to increase crop yields, were clearly in place by the early Tiwanaku IV period, or about A.D. 500 (Kolata 1991, 1993a).

In totality, then, the Tiwanaku state constructed an interlocking and redundant agricultural supply base resistant to collapse and disintegration. Yet despite an apparently secure basis for continued expansion and economic growth, the state and its colonies collapsed after at least seven centuries of successful functioning. The collapse came toward the end of the regional historical period denoted as Tiwanaku V (A.D. 800–1100). Its mechanism is only now emerging as a result of coordinated research into the functions and vulnerabilities of the agricultural base of the Tiwanaku heartland and colonies, together with climatological and ecological data from this period. Recent projects concentrating on Tiwanaku colonial outposts in the Moquegua Valley (Rice, Stanish, and Scarr 1989; Watanabe, Moseley, and Cabieses 1990), as well as at Tiwanaku proper (Kolata 1986, 1989, 1993b), have generated new knowledge that enables us to offer a general historical reconstruction of Tiwanaku's growth and subsequent decline, particularly with respect to its systems of state agricultural production.

In particular, data on climate variation obtained from cores taken in the Quelccaya ice cap (Thompson et al. 1988) in southern highland Peru have permitted us to make preliminary correlations between Tiwanaku culture history and changing ecological conditions, especially precipitation patterns. Such correlations form the basis of the collapse model for Tiwanaku and proceed in the first instance from statistical analysis of the Quelccaya ice cap data. This analysis indicates that an abrupt climate change took place in the south-central Andes during the post–A.D. 1000 era. Recent results from our research team's primary paleolimnological investigations in the southern Lake Titicaca basin corroborate the ice cap data independently.

The paleoenvironmental record of changing climate conditions can be compared with new settlement data from the Tiwanaku Valley and elsewhere in the Tiwanaku state's geopolitical sphere of influence. We show that environmental change in the form of a substantial, regional decrease in precipitation induced progressive collapse of the agricultural systems of the Tiwanaku colonies, followed by collapse of the raised-field systems in the core altiplano area. Because climate differentially affected the various types of agricultural systems supported in each of the dispersed state centers, local responses to climate change were varied yet predictable. The intent of this chapter is to present an integrated view of the coupling of climate and cultural process during the critical historical period in which the Tiwanaku state experienced political fragmentation and ultimate collapse.

## Climatological Data from the Quelccaya Glacier

The most highly resolved record of Andean paleoclimates derives from recent ice coring work at the Quelccaya glacier (Thompson et al. 1985, 1988). The Quelccaya ice cap is located in the Cordillera Oriental of southern Peru, approximately 200 kilometers northwest of Lake Titicaca (fig. 8.1). Thompson and colleagues (1988), by establishing a qualitative correspondence between annual precipitation at the meteorological station of El Alto near La Paz and annual changes in lake elevation, deduce that the Quelccaya record is a good proxy for the level of Lake Titicaca in the twentieth century.

In overview, for Tiwanaku IV and V times, the Quelccaya record indicates wetter periods from A.D. 610 to 650 and from 760 to 1040, and a period of decreased precipitation from A.D. 650 to 730. In the post-Tiwanaku period, from A.D. 1245 to 1310, the region experienced a severe precipitation deficit. High dust concentrations in the ice core, with peaks around A.D. 600 and 920 (fig. 8.2), have been associated with periods of major earth moving, including raised-field construction, in the altiplano around Lake Titicaca (Thompson et al. 1988). Prevailing winds from the altiplano transport particles of dust and organic debris toward the Quelccaya glacier, where they are deposited in snow layers. These particles serve as datable boundaries within the accumulated snow layers and as indicators of unusual events such as volcanic eruptions or, in this instance, large-scale earth moving with its attendant generation of wind-borne dust.

The proximity of the Quelccaya ice cap to Lake Titicaca and the main urban centers of the Tiwanaku state is significant in that climate history derived from analysis of ice cap data can be assumed to have paralleled the historical development of the state. The sections of the Quelccaya ice cap that have been analyzed so far provide a record of climate variation in the south-central Andes from A.D. 400 to 1980 (Thompson, Hastenrath, and Arnao 1979; Thompson and Moseley-Thompson 1987, 1989; Thompson et al. 1982, 1985). The basic data are cumulative measurements of annual snow deposits. The thicknesses of annual layers, measured in cores extracted from the ice cap, are shown in figures 8.3–8.5, which present data for the period from A.D. 800 to 1400.

In simplest terms, large values for snow layer thickness indicate heavy annual rainfall at lower altitudes; small values imply years of lower rainfall. Although numerous wet periods exist in the record as illustrated in these figures, and severe drought is certainly im-

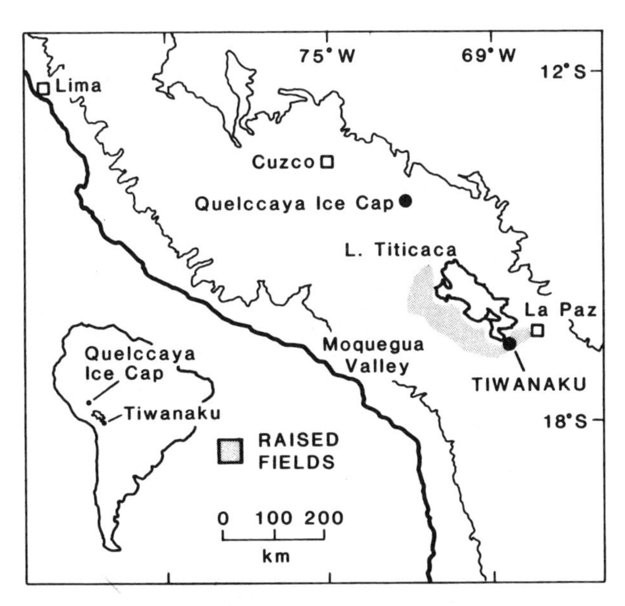


Figure 8.1. Locations of the Quelccaya ice cap and the Moquegua Valley in the south-central Andes.

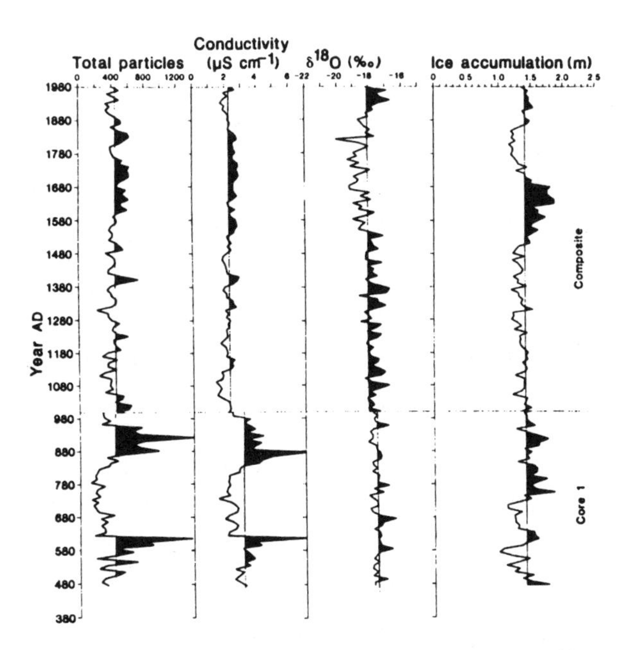


Figure 8.2. Total particles, conductivity, isotopic oxygen, and ice accumulation for the Quelccaya ice cap, A.D. 400–900 (from Thompson et al. 1988). Note particle accumulation peaks at A.D. 620 and 950.

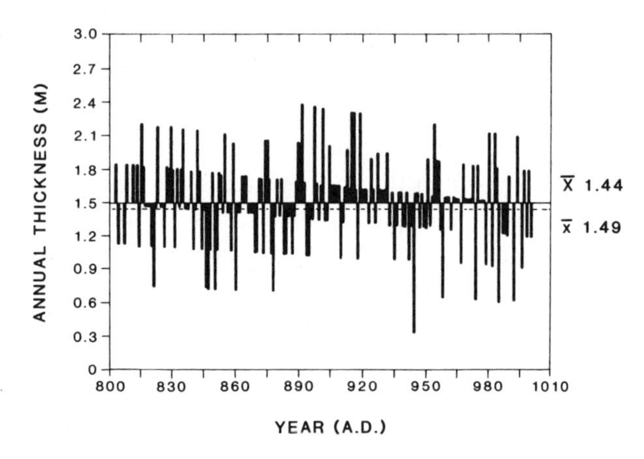


Figure 8.3. Thickness values for annual layers in the Quelccaya ice cap, A.D. 800–1000.

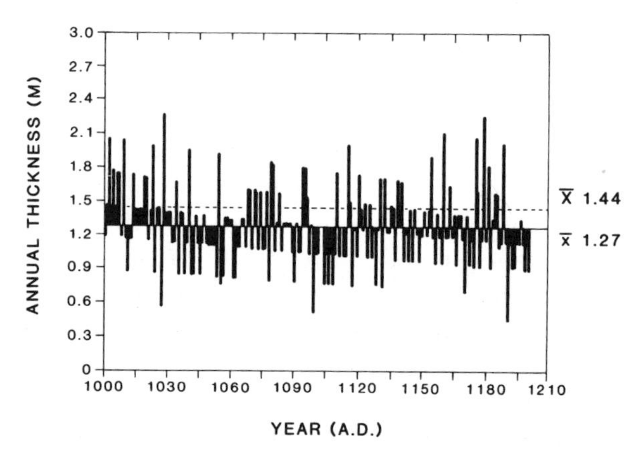


Figure 8.4. Thickness values for annual layers in the Quelccaya ice cap, A.D. 1000–1200.

plied for the period from A.D. 1245 to 1310, the data reveal clear trends only through statistical analysis. Over 200-year intervals from A.D. 800 to 1400, mean annual snow layer thickness progressively declined, as is indicated by the values shown in figures 8.3–8.5. The $\overline{X}$ and $\overline{x}$ values in the illustrations represent 200-year averages of snow layer thicknesses above and below the mean layer thickness, respectively. Replotting the data in terms of a three-year (fig. 8.6) and a nine-year (fig. 8.7) moving average from A.D. 800 to 1400 reveals more clearly the sequence of change in precipitation levels. Although vigorous fluctuations in precipitation certainly existed over decades, there was a statistically significant change in mean moisture level beginning after A.D. 1000.

If the ice core thickness distributions are integrated to emphasize mean changes in precipitation levels, a smoothed, time-dependent measure of precipitation can be obtained (fig. 8.8). The curve illustrated in

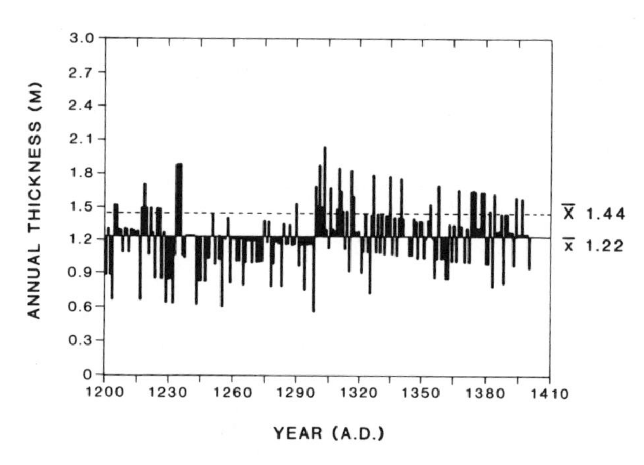


Figure 8.5. Thickness values for annual layers in the Quelccaya ice cap, A.D. 1200–1400.

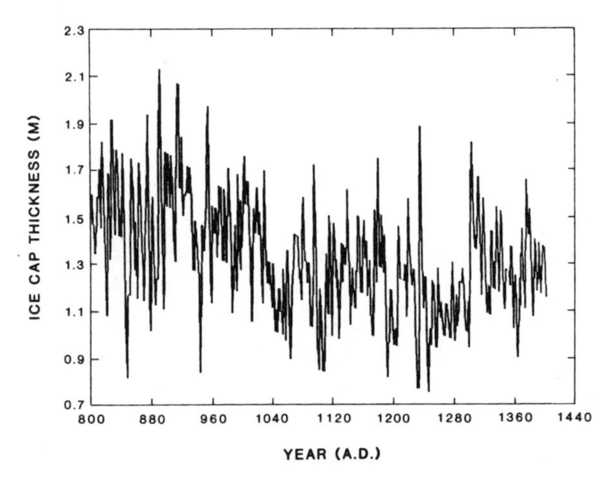


Figure 8.6. Three-year moving average of ice cap thickness values, illustrating the post–A.D. 1000 change in mean precipitation level.

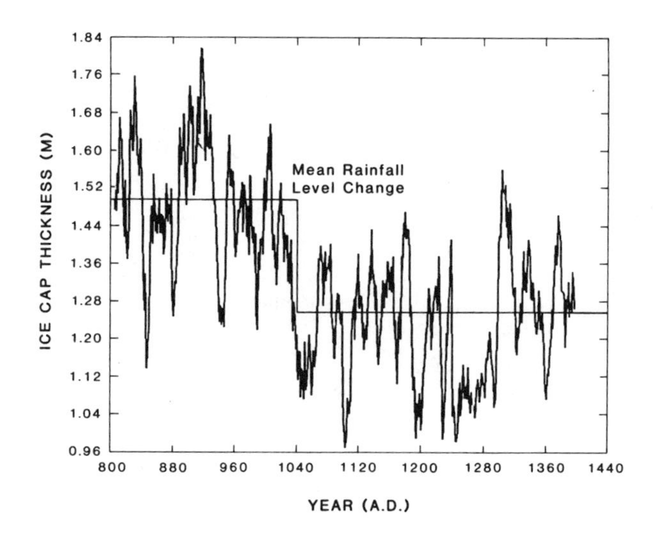


Figure 8.7. Nine-year moving average of ice cap thickness values. This plot provides an enhanced graphic display of the post–A.D. 1000 decline in mean precipitation level.

figure 8.8 is obtained by time integration of the ice cap data displayed in the nine-year moving average plot (fig. 8.7). Initially, the overall mean value of snow layer thickness over the entire time range of the plot is found. The area above this mean value is denoted as positive; the area below it is denoted as negative. The integration then reveals large-scale changes in mean layer thickness, while small fluctuations are deemphasized. Note that the integration parameter (y-axis) for the curve in figure 8.8 is given as "m-yr" (meter-year). In this curve, if the precipitation level is constant, for example, a linear rise is expected in the integrated result. Deviations from linearity indicate either excessive rainfall or drought, depending on the position of the integrated curve with respect to the linear result.

Figure 8.8 illustrates a gradual change in precipitation starting around A.D. 950, as is indicated by the slope change at that time (marked in the illustration as point A), followed by a precipitous change in moisture content commencing after A.D. 1000 (point B). This shift reflects the statistically significant change in mean level of precipitation from the pre– to the post–A.D. 1000 time period. A short uptick in moisture level appears in the curve at about A.D. 1300, followed by a decline starting about A.D. 1350 and extending at least to A.D. 1400. The departure of the integrated moisture curve from linearity in the period from A.D. 1050 to 1200 indicates several excursions of increased rainfall from the lower mean level characterizing the post–A.D. 1000 period as a whole. Generally, the integrated curve translates into a much drier climate on average in the years after A.D. 1000 than in earlier times.[2]

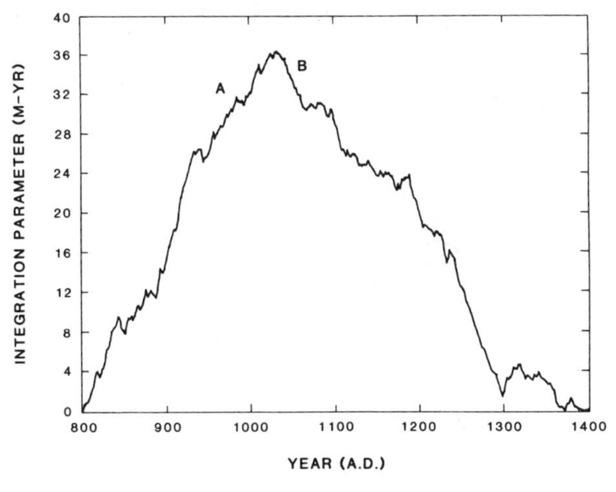


**Figure 8.8.** The curve derived through time integration of the nine-year moving averages of ice cap thickness displayed in figure 8.7.

In addition to changes in precipitation, an estimate of prevailing temperatures at the Quelccaya glacier can be obtained from isotopic $^{18}$oxygen ($^{18}$O) measurements taken along with those of ice layer thickness (Thompson et al. 1988). These measurements indicate a rise in mean annual temperature of between 0.5° and 1.0° C beginning around A.D. 1000 and persisting until at least A.D. 1400. Of course, this mean temperature increase should be interpreted in a statistical sense, considering that fluctuations of ± 1.0° C from the mean appear during this time period.

The A.D. 1000–1400 temperature rise has been observed in Europe as a phenomenon termed the "Medieval Warm Epoch" (Anderson 1991; Lamb 1965, 1982). Crops normally grown in the southern parts of Europe flourished even in the Scandinavian countries, leading to a period of economic prosperity throughout Europe. Vineyards and associated wine production peaked during this time, because of the mildness of the climate. The general rise in temperature was not, however, without negative collateral effects: devastating torrential rains occurred frequently in Europe in the fourteenth century, destroying the economic gains of earlier periods (Lamb 1965).

Judging from the Quelccaya ice cap data, the Medieval Warm Epoch appears to have extended into the Western Hemisphere; this climate change was probably a global phenomenon. Subsequently, the post–A.D. 1500 era was characterized by a drop in mean annual temperature of approximately 1.3° C, which lasted up to A.D. 1890. This phenomenon has been termed the "Little Ice Age" and again appears to have been a global effect (Grove 1988). During the A.D. 1000–1400 period in the Quelccaya area, both a temperature rise and a precipitation deficit occurred simultaneously. These phenomena may have been related, but it is problematic to couple them. For example, the first few centuries of the Little Ice Age were characterized by an average precipitation increase of 25 percent, while the later centuries saw a 20 percent decrease in mean precipitation (L. Thompson, personal communication, 1991).

## Climatological Data from Lake Titicaca

Our research team's paleolimnological work in Lake Titicaca supports the Quelccaya evidence for climate change (Binford and Brenner 1989; Leyden 1989).

According to pollen data from a lake sediment core, the lake level was significantly higher than usual between about A.D. 350 and 500, implying increased precipitation, decreased evaporation, or both. The 98centimeter-long core (22-VIII-86-1) was extracted from water 2.5 meters deep approximately 65 meters offshore northwest of the site of Lukurmata (see fig. 4.1) and represents about 2,000 years of sediment accumulation (Binford, Brenner, and Engstrom 1992). An elevated lake level is marked by a dramatic rise in pollen from aquatic macrophytes, specifically *Ruppia* (widgeon grass), *Myriophyllum* (water milfoil), and *Elodea* (water weed), and from the planktonic alga *Pediastrum boryanum* in the midcore section between 40 and 60 centimeters (see fig. 4.12). The sediments from 40 to 44 centimeters in this section have been radiocarbon dated to 1445 ± 210 B.P., uncorrected. This increase in aquatic macrophytes and planktonic algae co-occurs with a decrease in sedges, almost certainly totora (*Schoenoplectus totora*). Leyden (1989) interprets this pollen distribution as a result of lake level rising over the core site, drowning the sedges and promoting the expansion of aquatic macrophytes and algae (see chapter 4). Sediments in the upper 30 centimeters of the core then exhibit a resumed dominance of sedges and a concomitant decline in aquatic macrophytes (see fig. 4.12). The pollen distribution in the upper third of the Lukurmata core reflects a lowering of lake level and a return to littoral conditions at the coring site (Leyden 1989). Age-depth estimates on these sediments place this decline in lake level within the post–A.D. 1000 period of desiccation recorded in the Quelccaya ice cap.

Recent work on additional sediment cores extracted from the Wiñaymarka basin corroborates our inferences about changing lake levels based on the palynological data from the Lukurmata core (22-VIII-86-1). In this work, we are examining long-term lake-level fluctuations recorded in the stable isotope record preserved in lake sediments. Specifically, we are using the $\delta^{18}O$ signal in ostracods, gastropods, and bulk carbonates from radiocarbon-dated cores in the Wiñaymarka basin to obtain a high-resolution paleoclimatic record for the altiplano (Brenner et al. 1993). Preliminary interpretations of the stable isotope record analyzed for core 14-VIII-92-D are instructive. As summarized by Brenner and colleagues (1993), the dates and sediment geochemistry near the base of this core indicate a hiatus in sedimentation from before 6500 B.P. to about 3500 B.P., at a core depth 10 meters below the 1992 lake surface. This hiatus indicates a period of extreme aridity and extremely low lake levels. Evidence for a rapid rise in lake level beginning about 3400 B.P. is reflected in the Lukurmata core and in two other cores extracted from the lake around Huatajata and Guaqui, respectively (fig. 8.9).

As discussed in chapter 2, these lake-level changes are directly relevant to the early history of agricultural expansion in the southern Lake Titicaca basin. The core interval above 1.5 meters is of direct concern to our focus in this chapter—that is, the relationship between climate change and the agricultural collapse of the Tiwanaku state. Although it is rather subtly indicated in the gross stratigraphy of core 14-VIII-92-D, there appears to be a hiatus in sedimentation just be-

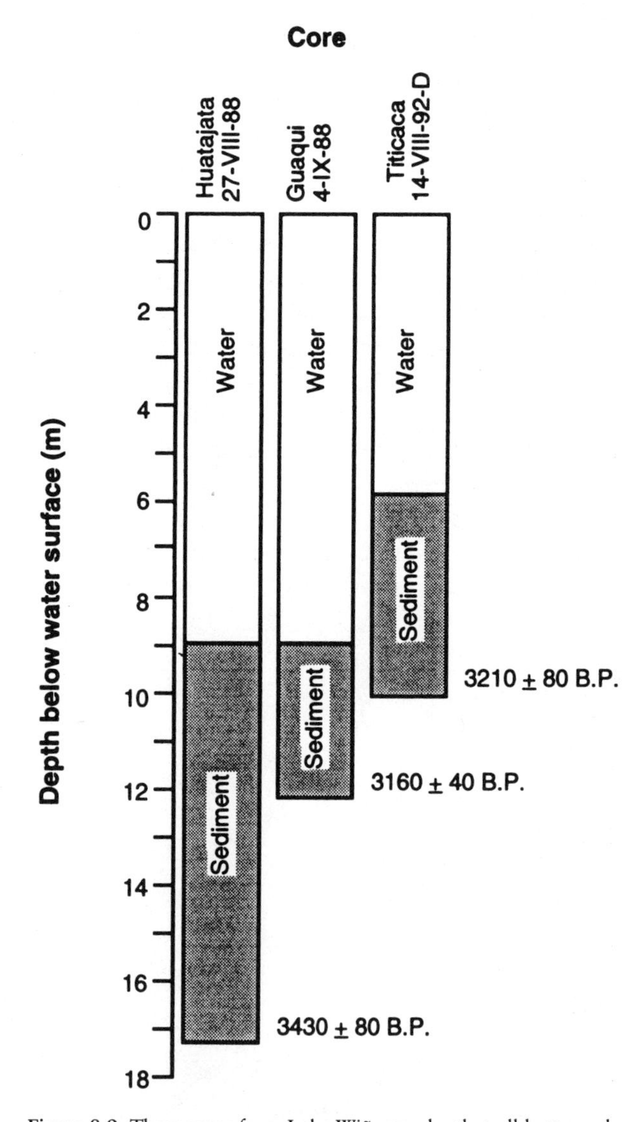


**Figure 8.9.** Three cores from Lake Wiñaymarka that all bottomed on indurated, fine-grained sediments. Dates near the core bases are similar, suggesting that water level rose quickly after about 3500 B.P.

low 1 meter in depth, signaled by the geochemical profile and by the greater than 1,200-year age difference between samples at 1.0 meter and 1.5 meters in the core. The $\delta^{18}O$ samples in this interval indicate a drying trend during the same period documented as relatively dry in the pollen record from the Lukurmata core (fig. 8.10). We should note that we currently have too few $\delta^{18}O$ sample points to confirm this drying trend to a satisfactory degree of confidence from stable isotope patterns alone. Work in progress should resolve this issue. Nevertheless, our interpretations of lake-level fluctuations (and, by inference, changing precipitation), grounded in stable isotope data and the pollen record, respectively, from lake sediment cores, are consistent with each other and with the patterns emerging from the independently derived Quelccaya ice cap data.

Our paleolimnological research indicates that periods of cultural change (initiation, intensification, and abandonment of agriculture) in the Lake Titicaca basin coincided with changes in the water balance of Lake Titicaca that are directly expressed in lake sediment cores (fig. 8.11).[3] In every core we have studied so far, there occurs a transition from gray clays and silts, with an erosion surface at the top of the gray clay, to organic, laminated sediments. The clay appears similar to inorganic clays of Pleistocene age that underlie organic-rich sediments in many neotropical lakes (Bradbury et al. 1981). These clays may be formed by a process of soil formation followed by flooding. When lake level rises, newly inundated mineral soils are saturated and reducing conditions are created, leading to gleyization, predominantly reduction of ferric iron ($Fe^{3+}$) in soil minerals to ferrous iron ($Fe^{2+}$). As the lake level rises further, organic sediments are deposited over the gley soil. Therefore, we interpret the gray clay as a mineral soil that developed prior to about 3500 B.P., indicating a period of lower lake level and drier climate, and the laminated, organic sediments as having been deposited during the higher stand after about 3500 B.P.

Radiocarbon dates at the transition from gray clay to organic lake sediments are concordant in all cores, despite the fact that the contact zone ranges over 10 meters in elevation and the samples were taken at sites more than 25 kilometers apart (fig. 8.11). Lake level must have risen rapidly when net precipitation in the Lake Titicaca basin increased. The lowermost date obtained from any of the cores (core A in fig. 8.11, at 3,789 meters above sea level) is 3540 ± 60 B.P. (the calibrated date, adjusted by 375 years for

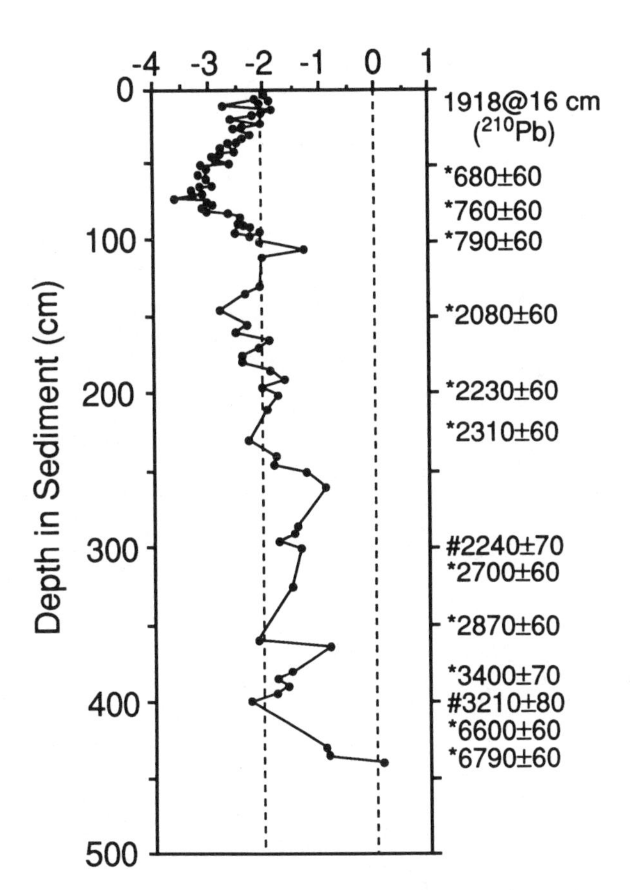


**Figure 8.10.** Values of $\delta^{18}O$ from ostracods (*Limnocythere* sp.) in Lukurmata core 14-VIII-92-D, and preliminary interpretation of the record. AMS $^{14}C$ ages are shown along the right side of the figure. Key: * = date on gastropod shell; # = date on sedge seeds (2240 ± 70 B.P.) or miscellaneous plant material (3210 ± 80 B.P.).

contemporary reservoir radiocarbon, is 1420 ± 117 B.C.) (see Stuiver and Reimer 1993). The lake was more than 19 meters lower than today until about 3,500 radiocarbon years ago but rose more than 10 meters during the subsequent 300 to 400 years. These lake-level data predate the paleoclimate record from the Quelccaya ice cap by more than 500 years.

Stable oxygen isotopes extracted from ostracod carapaces indicate highly evaporative lake environments both prior to 1300 B.C. (calibrated) and around A.D. 1100 (fig. 8.11, core E). The $\delta^{18}O$ of lake water in tropical regions, where there is a distinct dry season and most water loss is through evaporation, is controlled mainly by the ratio between evaporation and precipitation (E:P) (Fontes and Gonfiantini 1967; Gasse et al. 1990). Therefore, variations in $\delta^{18}O$ in monospecific samples of ostracods (*Limnocythere* sp. and *Amphicypris* sp.) are interpreted as having been caused by changes in E:P. The general decrease in oxy-

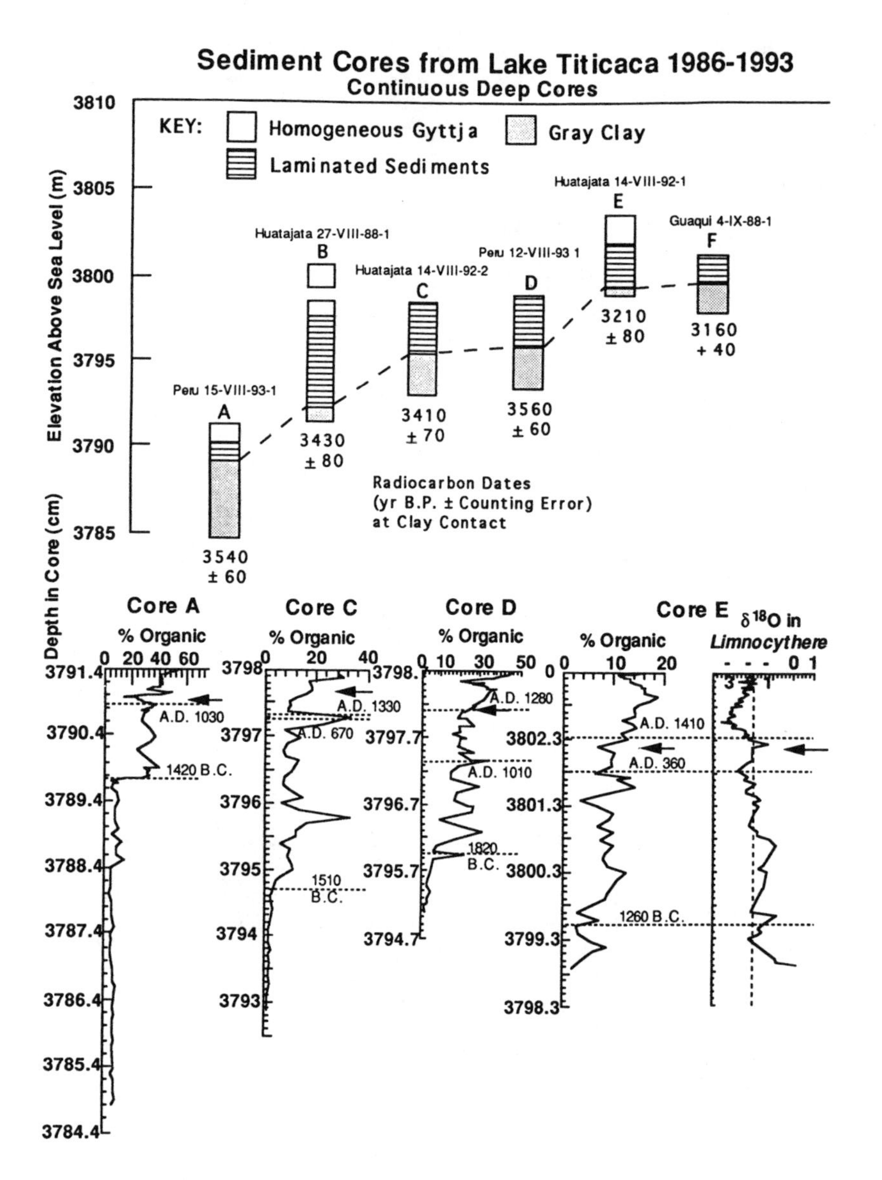


Figure 8.11. Selected gross stratigraphies, basal radiocarbon dates, $\delta^{18}O$ (for one core), and sedimentary organic matter content of six cores along a depth transect in Lake Wiñaymarka. Cores are composites of sediment-water interface cores, extruded and subsampled immediately, and cores taken with a square-rod piston corer. AMS radiocarbon dating was done at the Lawrence Livermore Laboratory, Livermore, California, on samples prepared at the Limnological Research Center, University of Minnesota, Minneapolis. The core stratigraphies are shown relative to elevation above sea level. Core field labels and water depth at the time the cores were taken are as follows: *a*, Peru 15-VIII-93-1 (16.6 meters); *b*, Huatajata 27-VIII-88-1 (8.8 meters); *c*, Huatajata 14-VIII-92-2 (11.1 meters); *d*, Peru 12-VIII-93-1 (9.3 meters); *e*, Guaqui 4-IX-88-1 (8.3 meters); and *f*, Huatajata 11-VIII-92-1 (2.1 meters).

gen isotopic ratios from 400 centimeters through 150 centimeters in core E indicates increased moisture and higher lake levels (fig. 8.11).

The paleolimnological evidence for drought at A.D. 1100 is less obvious than the evidence for the post–1500 B.C. lake-level rise, but it is indicative nonetheless (fig. 8.11). Sequences of radiocarbon-dated core sections demonstrate similar and steady sediment accumulation rates at all sites for most periods after about 1500 B.C. Sedimentation hiatuses, indicated by dates of very different ages in close vertical proximity, occur in the two shallower of the three cores that have been dated at close intervals. Hiatuses show clearly in cores C and E, but not in core A, which was deeper than the decline in lake level.

Lithological and chemical stratigraphies indicate a period between calibrated dates A.D. 1030 and 1330 during which sediments lower in organic matter and higher in bulk density were formed. These two dates were selected from cores A and C and are, respectively, the latest radiocarbon date before the sedimentation hiatus and decline in organic matter content and the earliest date after the hiatus and organic decline.

We interpret the sharp variations in organic matter content in the cores to be the result of a rapid and profound drought that resulted in a much shallower lake. The sedimentation hiatus in core C occurs at approximately 3797.30 meters above sea level, so the lake level would have been between this elevation and 3791.95 meters, the contemporaneous horizon in core A. Thus, the lake was at most 5.35 meters deep at the site of core A during the drought.

Littoral vegetation supplied large amounts of organic matter to the sediments at sites C and D when the lake was lower, and the lack of desiccation has preserved the higher concentrations. However, site D is closer to the shore than the locations of the other cores, so inorganic sediment generated by terrestrial erosion diluted the organic matter. Site C, although only 2 meters deeper than site D, is sufficiently deep to avoid desiccation in all but the severest drying periods. We interpret the peaks of organic content at 220 centimeters and 70 centimeters in core C to be the result of lower lake levels that brought the site into the littoral zone. Large amounts of organic matter were then deposited, as they are now in shallow water (Binford, Brenner, and Engstrom 1992:29–39). The lake declined further, exposing the site, but for a time short enough that when the lake rose again, new sediment buried the remaining organic-rich soils. The lake level was not far below the elevation of core C, and for at least the period of lower precipitation, it may have fluctuated much like that of the modern lake.

These data indicate a period of low lake level leading to drying and oxidation of exposed lake sediments, mineralization and proportional decrease in organic matter in the sediments from sites at higher elevations, increased but periodic exposure to littoral input of organic material at sites in middle elevations, and decreased input of organic matter at sites in lower elevations. Values for $\delta^{18}O$ in ostracod carapaces are heavier above, below, and through the zone of shallower lake levels, indicating a relatively higher E:P ratio. The consistent sedimentation hiatus seen at widely distributed coring sites indicates a lake-level decline of greater than 12 but less than 17 meters. The transition to the corresponding period of reduced ice accumulation in the Quelccaya glacier took only a few years, and the decline in level at Lake Titicaca may have been as abrupt. A simple climate–water budget model calculates that a 10–12 percent decrease in net precipitation from the modern average could cause the 12-meter to 17-meter lowering of the lake (Hastenrath and Kutzbach 1985). A decrease of 12 meters would reduce the surface area of the whole of Lake Titicaca from its current 8,490 square kilometers to 6,398 square kilometers; a drop of 17 meters would bring it to 5,859. The smaller Lake Wiñaymarka would drop from 1,400 square kilometers to less than 60. In effect, during the post–A.D. 1000 drought, most of Lake Wiñaymarka disappeared. Such a precipitation decline is within the range of interannual variability for the twentieth century and is less severe than that measured at the Quelccaya glacier.

## Raised-Field Chronology and Association with Settlement Patterns

Archaeological excavation of 193 randomly selected test trenches, along with survey in a 70-square-kilometer region of the Catari River basin, revealed the principal periods of construction, use, and abandonment of raised-field systems and their relationship with human settlement. Construction techniques for the raised fields were remarkably homogeneous across the sampled trenches. Most fields presented uniform profiles (fig. 8.12): they were constructed by excavating canals and mounding sediments between them to create a raised platform upon which crops were cultivated. Ancient cultivation horizons were usually well preserved in the profile as highly mottled, black, organic sediments. After the fields were abandoned, they eroded slightly and then were covered by 25 to 50 centimeters of homogeneous fine clay and silt derived from aeolian and fluvial sources, an erosional process continuing today. Recovery of terrestrial carbon samples as well as freshwater snails (*Taphius montanus*) from various stratigraphic contexts clearly defined the sequence of construction, use, and abandonment of the raised fields.

Ten of fourteen radiocarbon assays from raised-field construction and use contexts date between A.D. 600 and 1100, indicating that this was the most intensive period of raised-field cultivation (fig. 8.13, table 8.1). As noted earlier, this period of intensive agricultural activity coincided with increased precipitation in the region. A tight cluster of seven dates from post-abandonment sediments occurs in the interval between A.D. 1200 and 1300. These dated sediments accumulated after field abandonment; therefore the time of regional raised-field abandonment was prior to A.D. 1200. Although there is some evidence of small-scale use of the raised fields after A.D. 1100, the major period of regional construction and use of the system occurred in the late Tiwanaku IV and Tiwanaku V periods (A.D. 600–1100) (Seddon 1994).

Associated settlement patterns further support this conclusion. During the Tiwanaku IV and V periods, most settlement in the Catari River basin occurred in nucleated centers closely associated with raised fields (Kolata 1993a). Roads and elevated causeways frequently linked raised-field zones with these nucleated

**Figure 8.12.** Raised-field excavation profile. The trench extends from the middle of the raised field to the middles of the adjacent canals. Immediately below the surface are homogeneous clay sediments that accumulated after the field was abandoned. Note the internal structure of the original raised-field bed, which incorporates black organic cultivation horizons and, immediately below the post-abandonment sediments, a light, mottled loam that reflects field maintenance and canal cleaning events.

settlements. In contrast, after the collapse of the Tiwanaku state, settlement consisted of small occupations (< 1 hectare) dispersed throughout the basin, with no apparent orientation to the raised fields. This pattern is repeated in the Tiwanaku Valley and in areas of Tiwanaku-related raised fields in the Juli-Pomata region of Peru (Albarracín-Jordan and Mathews 1990).

Thus, direct dating of raised fields, as well as analysis of associated settlement patterns, indicates that the period of most intense raised-field cultivation occurred between A.D. 600 and 1000, and that raised field agriculture was no longer a major economic activity in the region by A.D. 1200. We directly associate this trajectory in the space-time dynamics of agriculture and associated settlement with the climatic change that was affecting the Andean altiplano in the era after A.D. 1000. This climate change had an agroecological impact on South American civilizations as profound as its historically documented effects on western European societies, cited earlier. The specific effects of these changes on Tiwanaku agricultural systems will be examined in detail in the next section. In sparest terms, however, we hypothesize that climate change in the form of persistent lowered precipitation in the post–A.D. 1000 period was the mechanism that triggered the collapse of Tiwanaku's agricultural base and ultimately the disintegration of the state itself. This is not to say that the drought is a complete explanation for the collapse of Tiwanaku's political system. The process of political collapse in the face of declining agricultural returns undoubtedly took place over a few generations and most likely entailed complex, historically specific instances of social competition, conflict, and realignment that are unrecorded in the archaeological record. Nevertheless, we propose that the post–A.D. 1000 climatic shift to chronic drought conditions was the *proximate* cause of the collapse of

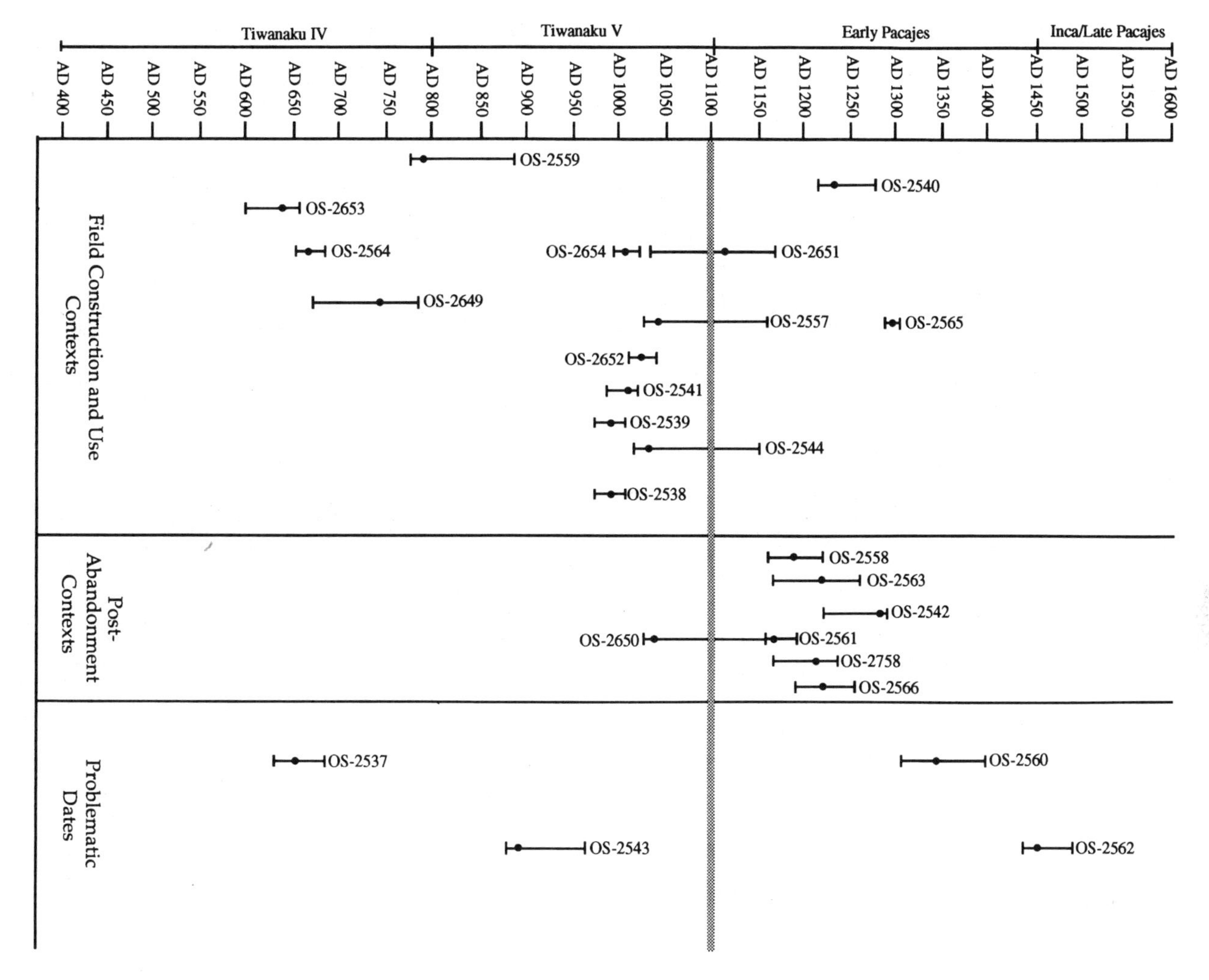


**Figure 8.13.** Radiocarbon dates from raised-field excavations in pre- and post-abandonment contexts. Note the tight cluster of post-abandonment dates between A.D. 1200 and 1300. The four problematic assays reflect two pairs of samples from identical stratigraphic contexts that returned highly divergent dates. All samples were processed at the National Ocean Sciences AMS (NOSAMS) Facility at Woods Hole Oceanographic Institution, Woods Hole, Massachusetts. Calibrated dates were calculated utilizing the Stuiver and Pearson (1993) calibration curve, with CALIB 3.0, by the University of Washington.

intensive, groundwater-driven agriculture and, ultimately, of the political fragmentation of the Tiwanaku state.

## Climatic Effects on Tiwanaku Agricultural Systems

In order to relate the foregoing climate data to the performance of Tiwanaku agricultural systems, we first defined relative vulnerability classes for agricultural technologies used in different geographic regions of the Tiwanaku state (table 8.2). The rank order of vulnerability of these technologies depends directly on (1) the relationship of water source and water redistribution techniques to field systems, and (2) the effects of drought conditions on the function of a given system. Because water supply ultimately relates to climate-dependent rainfall, fluvial runoff, or groundwater storage, the agricultural systems that rely on these sources will be affected differentially by rainfall fluctuations, as indicated in table 8.2. Here we discuss the type, water source, and vulnerability of Tiwanaku agricultural technologies in the altiplano and in the Peruvian south-coast valley of Moquegua (see fig. 8.1). Although the geographical focus of this volume is on Tiwanaku's immediate hinterland, questions of state collapse inevitably implicate colonial as well as core territories. Recent intensive research in

Table 8.1. Radiocarbon Dates from Raised-Field Excavations in the Catari River Basin, Grouped According to Archaeological Contexts

| NOSAMS Number[a] | Material | | Provenience | Context | $^{14}$C Age | Calibrated Years (A.D.) | Calibrated 1-Sigma Age Range (A.D.) |
|---|---|---|---|---|---|---|---|
| OS-2441 | Mollusk | 6 | 86-4-2 | Construction/Use | 1040 ± 35 | 1010 | 990–1020 |
| OS-2540 | Mollusk | 7 | 86-2-1 | Construction/Use | 820 ± 30 | 1230 | 1220–1280 |
| OS-2538 | Mollusk | 8 | 109-2-3 | Construction/Use | 1070 ± 30 | 990 | 970–1010 |
| OS-2539 | Mollusk | 10 | 88-3-3 | Construction/Use | 1070 ± 30 | 990 | 970–1010 |
| OS-2654 | Mollusk | 11 | 111-2-3 | Construction/Use | 1030 ± 35 | 1010 | 990–1020 |
| OS-2564 | Carbon | 11 | 111-2-3 | Construction/Use | 1360 ± 40 | 670 | 650–680 |
| OS-2651 | Mollusk | 11 | 111-2-4 | Construction/Use | 930 ± 30 | 1050, 1090, 1120, 1140, 1160[b] | 1040–1170 |
| OS-2649 | Mollusk | 12 | 112-3-2 | Construction/Use | 1290 ± 50 | 710, 750, 760[b] | 670–780 |
| OS-2557 | Carbon | 13 | 113-3-2 | Construction/Use | 950 ± 30 | 1040, 1150[b] | 1030–1160 |
| OS-2565 | Carbon | 13 | 113-3-3 | Construction/Use | 690 ± 30 | 1300 | 1290–1300 |
| OS-2544 | Mollusk | 14 | 134-4-2 | Construction/Use | 980 ± 30 | 1030 | 1020–1150 |
| OS-2652 | Mollusk | 16 | 114-5-3 | Construction/Use | 990 ± 30 | 1030 | 1020–1040 |
| OS-2559 | Carbon | 17 | 35-1-7 | Construction/Use | 1220 ± 40 | 790 | 780–880 |
| OS-2653 | Mollusk | 18 | 89-3-4 | Construction/Use | 1440 ± 45 | 640 | 600–660 |
| OS-2542 | Mollusk | 1 | 83-2-1 | Post-abandonment | 775 ± 60 | 1280 | 1220–1290 |
| OS-2563 | Carbon | 2 | 62-1-3 | Post-abandonment | 840 ± 45 | 1220 | 1170–1260 |
| OS-2558 | Carbon | 3 | CC33-1 | Post-abandonment | 875 ± 35 | 1190 | 1160–1220 |
| OS-2650 | Mollusk | 9 | 110-3-1 | Post-abandonment | 955 ± 30 | 1040 | 1030–1160 |
| OS-2561 | Carbon | 9 | 110-3-2 | Post-abandonment | 910 ± 30 | 1160 | 1050–1180 |
| OS-2566 | Carbon | 15 | 147-5-1 | Post-abandonment | 840 ± 35 | 1220 | 1180–1250 |
| OS-2758 | Carbon | 16 | 114-5-1 | Post-abandonment | 860 ± 40 | 1210 | 1170–1230 |
| OS-2537 | Mollusk | 4 | 63-3-1 | Problematic | 1410 ± 30 | 650 | 630–660 |
| OS-2560 | Carbon | 4 | 63-3-1 | Problematic | 615 ± 30 | 1320, 1340, 1390[b] | 1310–1400 |
| OS-2543 | Mollusk | 5 | 85-3-5 | Problematic | 1140 ± 30 | 890 | 980–970 |
| OS-2562 | Carbon | 5 | 85-3-5 | Problematic | 425 ± 45 | 1450 | 1440–1480 |

[a]All samples were processed at the National Ocean Sciences AMS Facility (NOSAMS) at Woods Hole Oceanographic Institution, Woods Hole, Massachusetts. Calibrated dates were calculated utilizing the Stuiver and Pearson (1993) calibration curve with CALIB 3.0 by the University of Washington. Multiple dates reflect several possible calibrations.

[b]The four problematic assays reflect two pairs of samples from identical stratigraphic contexts that returned highly divergent dates.

the Moquegua Valley permits us to draw a reasonably detailed portrait of the effects of climate change on a key Tiwanaku colonial territory.

## Altiplano Systems

As we have documented in earlier chapters, the immediate environs and near hinterland of Tiwanaku are characterized by extensive groundwater- and spring-water–supplied raised-field systems and by qochas.[4] Qochas are essentially sunken gardens excavated into the phreatic zone (Flores-Ochoa 1983) to exploit stored groundwater. We have strong circumstantial, but no incontrovertible, evidence that qochas were part of the technological repertoire of Tiwanaku farmers, at least during the Tiwanaku IV and V phases. Raised fields and qochas possess water source and redistribution attributes that render them resistant to drought conditions, placing them in our lowest vulnerability classes, 0 and 1 (table 8.2).

Two types of canal-fed raised-field systems are found in the Tiwanaku hinterland. One such irri-

Table 8.2. Vulnerability of Tiwanaku Agricultural Technologies to Fluctuations in Rainfall

| Vulnerability Class | System Type[a] | Water Source | Response to Rainfall Fluctuations |
|---|---|---|---|
| 5 | Spring-supplied localized systems | Shallow groundwater | Immediate |
| 4 | Rainfall-supplied terraces | Rainfall | Immediate |
| 3 | Canal-supplied river plain agriculture | Fluvial/surface flow | Immediate |
| 2 | Canal-supplied terrace agriculture | Snowmelt/rainfall | Delayed |
| 1 | Raised fields | Groundwater/ springs/fluvial | Delayed |
| 0 | Qochas | Deep groundwater | Delayed |

[a]Note that the agricultural technologies that exhibit delayed vulnerability, particularly raised fields and qochas, are associated with the core altiplano territory of the Tiwanaku state.

gation network was discovered in the Pajchiri area northwest of the Pampa Koani (Ortloff and Kolata 1989; and see chapter 5). This aqueduct-based network was driven by local, high-elevation spring water. A second and more extensive system of canal-fed raised fields is found in the valley of Tiwanaku and in the Catari River basin (see fig. 5.4). The canals supplying these fields drew water from local rivers and streams. If the fields had operated with surface runoff as their *sole* source of water, they would have been highly vulnerable to drought conditions (class 3). However, they were simultaneously supplied by groundwater, and they therefore retain a lower vulnerability rank (class 1). One other source of aquifer recharge exists in the Tiwanaku hinterland. Snowmelt from the Cordillera Real channeled water to a network of raised fields in the Pukarani area northeast of the Pampa Koani. The Pukarani network of raised fields depended upon this remote source of groundwater recharge and was therefore linked directly to the regional precipitation regime.

## Moquegua Valley Systems

Recent research in the Moquegua Valley has begun to clarify the nature and extent of Tiwanaku state expansion from the altiplano to the western Andean slopes and coastal zones of southernmost Peru (Goldstein 1989; Rice, Stanish, and Scarr 1989; Stanish 1989; Watanabe, Moseley, and Cabieses 1990). In many respects, the Moquegua Valley can be considered a paradigmatic case of Tiwanaku agricultural colonization outside of the altiplano. Aridity and difficult, broken terrain severely constrain agriculture in the 140-kilometer-long drainage area of the Moquegua Valley. Although this drainage system rises above 5,000 meters, less that 20 percent of the catchment area lies within the zone of seasonal rainfall. Consequently, cultivation requires artificial, canal-based irrigation. Not surprisingly, the utilization of scarce runoff is itself subject to topographic constraints, which divide Moquegua agriculture into four ascending zones (Moseley et al. 1991), labeled A through D in figure 8.14. The second zone (B), which lies at the heart of the valley, contains the largest expanse of arable land, comprising fertile flatlands around the confluence of the three major valley tributaries. This zone was the focus of heavy, long-term Tiwanaku occupation.

Tiwanaku occupation of the Moquegua Valley was the subject of preliminary work in the 1960s (Disselhoff 1968). More recent studies have identified more than a dozen sites (Moseley et al. 1991; Rice, Stanish, and Scarr 1989). Tiwanaku sites are concentrated in the lower agricultural zones where farming was supported by canal systems that reclaimed relatively flat land. Settlements range from multiroom farmsteads or hamlets to nucleated communities of several hun-

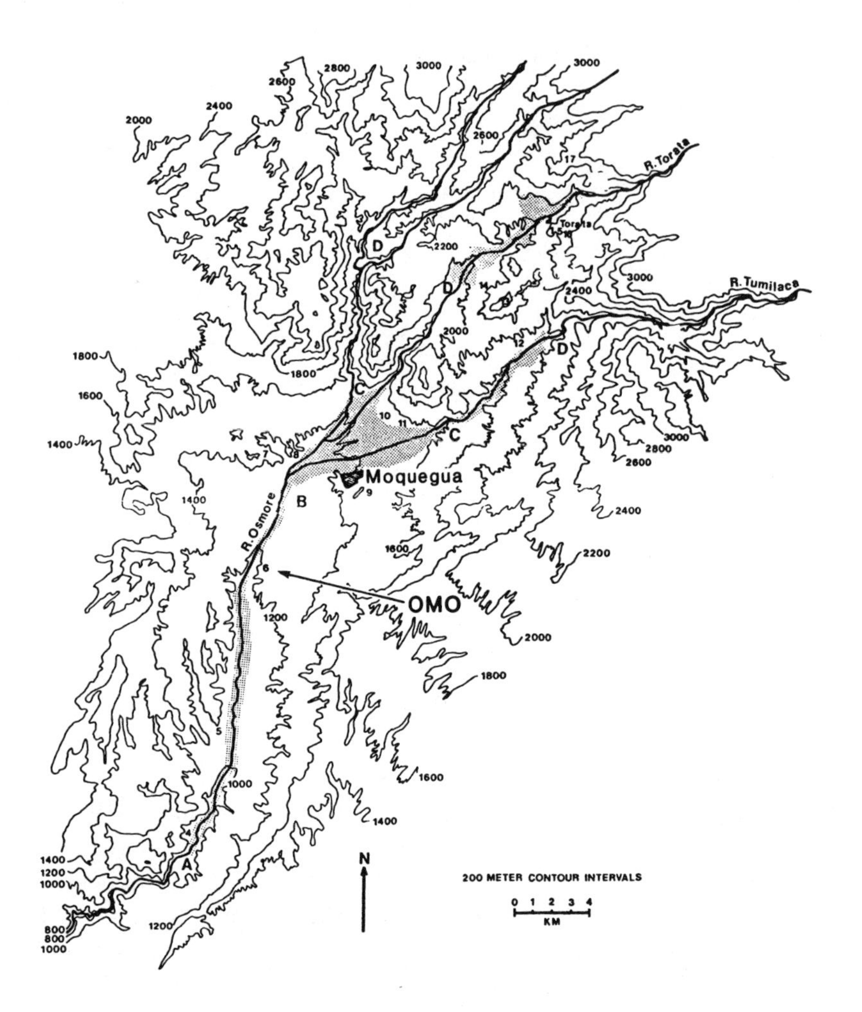


Figure 8.14. The four ascending zones of agricultural production in the Moquegua Valley, labeled A through D, and the Tiwanaku site of Omo. Small numbers denote other archaeological sites. (After Moseley et al. 1991 and Goldstein 1989).

dred structures grouped around plazas. There are special purpose sites such as the extensive settlement of Omo, where massive adobe architecture and a formal, stepped terrace layout imply an administrative function (Goldstein 1989). Three 50- to 150-room Tiwanaku settlements are situated at the base of Cerro Baul, immediately adjacent to irrigated bottomlands of the Torata and Tumilaca rivers (fig. 8.14). Significantly, however, there appears to be little or no Tiwanaku association with agricultural terraces at higher elevations; these are apparently post-Tiwanaku constructions (see note 4).

The Moquegua Valley is characterized by a multiplicity of agricultural techniques designed to exploit available water resources in varied forms. These techniques include rain-fed agricultural terraces, canal-irrigated field systems in the floodplain of the Moquegua River, high-elevation agricultural terraces provisioned with snowmelt-derived water by means of elaborate ridge-top canal systems, and local wetlands agriculture supplied by seepage from spring water and groundwater at coastal sites near Ilo (Clement and Moseley 1989). The rather unusual snowmelt-driven system of terraced agriculture in the sierra zone of the Moquegua Valley exhibits relatively intense usage from Tiwanaku V into post-Tiwanaku times. Irrigated floodplain agriculture in the Moquegua Valley appears to be earlier and associated with both Tiwanaku phase IV and V colonies.

## Vulnerability of Tiwanaku Agricultural Systems

Tiwanaku agricultural systems in both the altiplano core territory and its coastal colonial outposts reflect consummate skill in conception and construction. Nevertheless, both core and colonial systems failed and were abandoned in the period immediately after A.D. 1000. We argue that the proximate cause of this regional failure was the severe and chronic precipitation deficit recorded in the Quelccaya ice cap and in our Lake Titicaca sediment cores. Given the different ecological, technological, and organizational characteristics of the various agricultural systems, we further hypothesize that there was a distinct temporal sequence in the extinction of those systems, based on their relative vulnerability under extended drought conditions.

Agricultural systems in vulnerability classes 3, 4, and 5 are most directly linked to precipitation levels (table 8.2). In the chronic absence of rainfall, agricultural fields dependent upon the water sources that define these vulnerability classes are the first to fail. Such systems do not possess remote or delayed water delivery capacities. In contrast, systems of vulnerability class 2 are dependent upon snowmelt for water supply. Much like slow groundwater seepage, this source features a gradual, delayed release of stored water. Since accumulated snow and ice may represent water storage from past millennia, a rise in regional ambient temperature such as that which occurred in the post–A.D.1000 period can activate melting at the lower snow boundary and thereby provide a water source of long duration independent of prevailing moisture conditions. Such systems apparently provided water to the Moquegua terrace systems throughout post-Tiwanaku times.

The groundwater-based raised-field systems of the Tiwanaku hinterland are grouped as class 1 systems. Owing to the nature of the groundwater reservoir, evaporation through the surface is limited. Seepage into the canals of raised-field complexes is a similarly slow process further limiting the effects of evaporation. Because the collection zones supplying groundwater to the raised fields in the Tiwanaku hinterland are immense, and because this supply results from the integrated effects of rainfall infiltration and slow groundwater flow toward the field systems, depletion of groundwater is minimal under periodic, normal drought conditions. During periods of prolonged drought, however, the groundwater level will ultimately decline as resupply diminishes. Finally, class 0 systems are represented by qochas, which offer a simple technological response to drought conditions: they can be continuously excavated to follow a decreasing water table. Although least vulnerable to drought, by their nature qochas have limited planting surface areas and offer a low rate of agricultural return relative to labor invested.

Under chronic drought conditions, all of the agricultural systems categorized in table 8.2 will ultimately fail, but they will fail sequentially, not simultaneously. Systems that possess delayed delivery characteristics (vulnerability classes 0, 1, and 2) will sustain production longer than those directly tied to the precipitation regime (classes 3, 4, and 5). In short, in the presence of extended drought conditions, there is a definite temporal sequence of extinction of agricultural systems based on their degree of vulnerability. Given this sequential extinction effect, one immediate agroecological consequence of the climate change documented in this volume was shift in the agricultural supply zones available to the Tiwanaku state. These shifts in supply zone would in turn have generated significant social problems for a political system experiencing increasing economic stress.

As precipitation levels began to decrease gradually after A.D. 950, class 3 canal-supplied agricultural systems characteristic of the Tiwanaku V colonies in the Moquegua Valley were early casualties of reduced rainfall and reduced river flow rates. Those colonies relied almost exclusively on canal-fed irrigation systems to support their populations. Even more vulnerable to minor rainfall and runoff decreases were the small communities dependent upon groundwater seepage (class 5) along the Peruvian and Chilean coasts (Clement and Moseley 1989). Because only a small fraction of a river's flow recharges the groundwater reservoir, coastal communities depending upon springs and seepage to irrigate field systems were the first to experience minor changes in the water supply. These small, spring-based agricultural communities may have gone into decline as early as A.D. 850–950 (Bermann et al. 1989) with the initial shifts to a drier climatic regime evidenced in the integrated moisture-supply curve (fig. 8.8).

Despite the deterioration of the agricultural base of the Tiwanaku V Moquegua colonies, the heartland's agricultural system, dependent upon raised fields and, to a lesser degree, rainfall-supplied terraces (see note 3), was still relatively viable because of the time lag in groundwater change under incipient drought conditions. Furthermore, the heartland systems had excess agricultural capacity, supply far exceeding demand (Kolata 1991). Even if these fields operated at partial capacity owing to gradually changing groundwater conditions, harvests sufficient to sustain the local population were still possible. But the agricultural system as a whole would have lost substantial capacity for surplus production.

Ultimately, chronic drought conditions began to lower the water table in the raised-field complexes in the Tiwanaku hinterland, changing the delicate phreatic-zone moisture balance derived from differences between the height of canal water and that of the mound surface. Declining availability of freshwater caused subtle changes in the heat transfer characteristics of the raised-field systems (Kolata and Ortloff 1989). Drying of the soil surface layers, for example, changes the heat-conduction and moisture-transport characteristics of the raised fields, increasing chances of crop loss from frost damage (Sato, Fukuhara, and Boris 1990). The key problem, however, was the drought-related withdrawal of water from raised-field platform root systems as the groundwater level dropped. With a receding water table, there was no economically feasible way to reconfigure the water supply and restore production to levels similar to those achieved under fully functioning raised-field systems.

## Evidence of Changing Settlement Patterns

In our model of climate-induced state collapse, the heartland area was the last survivor, but only in spite of an observable loss in agricultural capacity from year to year. As the principal agricultural supply base declined predictably and irreversibly, centralized state control over an integrated agricultural landscape was replaced by regionalization and opportunistic exploitation of declining water resources (Kolata 1993a). Because available water resources were dispersed and limited, the size of the group deriving sustenance from each source was commensurate with that of the source itself. Post-Tiwanaku settlement patterns in the valley of Tiwanaku dramatically reflect this process of population dispersion and disaggregation.

In the Tiwanaku IV and early Tiwanaku V phases, the lower and middle Tiwanaku Valley were organized into an integrated agricultural production zone characterized by a distinct settlement hierarchy. Albarracín-Jordan and Mathews (1990) have identified a series of Tiwanaku IV and V phase settlements spaced regularly (approximately 2 kilometers apart) along the colluvial terraces on both the north and south sides of the valley. They classify these as secondary sites (ca. 3–10 hectares in size) and tertiary sites (ca. 1–3 hectares) within the settlement hierarchy and associate them directly with the administration of agricultural production on raised fields in the adjacent alluvial plain of the Tiwanaku River (see Albarracín-Jordan and Mathews 1990:maps 4 and 5). A large number of fourth-order sites in this hierarchical ranking were small mounds and sherd scatters (less than 1 hectare) directly associated with the raised fields themselves. In sharp contrast, the immediate post-Tiwanaku settlement pattern in the region exhibits a complete disintegration of this hierarchy and presumably of the underlying political and economic structures that were reflected in it (see Albarracín-Jordan and Mathews 1990:map 6). As Albarracín-Jordan and Mathews note (1990:191–92), the immediate post-Tiwanaku period ("Early Pacajes" in their nomenclature) was characterized by

> a proliferation of small sites that were distributed in a dispersed fashion throughout all of the microenvironments of the valley, including the intermontane zone, which had not been occupied previously. The secondary centers that characterized the Tiwanaku IV and V periods disappear as such, becoming converted into small habitation centers. These transformations suggest a change in the social order from a hierarchy of centralized administration to autonomous social groups reduced [in scale]. (our translation)

Although there are substantial numbers of sites in Tiwanaku's hinterland dating after A.D. 1000, they are widely dispersed across the landscape, and few exceed 1 hectare in size. The upper end of the previously existing settlement hierarchy (in terms of settlement size and presumed political complexity) was clearly truncated. Most dramatic in terms of settlement pattern transformations, the cities of Tiwanaku and Lukurmata themselves were virtually abandoned at this time. Radiocarbon dates on Tiwanaku V households in these cities cluster between A.D. 750 and 950, and no radiocarbon dates on domestic occupations are associated with these urban centers past A.D. 1000 (table 8.3). There was, in short, a dramatic redistribution of population in the Tiwanaku hinterland characterized by disaggregation and, more tellingly, complete deurbanization.

There is some evidence for localized raised-field cultivation in the post–A.D. 1000 environment (Albarracín-Jordan and Mathews 1990; Graffam 1990; Seddon 1994). However, despite occasional periods of higher precipitation that would have made this form of cultivation technologically feasible again, the earlier regional system of large-scale agricultural production was never reactivated. This observation illustrate the point that societies possess thresholds of irreversibility. Once fragmented, the precarious structures of organizational complexity characteristic of imperial societies never permit a return to the original state.

Stanish's (1994) recent settlement-pattern survey in the Juli-Pomata area on the northwestern margins of Lake Titicaca provides a portrait of agricultural col-

**Table 8.3. Radiocarbon Dates for Tiwanaku IV and Tiwanaku V Household Contexts from Tiwanaku, Lukurmata, and Selected Sites in the Moquegua Valley, Peru**

| Site | Laboratory Designation | $^{14}$C Years (B.P.) | Calibrated Years (A.D.) | Phase |
|---|---|---|---|---|
| Tiwanaku | SMU-5639 | 1170 ± 60 | 860 ± 80 | Tiwanaku V |
| Tiwanaku | ETH-6306 | 1460 ± 60 | 590 ± 60 | Late Tiwanaku IV |
| Tiwanaku | SMU-2330 | 1080 ± 210 | 950 ± 110 | Tiwanaku V |
| Tiwanaku | SMU-2367 | 1150 ± 80 | 880 ± 80 | Tiwanaku V |
| Tiwanaku | ETH-5680 | 1170 ± 65 | 860 ± 85 | Tiwanaku V |
| Tiwanaku | SMU-2468 | 1390 ± 50 | 640 ± 35 | Late Tiwanaku IV |
| Tiwanaku | SMU-2467 | 1130 ± 60 | 900 ± 70 | Tiwanaku V |
| Tiwanaku | SMU-2472 | 1200 ± 115 | 830 ± 130 | Tiwanaku V |
| Tiwanaku | SMU-2465 | 1110 ± 50 | 930 ± 60 | Tiwanaku V |
| Tiwanaku | SMU-2466 | 1170 ± 60 | 860 ± 80 | Tiwanaku V |
| Tiwanaku | SMU-2289 | 1185 ± 60 | 840 ± 80 | Tiwanaku V |
| Tiwanaku | SMU-2290 | 1120 ± 70 | 910 ± 85 | Tiwanaku V |
| Tiwanaku | SMU-2276 | 1070 ± 60 | 960 ± 60 | Tiwanaku V |
| Tiwanaku | SMU-2277 | 1130 ± 60 | 900 ± 70 | Tiwanaku V |
| Tiwanaku | SMU-2469 | 1190 ± 100 | 830 ± 15 | Tiwanaku V |
| Lukurmata | SMU-2165 | 1000 ± 230 | 1020 ± 220 | Tiwanaku V |
| Lukurmata | ETH-3180 | 990 ± 95 | 1045 ± 100 | Tiwanaku V |
| Lukurmata | ETH-3179 | 1180 ± 110 | 840 ± 115 | Tiwanaku V |
| Lukurmata | SMU-1920 | 1201 ± 96 | 818 ± 110 | Tiwanaku V |
| Lukurmata | ETH-3178 | 1085 ± 90 | 850 ± 100 | Tiwanaku V |
| Lukurmata | SMU-2117 | 1090 ± 60 | 950 ± 70 | Tiwanaku V |
| Chen Chen | HV-1076 | 1040 ± 65 | 999 ± 32 | Tiwanaku V |
| Chen Chen | HV-1077 | 930 ± 65 | 1105 ± 78 | Late Tiwanaku IV |
| Loreto Viejo | HV-1091 | 980 ± 70 | 1024 ± 84 | Tiwanaku V |
| Omo | Beta-26650 | 1120 ± 60 | 897 ± 53 | Tiwanaku V |
| Omo | Beta-26649 | 1170 ± 70 | 983 ± 93 | Tiwanaku V |

Note: Radiocarbon dates for Tiwanaku and Lukurmata are corrected and calibrated according to the Stuiver and Pearson (1993) calibration curve. Radiocarbon dates for Chen Chen, Loreto Viejo, and Omo are published in Rice et al. (1989:8) and were calibrated using the CALIB 3.0 radiocarbon program, University of Washington, Quaternary Isotope Laboratory.

lapse and settlement transformation in that region consistent with the scenario we have outlined for the Tiwanaku hinterland. He reports evidence of intrusive human occupation and tombs in previously productive raised-field complexes in the immediate post–A.D. 1000 period (Charles Stanish, personal communication, 1991). Provocatively, Stanish suggests that with the collapse of Tiwanaku raised-field agriculture in the region, there came a shift to increasing emphasis on camelid pastoralism to replace lost food resources. Such a shift would have entailed dramatic changes in the logistics of subsistence and, correlatively, in the structure of the prevailing social order, toward a more dispersed, mobile (and perhaps aggressive) society.

Relocation and regionalization of populations

around increasingly scarce water resources also occurred outside of the altiplano in the colonial outposts of the Moquegua Valley. This process of climate-induced settlement reorganization is directly reflected in the emergence of post-Tiwanaku groups in the upper Moquegua Valley sierra zones. Agriculture in the Moquegua region shifted away from the irrigated cultivation of the mid-valley floodplain characteristic of the Tiwanaku V colonies toward higher-elevation agricultural terraces tied to a restricted water supply derived from snowmelt and precipitation (Bermann et al. 1989; Rice, Stanish, and Scarr 1989). Water supply was now critical to survival, and defensive structures appear in profusion in the sierra zone, apparently guarding and controlling access to the supply canals (Kolata 1983; Rice, Stanish, and Scarr 1989). The water supply from the canals was limited, however, given declining precipitation and lack of replenishment of the sierra snowpack in the post-Tiwanaku environment.

## Beyond Tiwanaku: Regional Implications of the Climate Change Model

The implications of this agroecological model of state collapse reach beyond the specific case of Tiwanaku. Agricultural system collapse has been noted previously in other areas of the Andes in the period immediately after A.D. 1000 (Ortloff 1993). We propose that these other instances of system collapse were similarly related to the chronic drought conditions documented in this volume. The history of Chimu land reclamation in the Moche Valley on Peru's north coast offers a particularly intriguing forum for exploring the potential Andean-wide effects of this climatic change on large-scale systems of agricultural production.

The Chimu state's intervalley canal between the Moche and Chicama valleys on the Peruvian north coast is a classic example of engineering response to water-supply problems (Ortloff, Moseley, and Feldman 1982). This canal was designed and built at great labor cost to supply freshwater from the Chicama River to field systems in the Moche Valley that were clearly experiencing a significant water deficit. Ortloff, Moseley, and Feldman (1982) originally interpreted this water deficit as the result of localized tectonic uplift that physically stranded the intakes of entire canal systems. Despite considerable debate over this issue (Kus 1984; Pozorski and Pozorski 1982), the empirical evidence for uplift and canal stranding is compelling (Ortloff, Moseley, and Feldman 1983). The climatological data for the extensive drought characterizing this period provides a complementary explanation for the water deficit that stimulated the ultimately ill-fated Chimu attempt to capture water from the Chicama River. Tectonic and drought effects appear to have acted simultaneously to decrease the net water supply to the Moche Valley field systems.

Figures 8.15 and 8.16 summarize the results of previous quantitative research by one of the authors into the dynamics of, respectively, large-scale Chimu canal systems on the north side of the Moche Valley (Ortloff, Feldman, and Moseley 1985) and the smaller Carrizal spring system in the lower Moquegua Valley (Ortloff 1989). The decrease in canal flow rates through time shown in these figures is derived from measurements of changing canal cross sections and computation of flow rates through different canal configurations. Shown sequentially are the total flow rate of water supply systems, land area under cultivation, and the labor requirement for agricultural system construction.

Inherent in the changing dynamics of these systems is a significant decline in water supply in the post–A.D. 1000 environment and people's consequent struggle to survive by using increasingly complex engineering practices or alternative agricultural technologies. The Chimu state adapted to deteriorating environmental circumstances after A.D. 1000 by successfully establishing an aggressive tribute economy through territorial expansion and by applying sophisticated canal technologies to reconfigure irrigation systems continuously for optimum production (Kolata 1990; Ortloff, Feldman, and Moseley 1985). For the Chimu, reconfiguration of the agricultural supply base to the north of the Moche Valley and conquest of the far northern Lambeyeque polities between A.D. 1000 and 1300 were consistent with the drive to secure rivers with high-flow rates for irrigation agriculture and to control adjacent valleys to fortify the state's eroding economic base. Other, smaller polities, such as that focused around the Carrizal spring system in southern Peru, were incapable of substituting or generating new sources of wealth in the face of declining agricultural returns, as the Chimu did. For lack of efficient technical solutions providing an alternate agricultural supply or the ability to expand their resource base through aggression, these smaller-scale societies simply disappeared.

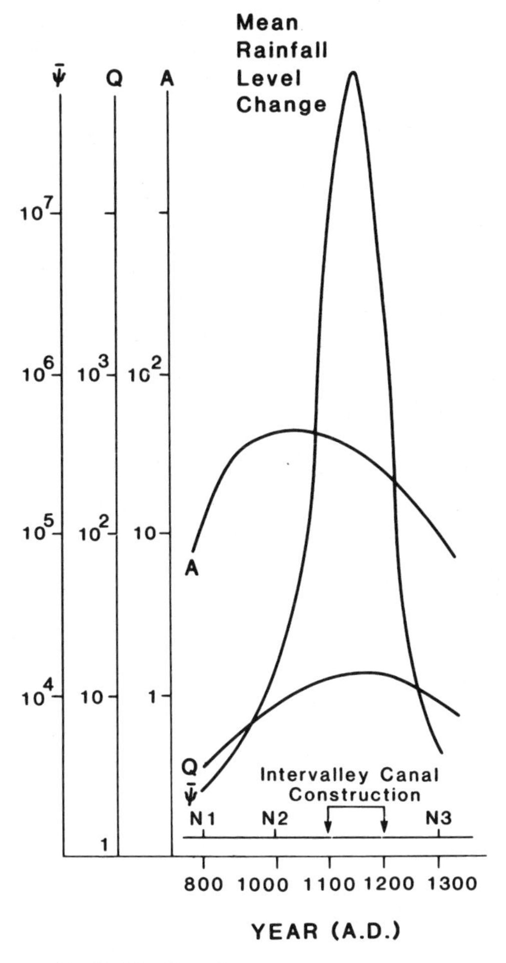


**Figure 8.15.** Selected diagnostics of the north-side Moche Valley canal system for the period between about A.D. 800 and 1300. Diagnostics include labor input (man-hours), canal flow rate (cubic meters per second), and irrigated land area (square kilometers). (Adapted from Ortloff 1989.)

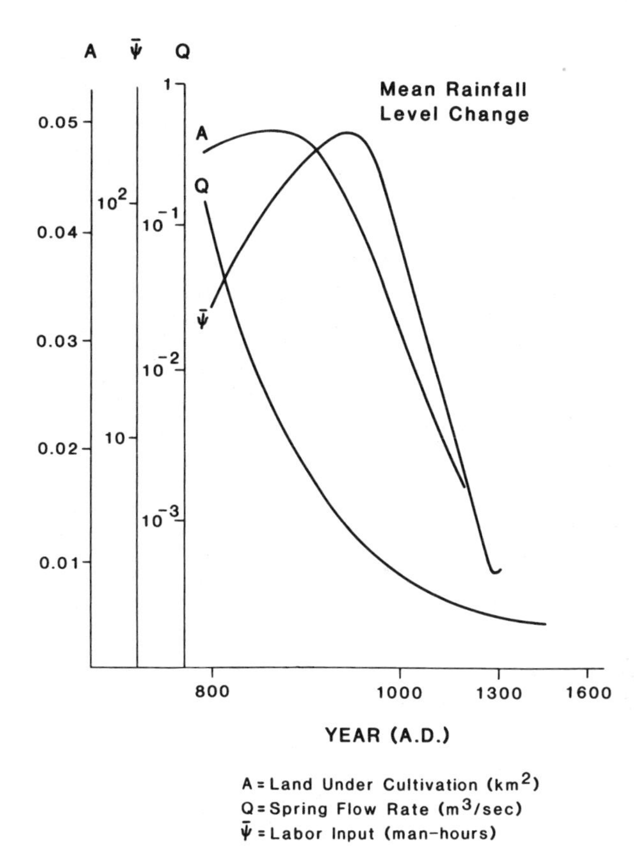


**Figure 8.16.** Selected diagnostics of the Carrizal spring system in the lower Moquegua Valley for the period between about A.D. 800 and 1300. Diagnostics include labor input, spring flow rate (cubic meters per second), and irrigated land area (square kilometers). (Adapted from Ortloff 1989.)

## Conclusion

The Tiwanaku state experienced the collapse of its agricultural base after A.D. 1000 because of a dramatic decline in mean annual precipitation commencing around A.D. 950. Climatic recovery, in terms of return to the precipitation levels of the pre–A.D. 1000 period, began only centuries later. Several higher rainfall excursions from the lower mean of the post–A.D. 1000 environment did occur, but even these brief precipitation pulses were truncated by an intensification of drought conditions between A.D. 1245 and 1310. Generally, in environmental terms, the post-Tiwanaku period from A.D. 1000 to 1400 was characterized by a significant water deficit that had severe negative impacts on systems of intensive agriculture. Categorization of the vulnerability of diverse types of Tiwanaku agricultural systems, for both the altiplano and its dispersed colonial network, suggests a sequential extinction of these systems based on their degree of linkage to the prevailing precipitation regime.

We propose that the collapse of these systems proceeded chronologically in order of their vulnerability. Heartland agricultural systems, composed primarily of raised fields, exhibited a delayed response to drought conditions and consequently were the last to fail. Because the center of the state was still intact as the colonies began to fail, the long-term drought slowly led people in the center to an awareness of the imminent failure of the agricultural system. Under such circumstances, an organized technical defense could be organized to maximize agricultural production in the heartland, which may have been accomplished by reconfiguring raised-field networks in areas of relatively higher groundwater near the shores of Lake Titicaca.

Ultimately, chronic drought caused failure of the core raised-field systems as well. With the collapse of this essential agricultural base, the Tiwanaku state's political structure fragmented. This process is reflected clearly in a dramatic change in settlement patterns that can best be characterized by the terms disaggregation, deurbanization, and dispersion of populations. The signal change in settlement and population distributions can be detected in the immediate Tiwanaku hinterland, in the Juli-Pomata region of the Lake Titicaca basin, and in the lower-altitude colonial region of the Moquegua Valley. We predict that future intensive settlement-pattern surveys in other areas of Tiwanaku hegemony in the south-central Andes will reveal similar shifts in population concentration.

Because Tiwanaku's surplus-producing agricultural system had been sustained for at least seven centuries, the intense drought of the post–A.D. 1000 period can be understood as an extraordinary episode of climate change beyond any other experienced during the formation and design of the raised-field system. Over the course of some 700 years, Tiwanaku society became dependent upon a system of agricultural production that was well adapted to the rigorous environmental conditions of the altiplano and could adjust to that environment's normal cycles of drought and inundation. The state organized labor on a large scale to construct raised-field systems in their final Tiwanaku IV and V configurations. The intricate drainage and water shunting systems that controlled groundwater level and intercepted runoff are eloquent testimonies to indigenous understanding of the hydrological environment and its manipulation. Nevertheless, Tiwanaku farmers were unable to respond to a drought of unprecedented duration and severity. In the prolonged decades of drought that ensued after A.D. 1000, production and storage capacity were insufficient to support the urbanized populations that had grown up in the lake district during earlier periods of agricultural expansion and prosperity. The end product of climate-induced deterioration of the agricultural base was predictable: Tiwanaku cities were abandoned and the surplus-extracting apparatus of state administration lost both its fundamental source of power and its social relevance.

Implicit in this model of drought-induced agricultural crisis and state collapse is the probability that the climate change recorded in the Quelccaya glacier and in sediment cores from Lake Titicaca was pan-Andean and perhaps even hemispheric in scope. The implications of this conclusion for Andean prehistory after A.D. 1000 are apparent: climate-induced agricultural crises and potentially radical transformations in settlement patterns should be detectable during this period in other regions of the Andes.

## Notes

A version of this chapter was previously published in "Climate and Collapse: Agroecological Perspectives on the Decline of the Tiwanaku State," by C. R. Ortloff and A. L. Kolata, *Journal of Archaeological Science* 20 (1993): 195–211. The version presented here incorporates new paleolimnological data that corroborate the hypothesis of climate change in the post–A.D. 1000 period. Our figures 8.2 through 8.7 are based on privileged, unpublished data and are reproduced here with the permission of L. G. Thompson.

1. The precise dating of the Tiwanaku collapse is a subject of some controversy. The traditional view is that the (terminal) Tiwanaku V phase persisted until A.D. 1200 at Tiwanaku (Ponce Sanginés 1972), as well as in some of its colonial enclaves in the yungas zones. A number of radiocarbon dates from Tiwanaku settlements in the Moquegua Valley seem to support this scenario. However, as is evident from table 8.3, recent radiocarbon dates from urban centers in the Tiwanaku heartland, specifically Tiwanaku and Lukurmata, suggest a terminal date somewhere between about A.D. 900 and 1100. Bermann and colleagues (1989) argue that Tiwanaku's Moquegua colonies collapsed prior to the decline of the Tiwanaku core area around Lake Titicaca, a view in agreement with the argument presented in this chapter. They suggest that the Tiwanaku collapse in the Moquegua Valley was complete by A.D. 1000. Since identification of the Tiwanaku V phase in the coastal colonial enclave depends principally on stylistic analysis of ceramics, it is conceivable that Tiwanaku and Tiwanaku-derived stylistic influences in ceramic traditions persisted on the coast after the political decline of Tiwanaku itself and of its colonial enclaves. This scenario is consistent with recent interpretations by Goldstein (1989) and other investigators of the Programa Contisuyu (Rice, Stanish, and Scarr 1989; Watanabe, Moseley, and Cabieses 1990).

2. A brief comment on the statistical methods employed in this chapter is in order. In analyzing the degree of dependence and correlation between two normally distributed ice cap thickness populations, we used the t-test to examine the hypothesis that mean precipitation levels were significantly different in the pre– and post–A.D. 1000 environments (Dunn and Clark 1974). We tested the null hypothesis that the means of the distributions from which

the two populations were drawn were identical. The null hypothesis was rejected, supporting the conclusion that a change to a drier climate took place after A.D. 1000. From analysis of input data files and use of standard statistical nomenclature, the following statistics were obtained: for the pre–A.D. 1000 group, n = 225, mean = 1.487, standard deviation = 0.388; for the post–A.D. 1000 group, n = 376, mean = 1.232, standard deviation = 0.316. Separate variances were t = 8.4566, df = 403.7, p = .00000; pooled variances were t = 8.7059, df = 599.0, p = .00000.

The probability that the ice cap thickness distribution from before A.D. 1000 comes from the same population as the distribution after A.D. 1000 is virtually zero. Assuming that the observed correlation between snow layer thickness and intensity of annual rainfall is correct, then from a statistical perspective the Quelccaya ice cap data provide firm evidence of a significant climate change in the form of lower precipitation levels (from those existing previously) in the post–A.D. 1000 environment. This lowered mean precipitation persisted for four centuries (ca. A.D. 1000–1410) despite several brief excursions of above-average rainfall (figs. 8.4, 8.5, 8.8).

3. This section of the chapter is drawn from an unpublished manuscript titled "Human-Environment Interactions: Climatic Thresholds and the Rise and Fall of an Andean Civilization," by M. Binford, A. Kolata, M. Brenner, M. Abbott, J. Curtis, J. Janusek, and M. Seddon. The paleolimnological analyses discussed here were conducted by Michael Binford, Mark Brenner, Jason Curtis, and Mark Abbott.

4. Albarracín-Jordan argues that artificial terraces in the valley of Tiwanaku were also part of the state's repertoire of intensive agricultural techniques (Albarracín-Jordan and Mathews 1990). These "agricultural" terraces, however, possess substantial quantities of cultural material (ceramics, ground stone, projectile points, etc.), suggesting that they were, in actuality, constructed to accommodate domestic architecture rather than intensive agriculture. Similar domestic terraces have been investigated at the Tiwanaku secondary urban sites of Pajchiri and Lukurmata. Extensive excavations of such terraces at Lukurmata revealed unequivocal evidence that they were employed for domestic architecture and not for agriculture (Kolata 1989). It is possible that some forms of house gardens were interspersed among the residential architecture on these terraces, but these would not have been of sufficient scale to constitute an intensive, state-managed agricultural system. Given these clear precedents and the presence of similar surface domestic debris on the terraces in the lower Tiwanaku Valley, the preponderance of evidence suggests that the Tiwanaku Valley terraces were also designed primarily for residential architecture and not for intensive agriculture. We accept Albarracín-Jordan's interpretation, however, to the extent that these terraces may have been utilized partly for supplemental, family-based agricultural production. In a previous paper, Kolata (1987b:38–41) argued that the massive agricultural terraces that do exist in the Tiwanaku area, such as on the island of Cumana northwest of the Pampa Koani, are primarily a post-Tiwanaku phenomenon. Considering the foregoing discussion, we see no compelling evidence to alter that conclusion.

# 9

# Rehabilitating Raised-Field Agriculture in the Southern Lake Titicaca Basin of Bolivia

## *Theory, Practice, and Results*

ALAN L. KOLATA, OSWALDO RIVERA, JUAN CARLOS RAMÍREZ, AND EVELYN GEMIO

Over the past decade, comprehensive scientific investigations of precolonial systems of indigenous agriculture in the Andean region have brought into sharp relief the strong potential for generating relatively high crop yields through non-capital-intensive systems of production. In particular, raised-field agriculture has recently been the subject of intensive research and small-scale projects of experimental field rehabilitation that underscore the potential for generating elevated yields of traditional highland Andean and introduced crops (Erickson 1985, 1988, 1992; Erickson and Candler 1989; Garaycochea 1987; Kolata 1991).

Pre-Hispanic systems of raised-field agriculture, if not quite ubiquitous in the Americas, are nevertheless widely distributed throughout Central and South America and, to a lesser degree, North America as well. They occur in climatic regions ranging from the humid tropics of the South American lowlands to the middle-latitude temperate zones of the upper Midwest in the United States. Interest in the problem of agricultural reclamation in perennially or periodically inundated landscapes has expanded dramatically in recent years. The raised-field complexes of the circum–Lake Titicaca region in Peru and Bolivia represent the largest virtually continuous expanse of this type of cultivation system in the world.

As detailed in preceding chapters, indigenous raised fields in the Andean altiplano are essentially large planting platforms elevated above the surrounding natural landscape. The planting platforms alternate with systems of canals to form distinct and rather complex hydrological units. Within a given segment of a raised-field system, approximately 50–70 percent of the area is given over to the planting surface itself. The remaining portion is occupied by intervening canals that derive their water from local fluvial networks, natural springs, or percolating groundwater. In certain ecological contexts, such as in perennially inundated landscapes, the primary function of raised fields is to promote drainage and lower local water tables to reduce the incidence of root rot (see chapter 6). In other settings, raised fields mitigate the hazard of killing frosts (chapter 5). Still other systems of raised fields appear to promote the conservation of water and the recycling of essential nutrients (chapter 7). These distinct effects of raised-field cultivation are not mutually exclusive.

This chapter presents an overview of our continuing efforts to rehabilitate raised fields in the hinterland of Tiwanaku. We describe our methods and data-collection protocols and evaluate the results of crop production on rehabilitated raised fields in various communities. Although we have been involved in rehabilitating raised fields since 1986, we concentrate here on results obtained during the 1990–91 agricultural season (August–May), with limited references to results obtained from earlier seasons. We do this for a number of reasons. First, the 1990–91 season was the first period in which we were able to implement a uniform data-collection protocol in every community participating in the rehabilitation project. For this period, therefore, our data are strictly comparable across the communities. Second, although we have production values for other seasons, the data for the 1990–91 season are the most thoroughly analyzed and amenable to interpretation. Third, the quantity of data collected during any one agricultural season is immense, and we are unable to present complete data sets for all seasons within the space of a single chapter. We believe, however, that the results of the 1990–91 agricultural season are representative of the research and development work we have been pursuing. Data from subsequent seasons will appear in future publications.

The results presented in this chapter include descriptions of the techniques and procedures employed in constructing and maintaining raised fields, a summary of production yields on raised fields from the various communities involved in 1990–91, and indices of insect infestations and plant pathogens. Variation in yields among the communities participating in the rehabilitation program are discussed in terms of both ecological and organizational variables. (The demographic and organizational implications of intensive, raised-field agricultural for the archaeological interpretation of Tiwanaku society are discussed in chapter 12.) Finally, we touch briefly upon the potential implications of rehabilitating raised fields for contemporary development. These results should be of interest to scholars in archaeology, agroecology, agronomy, and development.

## Background

The results summarized here stem from our work among 22 indigenous Aymara communities concentrated in the provinces of Ingavi, Los Andes, Pacajes, and Manko Capac of the Department of La Paz (fig. 9.1, table 9.1). More than 70 percent of the popula-

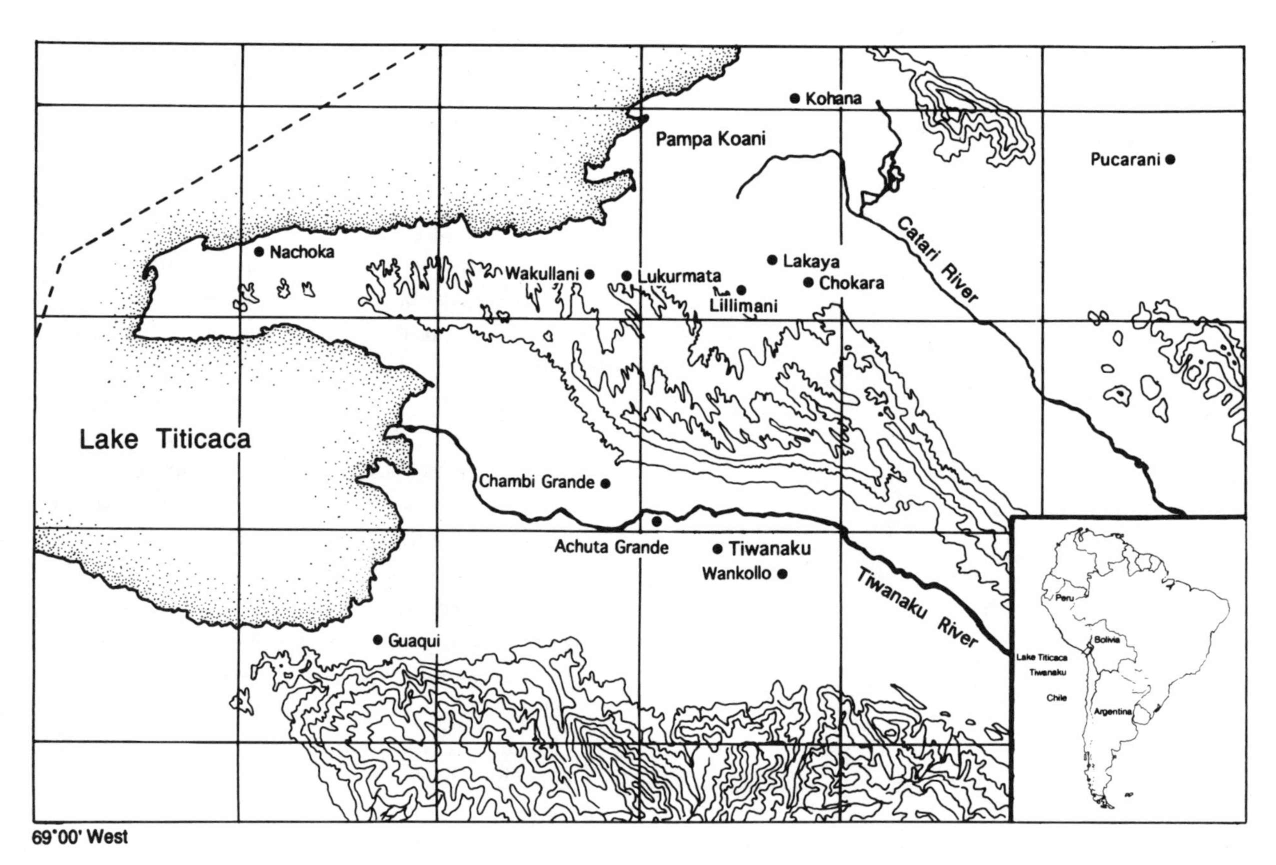


Figure 9.1. Locations of some of the communities participating in the raised-field rehabilitation study.

**Table 9.1. Areas of Raised-Field Rehabilitation by Community**

| Community | Reconstructed Surface Area in Hectares |
|---|---|
| Tiwanaku area | |
| K'araña | 10.00 |
| Wankollo | |
| Osco group | 1.00 |
| Hospital group | 0.87 |
| Niña group | 0.75 |
| Chambi Grande | 4.00 |
| Achuta Grande | |
| Group 2 | 2.00 |
| Group 3 | 1.00 |
| Yanarico | 1.00 |
| Pampa Koani area | |
| Chukara | 3.00 |
| Chukara CEMA | 1.00 |
| Kiuchapi | 3.00 |
| Lukurmata | 2.00 |
| Lillimani | 2.00 |
| Wakullani | 2.67 |
| Ñachoka | 2.83 |
| Kohana | 3.61 |
| Lakaya Baja | 3.00 |
| Lakaya Alta | 1.00 |
| Pukarani area | |
| Huayrocondo | 0.75 |
| Tujuyo | 0.75 |
| Warialtaya | 0.50 |
| Batallas area | |
| Santa Ana | 1.00 |
| Viacha area | |
| Hilata Santa Trinidad | 2.00 |
| Satatotora area | |
| Nasakara | 0.50 |
| Copacabana area | |
| Kusijata | 2.00 |
| Marka Kosko | 1.00 |
| Total | 49.98 |

tion in these provinces of the northern Bolivian altiplano practice subsistence agriculture. The remainder find income in service- and labor-related occupations. The predominant economic activity of these communities is subsistence farming on small plots of land using traditional agricultural techniques, ox-drawn plows, and hand tools (fig. 9.2). Cultivation is directly dependent upon seasonal rainfall and takes place on hill slopes (upland zones) and adjoining floodplains (pampas zones). A few communities with access to reliable, perennial water sources practice small-scale irrigation, but most are tied to a regime of dry farming. Virtually all rural families combine small-scale livestock raising with agricultural activities. The main crop is the potato (*Solanum* sp.), which is supplemented by various introduced and native crops such as broad bean (*Vicia faba*), barley (*Hordeum vulgare*), oats (*Avena sativa*), quinoa (*Chenopodium quinoa*), kañiwa (*Chenopodium pallidicaule*), oca (*Oxalis tuberosa*), and tarwi (*Lupinus mutabilis*). Production under this traditional regime of dry farming is depressed by frost and by nutrient-deficient (particularly nitrogen-deficient) soils. Average annual production of potatoes under this regime is 2 to 5 metric tons per hectare (MACA 1974, 1985).

The aggregate productivity of this subsistence-level cultivation is poor, given the ecological and economic constraints under which small farmers operate. Nutrient concentrations in soils in the upland zones of hill slopes and colluvial terraces are extremely low in comparison with those in the pampas zones (see chapters 4 and 7). Moreover, these upland soils are prone to extensive erosion. Successful cultivation on the flat terrain of the pampas, on the other hand, is inhibited by hydrological and meteorological variables. The pampas zone is perennially marshy and subject to inundation during the wet season. Throughout the year, intersecting water tables and ground surfaces create pools of standing water. These pools diminish in size as water evaporates and the level of Lake Titicaca declines throughout the dry season, leaving behind saline crusts, mostly $CaSO_4$, $CaCl_2$, and NaCl. Under these hydrological circumstances, a combination of waterlogging and surface deposition of soluble salts is inevitable, and the absence of constructed drainage systems results in saline soils. For dependable production in the pampas zones, artificial water-control systems such as those incorporated in the design of raised fields are required to maintain a locally regulated phreatic surface to allow drainage and leaching of salts by new freshwater.

In addition, traditional dry farming of the pampas zones frequently results in elevated incidences of crop loss from killing frosts as cold air drains from more protected upland zones down onto flatter, lower-lying terrain. Again, in the absence of raised-field technology with its frost mitigation properties, dry cultivation of the pampas zone is risk prone. Not surprisingly, contemporary campesinos utilize the pampas zone principally as unimproved pasture land with oc-

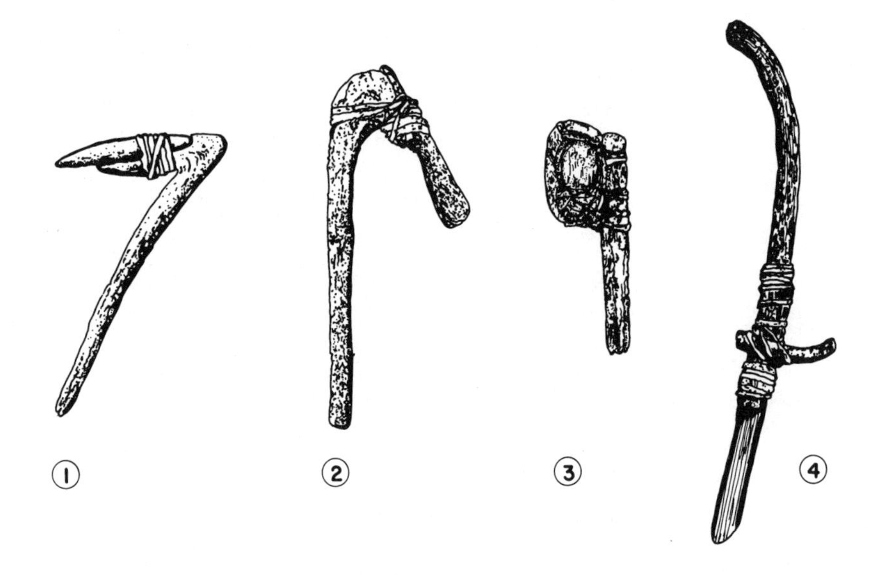


**Figure 9.2.** Traditional Aymara hand-held farming implements. 1 and 2, *liukana,* and 3, *kupana,* are all varieties of mattocks; 4, *hyuso,* is a digging stick or foot plow.

casional opportunistic *chakras,* or agricultural plots, placed strategically in areas of local topographic highs. In fact, small archaeological mound sites, which are rich in organic matter and provide a measure of drainage, are preferred locales for such chakras.

Additional difficulties afflicting the small farmers of this region include (1) a land tenure system characterized by exceptionally small landholdings (*minifundismo*), which has resulted in a scarcity of arable land available for extensive, more efficient agricultural production; (2) a deteriorating regional economic climate that has produced serious labor scarcity as campesinos migrate from rural areas to cities in search of alternative employment; (3) an emphasis on cattle production for meat and milk products in some areas, which has accelerated problems of soil erosion; and (4) poor agricultural management techniques resulting from a lack of information or inadequate access to capital. Among the most pernicious of these poor management techniques are the use of poor quality seeds, inadequate control of pests and crop pathogens, lack of crop rotation, inadequate systems for controlling soil erosion, and poor techniques for preserving harvested crops.

Within the region, 94 percent of the families with whom we work do not have access to sufficient land to produce enough food for their own needs. Average monthly family income is less than U.S. $70. Bolivian government statistics indicate that the low-income Bolivian family requires a minimum of $152 per month to satisfy basic subsistence needs. Not surprisingly, census data for the region indicate that approximately 80 percent of the population lives well below this poverty line. The direct ramifications of chronic low income on the health of women and children are particularly severe. Infant mortality is among the highest in the world (up to 167 per 1,000 in certain localities), and approximately 50 percent of all children under five are victims of inadequate nutrition. Life below the poverty line, underemployment, chronic low income, high infant mortality, malnutrition, and insufficient agricultural production are marked socioeconomic characteristics of the communities in which we work.

Because the ancient technology of raised-field agriculture is labor intensive rather than capital intensive, its rehabilitation promises to address two critical elements of underdevelopment in the area: inadequate agricultural production and inadequate opportunities for productive rural employment. Preliminary work in rehabilitating raised fields indicates that dramatic improvements are possible in the yields of both traditional Andean and introduced crops in comparison with yields generated by traditional forms of dry farming current in this region of the altiplano. Our research has demonstrated that (1) this native form of intensive agriculture is well adapted to the particular constraints on agricultural production in the Andean altiplano; (2) the rehabilitation of raised-field plots by a community-based work force is feasible and cost effective from both economic and social perspectives (rehabilitating raised fields entails only access to hand tools, sufficient improved seed stock, and community cooperation in integrating fields with sources of freshwater such as springs); and (3) communities participating in the experimental program of raised-field rehabilitation and maintenance experience enhanced yields of important subsistence and cash crops that contribute to growth in individual and community income.

## Methods of Field Rehabilitation

Some of the earliest experiments in rehabilitating raised fields were conducted by Puleston (1977), who worked with agricultural features associated with the Maya in Belize. The first successful experimental reconstruction of raised fields in the Lake Titicaca basin was undertaken by Erickson in 1981 in the Department of Puno, Peru (Erickson 1985, 1988a). Our own efforts at reconstructing raised fields on the Bolivian side of Lake Titicaca began with several unsuccessful attempts to recruit communities for an experimental program of field rehabilitation between 1979 and 1985. Our efforts to involve communities in the project were inhibited by a series of natural and political events. During the severe drought that affected the Andean altiplano in 1982–83, and subsequently during the catastrophic inundation of the circum-Titicaca region in 1985–86, our efforts were impeded by the ready availability of food and temporary employment opportunities spawned by large-scale disaster relief efforts. Simply put, our small-scale, experimental project could not compete with internationally sponsored aid programs. From 1982 to 1985, the political climate of the Bolivian altiplano was also disturbed by the country's chaotic return to democracy under Hernán Siles Zuazo's UDP government, after years of military dictatorship. The political instability and hyperinflation resulting from the UDP's inconsistent economic policies exacerbated already difficult social conditions in the altiplano. At that time, no communities were willing to risk a substantial investment of labor for the uncertain returns promised by the "nontraditional" agricultural technique we were promoting.

With the inevitable decline in international disaster relief by mid–1986, local communities began to listen to our proposals for a raised-field rehabilitation project that would rely principally on self-help. Ultimately, we achieved a working relationship with the community of Lakaya in July 1986. After the first season of successful production there (1986–87), more indigenous communities became involved each year. As of 1992, we were working in 52 communities with a total beneficiary population of approximately 2,500. All rehabilitated raised fields, termed *suka kollu* in Aymara, are located in the seasonally inundated pampas zones, which are either under the control of the communities as a whole in the form of commons (*aynoka* lands) or divided into discrete parcels as the private property of nuclear and extended families. Many private owners of these lands have migrated to La Paz in the past decade, leaving enormous tracts of land virtually abandoned or else under the stewardship of relatives who remain in the rural communities.

Before rehabilitation was begun on any raised fields, we first contacted the designated leaders of the community and described to them the potential advantages of this type of cultivation. These community leaders, who normally hold office for a year at a time, were responsible for disseminating this information to the community and deciding whether or not the town wished to participate. If the answer was affirmative, we asked the leaders to provide us with a list of people interested in becoming participants, the area where the field construction was to occur, and a letter requesting our support for the project.

Once the request was received and vetted for feasibility, we arranged a site visit to the community. There we evaluated the potential of the soils for the construction of raised fields and recorded information on available water sources and local slope variations. Normal data-collection protocols called for one or more test excavations in areas of potential field rehabilitation. These small soundings were designed to extract basic soil profile information, including presence and character of discernible soil horizons, depth of the arable stratum, depth to the water table, relative abundances of clay, silt, sand, and rarer inclusions such as volcanic ash, presence of gravel in the soil profiles, structure, texture, and organic matter content of the soils, and finally, soil pH. In addition, we conducted interviews to obtain data on the local frequency of frosts, wind direction, frequency and periods of precipitation, direction and flow of groundwater, and areas of pooling during the rainy season.

Once the site visit and basic evaluation of soils, water, and logistical feasibility were completed, we signed a *convenio,* or formal accord, with the community and its leaders. Our standard agreement calls for the project to provide seed stock for the first year of cultivation, basic hand tools (picks, shovels, mattocks, wheelbarrows), and technical assistance for the reconstruction and maintenance of raised fields. The first step in providing technical assistance was a formal set of lectures and practicums on the theory and practice of raised-field cultivation offered by project agronomists to the assembled participants. A set of three bilingual (Aymara-Spanish) technical manuals published by the project and detailing raised-field construction and maintenance procedures, were distributed during this first course. Since 1990, the course has also incorporated a bilingual videotape in which successful raised-field rehabilitators recount their own experiences. In addition, a subset of community members, designated by the community itself, is taken on a field trip to successful rehabilitation sites in other communities to discuss the process with people already participating in the project.

The bilingual video and site visits have been exceptionally successful in generating local interest for raised-field rehabilitation. The bilingual texts, on the other hand, are received with apparent enthusiasm, but most community members glance at them once and then file them away. They do not appear to serve effectively as field guides and technical manuals as they were originally intended. Although heavily based on clear, didactic graphics, the text portion is extensive. After we persisted in inquiring why these pamphlets were not frequently consulted, many community members informed us that they do not often read Aymara and that, in any event, they prefer to visit communities already engaged in raised-field rehabilitation and talk to people directly about their experiences. Although we continue to distribute the three texts, in light of these experiences we are reassessing our original plans to produce additional manuals.

The project concentrates on rehabilitating preexisting raised fields. Some community lands, however, are in areas without suitable, preserved raised fields, and in these instances we have designed and constructed new ones. The design of these fields is patterned as closely as possible on ancient models drawn from comparable ecological settings. Once the field locations are chosen, project personnel begin a practical demonstration of the construction methods for a group designated by the community. The basic principles and technology of rehabilitating (or constructing) raised fields are simple. Field systems are laid out by first cutting and clearing the canals adjacent to the planting platform. Teams of workers cut and turn the sod from the base of the intended platform to establish an appropriate foundation for the raised field. Then they mound the earth cut from the canals into the center to form the elevated planting surface itself (figs. 9.3, 9.4).

The construction of the elevated planting bed is one of the keys to the technological effectiveness of this cultivation system. By cutting and turning the surface sod and its underlying earth and by mounding this material into an elevated bed, cultivators significantly transform and enhance the soil structure of their agricultural fields. The process of constructing a raised field results in earth that is loose and well aerated, with the capacity to capture both water and air in micropores within the soil. This uncompacted, aerated soil structure increases the ability of growing plants to retain water and absorb essential, water-soluble nutrients. A loose, well-tilled soil structure may also permit farmers to plant their crops in closely packed, dense rows, resulting in higher yields. In addition to generating higher yields, close packing of

**Figure 9.3.** A team of workers in the Aymara community of Chokara cuts and turns sod in order to construct a raised-field platform.

Figure 9.4. Rehabilitated raised fields near the Aymara community of Lakaya.

plants reduces the otherwise formidable competition from weeds native to the altiplano.

In conjunction with project agronomists, community members next select a suite of crops for planting and decide on the locations of the individual crop-specific parcels within the raised field block. Potatoes and barley are the principal crops of choice among the participating communities. People also normally incorporate a few parcels of vegetables into their raised-field plantings. Less frequently, they plant quinoa and kañiwa in contiguous parcels or as field borders. Table 9.2 lists the principal crops grown on the project's rehabilitated raised fields, along with the optimal spacing between furrows and plants (where applicable). These optimal spacings were determined by experiment and by common practice.

If the raised fields have been in cultivation for more than one year, a preestablished plan of crop rotation developed in consultation with the community is followed. The project encourages crop rotation schemes to reduce the risk of insect infestations and plant pathogens. Of course, crop rotation also slows the rate of soil nutrient depletion, but this is not the essential reason for implementing rotation schemes on raised fields. The raised fields reconstructed by the project are continuously cropped without the need for a fallow period. Green manure and organic matter from adjacent canals are routinely incorporated into the topsoils of the planting platforms throughout the field maintenance cycle. This input of new, readily available macronutrients sustains the fertility of the fields indefinitely. Technically, there appear to be no physical or agronomic impediments to continuous cultivation on raised fields.

There is, however, a certain degree of *cultural* resistance to continuous cropping on the part of the indigenous small farmers of the region (a pattern also noted in Peru by Erickson and Brinkmeier [1991:14–16]). These farmers are accustomed to following a long-fallow regime on their traditional upland fields (Mayer 1979). This regime frequently takes the form of sectorial fallow of common fields (Godoy 1991) and a standard cultivation sequence of potatoes alternating with barley. In the Tiwanaku region, common sequences in a given field over a three-year period are potato-potato-barley, potato-quinoa-barley,

Table 9.2. Cultivars Grown by Aymara Communities on Rehabilitated Raised Fields

| Species | Optimal Distance between Furrows (cm) | Optimal Distance between Plants (cm) |
|---|---|---|
| *Solanum* sp. (potato) | 80–90 | 30–40 |
| *Vicia faba* (broad bean) | 60–80 | 20–30 |
| *Vicia villosa* (hairy vetch) | 50–60 | — |
| *Chenopodium quinua* (quinoa) | 50–60 | scatter |
| *Chenopodium pallidicaule* (kañiwa) | 50–60 | scatter |
| *Hordeum vulgare* (barley) | 40–60 | scatter |
| *Avena sativa* (oats) | 40–60 | scatter |
| *Triticum* sp. (wheat) | 40–60 | scatter |
| *Allium cepa* (onion) | 30 | 15–20 |
| *Allium sativa* (garlic) | 30–40 | 20–30 |
| *Raphanus sativa* (radish) | 20–30 | 15–20 |
| *Brasica rapa* (turnip) | 20–30 | 20–30 |
| *Brasica oleraceae c.* (cabbage) | 30–40 | 20–30 |
| *Beta vulgaris* (beets) | 20–30 | 20–30 |
| *Beta vulgaris cicla* (spinach beet) | 25–30 | 20–25 |
| *Daucus carota* (carrot) | 20–30 | 20–30 |
| *Lactuca sativa* (lettuce) | 25–30 | 20–25 |

and potato-barley-barley. After three years of cultivation, the fields are placed in fallow (*descanso*) for a period that varies from five to fifteen years depending on the particular soil and edaphic characteristics of the field. A substantial proportion of our training program concentrates on the economic benefits of continuous cultivation on raised fields. Overcoming small farmer skepticism surrounding the feasibility of continuous cultivation, which stems from decades of experience with long-fallow systems, is difficult. With continuous encouragement from project agronomists over the past five years, the number of farmers who have accepted this dimension of raised-field cultivation practice has slowly increased.

After the designated crops have been planted on the rehabilitated fields, project agronomists continue to offer training programs focusing on field and crop maintenance. Maintenance throughout the growing period entails early application of animal dung (*taquia*) as a soil amendment and natural fertilizer, manual weeding, pruning of damaged or weakened plants (*raleo*), and monitoring of the water level in the canal system. The last practice is perhaps the most critical of all maintenance procedures performed in the raised fields. In a number of instances, members of communities engaged in raised-field rehabilitation for the first time did not grasp the importance of maintaining appropriate water levels in the canals between fields. They treated the canals as a means of periodic irrigation rather than as an integral part of the cultivation system. After filling the canals to the appropriate level at planting time, they frequently diverted water for other purposes, such as watering cattle and other livestock. People's misunderstanding of the total contribution of the canal water to the successful functioning of the raised-field cultivation system, particularly its thermal properties and its role in sequestering biologically available nutrients, resulted in significantly depressed yields in these communities, often from severe frost damage. In response to such experiences, the project redesigned its training program to place greater emphasis on the critical step of maintaining water levels in the canals throughout the growing season.

The harvesting of crops on the reconstructed raised fields is accomplished in stages, depending on the crop type and the maturation of the plants. The normal harvest season for the principal planting extends from early March through May. Later we discuss the yields of our index crop (several varieties of potatoes) achieved in 22 communities during the 1990–91 season.

Once the harvest is completed, the project encourages a standard set of field maintenance procedures. Some communities permit livestock, particularly pigs and sheep, to root and graze on the after-harvest stubble. This practice contributes substantially to the pace of erosion of the field surfaces. Harvest activities themselves often cause considerable damage to the sidewalls of the elevated planting beds. These sidewalls are constructed of cut sod blocks (locally termed *tepes*), which, especially in newly rehabilitated fields, are rather friable and susceptible to crumbling. To prevent erosion of the planting surface and sedimentation into adjoining canals, the sidewalls are repaired annually after the harvest by replacing disintegrated sod blocks along the field borders. Frequently, in the process of repairing the field borders, communities will add additional topsoil to the field surface (fig. 9.5).

After-harvest maintenance of rehabilitated fields that have been in continuous production for more than three years includes the incorporation of organic matter dredged from the bottoms of the adjacent canals. This procedure recycles nutrients that have been sequestered in the aquatic environment of the canal systems (see chapter 7). Although recycling canal sediments entails substantial additional labor input, some communities have begun to incorporate this maintenance procedure routinely into their after-harvest activities. Informal discussions with the small farmers who have adopted this procedure indicate that they have made the conceptual linkage between recycled canal sediments and the maintenance or enhancement of soil fertility on raised fields, and that they have calculated that the cost-benefit ratio of the procedure is generally positive.

Despite their ready acceptance of green manure or organic muck as a natural soil amendment, many of the same farmers express a preference for commercially prepared chemical fertilizers. They appear to believe that industrial fertilizers are more effective than locally derived, naturally produced "biofertilizers" from the canal sediments. They also take into account the heavier labor cost of cleaning and redistributing the canal sediments, and as a result, they lobby whenever possible for direct grants of commercial fertilizer to avoid this additional investment. Lack of capital appears to be the principal limiting factor explaining the absence of agrochemicals in the local cultivation system. It remains unclear, however, whether farmers would be willing to substitute cash for labor if they did have access to sources of capital, such as agricultural credit.

## Production Results of the 1990–1991 Agricultural Season

During the 1990–91 agricultural season, the communities working with the project planted potatoes, barley, oats, broad beans, and, to a lesser extent, winter wheat, hairy vetch, quinoa, kañiwa, and a number of vegetables. The aggregate area in raised fields cultivated during this season was 50 hectares distributed among 22 communities (table 9.1). In addition to potatoes, the communities cultivated a number of grains on the raised fields. Apart from quinoa and the lesser quantities of winter wheat, these grains are used primarily as fodder for animal consumption. The project also encourages the experimental cultivation of vegetables, and most communities incorporated a few parcels into their fields (fig. 9.6).

The experimental cultivation of vegetables serves a

**Figure 9.5.** After the harvest, a farmer adds topsoil to a field surface.

**Figure 9.6.** Cosimo Uruchi, an Aymara elder from the community of Lakaya, looks at an experimental crop of lettuce grown in a rehabilitated raised field.

dual purpose: to diversify the crop inventory by introducing new species into the highlands via the raised-field system, and to diversify the diet by adding crops with supplemental proteins, vitamins, and minerals, each of which may help to improve the dietary (and ultimately the health) status of the participating communities. Vegetables are also a potential cash crop. In theory, efficient, large-scale production of vegetables such as onions, lettuce, radishes, and cabbages on raised fields could help generate an economic surplus and the promise of new sources of income for participating families. The complete roster of crops planted in 1990–91 appears in table 9.2.

The greatest area of rehabilitated raised-field land was given over to several varieties of potatoes, the crop currently of highest economic and social value (Arnold 1987) to the Aymara. Potatoes are the dietary staple of the inhabitants of the altiplano (Correll 1962; Ochoa 1990). Nearly all the produce is consumed at the household level, although some families dedicate a portion of their crop for sale in weekly rural markets, such as in the Thursday market in the village of Lakaya and the Sunday market in the village of Tiwanaku. These markets draw consumers from throughout the region, including substantial numbers of campesinos from neighboring Peru, some 30 kilometers away. Table 9.3 summarizes the physical characteristics of the five potato varieties planted during the 1990–91 season (Correll 1962). Varieties are listed according to their local Aymara names. Figure 9.7 illustrates the key, indigenous cultivated crops. The two principal potatoes planted by the project are the *sani imilla* and *huaycha* varieties, and these are treated as our index varieties for purposes of comparing yields on raised fields across the communities.

## Potato Production on Raised Fields: Evaluation Methods

The point at which potatoes were harvested was determined by the development of the vegetation and the tubers. The decision to harvest a given set of raised fields was made by project agronomists in conjunction with members of the participating communities. Generally, 150 to 180 days were required for the crops to complete their growth cycle. This period began with the planting of the seed potatoes and continued until the maturation of the tuber was complete. All harvests were completed with the direct participation of project agronomists and technicians who coordinated collection and recording of yields. Methods used to evaluate potato yields quantitatively were based on the following data-collection protocol.

Within a given community's block of rehabilitated raised fields, a set of randomly selected parcels, each of which covered a standard area of 50 square meters, was selected for complete measurement and evaluation. Every parcel contained at least two edges bordering on the adjacent canals. Additionally, in order to evaluate the development and yields of the different varieties of potatoes in relation to their position in the raised fields, plants were sampled from three distinct positions within each parcel: from each of the two edges of the parcel bordering on the canals and from the center of the parcel (coded on standard project forms as right, left, and center). These plants were harvested and evaluated according to the number and weight of tubers per plant and the maximum and minimum diameter of each tuber. The percentages of crops affected by frost, hail, plant pathogens, and insect infestations were also calculated.

Depending on the aggregate area of the raised

Table 9.3. Selected Characteristics of Aymara Potato Varieties

| Feature | Sani Imilla | Huaycha | Luk'i | Chiar Imilla | Wila Imilla |
|---|---|---|---|---|---|
| Maturation | 24–26 weeks | 24–26 weeks | 28–30 weeks | 24–27 weeks | 25–28 weeks |
| Plant height (m) | 0.6–0.7 | 0.5–0.6 | 0.4–0.5 | 0.6–0.8 | 0.6–0.8 |
| Growing shape | Upright | Upright | Ground hugging | Erect | Erect |
| Stems | Erect | Erect | Semi-erect | Erect | Erect |
| Foliage density | Compact dense | Compact dense | Open | Compact dense | Thick |
| Branching | Basal abundant | Basal | Abundant | Abundant | Basal |
| Blossoms | Abundant | Abundant | Abundant | Abundant | Abundant |
| Flower color | Violet | Pink | Violet | Pink | Pink |
| Skin color | Brown with violet tints around eyes | Pink with white tints | White | Black | Pinkish red |
| Tuber form | Round, oval | Oval | Multiple rounded forms | Round forms with deep eyes | Round forms with deep eyes |
| Flesh color | Creamy white | Yellowish white | White | Bluish white | Pinkish white |

fields, four to six such standard parcels were evaluated in each community. The parcels were completely harvested and the product was weighed in order to determine the yield per parcel. The yield per hectare (expressed in metric tons per hectare) for each community's raised fields was obtained by taking an average of the measured yields from these randomly selected parcels. In order to verify that the projected yield per hectare, calculated on the basis of the standardized parcels, was an acceptable measure of actual yield, we weighed the *total* production of the raised fields in five communities and compared this weight with that of the projected yields. In three of five cases, projected yield overestimated actual yield; in the remaining two cases, the actual yield was underestimated. The difference between projected and actual yields averaged 0.8 metric tons per hectare (mt/ha). The maximum difference between projected yield and actual yield was 1.7 mt/ha.

Two types of yields per unit surface area can be obtained for raised fields: gross yield, in which the total area of a hectare (10,000 square meters) is considered, and net yield, in which only the surface area under cultivation is considered. Net yield does not take into account the uncultivated surface area of the canals. The production results for each community, presented in the next section, are expressed in terms of net yields. In certain instances we also provide the figure for gross yield. Our calculation of net yields assumes that the cultivable surface area for each hectare of raised fields is 6,000 square meters, or 60 percent of the total surface area.

The following sections summarize production results on rehabilitated raised fields by area and by communities within areas. The two principal areas of project activities are the Tiwanaku Valley and the basin of the Catari River (fig. 9.1). For the sake of convenience, we refer to the Catari basin as the Pampa Koani area. These two areas account for 17 of the 25 groups with which the project was working during the 1990–91 agricultural season. Here we report the production data, along with brief evaluations of raised-field performance, for 15 communities that are representative of the production results and experiences of raised-field rehabilitation throughout the areas of project activity.

## The Tiwanaku Area

In the Tiwanaku Valley, the highest potato production on raised fields was obtained in the community of Achuta Grande, which achieved a gross yield of 39.3 mt/ha and a net yield of 23.6 mt/ha. We infer that these high yields were due in part to the excellent management techniques practiced by this community. Achuta Grande was the first community in the Tiwanaku Valley to participate in the raised-field project. Interviews with farmers from this community

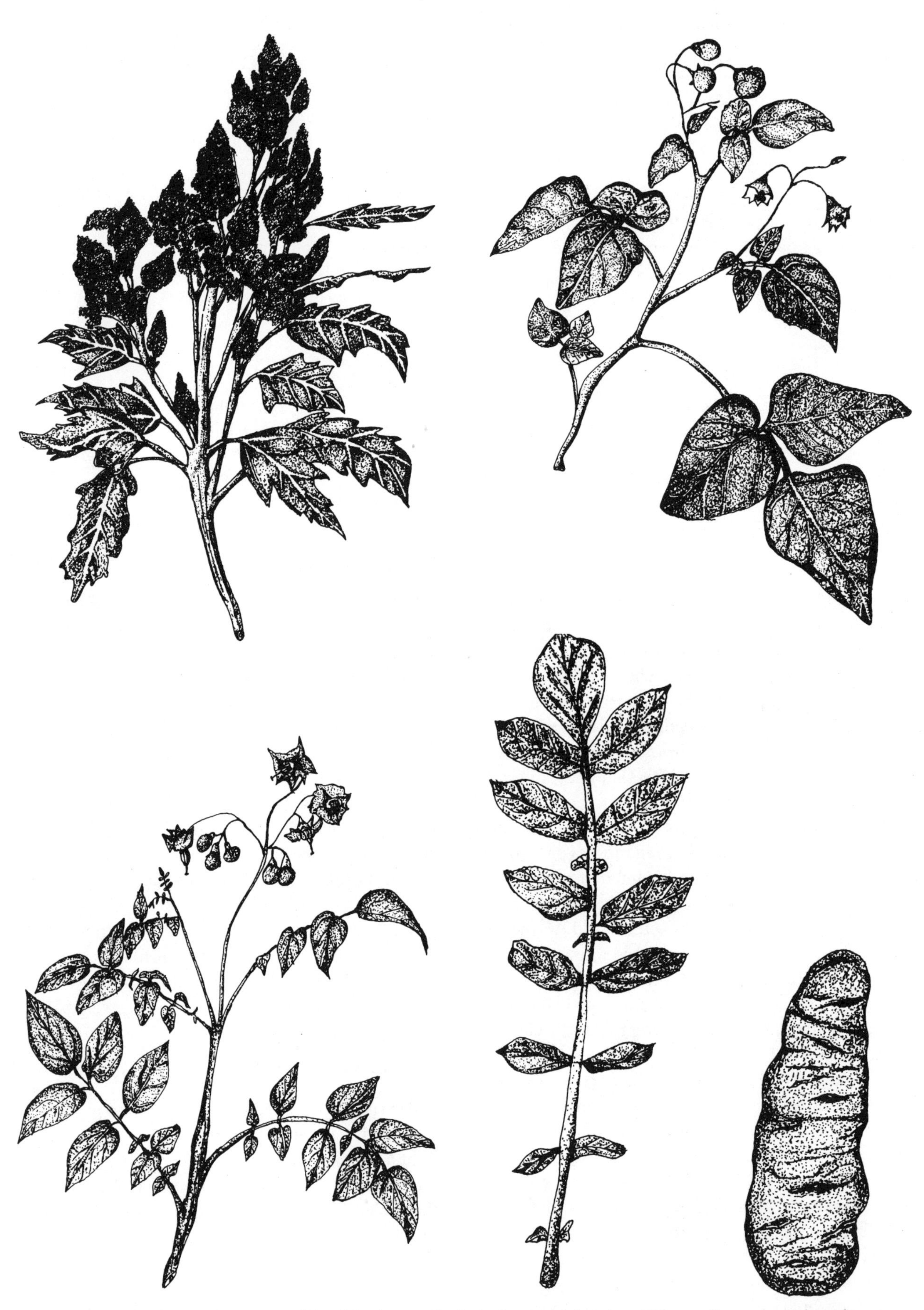

**Figure 9.7.** Four of the principal Aymara traditional food crops. Clockwise from top left: quinoa (*Chenopodium quinoa*), *huaycha* potato (*Solanum andigenum*), *jank'o luk'i* potato (*Solanum juzepezukii*), *sani imilla* potato (*Solanum andiginum*).

indicate that they feel a kind of pride of place and consider themselves to be model *suka kolleros* (raised-field cultivators). Achuta Grande's farmers enthusiastically engage in debate with project agronomists regarding the best techniques for managing raised fields and enhancing productivity, and they are meticulous about maintaining appropriate water supply to raised-field canals and about tilling, weeding, and fertilizing their fields. Under their own initiative, they apply organic fertilizers (principally dried animal dung) to the fields in a proportion of 3 mt/ha.

In contrast, the lowest yield in this valley was obtained from raised fields within the archaeological site of Tiwanaku itself, in the sector locally called K'araña. The raised fields of K'araña achieved a gross yield of 6.3 mt/ha and a net yield of 3.82 mt/ha. The K'araña fields are on common lands controlled by the village of Tiwanaku. In return for a portion of the expected harvest, the *sindicato* (union) of archaeological workers in Tiwanaku agreed to perform the labor of constructing and maintaining these raised fields. Because project personnel have a close association with the sindicato members, we requested more complete control over rehabilitation activities for the purposes of experimentation, a process that is more difficult to accomplish in other communities.

During the 1990–91 season, planting of the K'araña fields did not commence until early December, and some parcels were not planted until early January 1991. The normal planting period in the Tiwanaku Valley spans the period from mid-September to early November. This delay in planting was partly a matter of logistics (the sindicato was working full-time in the archaeological excavations until mid-December 1990) and partly the product of our experiments. We wished to determine the effects of delayed planting on the maturation of three varieties of potato: sani imilla, huaycha, and *chiar imilla*. The period between November and February is critical for the growth of these potatoes. Adverse meteorological conditions such as frost and hail, which occur with some frequency during these months, often have a devastating effect on maturing plants. The retarded growth of the K'araña raised-field plants caused by the delay in planting left them even more vulnerable to these conditions. Indeed, on the four standardized parcels that were selected for evaluation, the incidence of significant damage to plants from hail and frost was exceptionally high, ranging from 80 to 100 percent. The lower yields achieved in the K'araña fields were clearly related to this period of increased vulnerability to hail and frost.

Another factor contributing to the low yields may have been more relaxed attitudes toward field maintenance among the sindicato members. Because the K'araña raised-field plots were not the private property of sindicato members, there was weaker incentive to maintain them with the same degree of care demonstrated by the farmers of Achuta Grande. For instance, because sindicato members were absorbed with their personal, dry-farmed chakras, no organic fertilizer was applied to the K'araña raised fields, and weeding became a casual, unscheduled affair. Even though the yields on the K'araña fields were relatively low, it is likely that traditional dry-farming techniques could not have been used there at all.

#### ACHUTA GRANDE

The community of Achuta Grande had three contiguous hectares of land under cultivation during the 1990–91 season. This community is located in the middle Tiwanaku Valley in an area of high groundwater. The water supply for the raised fields derived from both groundwater percolation and from a small canal that community members redirected from the springs of Choque Pajcha in the southwest section of the archaeological site of Tiwanaku. The feeder canal was essential for maintaining appropriate water levels in the secondary canals between the elevated beds immediately after planting, which took place on October 27, 1990. By January 1991, there was sufficient rainfall and groundwater percolation that the community was able to divert the feeder-canal water for other uses. The soils of Achuta Grande's fields are unconsolidated alluvium of high quality; they can be characterized as silty clay loams, with organic matter in selected samples ranging from 7 to 13 percent. Soil pH ranges from 7.5 to 8.0. As indicated earlier, the high yields obtained by this community were due to careful, consistent field management techniques. Relatively high soil fertility was also clearly a contributing factor. Table 9.4 and figure 9.8 summarize the achieved net yields for the Achuta Grande raised fields.

#### CHAMBI GRANDE

The community of Chambi Grande lies in the middle Tiwanaku Valley. Community members cultivated 4 hectares of raised fields during the 1990–91 agricultural season. As in the case of Achuta Grande, the water source for Chambi Grande's raised fields combines groundwater percolation and a feeder canal drawn

Table 9.4. Net Yields of Potato Varieties from Raised Fields of 15 Bolivian Aymara Work Groups

| Work Group and Variety | Net Yield (mt/ha) | Planting Date | Harvest Date | Developmental Period (Days) |
|---|---|---|---|---|
| Achuta Grande | | | | |
| Sani imilla | 27.9 | 27/10/90 | 16/04/91 | 154 |
| Huaycha | 21.3 | 27/10/90 | 16/04/91 | 154 |
| Chambi Grande | | | | |
| Sani imilla | 22.1 | 11/11/90 | 18/04/91 | 157 |
| Huaycha | 27.1 | 11/11/90 | 18/04/91 | 157 |
| Chiar imilla | 19.9 | 11/11/90 | 18/04/91 | 157 |
| Wankollo Hospital | | | | |
| Sani imilla | 11.6 | 28/11/90 | 03/05/91 | 156 |
| Huaycha | 10.9 | 21/11/90 | 03/05/91 | 163 |
| Wankollo Osco | | | | |
| Sani imilla | 13.9 | 27/11/90 | 06/06/91 | 183 |
| Huaycha | 14.9 | 02/12/90 | 20/06/91 | 178 |
| Wankollo Niña | | | | |
| Sani imilla | 12.6 | 28/11/90 | 06/06/91 | 182 |
| Huaycha | 13.2 | 02/12/90 | 20/06/91 | 178 |
| Kohana | | | | |
| Sani imilla | 38.5 | 01/11/90 | 10/04/91 | 130 |
| Huaycha | 34.5 | 01/11/90 | 10/04/91 | 130 |
| Lukurmata | | | | |
| Sani imilla | 7.7 | 23/10/90 | 03/04/91 | 161 |
| Ñachoka | | | | |
| Sani imilla | 6.0 | 16/11/90 | 12/04/91 | 150 |
| Huaycha | 9.1 | 16/11/90 | 12/04/91 | 150 |
| Lillimani | | | | |
| Sani imilla | 7.9 | 26/10/90 | 03/04/91 | 158 |
| Huaycha | 8.5 | 26/10/90 | 03/04/91 | 158 |
| Chukara | | | | |
| Sani imilla | 16.5 | 26/10/90 | 03/04/91 | 158 |
| Huaycha | 18.7 | 26/10/90 | 03/04/91 | 158 |
| Chukara CEMA | | | | |
| Sani imilla | 11.8 | 16/10/90 | 03/04/91 | 168 |
| Huaycha | 8.0 | 26/10/90 | 03/04/91 | 158 |
| Wakullani | | | | |
| Sani imilla | 14.4 | 16/10/90 | 03/04/91 | 168 |
| Huaycha | 9.6 | 26/10/90 | 03/04/91 | 158 |
| Kusijata | | | | |
| Sani imilla | 19.9 | 24/10/90 | 10/03/91 | 136 |
| Huaycha | 6.2 | 16/11/90 | 16/04/91 | 152 |
| Santa Ana | | | | |
| Sani imilla | 5.3 | 15/12/90 | 29/04/91 | 152 |
| Huaycha | 3.6 | 15/12/90 | 29/04/91 | 152 |
| Hilata Santa Trinidad | | | | |
| Sani imilla | 13.2 | 12/12/90 | 06/04/91 | 132 |
| Huaycha | 16.4 | 12/12/90 | 06/04/91 | 132 |

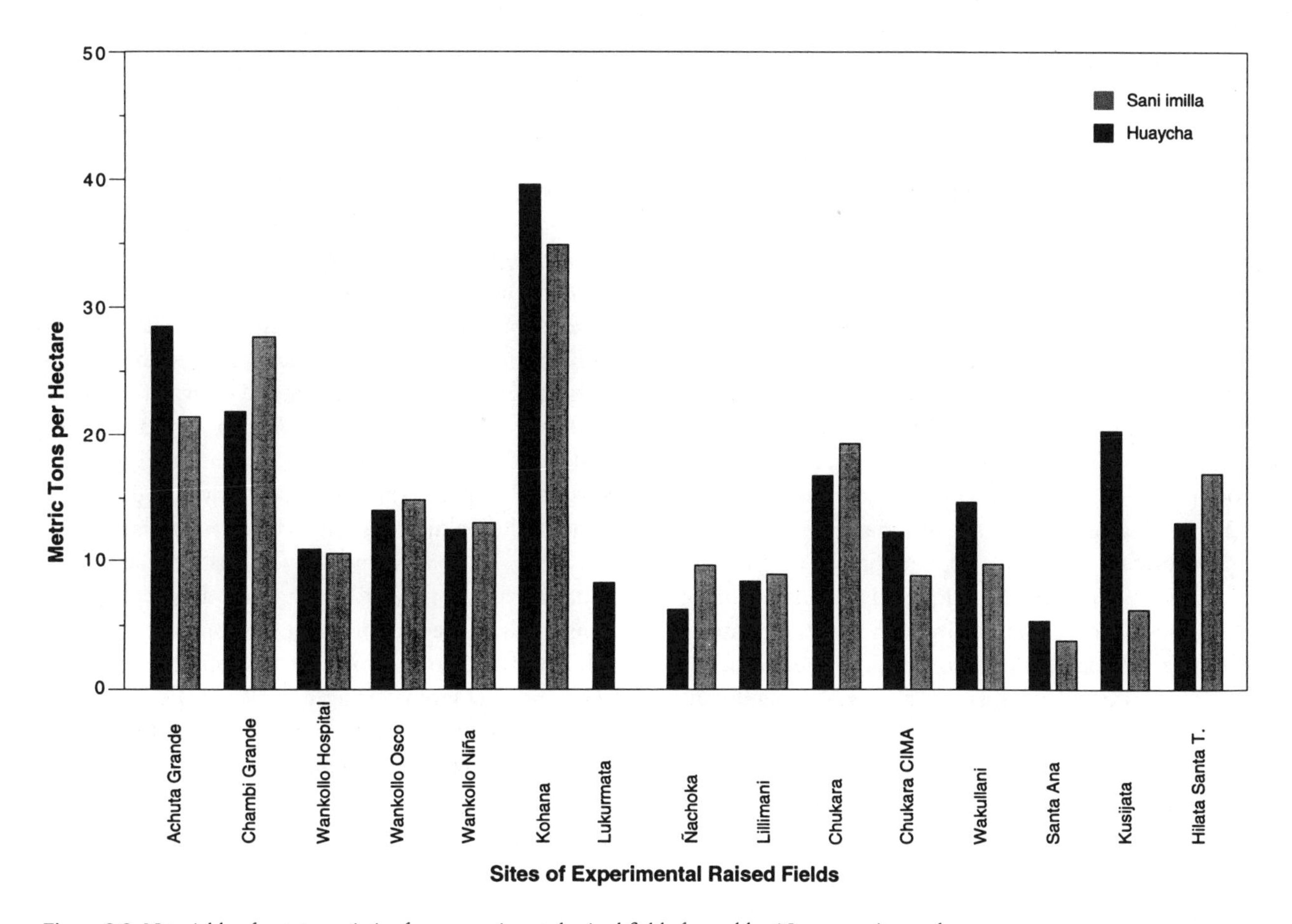


**Figure 9.8.** Net yields of potato varieties from experimental raised fields farmed by 15 community work groups.

from a local spring. Soils are generally similar to those of Achuta Grande, but with a higher admixture of sand. These soils may be characterized as sandy clay loams with a somewhat lower percentage of organic matter than those of Achuta Grande. Soil pH ranges from 6.7 to 8.0. Some of the soils on the raised fields exhibit an efflorescence of salts, principally $CaCl_2$ and NaCl. During preparation of the fields for cultivation, these salts were simply mixed in with additional topsoils drawn from the raised-field canals, and there is no evidence that the presence of these salts depressed yields (table 9.4, fig. 9.8).

#### WANKOLLO HOSPITAL, WANKOLLO OSCO, AND WANKOLLO NIÑA

The aggregate area under cultivation in the community of Wankollo, which lies immediately east of Tiwanaku, was 2.62 hectares divided among three separate work groups. During the 1990–91 season, these groups were experimenting with raised-field rehabilitation for the first time. We attribute the relatively low yields they achieved to internal organizational problems and incomplete grasp of the techniques entailed in raised-field construction and maintenance.[1] For instance, delays in planting were encountered among all three groups because the investment of labor in constructing the fields and cutting feeder canals from adjacent springs was higher than anticipated. After an extended series of meetings among the participants, the labor obligations of each member were finally sorted out. The delays, however, resulted in rapid and somewhat careless preparation of the elevated planting beds. The soil was neither aerated nor tilled properly. Substantial quantities of local gravels, sands, and clays were incorporated into the topsoil. Furthermore, despite repeated lectures and demonstrations by project agronomists regarding the importance of maintaining water levels in the raised-field canals, the Wankollo groups frequently diverted water for their livestock. Water levels in the canals fluctuated dramatically throughout the growing season, and at one point the canals were left completely dry for two weeks. Parent soils for the Wankollo raised fields can be characterized as sandy loams and have pH values that cluster around 8.0.

## The Pampa Koani Area

The highest yield from any of the raised fields in this study was registered in the Pampa Koani area. The community of Kohana, with 1 hectare under cultivation during the 1990–91 season, achieved a gross yield of 60.8 mt/ha and a net yield of 36.5 mt/ha. Significant variables explaining this high yield are superior soils, a constant supply of freshwater, and excellent management techniques, including significant input of organic fertilizer at a proportion of 3.5 mt/ha. In contrast, the lowest yield for the Pampa Koani area was obtained on 2 hectares of raised fields in the community of Lukurmata, which achieved values of 12.9 mt/ha gross yield and 7.7 mt/ha net yield. Lukurmata's low relative yields appeared to be the product of poor management techniques. For a time during the 1990–91 season, a dispute within the community caused field maintenance to cease. In addition, no organic fertilizer or other form of soil amendment was incorporated into Lukurmata's fields. Another factor contributing to this variability in production results was differences in the type and quality of soils.

#### KOHANA

The community of Kohana maintains 3.6 hectares of rehabilitated raised fields constructed during the 1989–90 and 1990–91 seasons. These fields are linked to a stable water supply provided by a feeder canal with intake from a local spring. The soils of the Kohana raised fields may be characterized generally as clay loams of high fertility. There are also substantial peat deposits in the vicinity of Kohana that have been used as soil amendments for agricultural fields in the past. This may partially explain the exceptional fertility of the Kohana soils. The high yields obtained by this community were the product of high soil fertility, careful seed selection, and proper management techniques. Kohana's raised-field cultivators, like those of Achuta Grande, were intensely interested in the courses and demonstrations sponsored by the project. On their own initiative, they sent community representatives to discuss raised-field technology with project agronomists at our office in La Paz, and they accompanied the agronomists on site visits in other communities. They constantly compared their own techniques with those of others participating in the project. This intense engagement with the technology clearly had a major impact in generating high yields.

#### LUKURMATA

Lukurmata placed 2 hectares of rehabilitated raised fields under cultivation during the 1990–91 season. Directly on the shore of Lake Titicaca, Lukurmata is at the foot of the Taraco peninsula, a large, aquifer-bearing Tertiary geological formation. This community enjoys a stable, if not consistently abundant, water supply even during drought years like that of 1982–83. Accordingly, the water supply to the Lukurmata raised fields was constant and derived from both a surface point source (a set of springs above the fields) and from groundwater percolation. There is a constant flow of surface water and groundwater through the Lukurmata raised fields to the lake edge. Soils are clay loams but do not possess the exceptional fertility of the Kohana soils. Physical conditions (soils, water supply) at Lukurmata are reasonably good and do not appear to explain the relatively low yields achieved during the 1990–91 season. We attribute these low yields to organizational problems and poor management techniques.

#### ÑACHOKA

The community of Ñachoka had 2.83 hectares of raised fields under cultivation during the 1990–91 season, supplied by a constant source of water from a spring-driven irrigation canal. Like Lukurmata, Ñachoka is in an area of high groundwater that contributes to the water supply of the raised fields. Ñachoka's soils are a mixture of clay and sand loams with irregular distribution but distinct stratification. The sandy loams tend to underlie the clayey loams. In general, these soils have a relatively high percentage of organic matter but are not exceptionally fertile. The low yields achieved in this community, which were well below the overall average for raised fields during the 1990–91 season, can be attributed to relatively poor quality soils, weak organizational infrastructure, and poor field management techniques. As in the case of Wankollo, Ñachokans diverted water from the feeder canals to accommodate livestock. In addition, planting in Ñachoka was delayed because of internal feuding in the committee responsible for organizing labor parties.

#### LILLIMANI

Lillimani cultivated 2 hectares of rehabilitated raised fields during the 1990–91 agricultural season. These fields were supplied by an irrigation channel that transported water from a spring approximately 1,000 meters south of the field. Like other communities along the colluvial terraces at the base of the Taraco Formation, Lillimani enjoys a relatively stable water supply from springs charged by seasonal rainfall and by infiltration from the aquifer in that formation. Lillimani's soils are locally variable and range in texture from clayey loams to significant admixtures of sands and gravels. Salt efflorescence was prominent in the fields, perhaps because of the marshy, wetlands character of the field rehabilitation site. During the rainy season in this area, the water table intersects the surface, forming standing pools from December to April. Subsequent evaporation of these pools leaves behind alkaline crusts of deposited salts.

The yields obtained by this community were relatively low. As in other cases, we attribute these depressed yields in great part to inadequate field maintenance techniques. The community rarely chose to follow project agronomists' suggestions regarding crop type, crop location, and crop rotation schemes. Furthermore, they refused to invest in the labor of collecting organic fertilizer in the form of either animal waste or canal mucks. Instead, they opted for a strategy of lobbying the project for direct grants of commercially produced fertilizers. Because one goal (and a principal philosophical strut) of the project is experimentation with non-capital-intensive forms of agriculture, we were unwilling to accede to this request. Virtually every community has requested commercial fertilizers in its initial negotiations with the project. After extended discussions and project demonstrations of the efficacy and cost advantages of locally produced biofertilizers, most communities incorporate a regime of canal mucking into their field maintenance procedures. The farmers of Lillimani remain an exception.

#### CHUKARA

This group was composed of farmers from the community of Chukara who cultivate aynoka, or communally owned lands. They had 3 hectares of communal raised fields under cultivation during the 1990–91 season. In addition, many of these farmers have reconstructed raised fields on their own privately held lands. The yields reported here, however, are those achieved only on the aynoka lands. In the concluding section of this chapter, we briefly discuss the implications of the private adoption of raised-field technology by Aymaras.

As in the case of Lillimani, the soils of Chukara are locally variable with an overall aspect of clayey loam. Freshwater supply to the fields comes from irrigation canals with sources in local, perennial springs. The efflorescence of salts is extremely prominent in the raised fields of Chukara. This area was completely inundated during the 1985–86 flood. The fields remained under water or were supersaturated for two years after this flood. As the waters receded, extensive deposits of salts were left behind. Despite these concentrations of salts, the net yields achieved on the Chukara raised fields cluster around the overall average. Either the soluble salts are not present in sufficient concentrations to depress productivity or there is sufficient flow-through of freshwater to purge the fields, reducing salt concentrations to levels that do not damage the crops.

The farmers of Chukara were among the original participants in the project, and their raised-field management techniques are among the best. Like the farmers of Achuta Grande in the Tiwanaku Valley, Chukarans take special care in preparing the seed beds and selecting seed that is healthy and free of plant pathogens. They are particularly sensitive to the need to maintain a well-aerated planting surface. They also apply organic fertilizer at a rate of approximately 3 mt/ha.

#### CHUKARA CENTRO DE MADRES (CEMA)

A second autonomous group working rehabilitated raised fields in the community of Chukara, the Chukara Centro de Madres (CEMA), represented an entirely different form of labor organization. In 1987, three women from the neighboring community of Lakaya formed a *centro de madres,* a flexible, informal association of women to rehabilitate raised fields for the benefit of themselves and their children. The positive results they obtained during their first three agricultural seasons stimulated the formation of Chukara's own centro de madres. The membership of these two autonomous associations partially overlaps. The three original *promotoras* (promoters) of the Lakaya CEMA took the lead in organizing work crews in the Chukara raised fields and acted as liaisons between the project and the Lakaya and Chukara CEMA groups. Land for the Chukara CEMA was rented from a local landowner who was a relative of one of the promotoras in a sharecropping arrangement. The Chukara CEMA entered into a formal, written contract with the landowner, agreeing to give him 25 percent of the produce from the fields in return for use of the land. All negotiations were conducted by the promotoras without the direct intervention of the project.

During the 1990–91 agricultural season, the Chukara CEMA planted 1 hectare of newly rehabilitated raised fields. Almost immediately it became apparent that the choice of land for the raised fields was problematic. Water supply was irregular and insufficient for the rehabilitated area. Water levels were low throughout the growing season and were incapable of meeting the hydrological needs of the fields and growing crops. Although ancient raised fields were rehabilitated, their original sources of water were a set of canals that were no longer operational. The Chukara CEMA was unsuccessful in its attempts to negotiate access to a local spring: the required canal would have cut across the prime pasture lands of an extended family that was unwilling to authorize the canal. Although the field management techniques of the Chukara CEMA were excellent, the water problem was never adequately resolved, and the result was relatively low yields (table 9.4, fig. 9.8).[2]

#### WAKULLANI

The community of Wakullani placed an aggregate area of 2.67 hectares under cultivation, all of which was constructed during the 1990–91 season. This area was divided into eight smaller subparcels reflecting the individual activities of distinct groups within the community. The soils of the rehabilitated raised-field area may be characterized as clayey loams with occasional gravel admixture. The Wakullani raised fields were supplied principally by groundwater.

Each of the eight subparcels achieved a different yield, ranging from 7.5 mt/ha to 39.6 mt/ha. This high variability is exceptionally interesting given that overall physical conditions (soil quality and fertility, water sources) were essentially the same over the eight parcels. There is the possibility that subtle differences in soil fertility among the parcels were partially responsible for this high variability. However, our principal hypothesis attributes the variability to differences in management techniques among the eight participating groups. Parcels in which the planting beds where poorly prepared generally produced the smallest yields. The parcel that produced the highest yield (39.6 mt/ha.) enjoyed high soil fertility, well-prepared planting beds, appropriate water levels throughout the growing season, consistent weeding and pruning practices, and the incorporation of organic fertilizers. The net yields reported in table 9.4 and figure 9.8 are the averages taken over the eight subparcels.

## The Copacabana, Batallas, and Viacha Areas

#### KUSIJATA (COPACABANA AREA)

The community of Kusijata lies immediately north of the modern town of Copacabana on the Copacabana peninsula (see fig. 9.1). Community members have access to a broad pampa on the shore of Lake Titicaca between Kusijata and Copacabana. Archaeological surveys of the area by one of the authors (Rivera) revealed traces of ancient raised fields on this pampa. Community members were enthusiastic about experimenting with raised-field technology, and they reconstructed 2 hectares during the 1990–91 season.

The Kusijata results are interesting in that they present another pattern of yield variability: differences between varieties of potatoes. The most productive fields were planted in the sani imilla potato variety and generated an average net yield of 19.93 mt/ha. Fields planted in the huaycha potato variety, on the other hand, achieved an average net yield of 6.23 mt/ha. Although there is normal variability in yields between varieties, a result of multiple interacting factors, the direction of variation is not consistent. That is, in some cases sani imilla outperforms huaycha and chiar imilla; in other instances, that result is reversed. We believe the extraordinary difference in achieved net yields between the sani imilla and huaycha varieties on the Kusijata fields resulted from differences in the time of planting of the two varieties, significant differences in the quality of construction work on the respective raised fields, and differences in the quality of field management. The huaycha variety was planted more than three weeks after the sani imilla variety on the Kusijata fields. This delay in planting (caused by a lack of availability of good quality seed) retarded the development of the plants relative to the sani imilla variety, placing them at greater risk of damage from hail, sleet, and frost. Delays in planting appeared to reduce the incentive of the Kusijata farmers to maintain the fields with the same level of care that they were providing the fields planted on schedule with the sani imilla variety. In particular, fields planted in sani imilla were systematically treated with substantial quantities of organic fertilizer (animal waste), whereas those planted in huaycha were given only casual applications.

#### SANTA ANA (BATALLAS AREA)

During the 1990–91 season, the community of Santa Ana in the Batallas area had a total of 1 hectare under cultivation. This hectare was divided into 16 smaller parcels, each cultivated by an individual family. The soils in the Santa Ana raised fields are highly variable in texture, ranging from clayey loams to localized areas with substantial interbedding of sands and gravels. Water supply to the individual parcels derived from small feeder canals cut from local springs and from a perennial stream. Groundwater percolation added a substantial component to the water supply during the rainy season from December to February.

We believe that the relatively low yields obtained by this community (table 9.4, fig. 9.8) were due principally to organizational problems that delayed both reconstruction of the raised fields and the planting period. Santa Ana was experimenting with raised fields for the first time during the 1990–91 agricultural season. From lack of experience, community members misjudged the amount of labor entailed in rehabilitating the fields. Casual disputes regarding equity in sharing the burden of labor escalated into major schisms. In the end, rather than working in a coordinated, communal fashion, the participating families took responsibility only for their individual parcels. Not surprisingly, this resulted in staggered completion times for the parcels as each family worked according to its own schedule. As the planting period passed, people completed their parcels in a flurry of activity, but with predictable results: the planting beds were badly prepared, with a substructure of highly compacted soils. Planting was delayed until December 15, 1990. Despite these problems, the community managed to achieve yields above the altiplano average for traditional dry farming, although significantly below the overall average for raised-field cultivation.

#### HILATA SANTA TRINIDAD (VIACHA AREA)

The community of Hilata Santa Trinidad constructed 2 hectares of new raised fields during the 1990–91 agricultural season. No pre-Hispanic raised fields are known from the Viacha area. The fields were designed by project agronomists following pre-Hispanic models drawn from the Pampa Koani, the area closest in hydrological characteristics to the Hilata Santa Trinidad lands. The soils can be characterized as clayey loams with localized gravel or sand and gravel admixture. Water supply to the fields was constant throughout the growing season and came from a deep community well. Despite delays in planting, Hilata Santa Trinidad achieved strong yields, near the overall average for raised-field cultivation. These yields were the result of good soil fertility and consistent field maintenance procedures. Yields may have been depressed, however, by insufficient preparation of the planting beds as community members struggled to complete field construction in time to plant the crops.

### Discussion of Production Results

Among the most interesting data collected during the 1990–91 agricultural season were those on the extensive variability in yields achieved on raised fields by the participating communities. There were even differences between individual field plots within communities. The causes of variability in production results were rarely attributable to a single factor, but certain common factors explain much of it: (1) differences in soil fertility, (2) differences in access to stable water supplies, (3) differences in time of planting, and (4) differences in raised-field construction and management techniques. The first two factors are essentially matters of natural resource distribution. The last two relate to the social dimensions of agricultural production: information dissemination, labor coordination, leadership qualities, community motivation, and the like. In a potential hierarchy of causation, the principal reason for relatively low yields in participating communities was poor field management, particularly with respect to water resources. A secondary cause was low soil fertility. Poor management of water resources resulted from either lack of an adequate, consistent source of water (a resource distribution problem) or, more often, misperception of the role of water in the total raised-field cultivation system (an informational problem).

These observations point to a key conclusion for any proposed program of raised-field rehabilitation in the altiplano. In the absence of extraordinary environmental stress (drought, flooding, extended frosts), incomplete dissemination or poor assimilation of technical information is the principal cause of low relative yields. Although this conclusion may appear obvious, the exceptionally disparate yields achieved by communities with excellent management techniques and those with poor or casual management techniques has focused our project's attention on improving tools for both disseminating technical information and assessing the assimilation of such information among the small farmers with whom we work. In short, social variables (communication, training, motivation) appear to be more important for achieving high yields on rehabilitated raised fields than agronomic, ecological, or natural resource variables.

Extreme variability in yields reduces the utility of calculating production averages for the aggregate total of 50 hectares of rehabilitated raised fields in production during the 1990–91 agricultural season. An overall production average, however, may still be useful for comparing the results from these rehabilitated raised fields with those of published regional averages obtained from traditional, dry-farmed fields and from rehabilitated raised fields on the Peruvian side of Lake Titicaca. We make such comparisons in the concluding section of this chapter. The average net yield for the sani imilla potato variety among the 15 evaluated communities was 15.3 mt/ha, with a range of 5.3 to 38.5 mt/ha. The average net yield for the huaycha variety was 14.4 mt/ha, with a range of 3.6 to 34.5 mt/ha. The combined average yield for the two index varieties during the 1990–91 agricultural season was 14.85 mt/ha.

Given the direct relationship of social variables to yields on rehabilitated raised fields, a more informative comparison entails calculating a two-tiered set of production averages: one for communities with strong organizational and management techniques and another for communities with weak organizational structure and poor management techniques. The criteria for evaluating the strength or weakness of a community's management techniques include quality of raised-field reconstruction, quality of planting bed preparation (well-aerated versus compacted), care in maintaining water levels in raised-field canals throughout the growing season, incorporation of organic fertilizers, efficiency of weeding, and maintenance of appropriate planting schedules.

According to these criteria, the communities with strong organizational structure and good management techniques are Achuta Grande, Chambi Grande, Kohana, Chukara, and Kusijata. The average yield in these "strong" communities was 24.5 mt/ha for the sani imilla potato variety, with a range of 16.5 mt/ha to 38.5 mt/ha (fig. 9.9). For the huaycha variety, the overall average yield was 25.5 mt/ha, with a range of 18.7 mt/ha to 34.5 mt/ha. The combined average yield for the two index varieties was 24.95 mt/ha in the "strong" communities.

The communities with weak organizational structure and poor management techniques include Wankollo, Lukurmata, Lillimani, Ñachoka, Wakullani, and Santa Ana. The average yield in these "weak" communities was 9.0 mt/ha for the sani imilla variety, with a range of 5.3 mt/ha to 14.4 mt/ha. For the huaycha variety, the overall average yield was 8.0 mt/ha, with a range of 3.6 mt/ha to 12.9 mt/ha. The combined average yield for the two index varieties was 8.5 mt/ha in the "weak" communities.

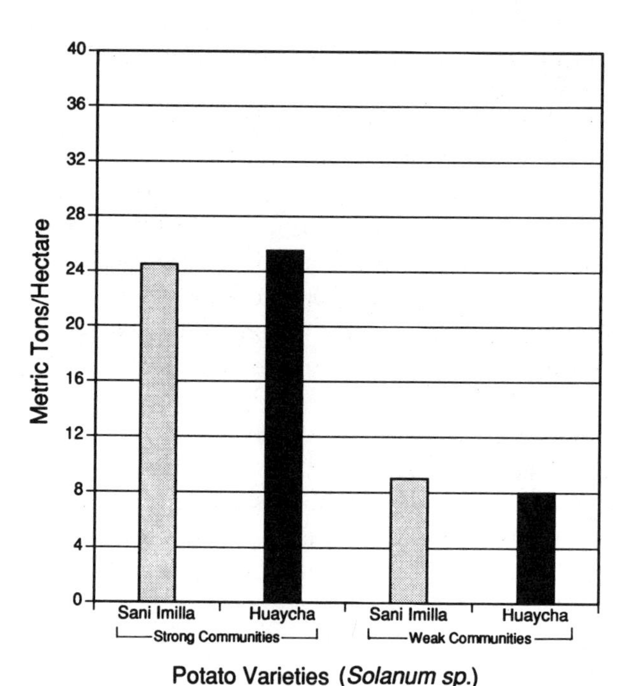

**Figure 9.9.** Comparison of average net yields from "strong" and "weak" communities.

Within this general characterization of "strong" (high-yield) and "weak" (low-yield) communities, there are, of course, anomalies and internal variations. For instance, the Chukara Centro de Madres practiced good field management techniques but achieved relatively low yields (11.8 mt/ha and 8.0 mt/ha for sani imilla and huaycha, respectively) because of the unexpected emergence of a "social fact"—the landowner's idiosyncratic denial of access to an adequate water supply. Yields also varied within single communities. For example, although the community of Wakullani is characterized here as using poor management techniques, the local reality was rather more complex. Wakullani's 2.67 hectares of rehabilitated raised fields were subdivided into eight parcels cultivated by different family units. The cultivators of one of these parcels achieved a net yield of 39.6 mt/ha, which was, in fact, the highest yield obtained from any rehabilitated raised-field plot during the 1990–91 season. At the same time, the cultivators of a second parcel achieved net yields of only 7.5 mt/ha, among the lowest achieved yields. The different yields on these two parcels within the same ecological context were correlated directly with the respective cultivators' motivation and engagement with project agronomists. To be perfectly accurate, yield assessments should proceed not from the frame of reference of the community as a whole but on a parcel-by-parcel and cultivator-group-by-cultivator-group basis. Aymara farmers do not act in lock-step fashion as a total collective. Rather, they behave opportunistically, as individuals and families, seeking the best personal strategies to improve their economic status. In this ultimately local sense, there are no "strong" or "weak" communities, only motivated and unmotivated farmers.

**Table 9.5. Principal Plant Pathogens and Insect Pests Identified in Aymara Crops**

| Type | Common Name | Scientific Name | Affected Part |
|---|---|---|---|
| Fungus | Potato warts | *Synchitrium endobioticum* | Tuber |
| Fungus | Scabies | *Spongospora subterranea* | Tuber |
| Fungus | *Kasawi* | *Stemphyllus consortiale* | Leaves/ stems |
| Bacterium | Rot | *Erwinia carotovora* | Tuber |
| Insect | Jumping flea | *Epitrix* sp. | Leaves/ stems |
| Insect | Thrips/*llaja* | *Frankliniella tuberosa* | Leaves/ flowers |
| Insect | White worm | *Phyllophaga* sp. | Tuber |
| Insect | Wire worm | *Ludius* sp. | Tuber |
| Insect | *Ticona* | *Copitarsia turbata* | Tuber |

## Insect Infestations and Plant Pathogens

Two biological factors can seriously affect agricultural production and net crop yields: insect infestations and plant pathogens. An important element of our field research entailed collecting and identifying insect pests and tracking infestations that might have an impact on total effective crop yields. We also identified, collected, and incubated plant pathogens in vitro.

Here we describe the range and intensity of occurrence of plant pathogens and insects that were found in the different communities at all stages in the development and harvesting of crops. Major plant pathogens and insect pests, along with their point of attack on potato plants, are listed in table 9.5.

### The Tiwanaku Area

#### ACHUTA GRANDE

In this community, during the period of maturation of the cultivars (which we refer to as the "developmental stage" or, in terms of field activities, the "tracking phase"), we identified the *kasawi* fungus (*Stemphyllus consortiale*) in 5 percent of the crops and the jumping flea (*Epitrix* sp.) in 1 percent. The 5-percent incidence of kasawi was relatively high, but the profusion of foliage on the potato plants in these fields mitigated the impact of this fungus, which affects leaves and stems. The pathogen did not have a significant impact on yields.

At harvest, we identified two fungi in the sani imilla potato variety: potato warts (*Synchitrium endobioticum*), with an incidence of 6 percent, and potato scabies (*Spongospora subterranea*), with an incidence of 3 percent. One parcel planted in the huaycha variety was found to be infected with bacterial rot (*Erwinia carotovora*), which causes softening and eventual rotting of the tubers, in 2 percent of the harvested crop. In order to eradicate these pathogens, we recommended a crop rotation regime to the community and suggested that they reduce the incidence of kasawi by manually removing and burning infected leaves, stems, and, where necessary, entire plants.

#### CHAMBI GRANDE

In this community's fields during the developmental stage, we discovered kasawi in 2 percent of the plants, jumping fleas in 3 percent, and thrips, or *llaja* (*Frankliniella tuberosa*), in 1 percent. The crops were not seriously affected by these insects during their developmental phases.

In the harvesting phase, we encountered different pathogens in the three varieties of tubers grown in these fields. We identified a virulent scabies caused by the fungus *Spongospora subterranea* in the chiar imilla and huaycha varieties. Because the incidence of infection was only 1 percent, the impact on the crops was insignificant and net yields were not affected. In the sani imilla variety, we identified the bacterial infection *Erwinia carotovora* in 1.5 percent of the plants. Given the low incidence of infection, the overall productivity and quality of the potatoes in these parcels was not seriously compromised. In the huaycha variety, we also identified larvae of Coleopteron (*Phyllophaga* sp.), known commonly as white worm. The proportion of plants with white worm infestation approached 2 percent.

#### WANKOLLO

Three separate raised-field parcels were reconstructed in the community of Wankollo (see table 9.1). Table 9.6 records the aggregate incidence of plant pathogens and insect infestations from these three parcels.

**Table 9.6. Percentages of Crops Damaged by Pathogens and Insects in Wankollo, Kusijata, and Santa Ana**

| Type | Wankollo | Kusijata | Santa Ana |
|---|---|---|---|
| Warts | 1.5 | 4.0 | 2.0 |
| Scabies | 1.0 | 6.0 | 1.0 |
| *Kasawi* | 2.5 | 2.0 | — |
| Rot | — | — | 1.0 |
| Jumping flea | 1.5 | — | — |
| Thrips/*llaja* | 0.1 | 5.0 | — |
| White worm | 3.0 | — | 1.0 |
| Wire worm | 1.0 | — | — |
| *Ticona* | 0.8 | — | 0.3 |

During the harvest, white worm was identified in the sani imilla variety with an overall incidence of 3 percent, while wire worm (*Ludius* sp.) was collected in 1 percent of the harvested tubers. The huaycha variety was slightly infested (0.8 percent) with *ticona* (*Copitarsia turbata*). The larvae of these insects did not reduce the overall productivity or quality of the crops. These larvae remain in the soil after the harvest, but it is possible to control infestations by deep tilling and removal of topsoil to truncate the insects' biological cycle. This is a labor-intensive technique, however, and communities will not invest in it until there is significant crop loss and yields decline below an acceptable level. Even then they prefer to place the infested fields in fallow. Raised fields, however, which offer the possibility of continuous cultivation, complicate the decision to abandon the fields. Reconstructed raised fields represent a significant investment in landscape capital. In the future, we may see an increase in prophylactic procedures on the part of communities that have invested in raised-field reconstructions.

## The Pampa Koani Area

#### KOHANA

During the developmental stage of Kohana's crops, we identified kasawi in 2 percent of the sani imilla potato variety and llaja in 1.5 percent. At harvest, we encountered white worm in 2 percent of the huaycha variety. Potato warts were identified in 3 percent of harvested tubers. Although the incidence of individual infestations and pathogens was low, their aggregate effect contributed to a reduction in product quality.

#### LUKURMATA

During the developmental stage of the crops, an infestation of jumping fleas and llaja affected 1 percent and 2 percent of the plants, respectively. During the harvest, white worms were recovered from 2 percent of the crops. Scabies affected 1 percent of the harvested tubers. These numbers were too small to significantly affect productivity.

#### WAKULLANI

The rehabilitated raised fields of Wakullani were subdivided into eight parcels. Two of the parcels, Lakori and J'anko J'anko, were completely free of harmful biological agents. Table 9.7 summarizes the incidence of plant pathogens and insect infestations in each of the others.

#### ÑACHOKA

No pathogens or insect infestations were identified at this site during the developmental stage of the crops. During the harvest, however, scabies was identified in 2.5 percent of the crops.

Table 9.7. Percentages of Crops Damaged by Pathogens and Insects in Six Parcels at Wakullani

| Parcel | Potato Warts | Scabies | *Ticona* | White Worm |
|---|---|---|---|---|
| Kapaquila | 1.0 | | | |
| Wilakollu | | 5.0 | 0.5 | |
| Asasita | | | 0.5 | |
| Jacha-Jawira | 3.0 | | | |
| Tilata | | 2.0 | 0.3 | 1.0 |
| Wila Waranka | | 2.0 | 0.5 | |

#### LILLIMANI

During the developmental stage, we identified kasawi in 1.5 percent of the crops. At harvest, scabies was found to affect 2 percent of the sani imilla variety tubers. Three percent of the huaycha variety were affected by potato warts.

#### CHUKARA

In the raised fields of the Chukara community group, kasawi was tracked in 2 percent of the plants during the developmental stage. At harvest, both the sani imilla and huaycha varieties revealed signs of scabies in approximately 3 percent of the tubers. We also found some evidence of rotting in tubers caused by *Erwinia carotovora*. In both varieties, less than 1 percent of tubers were affected by this bacterium. Two percent of the huaycha variety also experienced an infestation of white worms.

#### CHUKARA CEMA

In the agricultural fields of the Chukara Centro de Madres, jumping fleas were identified during the developmental stage in approximately 0.5 percent of the crops. Kasawi affected 3 percent. During the harvest, we discovered scabies fungi and potato wart in the sani imilla variety at incidences of 2 percent and 3 percent of the tubers, respectively.

### Kusijata (Copacabana Area)

In the rehabilitated raised fields of Kusijata, the incidence of plant pathogens was among the highest we encountered in any community. Table 9.6 summarizes the occurence of these pathogens, as well as the rate of infestation from llaja, which was discovered during the maturation of the crops.

We hypothesize that the high incidence of pathogens was the product of contaminated seed. Kusijata was the only community that insisted on planting seed potatoes derived from their own stock. We suspect that they chose not to accept the "foreign" seed offered by project agronomists precisely because they feared introducing pests into their fields. Ironically, the certified seed that the project employs is of higher quality than local seed stocks, exhibiting substantially lower incidences of plant pathogens and insects. For the 1991–92 agricultural season, the farmers of Kusijata decided to accept project seed stock and follow additional recommendations regarding crop rotation and intercropping on their rehabilitated raised fields.

### Santa Ana (Batallas Area) and Hilata Santa Trinidad (Viacha Area)

In the community of Santa Ana, plant pathogens were encountered in both the sani imilla and huaycha potato varieties (table 9.6). The huaycha variety was affected by potato warts and scabies. We identified potato warts, scabies, and tuber rotting in the sani imilla variety.

In Hilata Santa Trinidad, farmers cultivated several potato varieties, including sani imilla, huaycha, and two improved, introduced varieties, Cardinale and Alpha. Only the Cardinale variety exhibited evidence of infestation and/or pathogens, which included rot, scabies, and potato wart. The fact that only this variety was infected led us to infer that the original seed stock was contaminated.

### Summary of Plant Pathogen and Insect Infestation Data

Overall incidences of insect infestation and plant pathogens on rehabilitated raised fields in the Tiwanaku Valley were relatively low. Infestations were identified in less than 5 percent of the crops and plant pathogens in less than 3 percent. Overall incidences in the Pampa Koani area were similarly low: infestations were found in less than 3 percent of the crops examined and plant pathogens in less than 1 percent. In the case of Kusijata, the community with the highest incidence of pathogens and infestations, we attribute the problem to contaminated seed stock, a variable that is relatively simple to control with a measure of vigilance. The overall low incidence of pests and plant pathogens may be attributed to (1) precautions taken by project agronomists to acquire high quality, certified seed, (2) careful monitoring and treatment of crops during the growing season, (3) cultivation in areas of extremely long fallow with correspondingly low levels of plant pathogens and insect infestations (most of the rehabilitated raised fields are in areas that have not been intensively cultivated for nearly a millennium), and (4) the potential prophylactic effects of the 1985–86 inundation of the region, which may have truncated the biological cycles of insect pests. More speculatively, the raised-field cultivation system itself may contribute to the relatively low incidence of insect infestations. Because the planting surfaces of raised fields are surrounded on three sides by canals, water may form a barrier to some kinds of insects. This hypothesis is amenable to field testing. Despite some localized crop losses and reduction in product quality, in no case did insect pests or disease significantly affect the growth or productivity of cultigens on rehabilitated raised fields.

## Conclusion: Comparisons and Implications

In recent years, a realization and a consensus has begun to emerge among development-oriented agronomists that industrialized, capital-intensive agriculture represents only one kind of solution to the complex food-production problems of developing countries (Altieri 1987; Altieri and Hecht 1990; Kotschi et al. 1990). Modern, capital-intensive technologies were heavily promoted in developing nations throughout the 1960s and 1970s. Because such technologies offer impressive, immediate returns, their implementation still dominates strategies of agricultural development. Despite their ability to produce remarkable quantities of subsistence and cash crops, high-yield, capital-intensive agricultural systems developed according to models provided by the industrialized nations cannot address the critical food-production needs of isolated, rural communities that have little access to the centralized nodes of mechanized farming.

Since the early 1970s, even more fundamental questions have emerged concerning the assumed universal efficacy of the high-input–high-yield technologies characteristic of the "Green Revolution." As Bebbington notes (1992:3), this debate turns on a body of criticism focusing on at least five major issues:

> (1) that agricultural research has concentrated on a few crops and environments at the expense of others; (2) that many modern technologies have been biased against peasant farmers for agroecological and socioeconomic reasons; (3) that the introduction of modern technologies has eroded local cultural practice and identity; (4) that the technologies have created ecological problems; and (5) that the technologies have generated costly import dependencies.

The potential long-term sustainability (in economic, social, and ecological terms) of such capital-intensive technologies is increasingly coming under critical scrutiny. Even assuming that model projects of efficient, mechanized agriculture can be successfully implanted in some developing nations, their proximate result may be to increase yields per unit area, as well as aggregate crop production, but at the same time to significantly depress the demand for rural labor. Such model projects have not (and most likely cannot) generate sufficient employment opportunities to meet the demands of a rapidly growing rural work force. The end result of such an agricultural modernization strategy may well be to increase the rate of internal migration from rural areas to increasingly congested and overburdened urban settings. Poor rural farmers essentially substitute one marginal way of life for another. This paradox of development has engendered renewed interest by agronomists and other development specialists in projects designed to improve the efficiency and yields of traditional rural resource management and, especially, indigenous agriculture throughout the world (Altieri 1987; Bebbington and Carney 1990; Beyer 1980; Hatch 1976; Richards 1985). Raised fields may represent just such an indigenous technology with the capacity to contribute to regional economic development in the Andean altiplano.

### Raised-Field Productivity: Some Comparisons

From a purely technical and economic frame of reference, our experiments in rehabilitating Tiwanaku raised fields indicated substantial yield differentials between traditional dry farming and raised-field cultivation. The yields from the experimental raised fields compared favorably with those obtained from control plots using two traditional variants of altiplano agriculture, which have been monitored by the project since the 1987–88 agricultural season for purposes of direct comparison. The two traditional forms of agricultural plots were (1) shallow-furrow, rain-dependent plots, cultivated without the benefit of irrigation or the use of chemical fertilizers or pesticides but with small quantities of organic fertilizer, principally dried cattle manure, incorporated into the fields prior to seeding, and (2) shallow-furrow, dry-cultivated plots with chemical fertilizers and pesticides applied to both soil and foliage throughout the growing season.

The first control plot was established on a previously cultivated, gentle hill slope in the community of Lakaya, approximately 120 meters south of reconstructed raised fields in the pampas zone (see fig. 9.1). The plot chosen for cultivation had been in fallow for about five years. The second control plot was established in the community of Achuta Grande in the valley of Tiwanaku, 4 kilometers west of the village of Tiwanaku. This plot was cultivated on long-fallowed, flat land near the Tiwanaku River that had been used for the past 15 years exclusively for pasturage. This second control plot lies approximately 200 meters southwest of 4 hectares of rehabilitated raised fields in the pampas zone of Achuta Grande.

The first form of traditional cultivation—dry farming without commercial fertilizers—has been the dominant mode of peasant agricultural production in the Bolivian altiplano for nearly five centuries, even though it is patently inefficient. As indicated by the yield data in table 9.8, this form of unfertilized dry farming achieved an average of 2.4 mt/ha of potatoes on five cultivated parcels. During the 1987–88 growing season, 100 percent of the maturing plants on these parcels exhibited lesions from frost, with the bulk of the damage occurring during a hard freeze in February 1988. Among the individual parcels of cultivated land, 10–30 percent of the plants were superficially damaged by frost, and the remaining 70–90 percent were destroyed and yielded no edible tubers.

Predictably, the addition of commercial fertilizers (nitrogen, phosphorus, and potassium) to traditional fields (control plot 2) increased production substantially, to an average of 14.5 mt/ha on eight cultivated parcels (table 9.9). Despite this result, it is clear from a comparison with the data presented in table 9.4 and fig. 9.9 that the experimental raised fields significantly outperformed (in terms of both yield per unit area and cost per unit area) the two forms of traditional dry-farmed fields. On 12 cultivated parcels of experimental raised fields in the 1987–88 growing season, potato yields reached an average of 21 mt/ha, or nearly twice the yield of traditional fields treated with chemical fertilizers and over seven times the yield of unimproved traditional cultivation (Kolata 1991: table 1).[3] Furthermore, in that agricultural year, the percentage of the crop planted in raised fields that was affected by frost lesions averaged only about 10.5 percent, a radically different and much smaller proportion of frost damage than that experienced in the two control plots.

Similar experiments in raised-field rehabilitation were conducted in the altiplano of Peru on the northern side of Lake Titicaca by a team of archaeologists and agronomists during the early and mid–1980s (Erickson 1988a, 1988b). Their results are instructive

**Table 9.8. Potato Yields from Control Plot 1, 1987–1988, Using Traditional Dry Farming without Commercial Fertilizers**

| Parcel | Surface Area ($m^2$) | No. Plants | Weight (kg) | Weight per Ha (mt/ha) |
|---|---|---|---|---|
| 1 | 18.00 | 60 | 4.00 | 2.222 |
| 2 | 17.50 | 63 | 4.50 | 2.571 |
| 3 | 18.25 | 61 | 4.60 | 2.520 |
| 4 | 18.50 | 61 | 5.00 | 2.703 |
| 5 | 17.80 | 62 | 3.80 | 2.135 |
| Total | 90.05 | 307 | 21.90 | 12.151 |
| Average | 18.01 | 61.4 | 4.38 | 2.430 |

**Table 9.9. Potato Yields from Control Plot 2, 1987–1988, Using Traditional Dry Farming with Commercial Fertilizers**

| Parcel | Surface Area ($m^2$) | No. Plants | Weight (kg) | Weight per Ha (mt/ha) |
|---|---|---|---|---|
| 1 | 18.40 | 45 | 26.0 | 14.130 |
| 2 | 17.00 | 40 | 26.5 | 15.588 |
| 3 | 18.00 | 40 | 23.0 | 12.777 |
| 4 | 19.00 | 40 | 26.0 | 13.685 |
| 5 | 16.00 | 41 | 14.0 | 8.750 |
| 6 | 16.50 | 46 | 22.5 | 13.636 |
| 7 | 16.50 | 51 | 30.5 | 19.062 |
| 8 | 17.50 | 44 | 32.1 | 18.342 |
| Total | 138.40 | 347 | 200.6 | 115.970 |
| Average | 17.30 | 43.3 | 25.1 | 14.496 |

and generally consistent with ours (table 9.10). The Peruvian team apparently did not plant control plots of traditionally cultivated fields for direct comparison, but rather relied on regional averages for the Department of Puno derived from statistics compiled by the Peruvian Ministry of Agriculture. These averages of regional potato production on traditionally cultivated plots range from 1.5 to 6.0 mt/ha, which compares well with our own result of 2.4 mt/ha. On raised fields that were not treated with fertilizers over a three-year production cycle, the Puno group generated an average of 10.65 mt/ha, with a range of 8.3 to 13.0 mt/ha.

As can be seen in table 9.10, production figures varied considerably over time and space; some areas did particularly well in a given year. Even within individual blocks of reclaimed raised fields there was considerable variability in yield, depending on whether seeds were placed in the center or along the edge of a cultivated plot (Erickson 1988), an experience replicated in our own work. The average net yield of potatoes achieved on raised fields by the Puno group were lower than those obtained on the Bolivian side, although the pattern of enhanced production on raised fields in comparison with traditional fields was identical. The higher yields obtained in the Bolivian communities may relate to slight climatic differences between the northern and southern sides of Lake Titicaca: the area around Puno is at a higher altitude and consequently is somewhat more prone to frost damage than is the Bolivian side. Moreover, the planting and cultivating protocols practiced by the Puno group appear to have differed from our own: the Bolivian Aymara communities rehabilitating fields routinely incorporated organic fertilizer (green manure or animal waste) into the fields during construction, tilling, and sowing.

**Table 9.10. Potato Yields from Rehabilitated Raised Fields in Huatta, Peru**

| Field Name | Surface Area (m²) | Yield (mt/ha) 1981–82 | 1983–84 | 1984–85 |
|---|---|---|---|---|
| Machachi | 110 | 6.760 | | |
| Candile | 73 | 10.119 | | |
| Chojñocoto I | 702 | | 13.652 | 8.573 |
| Chojñocoto II | 2025 | | | 5.186 |
| Chojñocoto III | 1449 | | | 11.036 |
| Viscachani pampa | 1405/1625 | | 12.536 | 12.309 |
| Pancha pampa | 815 | | | 10.990 |
| Average yield per ha | | 8.440 | 13.094 | 10.441 |
| Combined average per ha | | | 10.658 | |

Source: Erickson (1988:table 8).

Despite the differences in raised-field production between the Peruvian and the Bolivian experiments, the general trend of significantly enhanced yields on reclaimed raised fields appears to be established beyond a reasonable doubt. At a minimum, cultivation on reclaimed raised fields results in production two to three times greater than that obtained by traditional methods. Moreover, as Erickson (1988a:245) points out, raised fields are remarkably efficient in terms of the ratio of seed to producing plant: "In comparison with traditional fields, only half the seed is necessary for planting a hectare of raised fields since half the area is uncultivated canal. These high production rates are even more impressive when considering that a hectare of raised fields has only half the number of plants of a traditional potato field." If the experiments of both research groups have produced reliable results, then raised fields represent a prime example of continuous, efficient, and potentially sustainable cultivation—a system of intensive hydraulic agriculture that requires no extended periods of fallow.

## Raised Fields and Regional Economic Development

The search for local, contextually sensitive alternatives to imposed systems of industrialized agriculture has generated a new subfield of research: agroecology, or sustainable agriculture. From the perspective of agroecology, we can perceive the contours of a new model in agricultural development that works within an analytical frame of reference that can be termed the ecological systems approach, or, more concretely, the farming systems approach. In contrast to the imposed model of industrialized agriculture, the farming systems approach to development attempts to understand the physical and organizational aspects of an agricultural system within its preexisting local context. As Turner and Brush (1987:3) phrase it: "The fundamental premise is that the understanding of agriculture is facilitated by a holistic perspective that integrates the socioeconomic, political, environmental, and technological elements of the system. Emphasis is placed on the micro- or mesospatial scale—the farm, the village or a small area—as the unit of analysis."

The goal of applying such a context-sensitive approach in a development project is to enhance productivity by making increasingly efficient use of traditional systems, subtly transforming traditional technologies in productive directions without entirely supplanting them. A farming systems approach examines agricultural production in its environmental, political, economic, and social context and then attempts to identify the locally limiting factors that constrain efficient agricultural production. These local constraints may be physical (excessively acidic soils, for example), or they may be social and political in nature (land tenure disputes, differential access to capital, etc.). The long-range objective of the farming systems approach applied in a development context is not simply to *replicate* traditional systems of agriculture like the raised fields of the Bolivian high plateau. Rather, the goal is to extract from these systems, which generally have evolved as local solutions to farming problems over many centuries, those features which permit long-term maintenance of the system of production in its environment and then to adapt those features to the contemporary cultural context.

As yet, we are a long way from establishing whether the model of the raised fields with which we are experimenting represents a successful application of the farming systems approach. Several years of intensive, interdisciplinary research remain before we will know whether the elevated crop yields generated during the first eight years of the experiment can be sustained over the long run. We believe, however, that the technological foundations of raised-field agriculture as a cultivation system efficiently adapted to the environmental constraints of the Andean altiplano are already well established. That is, we argue that in terms of its ability to generate enhanced yields, raised-field agriculture has demonstrated and will continue to demonstrate remarkable success. But it is the resolution of the social and cultural problems of introducing raised-field agriculture to rural communities that will be critical to its long-term sustainability. One nontechnological component that is critical to the broader success and implementation of this experiment is clear. Extensive areas of raised fields will never be rehabilitated or newly constructed if the agents who promote this traditional system rely heavily on the kinds of external incentives, such as purchased wage labor, that are common in large-scale development schemes. The imposed modes of organization and the structural incentives that characterize these development schemes may work in the short run, but they rarely seem to take on a vitality and an integrity of their own.

Our experiences with the raised-field rehabilitation project confirm the essential wisdom of rural development objectives and designs that, as Walter Goldschmidt (1982:81) noted over a decade ago,

> (1) recognize the existence of social structures which organize the collaborative energies of people and are, therefore, instrumentalities for technical accomplishment, (2) appreciate the central importance of existing cultural values as systems of sentiment and sources of individual motivation, which give meaning and satisfaction to the daily lives of people, and (3) utilize and build upon indigenous technical knowledge and the cumulative experiences of the people themselves.

Writing in a similar vein, John Hatch (1976) commented that the small farmer's expertise constitutes "the single largest knowledge resource not yet mobilized in the development enterprise" and is a source of experience and knowledge we "simply cannot afford to ignore any longer."

As the economist Vernon Ruttan (1988) argued, local knowledge and social systems are the rich and often unappreciated "cultural endowments" that can make some forms of positive institutional change less costly. But recognizing and strategically employing these cultural endowments can also do something more subtle and socially meaningful than offer merely the economic utility rightly perceived by Ruttan. As we have discovered in the raised-field rehabilitation project, explicitly incorporating local knowledge, local values, and local needs into the development enterprise can stimulate an enhanced sense of community participation, self-determination, creativity, and entrepreneurship. We suggest that the long-term success and efficient application of raised-field agriculture will turn on the internally generated, entrepreneurial behavior of the would-be clients of development: the Aymara villagers themselves. Understanding that these villagers are not some archetypal, closed corporate peasant society but a collectivity of individuals and families with a marked sense of individual worth and a penchant for entrepreneurship is critical to shaping development projects that take full advantage of the Aymaras' own concepts of fluidity and permeability in community structure and labor organization. If development personnel work under such a contextualized approach—from the perspectives of the indigenous farmers themselves—then raised-field agriculture may come to represent one option with which the chronically poor, isolated communities of the Andean altiplano can intensify food production and generate essential surplus income.

## Notes

1. When we refer to relatively low yields here and in subsequent evaluations of raised-field production, we mean low relative to average net yields on raised fields. Average net yields from traditional, shallow-furrow, dry-farmed fields in the northern Bolivian altiplano range from 2 to 5 metric tons per hectare. Clearly the "low yields" on raised fields reported here are substantially higher than those obtained by traditional dry cultivation.

2. It is worth nothing here that during the 1991–92 agricultural season, the Chukara CEMA resolved this water problem by recruiting the family that could provide access to the critical spring source. The yields from the original hectare plus an additional 2.6 hectares of rehabilitated fields rose to an average of 14.8 mt/ha during the 1991–92 season, despite relative drought conditions throughout this part of the Bolivian altiplano.

3. Note that the aggregate average net yield of 21 mt/ha in the 1987–88 season compares favorably with results from the 1990–91 season. For purposes of comparison, recall that we calculated three separate average net yields for 1990–91: (1) "strong" community yields, 25.5 mt/ha; (2) "weak" community yields, 8.5 mt/ha, and (3) the aggregate average for all communities, 14.85 mt/ha.

# 10

# Participant Observation with the Lakaya Centro de Madres

ALICE B. KEHOE

My participation in Proyecto Wila Jawira began as an opportunity to broaden my experience of American Indian communities during a sabbatical leave. A discussion with Alan Kolata in January 1988 suggested the feasibility of working under the auspices of the project and specifically of observing the Centro de Madres in the village of Lakaya, one of the principal communities engaged in the raised-field rehabilitation work in the Pampa Koani region of the Catari basin. The Centro de Madres is a unique work group among the villages participating in the project, and its presence in Lakaya promised an opportunity to compare contrasting work groups within one community. A second feature of the centro that made it seem particularly suited to my involvement was its leadership by persons of my own gender, a factor likely to facilitate participant observation.

Lakaya was one of the original villages participating in Operación Rehasuk (*reha*bilitation of *suk*a kollus; *suka kollu* is the Aymara term for raised fields), which is the field rehabilitation component of the larger Proyecto Wila Jawira. The constituent communities of Lakaya formed two principal work groups, one known to project personnel as "the Uruchis" after the principal family of the group, and the other as the Centro de Madres. Project personnel mentioned to me a third group, men from the local *sindicato rural,* but I did not observe them as a distinct group during my residence.

Like its sister villages along the Pampa Koani, Lakaya became enthusiastic about rebuilding the Tiwanaku raised fields after an excellent harvest from the 1987 rehabilitated fields. This enthusiasm, shared by project personnel, stimulated an expansion of rehabilitation activities but also potential problems in allocating project funds and supervision. For this reason, both directors of the project, Alan Kolata and Oswaldo Rivera, along with Kevin Healy of the Inter-American Foundation, partial funder of Operación Rehasuk, wanted ethnographic observation of suka kollu work in at least one of the villages.

## Lakaya and Its Historical Background

In the village of Lakaya, I watched an Aymara community live in a bilingual, bicultural world where Spanish words and the European cultural premises behind them ill fit Aymara life. Lakaya's Centro de Madres, on which I focused my study, is neither a center nor primarily of or for mothers. The inappropriateness of the group's name is, to the centro's Aymara organizer, but another instance of the impossibility of adequately translating her universe into a Hispanic one.

Lakaya lies on the lowest slope of hills bordering the basin of Lake Titicaca. About a kilometer of flat pampa stretches north to the marshy shore of the lake; behind the village, to the south, is a valley occupied by the hamlets of Lillimani and, at the head of the valley, Lakaya Alta. These three settlement clusters, together with scattered farmsteads on the pampa and in the valley, form a community. Similar communities are a kilometer or two apart on the gravel highway running east-west along the edge of the hills. La Paz, the capital city, is about 75 kilometers inland.

The Bolivian altiplano has been ruled by conquerors at least since the 1460s when the Cuzco Quechua Inca empire overran the Bolivian Aymara states. Throughout the first millennium A.D., the altiplano had been tributary to the great city of Tiwanaku, which had filled much of the pampa with its sophisticated system of raised fields and canals capable of maintaining high crop yields. It is unclear whether Tiwanaku was Aymara or, possibly, Uru (Puquina speakers [Hardman 1985:626]). At the Spanish conquest of the Bolivian altiplano in 1538, Aymaras were the locally dominant peoples under the Inca, with Uru a landless laboring class (Bouysse Cassagne 1987:161, 373; Manelis de Klein 1973). The Aymara were said to be mountain people, Uru the creatures—not really human—of the lake (Bouysse Cassagne 1987:366–69; Dillon and Abercrombie 1988:67).

Aymara is the language of Lakaya. Many older women are monolingual, and few men or women middle-aged or older can converse readily in Spanish. Younger adults can speak Spanish, although most have a marked Aymara accent. Only the young men, who are likely to have worked in other provinces, speak Spanish well. Spanish is the sole language of instruction in the village primary school. One radio station broadcasts much, though not all, of its programming in Aymara, and this station is commonly tuned in by Lakayans on their battery-operated sets. Neither television nor films are viewed in the village, which lacks electricity. Most of the women and older men are illiterate.

For 400 years, the Aymara worked on Spanish haciendas. In the 1570s, Viceroy Francisco Toledo established *comunidades indígenas* by nucleating Indian villages, averaging 142 inhabitants, into towns averaging 2,900 residents (Klein 1982:39; Yambert 1980:62–64). Toledo intended to preserve Crown rule over the Indians rather than allow the growth of a Hispanic landowning class, the hacendados. Indians were to be based in households under male heads 18 to 50 years old. These adult men, termed *originarios,* had land rights through their membership in an indigenous ayllu and paid tribute tax and *mita* (corvée) labor. No other men, or women, were directly taxed (Klein 1982:51–52). Severe depopulation through epidemics during the sixteenth and seventeenth centuries resulted in an insufferable burden of taxes on many of these originarios, forcing them to abandon their ayllu lands and seek wage labor as untaxed *forasteros* ("strangers"). Hacendados employed the laborers, strengthening the power of the Hispanic landed class. Comunidades indígenas remained the principal settlements of rural regions, but haciendas controlled the Aymara of the Lake Titicaca pampas accessible to the city of La Paz (Carter 1964:9; Klein 1982:53). La Paz grew steadily as the center of Indian markets drawing on altiplano and yungas (lower altitude valleys) agricultural production (Klein 1982:68). Toward the close of the nineteenth century, the penetration of the altiplano by international capitalist development consolidated hacendado power at the expense of the Indian producers (Klein 1982: 164; Spalding 1980:82–83).

In a book developed from a 1974 symposium, Orlove and Custred (1980:21–36) argue that it has been traditional to view haciendas and Indian corporate peasant communities as the basic units of Andean rural societies. This, they believe, distorts the true basis of these societies, which they aver to be the peasant household "based on the nuclear family . . . neolocal," with unmarried siblings or aged parents of either spouse possibly included. The "man of the household" (i.e., husband in the nuclear family) "acts as an intermediary . . . [who] arranges interhousehold labor exchanges and represents the household at local political assemblies" (Orlove and Custred 1980:37). Orlove and Custred admit that their view of Andean societies has been influenced by reading Chayanov and also Sahlins's *Stone Age Economics* (1972). In the same volume, van den Berghe (1980:167) disagrees with Orlove and Custred's model, insisting that the division of rural society into haciendas and Indian communities is the structure understood by the people themselves, and this emic view ought to be respected.

Haciendas disappeared from the Bolivian altiplano with the 1952 revolution and its 1953 agrarian reform decree, which followed seizure of many haciendas by peasants organized into *sindicatos campesinos*, or rural laborers' unions (Klein 1982:234–35; Simmons 1974:4). In Lakaya and its neighboring communities, the hacienda buildings, including the Catholic churches, have fallen into disrepair. The villagers remember the hacendados as absentee landlords enjoying their wealth, for most of the year, in La Paz (confirmed by Victor Andrade, quoted in Carter 1964:9). Lakaya is now essentially a self-regulating comunidad indígena. Its members obtain their living by farming family holdings supplemented with shared pasture on the communal land of the pampa. Population is somewhat adjusted to the fixed landholdings by the practice of unmarried (including widowed) adults assisting cultivator relatives by contributing labor and seed, these inputs entitling the single persons to shares in the family farm harvest.

Social structure in the community may appear to be based on nuclear families represented by the husband, as described by Orlove and Custred. This appearance reflects four centuries of Spanish governance, beginning with the designation of originarios and continuing to the present Euro-Bolivian assumption that a patriarchal nuclear family is the expected, proper, and morally correct societal unit. This formation is seen as the basic producing, consuming, and census unit (it has the great virtue of being discrete and easily counted). With four centuries or more—it may have been used by the Incas, too—of use by governments behind it, the nuclear family can be easily positioned in models such as that of Orlove and Custred's. Yet other students of Andean societies, such as Carter (1964:65), the Buechlers (1971:38, 50), Collins (1983), and Arnold (1987), have concluded that the extended family or bilateral kindred is the meaningful social unit in an Aymara community. Buechler and Buechler (1971:38) add, "It is difficult to give a clearcut definition of the [Aymara] family as a delimited unit."

Miracle and Yapita (1981:46) supersede the disagreement between social scientists by asserting that the individual and the community are the important constituents in Aymara societies. The *formal* structure of the community, enforced by the government, follows the Western liberal democracies' privileging of the patriarchal nuclear family. When this form is not being called up in conformance to outsiders' requirements, the Aymara can operate in their own universe. The Aymara community is the unit of "enduring, diffuse solidarity" (Schneider 1980:53) corresponding to the Western family.

Within the Aymara community, the most basic distinction is between human and nonhuman (Hardman 1981:12). Although Hardman does not put it this way, the distinction is in a sense grammatical gender because it is syntactically obligatory. Kinship terms are differentiated on the basis of two oppositions, male and female, and generation (older and younger) (Pyle 1981:80). The language distinguishes four persons, fourth person including both speaker and addressee plus or minus others (Hardman 1981:10). These linguistic constructions support, or impose, a particular emphasis on the human dyad of speaker and addressee. Lakayans consider it strange to wish to be left alone. They teach that being solitary is to be vulnerable to destruction, often expressed as vampires roaming the dark night seeking imprudent, unprotected victims. The community is composed of human individuals living with each other. This was the social and historical context in which I began my study.

## The Study

The method employed in this study was participant observation. I do not speak or understand Aymara. Villagers informed me that it would take a year to learn the language; therefore there was no point in my attempting to learn it during the weeks I would be in Lakaya. Inability to understand conversation around me was, of course, a drawback, but it had its advantage in that people could speak among themselves without inhibitions, knowing I did not understand. On September 16, 1988, I moved to Lakaya. The first week, I stayed in a house on the north side of the village plaza. This house had a street-level room and an upstairs room, but no access to a patio. The next week I moved to a house on the south side of the plaza, where I lived until I left on October 23. (Lakaya villagers are not accustomed to renting houses. The houses were lent to me through the agency of doña Bonifacia Quispe. When I realized that the dueña of the second house, like that of the first, had not understood that I intended to pay her for the use of her house, I asked Bonifacia to negotiate a rent, and the dueña agreed to let the house to me for the duration of my stay.) This house consisted of a second-floor room reached by a stair from the patio behind it. Both houses were ideal for my purposes because they had windows giving good views of the plaza and village activities. In addition to my daily experience of life in Lakaya, I walked to Quiripujo, Chukara, Korila, Muncaña, Chojasivi, Lukurmata, and inland into the hills, and conversed in Spanish with people from all these localities.

Doña Bonifacia Quispe, president of the Lakaya Centro de Madres, was my sponsor and hostess during my residence in Lakaya. She permitted me to eat with her or arranged for my meals, obtained my housing, guided my participation in activities, allowed me to observe her daily life, guarded me from "molestation," and, through her warm-hearted concern, made my six weeks in Lakaya a thoroughly rewarding experience. Whatever worth there may be in this report is the result of Bonifacia's intelligence and goodwill.

Twenty-five at the time, La Bonifacia (as she is known to the community) was a *soltera,* an unmarried woman. She lived with her widowed mother in a small house on the plaza; the family's house-plot and farmland, at the head of the valley in Lakaya Alta, was used by Bonifacia's older brother and his wife, Paulina. As Hardman (1981:3) remarks, "Within the framework of a corporate society, the Aymara are an entrepreneurial and individualistic people," and Bonifacia exemplifies these valued characteristics. The two women, Bonifacia and her mother, could obtain food by assisting relatives through providing seed and sharing in field cultivation, as I observed (see also Carter 1964:50–51). Bonifacia obtains cash by selling *refrescos,* bottled soft drinks wholesaled by trucks coming into the village about twice weekly. She provided the refrescos for the Red-and-Black soccer team at their regular Thursday afternoon games at the village field and when the team met for planning strategy and pep talks at her house on Wednesday evenings before the games. Five other women with homes on the plaza, including Bonifacia's cousin Felipa, also sell refrescos. Bonifacia and her mother weave and sell their product; because the family's sheep died from a disease epidemic along the lake, the women must buy wool, and this reduces their profit from weaving. Once, Bonifacia migrated to La Paz and obtained work as a household cook, but feeling her competence insulted by her employer's demanding directions, she left the job after a month. There seemed little scope for La Bonifacia's entrepreneurial ability until Proyecto Wila Jawira contacted the village.

Operación Rehasuk initially met with some skepticism in the villages, but because it offered immediate rewards and did not appear to demand a great deal of time, 57 men in Lakaya and somewhat smaller groups in other villages signed up. The groups followed the expected Hispanic pattern of hierarchical male leadership, with participating women subordinate to their husbands or fathers. This pattern was that of the sindicatos through which Bolivian campesinos fit into the contemporary Bolivian political economy.

La Bonifacia, eager to break out of the stranglehold in which poverty held her, conceived the revolutionary idea of organizing women into their own sindicato. The only women's organizations she had heard of were the centros de madres set up in the La Paz Indian barrios for maternal and child health education and delivery. She borrowed the name for her organization. There are actually a number of organizations for campesinas in Bolivia, of which the most famous is the Comité de Amas de Casa of the Potosí mining town of Siglo XX, led since 1963 by Domitila Barrios de Chungara. Lacking newspapers and even a radio, Bonifacia Quispe does not know of these organizations. Bonifacia broached her idea of a women's work group to Kolata and was pleasantly surprised at his willingness to accept such a group. She organized a set of officers for the group: herself as president, her best friend, Ana María Limachi, as vice-president, her cousin Felipa Uruchi as recording secretary, her brother's wife, Paulina Quispe, as treasurer, and her cousin Josefina Fernández as voting member-at-large. Of these five women, the first three are solteras in their twenties. Josefina is married with two young children, and Paulina, married, has older children. Only Felipa and Ana María are literate. A list of 50 women's names was delivered to the project as the Lakaya Centro de Madres. They were assigned a set of raised fields next to the set assigned to the conventional work group, and they successfully rebuilt, planted, and harvested these fields.

Aymara women are expected to be productive and responsible adults (Hardman 1976:2–5). Young children of both sexes tend animals and younger siblings; adolescent girls work in the fields as well as in the homes and are encouraged to exhibit initiative, even engaging boys in public horseplay. The majority of market vendors are women. Aymaras admit the superior upper-body strength of men and delegate to men tasks that demand strength, such as breaking sod, but women will do such work, adjusting to it by teamwork or more frequent rest breaks. In conventional (Hispanic) agriculture, a man guides the plow pulled by a pair of cattle—keeping the wooden plow in the furrow requires considerable strength—while a woman walks behind him, sowing and covering the furrow. The Centro de Madres is assisted by members' husbands, fathers, and adolescent sons, who break sod and do the heaviest shoveling. The entrepreneurial initiative shown by the three solteras who organized the centro and the work performed by centro members in the fields are quite within Aymara expectations.

To observe the work, I stayed around Bonifacia, assisting in such activities as I could (e.g., the work on the suka kollus or washing my clothes in the stream when she did hers) and simply watching activities (e.g., weaving) in which I could not participate. Each day, I wrote up my observations in a small notebook; although I carried this notebook always with me, in a bag with a small camera and a windbreaker (we joked that this bag was my *awayo,* or carrying cloth), writing in it usually brought people's attention and curiosity, so most of my writing was done when alone in my room, before and after the day's activities. I took photographs of activities, explaining that these were primarily to show the project directors and agency heads the achievements of the villagers engaged in Operación Rehasuk. Because it was crucial to the success of my work that I disturb the daily activities of the villagers as little as possible, I did not take photographs surreptitiously against subjects' will or when it would appear intrusive.

Each day began with breakfast between 7:00 and 8:00, usually brought to my room by Bonifacia or another member of the centro de madres, sometimes taken in the home of Bonifacia or that of the centro secretaria, Felipa Uruchi. At 9:30, I would go to Bonifacia's house to set out for the suka kollus or to observe her other activities. Noon lunch, the main meal of the day, would be at the home of Bonifacia, Felipa, or the Fernándezes (parents of the centro's *vocal,* Josefina Fernández), occasionally in my house or its patio, in the field, or once in a farmhouse patio. I always ate what I was served, asking that I share in meals. But frequently I was given different and a little better food than my eating companions—for example, rice or macaroni as well as potatoes, when they ate only potatoes, and some protein (cheese or a fried egg) when they had none. My companions also noticed that I ate *chuño* (freeze-dried potatoes) dutifully but without relish and that I disliked the most common fish, so they ceased adding these to my plate. However, even when my own lunch was superior to theirs, I could observe what they ate. Coffee and bread were served at Bonifacia's or Felipa's after work, around 5:30 P.M., and about 8:00 P.M., supper—almost always potato soup—usually in my house because the women enjoyed its space and candlelight. For the first three weeks that I was in Lakaya, one or, more often, two women of the centro slept in my room with me (they feared I would foolishly open my door to vampires). I was with women from the centro every day, continuously except for an hour after breakfast and an hour or so before supper.

For nearly all of my stay, I was the only non-Aymara in the village and the only foreigner in the district. Project personnel came to the village to inspect the work on suka kollus on an average of once a week, but for two and a half weeks of my stay, none came. Project coordinator Anita Spielvogel did come and stay with me in my house for several days in mid-October. I accompanied Anita as she met with the suka kollu work groups from the five participating villages.

## Discussion

The two raised-field work groups of Lakaya in 1988, "Lakaya I" and Centro de Madres, present contrasting organizational styles and modes of collective action. Lakaya I conforms to the standard pattern for Aymara labor groups. It is largely but not exclusively composed of adult men; about one-quarter of a usual day's work force consisted of women and boys in their early teens. (Older youths work like men.) The men usually form a single long line along the field and work in unison. Centro de Madres workers, in contrast, form into small groups of three to five people, each only roughly coordinated with others, scattered along the field. This mode accommodates the greater range of physical capacities within the centro, whose groups are about three-quarters women, among whom are several elderly women who tire quickly. About a dozen men and youths regularly work with the centro in the name of, or to assist, female kin (*como maridos,* "as if married," I was told, although clearly some worked *como hijos,* "like sons," or *como padres,* "like fathers"). No men's names appear on the official list of centro members; some of the men who frequently assist the centro have their names on (and receive tools from) the Lakaya I list. Policarpio Orosco, at least, does not appear on either list except to sign for his young daughter. When I suggested to Bonifacia that the centro sign men on as auxiliary members, she shrugged: a person's name on a list does not seem important so long as one receives the pick and shovel and the share of the harvest due.

It is my impression that the centro work groups are approximately as efficient, in terms of work output, as the conventional work group of Lakaya I. Both Lakaya I and the centro groups take formal rest breaks of about the same duration and frequency. A significant research question should be whether the more disciplined work mode of the Lakaya I group actually is, overall, more productive than the less structured work mode of the centro group. A complicating factor in comparing the two Lakaya groups would be the higher proportion of older women in the centro group versus the higher proportion of able-bodied men in Lakaya I. If the overall difference in amount of field land rehabilitated per work day is negligible, that would strengthen the appeal of raised-field rehabilitation because it would emphasize that flexibility in group size and composition, even from day to day, is not a handicap.

There is a second noticeable difference in modes of operation between Lakaya I and the Centro de Madres. When decisions are to be made within the group, Lakaya I men stand in a tight cluster around the few men who will be speaking. The men may remain standing and listening for half an hour or more. Centro members sit in small groups, two to five or so, around an open space. Leading speakers sit a little closer to the inner rim of the circle (or oval, if members are sitting along a facing pair of ancient suka kollu platforms). Two or three women in addition to the leaders (centro officers) will speak; then, after what is felt to be sufficient discussion, when it appears a consensus has appeared, an oral vote of approval is taken. Sometimes a show of hands is also requested. The Lakaya I group does not seem so committed to the democratic process. In meetings, as in work, the men form a marked geometric structure and most of them merge into a common body, which can seem threatening. Women appear unstructured and, being seated, unthreatening. The men who may be attending a centro meeting usually sprawl on the grass behind the loose circle of women. Most of the women spin or knit during meetings, and some nurse babies, furthering the image of weak organization. Men standing in their meeting circle do not engage in any other occupation, making their meeting appear to be important, that is, requiring members' full concentration. On the other hand, when the Lakaya I meeting takes place in the village, beer may be offered, and the meeting eventually degenerates into loud, drunken protestations. Beer is never offered during centro meetings, only soft drinks.

The physical contrast between the men's tightly ordered group and the centro's informality is not, I believe, a contrast between male and female patterns of behavior; it is a contrast between organizational styles, one external to the community and one internal to it (cf. Albó 1987:407–13). The Centro de Madres group follows what may be termed communitarian behavior: "the ideal structureless domain," collocated with "structural inferiority, lowermost status, and structural outsiderhood . . . harmony . . . fertility, health . . . universal justice, comradeship . . . equality . . . absence of [private] property" (Turner 1969:134; cf. Buechler and Buechler 1971:54–60; Simmons 1974:129, 143, 147–48). The group was created by and out of Indian campesinas, a class that in Bolivia is structurally inferior, of lowermost status, and outside the national structure of power. The centro campesinas seek, and practice, harmony, comradeship, justice, and equality as they work on the communal fields to obtain fertility and health. Lakaya I, the predominantly men's group, in contrast to the centro, was elicited by agents outside the community. These agents were familiar with structured work gangs and accustomed to listen to an official or overseer. Although they worked in leaderless egalitarian complementarity with women relatives in their own fields, on outside projects they held the status of male head of household, representing the household and responsible for its women if any labored with them in the project. Aymara men have four centuries of experience of this structure.

## Conflicts

Two problems were much discussed in centro meetings during my stay in Lakaya. One problem, endemic to any active group, is that of *faltas,* "no-shows," people who sign up and come to receive the benefits but do not come on working days. This is the classic free-rider problem that affects virtually all collective work groups. Felipa Uruchi keeps a careful record of who comes to work (not, be it noted, of precisely how much work a person contributes). The problem of faltas came to a head in October when the project insisted that only active members of Lakaya groups could receive picks and shovels. Centro members spent several half-hours after the day's work in the raised fields specifically discussing how to deal with faltas and held an extraordinary evening meeting October 12 in the plaza in front of Bonifacia's house—two and one-half hours sitting on the curb and cobblestones in the cold on a dark, windy, moonless night, the night before Anita Spielvogel's expected visit—to reach a decision. Spielvogel's suggestion to cut the faltas from the list of members was reluctantly accepted, but not as a final decision. More discussion of the issue ensued after the pick-and-shovel distribution. The issue involves the integrity of the *comunidad* and Aymara emphasis on courtesy toward other persons (Johnsson 1986:23), especially those with whom one is in frequent contact. The issue can be seen as a conflict between Western and Aymara cultures: Western privileging of atomistic individualism versus Aymara valuing of tolerance toward fellow members of one's community—the latter part of Aymara strategies of survival under centuries of foreign exploitation.

The second problem arose during my stay. The two Lakaya groups came into conflict over expanding their raised fields. Project co-director Oswaldo Rivera had pointed out ancient raised fields east of the men's group's fields as an area to be developed, and each group was eager to increase its acreage. Although people in the neighboring village of Chukara had begun rehabilitating and even building from scratch a few raised fields independently of the project, the Lakayans hesitated to proceed without direction from project personnel, fearing to jeopardize this profitable relationship, and in any case they needed seed from the project.

On Friday, September 30, after discussion in a centro meeting following a workday on the suka kollu, the five officers of the centro, accompanied by Plácido Fernández (uncle and father to centro officers, as well as treasurer of Lakaya I) marched over to the Lakaya I group gathered at their raised fields. Earlier in the afternoon, Paulina Quispe and Josefina Fernández had gone over and talked with members of Lakaya I. After politely drinking glasses of soft drinks proffered by the two young men serving the Lakaya I group, Bonifacia set out the reason for the formal visit: the centro wished to rehabilitate the suka kollus to the east. A dozen Lakaya I men then stood up in a tight cluster to discuss among themselves the centro's claim. Next, several of these men accompanied the centro delegation to the easternmost rehabilitated field. Waving his arms over the ancient ridges before them to the east, one of the Lakaya men counted to eight (in Spanish—Lakaya Aymaras generally use Spanish numerals to count) and declared that these would be rehabilitated by the Lakaya I group. "Aqui es mi terreno" (this is my land), he explained to me in Spanish, a claim he reiterated with much emotion later that night, after he had become drunk. "¿Sabes? ¡Es mi terreno, mi terreno como muchacho!" The five centro officers left the Lakaya I group muttering and jeering, but señor Fernández stayed behind, quietly talking with a couple of other Lakaya I leaders. After the work groups dispersed, about a dozen Lakaya I men clustered in front of President Isidro Cruz's house on the plaza, drinking beer and discussing the issue.

I asked Felipa Uruchi how the dispute would be settled, and she replied, "Por la comunidad." When I asked how the community would settle it, she merely repeated, "La comunidad." When I asked if the *alcalde* (mayor) would give a decision, she stared at me as if that were an absurd notion, and shook her head. She told me that all vacant (i.e., not cultivated) land within the community is generally available on a first-come basis, and the centro was following this principle in making its claim formally before the community. The dispute had not been settled when I left Lakaya on October 23, although there had been no further formal meetings and the open antagonism between the two groups had died down after about a week.

So far as I could observe, the mechanism of settlement was quiet discussion between respected leaders within the groups, brokered by Plácido Fernández acting literally as go-between. Fernández is intimately involved with the leaders of both groups, deeply respected, and accustomed to conducting diplomacy. The Aymaras' high valuation on mutual respect forced the opposing groups to restore proper demeanor to their encounters and to entertain the negotiations offered by don Plácido, who seems much like the Quechua village *sindicato dirigente* (leader), don Dionisio Guzmán, described by Simmons (1974:147–48), a "giver of land (in dispute), resolver of conflict." It appears to me that although Lakaya I had formed itself according to the structure normal for externally elicited groups, when it was involved in an internal community matter it reverted to the "structureless domain" governed by consensus.

## Conclusions

The Lakaya Centro de Madres is revolutionary in the Hispanic world of Bolivia (compare Barrios de Chungara [1980:50]: "Somos políticas, somos revolucionarias . . . queremos tener mejores condiciones de vida"). In the Aymara universe, it is revolutionary only in that it has been formally recognized by the Hispanic world. For 400 years, the voice of the Aymara world was muted by the Hispanic governing class (Platt 1987). Even anthropologists described Aymaras as "negative and violent" (Bastien 1978:xvi), "'dull', 'stolid', and 'unimaginative' . . . drabness and monotony [characterize] Aymara culture" (Tschopik 1947:501). Tschopik saw "irresponsibility," "submissiveness," "disorderliness," and "utilitarianism" to be dominant in Aymara personality (Tschopik 1951: 182–85). Simmons, studying Quechua-speaking Bolivian communities, described the campesinos' beds as "seldom made . . . a jumble . . . lacking in a sense of order, of symmetry; this mirrors, one feels, the lack of organization of their symbolic life, a certain apathy and confusion" (Simmons 1974:24–25). Tschopik and his predecessors and Simmons aligned themselves with the Hispanic class. Those anthropologists who lived and worked collaboratively with Aymara campesinos, including the Buechlers, Carter, Hardman and her associates, and Johnsson, give a radically different picture, one that corresponds to my own observations of a warmly gracious people.

The difficulty of understanding Aymara societies is more than a matter of class alignment. Aymaras living in the Hispanic world are like Aymara Spanish, which substitutes the three Aymara vowel phonemes for the five Bolivian Spanish vowels, does not give phonemic status to the distinction between /d/ and /t/ or /p/ and /b/, and drops final syllables in the manner of Aymara syntax. The resulting speech is intelligible to the Spanish speaker but distinctly Aymara. Parallel to Aymara Spanish are what Briggs (1981) has labeled Missionary, Patrón, and Radio Aymara. These jargons use Aymara words in Spanish or English phonology and syntactical constructions and are particularly lax in the use of Aymara politives (Briggs 1981:176–77). The linguistic codes reflect the incongruence between Hispanic expectation of marked hierarchies and Aymara valuation of mutual respect.

The anthropological axiom that primitive and peasant societies are organized on principles of kinship, in supposed contrast to the Western rational system of achieved statuses, befuddled students of Andean societies for generations. Ethnographers of Andean societies, including the Bolivian Aymara, searched for the kin units they expected to be the basic components of these societies. Debate ranged over the persistence of ayllus, first met as the unit of Inca local governance. Standard anthropological theory prompted the assumption that ayllus were composed of kin, although data on the incorporation of immigrants into ayllus indicated that they were territorial units marked by common attendance at earth shrines (Bastien 1978:191; for other discussions of ayllus, see, e.g., Allen 1988; Guillet 1981; Julien 1988; Rasnake 1986; Salomon 1987:160–64; Schaedel 1988). Tschopik (1947:542) baldly stated that the Aymara extended family, which he termed the basic social unit, is patrilineal and patrilocal, claims which no later ethnographer would accept. Not until the 1980s could anthropologists concede the concept of communities of independent individuals as the basic unit of Aymara society.

Aymaras consider it essential that children be raised by married couples. Families of husband, wife, and child (who may be a grandchild) are therefore a very common residential unit. Unmarried (including widowed) adults share homes with others, usually kin, because they feel unprotected when alone. Households are economic units. These observations enable the anthropologist expecting kinship units to be basic to the society to make a case. From this conventional point of view, the Lakaya Centro de Madres could be termed an extended family enterprise, with four of its five officers related and other extended families represented in the centro membership.

Working more directly from the suite of data, a better interpretation begins with the Aymaras' own emphasis on the community, coupled with the high valuation placed on the individual. From this perspective, we can see the encouragement of entrepreneurship, including both local initiatives such as the Centro de Madres and also circular migrations (Lewellen 1978). Migrants usually stay with others originally from their own community, often kin if only because most members of the community can trace some relationship to most others. It is not wrong to see kin relationships, but to emphasize these rather than the community bond or to assume that ascribed kin roles dominate behavior obscures the strength of Aymara valuation of the individual and of complementary equality (Johnsson 1986:16, 22–23).

The political economy of the Aymara village of Lakaya is based on the several hundred adults who are collectively the comunidad. Individual entrepreneurship can transcend the physical boundaries of the community without necessarily jeopardizing the entrepreneur's membership in the community (Miracle and Yapita 1981:46–47). The community is permeable to those who respect its members (Hornberger 1987:21). Thus, Lakayans can work in La Paz and more distant provinces and can accept vendors to their Thursday market, schoolteachers, soccer coaches, local employees of the Children's Plan charity, raised-field rehabilitators, and other incursions from outside. The respect due every human encourages tolerance. If Lakaya may appear backward, static, locked into the eternal cycle of agricultural seasons, that is the tourist's view; in fact, the community is lively and eager for opportunities. Four hundred years of peonage, ended only in 1953, left the village poor, and Bolivia's economy has given it few options.

Lakaya is an Aymara community in an Aymara world that exists in the Fourth World, encapsulated within a foreign nation. Anthropological conventions fit it as poorly as the borrowed Spanish title Centro de Madres fits the Aymara work group organized by La Bonifacia. To understand the political economy of the village it is necessary to realize that encapsulation provides two patterns of Lakayans, the national Bolivian and that which is seen as Aymara. The raised-field rehabilitation project elicited one pattern and stimulated the other. Individuals moved from one to the other even on the same day: a man might labor sindicato-style for Lakaya I and then go work beside the women on the Centro de Madres suka kollu, or a woman might take a subordinate role assisting her husband or father in Lakaya I, then return to the centro group where she would participate actively in its discussion. An outsider seeing only that the mode of production looks identical, conforming to the project's directives, would not know that to Lakayans, the Lakaya I group was externally elicited and the Centro de Madres internal to the community. From this difference flow contrasting organizations of labor and decision making.

## Note

This chapter contains substantial material published previously in "The Centro de Madres in the Village of Lakaya, Bolivia," by Alice B. Kehoe, in *Marxist Approaches in Economic Anthropology,* edited by A. Littlehead and H. Gates, pp. 133–99, Lanham, Maryland: University Press of America.

# 11

# Ethnodevelopment of Indigenous Bolivian Communities

## *Emerging Paradigms*

KEVIN HEALY

Since the late 1970s, Bolivia has undergone a revitalization of indigenous technologies, knowledge, resources, sociocultural values, and political institutions. This cultural revitalization often involves the rediscovery and recuperation of knowledge or institutions such as the ancient technology of raised-field agriculture that is the principal subject of this volume. In its cumulative effects, this process is helping to decolonize institutions, practices, attitudes, and strategies of change in contemporary Bolivian society. Grassroots and nongovernmental organizations (NGOs) and international and sometimes state agencies have participated in one or more aspects of this effort in every region of the country (fig. 11.1).[1] Although only a minority of state and nongovernmental organizations show elements of pro-indigenous orientation, the numbers of those who do continue to grow and gain influence.

In this chapter I present diverse examples of an emerging ethnodevelopment and political paradigm. Institutions that have shifted their focus from a "peasant" to a "Native American" approach and those that have promoted a Native American perspective receive detailed attention. Examples of such change include activities involving native Andean crops, tree species, and medicinal plants, indigenous languages, weaving traditions, diverse sociocultural expressions, indigenous authority positions, traditional political organizations, and modern political parties. This spreading cultural revitalization in Bolivia has been stimulated by diverse factors such as increasing democratization, the international environmentalist movement, activism by foreign and national anthropologists, agronomists, and botanists, the emergence of an indigenous intelligentsia and a native Katarista movement, and, most recently, the quincentennial of the European invasion of the Americas.[2]

The cultural revitalization movement challenges the rural modernization strategies that have held sway in Bolivia since the 1940s. These strategies, similar to those of other Andean republics, reflected both the country's condition of internal colonialism and its dependency on production and consumption models imported from Western industrial countries. Various Bolivian intellectuals have identified Bolivia's internal colonialism as the central problem of its underdevelopment (Albó and Barnadas 1984; S. Rivera 1990). The persistence of discrimination by dominant institutions (economic, social, and political) against people of indigenous descent in the cities and small towns is one of the country's enduring historical legacies. From public schools, the courts, and marketplaces to the state's ministries and corporations, anti-indigenous biases are at work against the majority of the population.[3] Moreover, the state's foreign-funded modernization programs have tended to reinforce these patterns by devaluing the culture and resources of the indigenous population.

## Revitalization of Andean Crops

From the 1940s into the 1990s, the Bolivian state's rural modernization strategies gave the development of Andean food crops disproportionately small budgetary support and investment. Agricultural research, infrastructure, credit, marketing, and foreign exchange were focused on the country's "modern" commercial farmers and ranchers operating in the tropical and subtropical lowlands while ignoring the population majority, the indigenous producers in the highlands (Heilman 1982; Whitaker and Wennergren 1982). Major national and foreign economic resources underwrote the expansion of commercial and export commodities in the lowland Santa Cruz and Beni regions, at the expense of native crops.

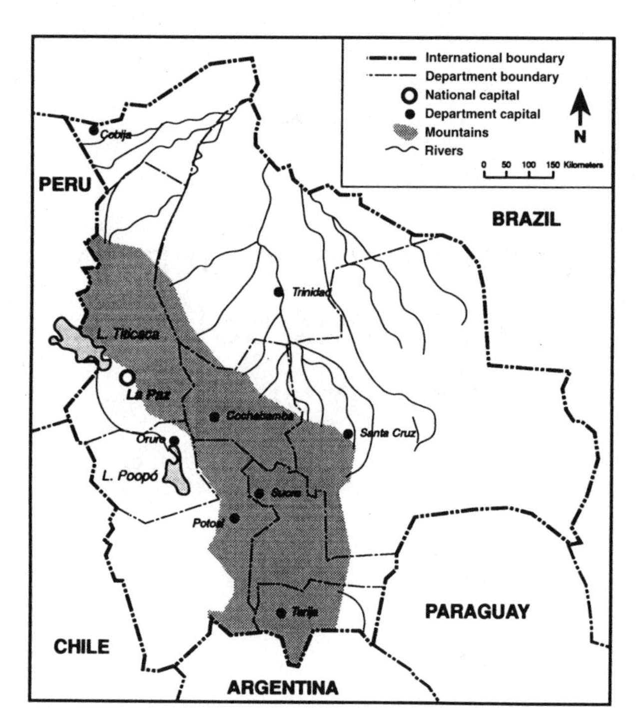


Figure 11.1. Modern political divisions of Bolivia.

The relatively significant support for resettlement and colonization programs in the tropics was another manifestation of this anti-Andean bias. Economic potential in the tropical lowlands was deemed by entities such as the United States Agency for International Development (USAID) to be much greater than that in the highland regions of the country (USAID 1974). This assumption stemmed from ignorance about both the fragility of tropical soils and the past achievements of highland agriculture. The analysis took an overoptimistic view of colonization schemes, perhaps influenced by the United States' experience of expansion in its own western region. Following the period of heaviest funding for colonization, a comprehensive study of its impact in lowland areas demonstrated that the trade-off for highland agriculture was too great a cost for Bolivia's overall development prospects (Wiggens 1976).

In addition to the biases in national agricultural policy, the importation of donated wheat from the United States under the PL 480 program beginning in the 1950s altered consumer preferences for traditional Andean grains and other food crops (National Research Council 1989; Prudencio Bohrt 1990). The flooding of Bolivian markets with wheat flour and bread induced changes in food tastes that led to a further decline in the dietary importance of native Andean grains such as quinoa and *kañiwa* and legumes such as *tarwi*. This import and food policy was an example of rural modernization's reinforcing neocolonial biases against "Indian foods."

The most widely produced and consumed crop in Bolivia, the potato, illustrates the public policy of neglect and exclusion (Dandler and Sage 1985). The potato is native to the Andes, and its various species have been used by some 95 countries as a principal food crop. Meanwhile in Bolivia, potato acreage yields and profitability have been in decline for decades (Godoy and Franco 1992:37; Hoopes and Sage 1982). Indeed, some of the lowest potato yields in the world have been documented in the highland Chuquisaca and Potosí regions of Bolivia. The modern technology for growing potatoes using imported chemicals for fertilization, pest control, and other purposes is increasingly economically unviable for Bolivia's producers, particularly smallholders (Gutierrez 1990). Although Bolivia established its own national potato seed certification program in the early 1980s, critics have argued that it supports mostly hybrids, with only a handful of native varieties, despite a huge seed pool of the latter from which to draw for promoting Andean biodiversity and long-term food security (Rea 1985).

In the mid-1970s, a small group of Bolivian and

foreign scientists working against these anti-native food policies forged ahead to sponsor international conferences, educational seminars, and incipient research programs calling attention to the valuable food crops ignored by development planners (National Research Council 1989). Peruvian universities played a crucial role in revitalizing research on Andean food crops, eventually influencing Bolivian institutions to do the same (Tapia 1990). This pioneering work stimulated efforts at recovery and revitalization of Andean crops in recent years. For example, one agronomist helped organize the first workshop (Primer Taller Nacional sobre Recursos Fitogenéticos) in 1983 to teach Bolivian agronomists in state agricultural agencies about germ plasm in order to preserve native seed species. This workshop was stimulated by a similar one held for the Southern Cone countries of South America as a whole. The Bolivian participants had been alarmed at the "genetic erosion" of native germ plasm through droughts, floods, and substitution of more productive hybrids (Rea 1985:48). They concluded that 180 cultivars in the fields of Andean farmers were living germ plasm banks and should be conserved, protected, and propagated.

Here I discuss five Andean crops that have experienced a recent revalorization in Bolivia. The first of these is the *papa amarga,* or bitter potato. Recently there has been an unprecedented upsurge in interest by the state and NGOs in this potato species. Papa amarga (estimated to be 15 percent of the total potatoes planted in Bolivia) flourishes in difficult Andean areas prone to frost, hail, and drought. A reassessment of the papa amarga's attributes has begun, and Bolivian and Peruvian agricultural scientists shared a wide range of related research findings at a roundtable, the Primera Mesa Redonda sobre la Papa Amarga, in 1991. The purpose of this event was to "understand and interpret the rationality, logic, and wisdom of the peasantry in its use" of the potato (Rea 1991). Agricultural researchers presented papers on topics such as the number of native varieties, the size of cultivated areas, how the papa amarga is used in preparing Andean freeze-dried potatoes (*chuño* and *tunta*), and its drought-resistance qualities. NGOs such as AGRUCO (Proyecto de Agro-Biología de la Universidad de Cochabamba) soon mounted programs to support this type of potato, and state research stations in La Paz and Cochabamba subsequently collected some 250 samples of papa amarga with which to conduct scientific experiments. The NGO known as SEMTA (Servicios Educativas de Tecnologías Apropriadas) identified nine varieties of bitter potatoes in the altiplano province of Pacajes alone (Birbuet 1992:86).

Quinoa is an example of an Andean grain that was substantially revived during the late 1970s and 1980s. A hardy protein crop, quinoa has been adapted to the harsh altiplano conditions of Bolivia over millennia (National Research Council 1989). Although quinoa had been negatively affected by wheat imports and state rural modernization priorities that favored lowland agriculture, individual agricultural researchers began modest efforts to recover the grain during the 1950s and 1960s (Cusack 1983). During the mid-to-late 1970s, interest in quinoa took a quantum leap, evidenced by a proliferation of publications and increased involvement of university and experimental stations conducting field tests to improve the grain and its production technology (Cusack 1983). In 1977, a conference entitled "Primer Encuentro de Productores de Quinoa Sur Altiplano" was organized by the cooperative federation Operación Tierra in Nor Lipez, Potosí. A later example of such support was the first Andean regional meeting on agricultural germ plasm organized by three international agencies in 1991, which targeted quinoa as a priority crop (CIRF 1981).

Another major impulse toward revitalizing production has been the rising demand for quinoa in health-food stores in the United States and western Europe. The growing export market has helped to reverse trends toward declining quinoa production and yields in the Bolivian Andes. By some estimates, quinoa production has increased fourfold in the important Lipez region of Potosí in recent years. Since the mid-1980s, indigenous producers' associations such as the Asociación Nacional de Productores de Quinoa (ANAPQUI) (Potosí and Oruro) and Operación Tierra have been exporting their own quinoa and multiplying the num ber of quinoa processing plants in rural areas. Attractive prices offered by international health-food chains have revivified interest in quinoa production among altiplano peasant farmers, while at the same time these buyers discourage the use of chemically based production technologies. International organizations in Bolivia are also beginning to embrace the cause. The World Food Organization, Programa Mundial Alimienta (PMA), and USAID recently used quinoa for distribution in maternal child-care programs in a microregion of Cochabamba. Networks of health-food stores with quinoa-based products have emerged in Bolivia's own urban centers. A parallel phenomenon has been the proliferation of new Bolivian recipe books on quinoa during the 1980s.

Tarwi is a third example of a highly nutritious Andean food crop whose recovery is now in full swing. Tarwi is a legume native to the Andes that has greater protein value than soybeans and peanuts, grows in marginal soils, and efficiently fixes atmospheric nitrogen (National Research Council 1989:181). In 1976, tarwi did not appear on the Ministry of Agriculture's list of Bolivia's most important food crops (Zuvekas 1977). Tarwi's national rediscovery began in 1978, when agricultural engineers from the regional development corporation in Cochabamba, CORDECO, learned of its qualities through Peru's national program of "Cultivos Andinos." However, CORDECO's support program to stimulate tarwi production among peasant farmers ran aground on bureaucratic and political limitations that hamper state effectiveness in peasant development programs. Subsequently, tarwi's revitalization in Bolivia was propelled by the initiatives and program continuities of NGOs. In 1982, the Centro Agrícola de Servicios de Desarrollo (CASDEC), a Cochabamba NGO, began a diverse program (agricultural credit, technical assistance, seed, customer promotion) to promote tarwi production and consumption in both urban and rural Cochabamba, surpassing CORDECO's increasingly lackluster outreach to small farmers.

By the 1990s, there were half a dozen Cochabamba NGOs supporting tarwi production, an active association of tarwi peasant producers in Cochabamba, university-based tarwi research programs in La Paz, Santa Cruz, and Cochabamba, and six small businesses in Cochabamba marketing tarwi flour and a variety of related products (bread, cookies, etc.). On a small trial basis, tarwi had been promoted in school lunch programs for low-income children and distributed among mothers' clubs. CASDEC helped organize the first Asociación Impulsora de Tarwi, comprising both public entities and NGOs. Although tarwi promotion programs have been ineffective and short-lived in the public development corporation in the Chuquisaca region (known as CORDECH), such programs spread to the Potosí and Lake Titicaca regions of La Paz via the rural development activities of NGOs. Current estimates for tarwi production reach 3,000 hectares in rural Bolivia (PROCAMPO 1991).

An equally vigorous rediscovery and recovery of an Andean crop has been taking place with amaranth. This crop apparently had disappeared for centuries in the Andes, primarily because of European colonization (Kietz 1992:103; National Research Council 1989:141). Prior to its relatively recent reinsertion into some Andean societies, however, it had spread widely to Africa, Asia, and North America. Amaranth is an extremely valuable source of protein and is adaptable to a wide range of environments. In Bolivia, the decision among NGOs to revitalize amaranth emerged during a 1986 seminar focused on the role of internationally donated food aid (Kietz 1992:157). In 1990, a seminar called "Primer Encuentro Interdepartamental del Amaranto," with the participation of 40 Bolivian and foreign professionals, opened discussion on diverse ways to support this Andean crop (CIEP 1990). This seminar led to the organization of the "Red Pro-Amaranto" (Pro-Amaranth Network) (CIEP-UTAB 1991).

As in the case of tarwi, new plans grew out of prior experiences. The amaranth network began by introducing genetic improvements into local Bolivian varieties to recover the pre-European status of the crop (Kietz 1992:160). Subsequently, several NGOs initiated small projects in the regions of La Paz, Cochabamba, and Tarija to provide seed and technical assistance to farmers. Bolivian institutions also have opened new markets for amaranth via school breakfast programs in low-income neighborhoods, and local businesses used amaranth for making health products for middle- and upper-class consumers in the capital city. The first-place prize at the national fair of small industry in 1992 went to an entrepreneur using amaranth in health-food products.

The final Andean crop I consider here whose value has recently been celebrated and reaffirmed is coca. This crop, of course, is a special and hotly contested case with a high international profile. Ironically, the revalorization of coca in Bolivia is a grassroots response to international multilateral and bilateral pressure to eradicate the coca leaf as a counternarcotics measure. Internationally inspired programs of coca reduction and eradication set off a furious defense of the leaf by producers beginning in the early 1980s (Healy 1989, 1991)—a social movement recently supported by the Bolivian state itself. To resist crop eradication schemes, coca leaf growers in the Chapare district and, to a lesser extent, in the yungas region of the Department of La Paz defended themselves via their *sindicato* (union) organizations. To advance their political interests, they also created the first national association of coca leaf growers, Asociación Nacional de Productores de Coca (ANAPCOCA), and together with Peruvian producers in 1989 held the "Primer Encuentro Andino de Productores de Hoja de Coca."

The sindicatos publicly defended coca as a "sacred leaf," a "renewable resource," and a fundamental pillar of native Andean culture. To defy outside pressures for eradication, they have organized annual "coca-leaf chew-ins" through networks of grassroots support, made speeches at political rallies celebrating the coca leaf's positive qualities, undertaken an international campaign to decriminalize the coca leaf, and spread the pro–coca leaf cause via local, regional, and national peasant sindicato congresses and political mobilizations (Healy 1989, 1991). As a result, the national confederation of peasant workers in Bolivia (CSUTCB) maintains a permanent committee defending coca, rating it as a high priority in its national agenda for protecting peasant rights and interests. The coca growers' sindicatos elaborated their own plans for diversifying and exporting products such as coca-based toothpaste, wine, marmalade, and syrups for depressing appetite.

In 1992, the Bolivian state itself demonstrated an unexpected shift in policy to support the coca leaf. Previously, in 1990, the Paz Zamora government had, at the Cartagena drug summit, proposed a "coca for development" thesis. This thesis signified Bolivia's interest in trading its coca fields in the tropical Chapare region for massive financial resources from the Western industrial countries in the form of investments to replace the coca-cocaine economy. Under the previous government, laws had been passed by congress placing the coca leaf in the category of "dangerous substances" while establishing a 10-year time frame for its complete eradication in the Chapare, its major production area. There were also threats by the United States government to destroy coca leaf fields in the Chapare through aerial spraying with toxic chemicals. On the other hand, the new law contained clauses allowing legal production in the yungas zones to satisfy the internal consumption demand from Bolivia's indigenous rural populations.

The government policy shift in 1992 appeared to be influenced by the potential for worldwide marketing of coca tea (*mate de coca*) and related coca products and the prospects for "industrializing" the coca leaf for export sales. The Bolivian government sponsored discussions in the United States to secure support for this new strategy and lobbied the World Health Organization and the National Institutes of Health for laboratory analyses and supportive statements on coca's cultural and potential pharmaceutical importance. By elevating the status of coca and its new derivatives to that of a legal industrial export, the Bolivian state was in effect bestowing an important value on this traditional Andean crop. During the 1992 quincentenary year, state employees were encouraged to use green coca-leaf pins in the presidential palace and various embassies around the world.

## Recovery of Native Agricultural Knowledge

State modernization programs in the highlands between the 1940s and 1980s operated on the premise that the technical resources and skills for developing the rural economy should originate outside the country and its native communities. The assumption was that little of technical or pragmatic value could be found among the indigenous populations themselves.[4] After the Bohan Mission report, the U.S. government established the Servicio Agrícola Interamericano (SAI) as an autonomous entity run by U.S. officials to promote rural modernization activities. Over the following decades, it introduced programs with 4-H clubs, home economists, and U.S.-style agricultural extension. SAI attempted to transform a Bolivian university into a land-grant institution to conduct agricultural research, modeled Bolivia's rural credit program on the U.S. Farm Home Administration Program, and imported development experts from land-grant institutions in states such as Utah that resembled the altiplano environmentally (Heilman 1982). In the mid-1970s, USAID and the Bolivian government organized the Servicio Nacional de Desarrollo de Comunidades under guidelines of the United States Public Administration Service (Valdivia and Martínez 1993:4). Within this framework for modernizing farms, the Bolivian extension agency was the key factor, and peasant farmers remained "backward and passive" recipients of external guidance and support. This approach achieved some gains in productivity by developing a native potato variety (Zuvekas 1977), but its thrust ignored the value of indigenous knowledge about farming.

During the 1960s, the rural extension programs were incorporated within the Ministry of Agriculture and Peasant Affairs, with heavy financial dependence upon and guidance from USAID. Bolivian government officials and professionals demonstrated little interest in tapping indigenous knowledge about agriculture and animal husbandry. Indeed, many agronomists employed by the ministry were sons of expropriated landowners whose farms had been turned over to indigenous farmers. Institutions such as the Servicio Nacional de Desarrollo de Comunidades, the Instituto Boliviano de Tecnología Agrícola (IBTA), and the Banco Agrícola did little to arrest the process of land degradation, falling rural incomes, and declining agricultural productivity.

There have, however, been a handful of institutional efforts during the 1980s and 1990s to reverse this pattern of external dependency and internal colonialism, even within USAID itself. A book titled *Nuestros conocimientos* ("our knowledge"), published in 1983, provides an example. Organized by USAID consultant John Hatch and Aymara anthropologist Mauricio Mamani, the book documents indigenous production systems from the perspective of the peasants themselves. Hatch had 127 farmers record in diary form their day-to-day tasks, outlooks, and experiences. For example, they recorded information about the allocation of labor time for the myriad household and farming tasks required for survival. Rituals used to predict the weather, prevent hail or frost, enhance animal fertility, and appeal to mountain spirits for a better harvest also appeared in their diaries (Hatch 1983). The result was a "textbook" that represented a contribution of peasant knowledge to the outside world, especially to development specialists designing rural modernization programs. Despite this laudable effort, there was little evidence of revised thinking in USAID policy priorities or recognition of indigenous resources during the 1980s.

The Centro de Desarrollo y Comunicación Rural (CENDA) in western Cochabamba collected local knowledge from communities through a participatory social research program about the economic and cultural management schemes of the indigenous population. This research, lasting several years, enabled CENDA to discover the farm-level indigenous decision-making framework and disseminate this knowledge for community analysis through multiple media and training channels, including posters, radio shows, and booklets. This approach led to the recovery of native potato and tree species, traditional health practices, and specialized knowledge for forecasting climatic changes pertinent to agriculture. By establishing a competition among community elders, CENDA identified the best forecasters. It also reinvigorated the local sindicato with a mission of cultural revitalization.

Servicios Múltiples de Tecnología Apropriada (SEMTA), conducting development programs in the Pacajes region in the central altiplano near the Chilean border, also focused on recovering indigenous knowledge to orient its strategy for rural change and development. SEMTA's community-based research identified "Andean indicators" used by the local population to forecast weather changes affecting agriculture (Birbuet 1992:72–79). It discovered how the flowers of specific native grasses, shrubs, and cactus plants and the behavior of birds, wild rabbits, and foxes were observed as signs of agricultural conditions during the growing season. It recovered 70 such Andean indicators to disseminate through publications and training programs. After experiments with U.S.-style "appropriate technology" projects, SEMTA concluded that the most viable local development strategy for livestock production was the recovery of native pastures.

In the altiplano of Oruro, the Centro de Capacitación Integral de la Mujer Campesina (CIMCA), a rural women's training center, began the 1980s using conventional community diagnostic methods from the field of social work. By the end of the decade, CIMCA was recovering native women's cultural practices and collecting knowledge in the communities about the use of native plants for treating the health problems of cattle and sheep. In Cochabamba, AGRUCO shifted its focus toward greater appreciation of indigenous knowledge. AGRUCO's program in the 1970s resembled an effort to bring European-style organic agriculture to Bolivia through local research and dissemination to grassroots organizations and NGOs. Its experiments included composting, the utilization of organic fertilizer, and programs to produce and exploit bio-gas (Augstburger 1990: 12). Subsequently, AGRUCO adopted an "agro-biological" approach, continuing to consider peasant attitudes as backward and the land parcel as the target for externally induced agricultural innovation (Augstburger 1990:14). Yet, over the course of the decade, AGRUCO's experiences with indigenous populations prompted it to move from its holistic "agro-biological" approach to an "Andean agro-ecological" approach. The latter perspective consisted of understanding the cosmological vision and indigenous technical knowledge of the Andean people as AGRUCO's point of departure for technological improvements. This culturally based, holistic approach began to use indigenous knowledge for agricultural development (Delgado 1989).

In practical terms, AGRUCO values the joint efforts of technicians and peasants working together rather than the unilateral flow of information characteristic of conventional modernization programs (Augstburger 1990:15). By focusing on indigenous knowledge systems, AGRUCO turned the social class notion of the "backward and unresponsive peasant" on its head (Augstburger 1990:17). Because of its active training program for NGOs, AGRUCO influences other agricultural development programs in highland Bolivia. Its outreach efforts include Cochabamba University thesis projects related to the agro-Andean approach and using these concepts for curriculum reform in the faculty of agronomy, which had evidenced little previous interest in indigenous knowledge.

A prime example of revalorizing indigenous knowledge is the recovery of raised-field agriculture (*suka kollu*) in the Lake Titicaca basin. In the late 1970s, archaeological research on both the Bolivian and Peruvian sides of the lake revealed that raised fields used for grazing had been the locus of an ancient agricultural system of the Tiwanaku civilization (ca. 300 B.C. to A.D. 1000). This highly productive technology produced food surpluses to satisfy the needs of a sizable indigenous population. In the mid-1980s, a group affiliated with Bolivia's Universidad Católica and the University of Chicago began experiments using this technology in the Lake Titicaca region. Elements of this research and development program are related in chapters of this volume, especially chapter 9. This group promotes and supports the efforts of local community organizations such as sindicatos and mothers' clubs in reconstructing the raised fields. Agronomy students from the rural, Tiwanaku campus of the Universidad Católica also participate in the reconstruction efforts as part of their curriculum. Outreach programs incorporate videotapes and bilingual texts to promote and explain the benefits of this native technology.

As described in chapter 5, the indigenous raised field technology utilizes water and solar energy to modify nighttime temperatures and enable food crops to survive frost damage with yields above contemporary levels. This altered microclimate provides for a measure of food security that had been lost in pre-Hispanic times by indigenous populations in the Titicaca basin (see chapter 8). The lack of food security due to recurring frost is a main contributor to rural poverty and urban migration in this area. The raised-field system also offers a chemical-free technology for potato production alternative to conventional approaches that have become both environmentally unsound and economically unviable. The recycling of naturally occurring nutrients enhances the economic and environmental benefits of this technology (see chapter 7). Through collective work schemes, several thousand farmers have had direct exposure to raised-field technology in Bolivia, and as of 1994 some 200 hectares have been put into experimental production on plots distributed among 52 communities from several altiplano provinces. The Bolivian activities also include a comprehensive program of scientific investigation of the physical and technological dimensions of raised-field agriculture by foreign and national scientists. The project organizers created a new NGO, Fundación Wiñaymarka, to expand their activities into analyzing and rehabilitating abandoned agricultural terrace systems in the region.

The Bolivian project has received extensive media attention both in Bolivia and internationally. This media exposure has begun to stimulate considerable national pride in the sophistication and potential contemporary application of this native technology. Between 1990 and 1992, the president of Bolivia, Jaime Paz Zamora, participated in several well-publicized planting and harvesting ceremonies on the raised fields to focus attention on the project. The Bolivian army developed "Plan Verde" to use conscripts to promote this technology through experimental plots in various regions of the altiplano. In 1993, an incipient NGO program of reconstructing raised-field agriculture also began in the lowlands of the Beni region.

Simultaneously in Peru, several hundred hectares have been rehabilitated for production in at least 100 indigenous communities (Erickson and Brinkmeier 1991). Up to a dozen NGOs, as well as state agencies engaged in rural development, have reintroduced the technology in communities of the Puno region of the Titicaca basin.

The publishing program of Historia Boliviana (HISBOL) is another example of indigenous knowledge recovery. For decades, most studies in rural communities on Andean agriculture, indigenous cultures, and other, related topics were conducted by North American, British, and French social scientists. Very little of their work had been published in Spanish prior to 1980, thereby remaining inaccessible to the Bolivian readership (Albó 1983). In 1983, HISBOL began translating into Spanish and publishing in pocket-sized books much of this mostly anthropological, sociological, and historical work. This program opened a rich vein of material on Andean and Amazonian rural life for Bolivian readers. The emergence of indigenous (especially Aymara and other national) scholars contributed to the tremendous growth in HISBOL publications during the second half of the 1980s. HISBOL's publishing program has played an important role in advancing a new paradigm for thinking about national rural development and contemporary political issues.

## Recovery of Native Tree Species

After decades of misguided modernization efforts, highland and lowland reforestation programs have recently reflected an unprecedented appreciation for native tree species. Bolivia's altiplano and valley regions suffered serious deforestation and land degradation for centuries. Factors leading to this environmental decline included mining, overgrazing, agricultural intensification, and the demand for fuel from growing rural populations (Godoy 1984:369; Rist and San Martín 1991:23; West 1984). Enthusiastic promotion of the eucalyptus tree by national development agencies to the exclusion of native varieties reflected a rural modernization bias toward imported resources and quick results from investments rather than long-term environmental planning and the conservation and propagation of native resources.

An important Bolivian actor in the reforestation arena, the Corporación de Desarrollo de Chuquisaca (CORDECH), pursued this conventional modernization approach on the Andean landscape. Between 1969 and 1989, CORDECH primarily grew imported eucalyptus and pine tree seedlings in its huge centralized nurseries (CORDECH-COTESU 1989). It distributed donated foodstuffs from the United States in rural communities in return for cooperation in transplanting seedlings. Because of its rapid growth, the eucalyptus tree enjoyed popularity among regional planners, engineers, and the peasants themselves. The reforestation program was intended to create sources of energy (fuel to be used or sold for cooking and mining) and to enhance a picturesque mountain landscape. This focus overlooked the accelerated degradation of natural resources underway in this region. The eucalyptus tree, while providing wood for construction and fuel, tended to siphon off soil nutrients and water from field crops, while its shallow root system failed to prevent erosion. CORDECH's top-down reforestation approach ignored the native tree species of the southern mountain valleys that had contributed to the local peasant economy for a millennium or more (as sources of fuel and forage and in soil conservation). This strategy devalued indigenous knowledge about native tree management and the multiple economic and cultural uses for this resource.

With encouragement from an environmentally conscious donor, the Corporación Técnico Suiza (COTESU), in 1990 CORDECH began promoting native tree species for its mountain environment. CORDECH made an inventory of traditional agroforestry practices and the uses of native species by the local indigenous population in Chuquisaca (CORDECH-COTESU 1992a:8). It expressed interest in 33 native trees in particular, including *churqui, sirado, tipa, jarcka, algarrobo,* and *soto* (CORDECH-COTESU 1992b:11), and it decentralized its nurseries by placing them in seven different provinces under the management of local NGOs. CORDECH contracted local rural schoolteachers as extension agents and utilized the school systems' infrastructure to carry out its reforestation plan.

CORDECH's thrust represents a growing trend throughout Bolivia. In the Cochabamba region, COTESU successfully encouraged that department's regional development corporation, CORDECO, to adopt a reforestation strategy using native tree species. Cochabamba NGOs such as CENDA, Radio Esperanza, and a half dozen others were doing the same in their reforestation and agroforestry programs with communities and grassroots organizations. The Programa de Desarrollo Alternativo Rural (PDAR), the government entity engaged in "alternative development" for reducing coca leaf production, promoted native trees in its rural programs in highland communities to slow migration from the Mizque area of Cochabamba to the Chapare's coca-cocaine industry.

In the lowland Santa Cruz region, NGOs and quasi-public entities have been active in this kind of reforestation. The Mataco indigenous people are using reforestation with native trees to attain raw material for making a variety of income-generating artisan products. The Centro de Investigación Agrícola Tropical (CIAT) (which had promoted mostly exotic forage and legumes), together with the Misión Británica en Agricultura Tropical, has implemented research projects that attempt to regenerate the natural vegetative cover of native bushes, pastures, and forage trees for sustainable cattle-raising activities. This recovery of native tree species is taking place both in the semiarid Chaco region and in the mountainous province of Valle Grande. CIAT also has identified four native tree species for promotion among peasant colonists in the Norte de Santa Cruz zone. Meanwhile, in Bolivia's altiplano region, the rural campus of the Catholic University and other local NGOs have shifted their reforestation priorities from eucalyptus and pine trees to the native *quishuara* tree.

## Recovery of Native Medicinal Plants

In the decade after 1980, an impressive revival took place in the recovery of medicinal plants that previously had received more public hostility than support from Bolivia's nonindigenous social order. Among a broad sector of the population, there has been a growing interest in herbal and related natural medicine. This cultural reawakening was triggered in part by Bolivia's hyperinflationary crisis between 1982 and 1985. Astronomical price rises encouraged members of the lower and middle classes to seek medicinal plants as alternatives to pharmaceuticals sold in local stores. Although arising from pressures in the national economy, the support for herbal medicine rapidly took on the character of a cultural movement.

A prime example is the Sociedad de Medicina Tradicional (SOBOMETRA), an association of grassroots and middle-class health activists, which has played a dynamic leadership role. Working through its national and regional affiliates, it has held frequent congresses, signed agreements with the national public health school to change its anti-indigenous orientation (SOBOMETRA 1986), organized health clinics in the cities of La Paz, Cochabamba, and Santa Cruz, and conducted training programs, seminars, and international meetings on traditional Andean medicine.

SOBOMETRA has also coordinated activities for many other NGOs and grassroots organizations for training programs in traditional medicine. Bolivian rural populations demonstrated tremendous interest in relearning this traditional knowledge and reducing the costs of medicines. Growing interest in medicinal plants in both the highlands and the lowlands led to a proliferation of scientific books, popular publications, training programs, educational radio shows, newspaper columns, and pamphlets containing descriptions of medicinal plants and their uses among the highland and lowland ethnic groups. Traditional medicine clinics such as the Centro de Promoción Naturógica y Atención Wancollo (CEPRONAW) appeared in various altiplano provinces.

Some NGOs began using traditional healers as health practitioners in their rural programs. The Cruz Roja Suiza (Swiss Red Cross) in the Chaco microregion of Izozog has co-managed a rural health program together with the indigenous Guarani. In its clinics and hospitals, it employs 12 different remedies using medicinal plants. CENDA replaced its rural health program based upon Western-style clinics and community health promoters with a program of joint consultation for local residents with traditional healers (*jampiris*) and medical doctors in the zone (Alva et al. 1993). After poor results with its provincial hospital services, the Instituto de Capacitación (INCCA), also in Cochabamba, opted to train and work with traditional midwives in its rural health programs.

An NGO in the Valle Grande area of Santa Cruz used survey research among the peasant population to identify 115 medicinal plants (Carrizo 1993:117). Other examples include CENDA's research on the efficacy of traditional medicine practitioners through follow-up interviews with patients receiving treatment, and a North-American woman's didactic publications on folk remedies based on 20 years' work among Aymara and Quechua peoples (Papik 1987). SEMTA, a La Paz–based NGO, supported the *kallawayas,* the well-known traditional medical practitioners from the Charazani area, in managing innovative health clinics and publishing herbal remedies (Cajías and Girón 1987; Ranaboldo 1986). A new research organization, PROMENANT, established modest experimental centers on medicinal plants in diverse environments and climatic zones and began a small marketing program for remedies using medicinal plants. Subsequently, several national universities began research programs with medicinal plants. There has been increasing interest in using ethnographic knowledge about communities to understand indigenous health problems and the role of traditional midwives in health-care delivery (Huanca and Aguilar 1992).

The year 1984 marked unprecedented governmental interest in herbal medicine. That year, an executive decree by the Bolivian state gave herbal medicine practices official status and therefore greater legitimacy in the public health field (CEE 1988:83). In 1987, following a national congress attended by Aymara, Quechua, and Guarani indigenous representatives, SOBOMETRA held the "Primer Congreso Continental de Medicina Tradicional," which led to the "Primer Consejo Latinoamericano de Medicina Tradicional." In 1993, the governmental program Fondo de Inversión Social (FIS) financed both the first issue of a new magazine, *Revista de Medicina Tradicional,* which promotes ideas and disseminates experiences in this emerging field, and related programs promoting traditional medicine with the Centros de Formación y Capacitación en Medicina Tradicional.

## Recovery of Native Languages

In recent decades, Native American languages have been utilized as resources by public and private entities to foster educational reform, indigenous cultural identity, organizational solidarity, and improved educational performance among rural populations.[5] The indigenous languages of Aymara, Quechua, and Guarani have been used for primary schooling and adult literacy programs.

These programs have had to break through biases embedded in the sociopolitical system of Bolivia. The movement toward supporting rural schooling as a citizenship right expanded with the 1952 social revolution under the Movimiento Nacional Revolucionario (MNR), and rural schools proliferated in the countryside. Revisionist social and political thinking, however, criticizes the MNR educational model as monolingual and essential to a "civilizing" mission with an implicit goal of assimilating the majority indigenous population into the Western cultural values of a criollo-mestizo urban political elite. The rural school became an important modernizing instrument of the state for transmitting criollo-mestizo citizenship values to successive generations of indigenous schoolchildren (Cárdenas 1991:49).[6] This educational policy imposed the language of the cities on rural schoolchildren, who spoke native languages almost exclusively (Huanca 1991b).

Critics have charged that the exclusive use of Spanish in the classroom eroded cultural identity (homogenizing vital indigenous culture into a common national framework) and impeded school performance and educational advancement for rural youth. This educational policy was another sign of the prevailing anti-indigenous biases of internal colonialism that characterized Bolivia's sociopolitical order. The policy of monolingualism exacerbated problems of high drop-out rates, grade repetition, underutilization of educational facilities, low self-esteem, and retarded educational achievement and advancement (CEE 1988:33).

In contrast to the state's monolingual educational models, during the 1980s the Catholic bishop's Comisión Episcopal sponsored bilingual educational experiments in Aymara and Quechua on a small scale in the rural primary schools. Another agency, the Instituto de Lengua y Cultura Aymara (ILCA), managed by Aymara professionals, promoted both use of the Aymara language and the study of Aymara linguistics in rural high schools of the northern altiplano.

The bilingual education programs' use of indigenous languages during the 1980s contrasts with the practices of earlier programs of the Summer Institute of Linguistics (SIL) and USAID during the 1970s. The latter's modernization approaches were geared toward expediting the assimilation of Spanish as the primary language and cultural assimilation into dominant, urban-based social values (Albó 1991:331). SIL in particular is infamous for the anti-indigenous rhetoric of its religious conversion methods and its literacy training programs for isolated ethnic groups in eastern Bolivia.

Important bilingual educational experiences are also taking place in the Cordillera province of Bolivia's Santa Cruz region. Within a network comprising 25 schools, 100 teachers, and 1,000 schoolchildren, students use Guarani for the first two grades, then combine Guarani with Spanish for subsequent primary school grades. The program draws from local history, culture, and ecology for its school texts to ground the curriculum in the life of the people of the area. The new bilingual education movement has focused on the concept *educación intercultural,* which replaces the practice of cultural domination with that of mutual respect between the Spanish and indigenous worlds and a revalorization of the indigenous cultural system in particular. Organizations such as the Centro de Investigación y Promoción del Campesino (CIPCA), TEKO-Guarani, UNICEF, the Fondo de Inversión Social (FIS) of the Bolivian government, and the Asamblea del Pueblo Guarani (APG), a federation of Guarani communities, have joined together to implement the project. UNICEF support has imparted prestige and legitimacy to this process, as well as providing essential resources for bilingual education within the Ministry of Education. For its part, the APG plays a key role in mobilizing local community support and involvement in the Cordillera province (Chumiray 1992; D'Emilio 1991a, 1991b).

In the Rayqapampa zone of western Cochabamba, CENDA, together with local peasant sindicatos, has established several bilingual primary schools employing local indigenous people as schoolteachers. By leveraging support from UNICEF, the national confederation of Bolivian peasant workers (CSUTCB), and the Ministry of Education, the rural sindicatos successfully defended their experimental school against pressures for closure from the national teachers' union. In the mid-1980s, the Centro Cultural Masis, a cultural center based in the city of Sucre, founded the first bilingual rural school (Quechua-Spanish) for the Chuquisaca region.

The bilingual education cultural movement has reoriented adult literacy programs as well. Prior to the 1980s, the Bolivian government had conducted its only national adult literacy campaign in the Spanish language. From 1982 to 1985, the Unidad Democrática Popular (UDP) became the first Bolivian government to use native languages in a national literacy campaign. To accomplish this, a new government entity, SENALEP, was established. SENALEP immediately organized commissions of advisors from among NGOs, indigenous groups, linguists, sociologists, educators, and anthropologists to design a new approach to adult literacy. This collaborative approach between public and NGO sectors generated bilingual literacy materials and training opportunities. The resulting texts had a strong and positive ethnocultural focus. For the first time in Bolivia's history, the national government recognized indigenous culture and language as part of the nation's patrimony (J. Rivera 1991:15).

SENALEP also engineered the signing of a presidential decree to unify and establish official alphabets for Aymara, Quechua, and Guarani (J. Rivera 1991:4). Although weak budgetary support and the crumbling UDP governing coalition ultimately undermined SENELAP's work, the literacy materials were put into use throughout the country by NGOs and grassroots organizations with their own programs.

Another instance of this new style of adult literacy program is that of TEKO-Guarani. Targeted toward thousands of Guarani speakers in the Cordillera province of Santa Cruz, this program was organized during the early 1990s. TEKO-Guarani conducted community-based research to recover 150 words from the local Guarani dialect for incorporation into the educational texts. TEKO-Guarani subsequently sent selected Guarani literacy trainers to provide identical programs for Guaranis confined to haciendas in the southern Chuquisaca region.

National political elites have also turned an interested eye toward bilingual education programs for rural communities. In 1994, the national congress passed a law giving official status to 15 indigenous languages (Cámara de Senadores 1992). The law enables indigenous peoples to be educated in their own languages as well as in Spanish. Bolivian ex-president Paz Zamora opened Bolivia's first bilingual education office within the Ministry of Education. Under his administration, with support from UNICEF, some 92 experimental bilingual primary schools for Aymara- and Quechua-speaking indigenous people were put into operation. In addition, the Equipo Técnico de Apoyo a la Reforma Educativa (ETARE), which was established to oversee Bolivian educational reform during the 1990s, made bilingual education central to its evolving plan. According to informed observers, the bilingual education cause has been one of the strongest rallying cries of the peasant and indigenous organizations in recent years (Albó 1991:331). The election of Víctor Hugo Cárdenas, one of the nation's visionaries and experts on bilingual and intercultural education, to the office of vice president in 1993 is a recent signal of widening support for bilingual education.

## Recovery of Native Textile Art

The rediscovery and recuperation of handwoven textile traditions by NGOs and artisans represents another departure from the rural modernization schemes of past decades. Since the 1950s, foreign, private, NGO, grassroots, and governmental organizations have taught skills throughout rural areas in knitting, crocheting, embroidering, appliquéing, sewing, and weaving (on pedal-operated looms of European origin) in order to promote income-generating handicrafts. Despite their makers' apparently low remuneration, handicrafts (for garments and decorative and functional household items) have become important elements of peasant household survival strategies. Income from handicrafts frequently is more important to a low-income family than earnings from agricultural and livestock activities, and weaving also provides additional clothing for rural families. Foreign funders, state agencies, local NGOs, artisan associations, production cooperatives, church parishes, and mothers' clubs have advanced handicraft production as an income-generating activity throughout the country.

Rural modernization strategies overlooked the economic development potential of handwoven textiles produced mostly by women on looms of pre-Columbian origin. The lack of promotion of an ethnic art form that was a vibrant hallmark of Andean culture reflects condescending, neocolonial attitudes toward Andean ethnic dress and related ceremonial uses in rural communities.[7] Andean textile traditions have felt the negative impact of the penetration of urban values and capitalist markets into rural communities. Modern market pressures led to the widespread replacement of articles of dress made from homespun wool with inexpensive, machine-made shirts, sweaters, and blouses of synthetic fiber. Clothing donations to Bolivia from Western nations have also undermined traditional dress styles.

By ignoring native textile work, foreign development agencies tended to overvalue imported technologies and resources. An example of this approach in a rural modernization project of the early 1970s was the German introduction of European looms and related weaving technologies and programs in the rural area of northern Chuquisaca, ironically in proximity to some of the most sophisticated native textile production in Bolivia. The weaving center produced handbags, wall hangings, and Colombian-style ponchos (*ruanas*) in an enterprise that died by the end of the decade from lack of sustained local interest and viable markets.

Although state and private agents of rural modernization failed to recognize the potential of native art, middlemen and shopkeepers in the cities of Sucre and La Paz perceived the commercial value of selling it to tourists. As in Peru, since the 1960s native textiles from highland areas have been acquired cheaply by itinerant middlemen and marketed to foreigners in the shops and sidewalks of Bolivian cities (West 1989). Over time, the textiles' demonstrated appeal to foreign tastes and interests had the side effect of spawning Bolivian collectors of native textiles.[8] It also led to large profits for international dealers of this art form, prompting NGOs such as Acción Cultural Loyola to sponsor textile exhibitions in the cities of Potosí and Sucre with the intent of diffusing awareness among indigenous people of the real value of their work.

The latest commercial trend in native textiles, mostly shawls (*awayo*) and overskirts (*ajus*), especially from the Norte de Potosí region, is refashioning the designs onto other products (e.g., handbags, duffle bags, backpacks, shirts, jackets, bicycle seats, vests, and leather goods such as shoes and briefcases). Urban entrepreneurs and artisans from Cochabamba, Potosí, and La Paz cut the textile pieces into fragments and apply them in a pastiche to a range of utilitarian products for tourists and export markets, including museum shops in the United States. This textile "recycling" allows the artisans to accent the exotic and ethnic, creating products with foreign tourist appeal.

Following the quincentennial of the Columbus landing, a domestic market for these products suddenly appeared among Bolivian students as an expression of national revalorization of the *awayo*. High-school and university students from Bolivia's major urban centers began wearing and using them in this new fad of ethnic identification. Yet despite the "revalorization" of native textiles for this commercial purpose, few economic or social benefits trickle down to the rural women weavers.

In contrast, a cultural revitalization effort that benefits rural weavers in multiple ways has taken place in the Chuquisaca and Santa Cruz regions. An NGO, Antropólogos del Sur Andino (ASUR), has mobilized women weavers and other members of local communities to increase their income significantly, to revive high-quality textile traditions, and to enhance cultural pride among the participants. In 1986, ASUR began a program to recover traditional textile production, first among the Jalq'a ethnic group and later among the Tarabuco. ASUR has assisted more than 400 women weavers from some six Jalq'a communities in recovering their original designs and techniques, which had been discontinued some 20 years earlier. In the neighboring Tarabuco area, they have worked with 300 weavers in seven communities to reverse textile decline and open better marketing channels. Led by anthropologists, ASUR bases its development strategy on in-depth ethnographic and ethnohistorical research (Dávalos, Cereceda, and Martínez 1992). With weavings from the Jalq'a, ASUR sponsored the first exhibition of native textiles in the National Museum of Art in La Paz.

The Jalq'a revival has enabled weavers to recover their original designs, color schemes, and associated production techniques while significantly increasing family income (Healy 1992). ASUR has mounted major traveling and permanent textile exhibitions both to educate the general public at home and abroad about Andean cultural values and to open textile markets for pieces of high quality. Indeed, ASUR has demonstrated that high standards of workmanship go together with increased income and cultural pride. Most recently, they have organized a grassroots federation that links the Jalq'a and Tarabuco weaving communities for joint training and organizational and marketing programs. The ASUR revival has caught the attention of agencies such as the Fondo de Inversión Social and the Fundación Cultural Quipus (which is launching Bolivia's largest folk-art museum), two national institutions with the resources to spread such developmental and cultural approaches to other Andean communities.

Another highland effort to revalorize textiles as a source of economic and cultural development began in the 1990s under the sponsorship of the Programa de Autodesarrollo Campesino (PAC) in the Bustillos province of northern Potosí. It has established production revitalization programs and published several books that highlight the textile traditions of the Chayautaka and Laymi ayllus (traditional territorial and kinship units) to bring recognition to this developmental and cultural resource (López, Flores, and Letoureux 1992).

The Centro de Investigación y Diseño de Artesanía Crucena (CIDAC), from the Santa Cruz region, began a similar revival among the Guarani women of the Izozog zone in the Bolivian Chaco and among Guarayo women from the indigenous town of Urubicha. Since 1984, the number of Guarani participants has grown from a dozen to over 60 weavers working with cotton tapestries and hammocks bearing the traditional Guarani motifs, and 150 women are making hammocks in Urubicha. Like ASUR, CIDAC has been able to revive high-quality weaving, conduct related sociocultural research, and foster self-management among weavers (via the grassroots organization ARTECAMPO) for their production and marketing program.

A different kind of textile recovery and revalorization took place in Potosí under the auspices of the NGO known as PIO XXII. To improve its adult literacy program for Quechua participants, PIO XXII encouraged women to conduct difficult first-time writing exercises by drawing symbols from their native textiles. This practice strengthened the cultural value of the textile traditions and affirmed their capacity to communicate social information. Elsewhere, the Fundación Cultural Quipus began producing gift-wrapping paper using the red and white textile designs of the Charazani ethnic group in the La Paz region. An NGO in Oruro recovered the animal and stick-figure motifs found in cave paintings from ancient pre-Columbian civilizations in Bolivia for use as designs in large woolen rugs that enjoyed popularity and commercial success in the capital city.

During the 1980s, there was a recovery of natural plant dyes for use in textiles and other products (e.g., food coloring). Plant dyes were essential ingredients in native textiles from pre-Columbian times into the nineteenth century. NGOs have published manuals on the use of natural dyes and introduced them through artisan training programs (Cajías and Fernández 1987). By using natural dyes, artisan producer associations in Cochabamba, Tarija, and La Paz have enhanced the foreign marketing appeal of their products. For example, Artesanías la Khochalita, comprising 560 rural and urban artisan families in the Cochabamba region, uses 10 different plants for colors in its sweaters, caps, socks, jackets, vests, rugs, and wall hangings. The best-known example of a natural dye product is cochineal, which produces 10 shades of red. Cochineal has become a Bolivian export, and NGOs and private entrepreneurs have promoted its production with loans and technical assistance for producers. Similarly, grassroots associations of peasant cochineal producers are playing key roles in expanding production and marketing.

## Recovery of Native Sociocultural Values

In addition to recovering Native American languages via adult literacy and rural schooling, NGOs and grassroots organizations such as peasant sindicatos have been promoting Andean sociocultural values in various ways. This social process frequently resembles an institutional shift from a "peasant" to a "Native American" approach for developmental and sociopolitical participation. The change in focus represents NGO recognition that cultural resources which revalorize ethnic identity are important factors for building grassroots organizations to address rural development problems.

An example of this phenomenon is the organization of new music and dance festivals, especially by NGOs working in the Andean area, typically involving thousands of peasant participants.[9] Festivals involve reviving not only native music, song, dance, and ethnic costumes but also a wide range of musical instruments themselves. The main festival event brings together music and dance groups from many indigenous communities at a central provincial location. It is frequently the culmination of numerous local festival competitions organized to prepare and select participants. These new festivals were endorsed as one of the most effective ways to maintain traditional Andean culture at a large workshop of indigenous leaders sponsored by the NGO UNITAS (UNITAS 1991:36).

Acción Cultural Loyola (ACLO), one of the largest rural development NGOs operating in the southern regions of Chuquisaca, Potosí, and Tarija, began organizing cultural festivals in 1983. These events, based on broad indigenous participation, often through close coordination with the rural sindicatos, have continued over the course of a decade. The Instituto Politécnico Tomás Katari (IPTK), one of Bolivia's largest NGOs in a microregion of Potosí, held an annual Festival Folklórico "Tomás Katari" during the 1980s (*En Marcha,* no. 182, 1985, p. 12). Another of the largest and most prestigious NGOs in Bolivia, CIPCA, also recently incorporated indigenous festivals as part of its rural development plan for the altiplano area. In the Chuquisaca region, the Centro Cultural Guarani-Quechua has been organizing festivals since the early 1980s to bring together lowland and highland indigenous peoples (Ulpana 1981).

In Santa Cruz in the early 1980s, the Casa de la Cultura, which had devoted most of its efforts to presenting music and dance from other nations to its urban public, organized the "Primer Festival de Culturas del Oriente Boliviano Sombrero e Sao." This experience led to biannual festivals and the region's first folkloric ballet. In the Norte de Potosí region, the Sociedad Andina Pusisuyu fosters community participation in traditional festivals during the agricultural production cycle as a strategy to help reconstruct an Andean cosmological vision of the stewardship of natural resources. Pusisuyu's Quechua agronomists support traditional festival music and dance for its inextricable links to the community's collective commitment to improving productive activities.

Perhaps the most sophisticated approach toward the recovery of traditional music and dance has been adopted by a Swiss-supported cultural institution, the Centro Portales, in its "Luz Milla Patiño" program based in the city of Cochabamba. From the late 1960s through the mid-1970s, Centro Portales's primary music promotional activity was awarding scholarships to Bolivian students to study classical music in Europe. Subsequently, Centro Portales changed its focus to sponsor concerts of indigenous and criollo music in urban Cochabamba. It began highlighting the "exotic" elements of indigenous culture for appreciation by a nonindigenous population. Its institutional effort at recovering these cultural expressions was to make long-playing records for commercial sale. In 1984, however, under the guidance of a Bolivian anthropologist, Centro Portales began working through grassroots organizations themselves—namely, sindicatos and ayllus—to hold festivals in provincial localities. This new arena of cultural revitalization has allowed indigenous leaders and NGOs from the selected regions to participate in year-long planning and research efforts that examine local music and dance history, its relationship with the production cycle, and views of community elders about festival traditions. This methodology builds intra-ethnic solidarity and appreciation for ethnic identity by allowing groups to learn of one another's traditions.

The regions of Potosí, Beni, and Tarija have also participated in this grassroots cultural revitalization program. In the Tarija region, for example, more than 40 local festivals took place in preparation for the main event, which attracted 3,000 participants. Thus the music festivals have mobilized the sindicatos and indigenous organizations toward another affirmation of their ethnic identity as a kind of collective defense against the cultural discrimination of urban Bolivia.

This form of cultural mobilization has inspired grassroots organizations (local and subregional sindicatos and indigenous ayllus) to organize their own festivals of traditional music and dance. In remote places such as the town of Poroma, the Nor Cinti province in Chuquisaca, and the province of Cercado in Oruro, new festivals have been organized since the later half of the 1980s to celebrate Andean ethnic identity (*En Marcha,* no. 182, 1985, p. 12; no. 242, 1990, pp. 6–7; no. 243, 1990, pp. 4, 12). National sindicato leader Juan de la Cruz Vilca helped revitalize a festival in the Oruro region that had disappeared at the end of the colonial period. The celebration of the Aymara New Year as an event in the national calendar has gained new popularity among various altiplano indigenous sindicato leaders and their advisors.

The massive entry of students from provincial areas and small towns into the national universities during the 1980s pushed the cultural recovery of Andean dances in urban arenas as well. Students have been reviving traditional carnival and other autochthonous dances in the cities of La Paz, Potosí, and Sucre in recent years. Student associations and academic departments organized the "Primera Entrada Folklórica Universitaria," which takes place annually and involves dozens of dance troupes with elaborate costumes and musical instruments and repertoires representing diverse Andean traditions. In addition to music and dance, the troupes display ethnic costumes in a virtual fashion show of traditional textiles. In Sucre at the end of the 1970s, the Centro Cultural Masis created a music and dance school that pioneered this massive dance participation during the 1980s. Also in the 1980s, the country's first youth orchestra using traditional Andean wind instruments offered concerts in Bolivian cities.

Another cultural recovery effort on behalf of Andean song took place among anthropologists and linguists working in the Norte de Potosí region. These fieldworkers rediscovered songs about specific food crops (potatoes, corn, wheat, green beans, barley, quinoa, oca, and coca) that indigenous women sang to the seeds as part of a planting ritual (Arnold and Yapita 1992:113). This tradition has been lost in many areas of the altiplano, but the authors identified its use among ethnic groups in Norte de Potosí through a *yatiri* (shaman) in the area.

The second Aymara newspaper (*Jayma*) appeared in La Paz during the 1980s, along with the first Aymara television show in the capital city. CENDA produced an important bilingual (Quechua-Spanish) newspaper for the rural indigenous population in the western Cochabamba region, and ACLO's rural newspaper, *En Marcha,* shifted its peasant and exclusively social-class-based focus increasingly toward cultural revitalization themes during the 1980s and early 1990s. Advances in indigenous media and social communication activities increased via the emergence of the Asociación Nacional de Comunicadores Nativas (ANCIN) in La Paz and Cochabamba to promote its cultural values and sponsor training programs for Native American announcers from educational and commercial radio stations.

In recent years, NGOs have fostered the recovery of poems, proverbs, and folktales as expressions of the indigenous oral literature.[10] The educational radio station, Radio San Gabriel (RSG), which has over two million Quechua and mostly Aymara listeners, started a radio show in the early 1980s that elicited write-in folktales from Aymara community members. These stories were read over the air during a 15-minute program. By the end of the decade, the popular show had grown to a half-hour weekly program and RSG had collected for its archives some 3,000 folktales. In other programs, RSG has collected nearly 1,000 Aymara poems and some 3,000 altiplano folk songs for its broadcasts promoting Andean culture. RSG has also sponsored competitions among the rural altiplano population for the best community histories as a way to offer incentives for cultural recovery. The many ways in which RSG has become popular as a voice of indigenous interests has led to its image in some quarters as the "Ministerio de Asuntos Aymaras."

An Aymara intelligentsia has introduced oral history techniques to enable Bolivia to recover an indigenous view of its history. Researchers for the Taller de Historia Oral Andino (THOA), for example, discovered a large indigenous underground network during the 1920s under the leadership of Santos Marka Thola, a traditional authority figure. Through the collection of oral histories, THOA revealed this impressive, unknown social movement and its charismatic leader who mobilized ayllus to exert pressure on state policy makers of the national oligarchy (THOA 1984). THOA turned this historical narrative into a radio novel with a following among millions of rural Aymara and Quechua listeners. In addition, the emergence of UNICEF's publishing program in bilingual education enabled the written oral history materials generated by THOA and other NGOs to be put into texts for rural public elementary schools.

An outstanding example of the use of the oral history genre is a revisionist work on the Chaco War (Arce 1987). Using stories by indigenous ex-combatants, the author provided a radically different perspective from those of the numerous military and diplomatic histories that had educated Bolivians about this historic episode. The indigenous point of view conveyed how a structure of internal colonialism functioned in wartime.

Related publication genres from oral history are the autobiographies and biographies of prominent indigenous or peasant personalities. Examples include the story of an Aymara woman (Condori 1989), the life stories of leaders from the Uru-Murato ethnic group in the Oruro altiplano (Miranda and Moricio 1992), the story of an indigenous leader of the Kallawayas during the agrarian reform (Ranaboldo 1987), and a forthcoming autobiography of Luciano Tapia, a leader in indigenous politics in Bolivia.

A different expression of cultural revitalization took place among the Guaranis of the southern Cordillera province. In 1992, for the first time, the indigenous federation Asamblea de Pueblo Guarani (APG) sponsored a 100-year anniversary commemoration of a local massacre of Guarani peoples (Centinario de la Masacre de Kuruyuki 1892–1992) to "recover and revalorize the cultural and historic memory of the Pueblo Guarani." The two-day event of marches, rallies, and festivities became the largest concentration of Guaranis within memory, bringing participants from as far away as the Argentine Chaco. The Bolivian president attended and listened to petitions for land rights made by APG leaders in the Guarani language. This event served not only to "recover and revalorize" the history of the Pueblo Guarani but also as an impulse for socioeconomic development in the region (Asamblea de Pueblo Guarani 1992).

Among the Aymara and Quechua peoples, the use of an indigenous flag, the *wiphala,* has increased greatly in recent years, especially in relation to the

Columbian quincentennial. The wiphala, which consists of a checkerboard pattern in a vibrant rainbow array of colors, was used by the protagonists in the indigenous anticolonial movements. It has again become the most visible and popular symbol of the regional and national peasant sindicato protest marches and indigenous dances performed on the streets for the "Entrada Folklórica Universitaria." The flag appears on pins, pamphlets, booklets, letterheads, calendars, publication covers, and posters to promote Andean cultural identity. NGO training courses provide know-how for making the wiphalas in a variety of sizes and forms.

Local sindicatos have passed formal resolutions to increase the use of wiphalas in meetings, assemblies, and congresses. New educational materials explain the origins and meanings of the wiphala (*El Pututu*, no. 19/20, 1991, pp. 1–2). A political party, El Movimiento Indio de Liberación Wiphala (MIL-Wiphala), formed in 1988, used the flag's name. By passing an executive decree in the 1990s establishing the wiphala as a national emblem and placing it in front of the presidential palace and the mayor's office in La Paz, the Bolivian state also participated in this revitalization of the Andean indigenous flag.

## Revitalization of Native Authority and Organizations

Bolivia's 1952 social revolution and agrarian reform displaced or marginalized indigenous organizations in many areas of the country. The sindicato form of organization became the grassroots vehicle for implementing sweeping land reforms in the highland areas of the country and for mediating between rural localities and state officials.[11] This apparent displacement of the ayllu by the sindicato was most common in areas of former hacienda landholdings. According to informed analysts, this anti-indigenous organizational model was part of MNR's "historic project" to assimilate the indigenous population into the mainstream of Latin American urban cultural values (S. Rivera 1990).

Forty years of rural sindicatos have failed, however, to eliminate traditional indigenous organizations such as the ayllu from the institutional landscape of Bolivia.[12] Pockets of traditional leadership and organizational forms persisted in regions such as Oruro, Potosí, Chuquisaca, Beni, and Santa Cruz, despite the pervasive political, social, and economic pressures to weaken and marginalize them. In some areas, they have continued side by side with the sindicatos in a pragmatic modus vivendi. The sindicato has served "outward" relations and representation while the ayllu handled the "internal" matters of indigenous and community affairs.

During the late 1980s a renewed appreciation emerged among various NGOs and grassroots organizations for traditional leadership roles and their holders (CSUTCB 1989). NGOs such as THOA, ASUR, and UNITAS sponsored workshops, seminars, and meetings that, for the first time in modern history, pulled together authorities from traditional indigenous organizations and backgrounds. Traditional leadership categories include, for example, ayllu leaders such as *jilacatas*, caciques, *amautas, kurakas,* and alcaldes. The objective behind this cultural promotion is to revive these leaders' roles and influence and to help gain broader acceptance for traditional organizational structures in national society.

THOA sponsored three meetings of traditional leaders from the La Paz and Oruro regions and subsequently published their testimonies and autobiographies in booklets for distribution throughout NGOs, radio stations, and grassroots organizational channels as part of its oral history recovery program (Huanca 1991a).

For the first time, the Confederación Única Sindical de Trabajadores Campesinos de Bolivia (CSUTCB) invited *las autoridades originarias* ("Jilacatas, Jilankos, Segundos, Capitanes, Ordinarios, Caciques") to participate in its national congress of peasant sindicatos (Pacheco 1992:156). The sindicato federations from the Oruro region also sponsored four "Cabildos de Autoridades Originarias" to raise their profile and participation in regional civic affairs (Pacheco 1992:342). There are also cases of prominent ex-sindicato leaders who switched orientations to identify with the spreading native movement. The best-known example is Génaro Flores, the former secretary general of CSUTCB for many years. Flores had run the course of his sindicato leadership career and was able to achieve new status and authority as an ayllu leader in his altiplano home province of Aroma.

El Programa de Autodesarrollo Campesino (PAC), organized by the Bolivian office of the European Economic Community (EEC), organized meetings and congresses of jilacatas and other communal authorities ("Los Encuentros Intercomunales") in the Oruro region during 1987 and 1988. An anthropologist on PAC's staff published a map of the remaining 140 ayllus in the region as part of an effort to locate these leaders and demonstrate their pervasiveness and legitimacy (Izko 1992:72). PAC's new institutional focus on the region's indigenous peoples also represented an effort to revitalize the leadership roles of this marginalized cultural sector.

The activities by NGOs, sindicatos, and other institutions to revive traditional authority positions flourished during the quincentenary events in 1992. In the regional capitals of Potosí and Chuquisaca, congresses of traditional leaders were held in the weeks leading up to October 12 (*En Marcha,* no. 264, 1992, p. 2). The Potosí meeting of Quechua speakers, La Primera Asamblea de Autoridades Originarias, organized a "Consejo de Autoridades" and among its proposals suggested that Bolivians "rebaptize the names of streets, plazas and provinces to reflect their traditional heroes" (*En Marcha,* no. 265, 1992, p. 5). On October 12, a march and rally of 50,000 indigenous participants, the largest Columbus Day protest in the hemisphere, took place in the capital city of La Paz. On the following day, CSUTCB sponsored the first national Asamblea de Nacionalidades. In the city of Sucre, the hemisphere's second largest protest was held, with 25,000 participants.

Another, related expression of such cultural revitalization occurs when NGOs, both national and foreign, shift from advocating conventional Western organizational forms to advocating indigenous organization in implementing their rural modernization programs.[13] PAC's experience in Oruro offers a good example of this change in thinking. In the ayllu areas of Oruro, instead of continuing to use spontaneously organized peasant "work groups" for channeling various technical services, PAC changed its approach to work through the ayllus themselves (Izko 1992:103). Moreover, this new interest in reenergizing the role of traditional indigenous organizations has involved development institutions from across the political spectrum.

CIPCA's regional office in the southern Chaco region represents a fascinating case of a left-wing organization reorienting its focus toward local organizations. Since the mid-seventies, CIPCA had promoted sindicatos in its rural development strategy for the Cordillera province of the Chaco. In 1983, however, responding to petitions in sindicato congresses from Guarani indigenous people themselves, CIPCA opted to change its grassroots organizational model for rural development to that of the *capitanía* (*mburuvicha*), the traditional Guarani form of organization. CIPCA subsequently helped the numerous capitanías to federate into a dynamic and effective microregional organization (APG) defending Guarani social and political interests and coordinating small-scale development projects. The APG subsequently undertook a campaign to reorganize Guarani communities into *mburuvichas* in the Tarija region and a similar campaign among peones in the haciendas of southern Chuquisaca. At the other end of the political spectrum, in the early 1980s the Christian Children's Fund, under an anthropologist advisor in a microzone of Oruro, changed its modus operandi from one of channeling financial support directly to individual families to one of supporting a traditional ayllu's socioeconomic development agenda.

In the Beni region, the NGO known by the acronym CIDDEBENI, which had advocated using forest resources to generate revenues for the regional economy, switched its orientation to champion the cabildos and their multiethnic federation's opposition to the powerful timber interests engaged in deforestation.[14] During the 1980s, the international donor agency Oxfam America began emphasizing indigenous-focused socioeconomic development projects. For example, in the Potosí region, it supported a local NGO working within the framework of the ayllu organization of the Yura ethnic group. Also, from the early 1980s forward, the Inter-American Foundation gave high priority to cultural revitalization in its project funding criteria.

In addition to NGOs, there are cases of grassroots organizations that have emerged with a stronger ethnonationalist ideology. The country's largest organization of quinoa producers, Asociación Nacional de Productores de Quinoa (ANAPQUI), exports to western Europe and the United States. Ayllus from the Oruro region belong to ANAPQUI, and the federation's organizational objectives include supporting the spread of the Andean ayllu as an important institution. In the Lake Titicaca basin, two grassroots organizations underwent an institutional facelift to recover their indigenous identity. In a series of meetings, the sindicato federation for Ingavi province passed resolutions to make its sindicato *secretarios* into *autoridades originarios* by adopting the full ayllu nomenclature for its most representative and important organization. In the nearby Jesus de Machaca zone of the altiplano, the local sindicato federation decided to reconstitute itself as an ayllu to protect its traditional land claims with colonial-period documents. In a similarly opportunistic move, an urban organization, the Federación Sindical Única de Trabajadores

Campesinos Radio Urbano y Sub-Urbano El Alto reconstituted itself as the Federación de Ayllus y Communidades del Distrito in an effort to eliminate its municipal tax burden (HOY, 20 November 1992, p. 8).

With the assistance of Bolivian anthropologists, the Federación del Ayllu del Sur de Oruru (FASOR) emerged in the Chayapata zone to revitalize the role of ayllus in that region (Pacheco 1992:282).[15] Representing ayllus from four provinces of Oruro, FASOR has pulled together Aymaras, Quechuas, Urus, and Chipaya ethnic groups with the objectives of defending their communal cultural values, recovering their history, installing a regional self-government involving traditional ayllu leaders such as caciques, jilacatas, and alcaldes comunales, strengthening the ayllu as a social and economic organization in rural development projects, and defending the region's natural resources (FASOR 1992). Similarly, in Bustillos province the seven ayllus organized themselves into a federation and operated their own radio station for several years. The effect of these activities was to focus organizational identity and promote an autonomous Andean ideology.

Indigenous women's organizations have also joined the cultural revitalization movement. In 1980, under the wing of the CSTUCB, the Federación Nacional de Mujeres Campesinas Bartolina Sisa emerged in a congress attended by 2,000 delegates from diverse ethnic groups of the highlands and lowlands (Cárdenas 1988:528). In the Bolivian workers' May Day parade of that year, for the first time in Bolivian history indigenous women in ethnic attire marched on a massive scale to demonstrate their presence and political thinking (Cárdenas 1988:529). In 1990, the women's federation reconstituted itself and added and emphasized indigenous elements in its program. It created new leadership positions overseeing territorial rights for *naciones originarias y indígenas* (Pacheco 1992:290). Its new program called for the revalorization of many expressions of its pluricultural identity, including native religion and the communal organization of the Andean ayllu (Pacheco 1992:304).

In the southern part of Chuquisaca, the Centro Cultural Guarani-Quechua organized the "Primer Encuentro de Pueblos y Comunidades de Guaranies de Chuquisaca" in the town of Muyupampa in 1987. In a region where traditional haciendas prevailed, this was a bold, unprecedented act of self-determination that aroused the concerns of landowners in the area. The meeting sought to revitalize the traditional capitanía organization and the role of the capitanes for the first time in the modern era.

During the 1980s, regional multiethnic federations emerged for the first time in the eastern Beni and Santa Cruz lowland regions. An NGO in Santa Cruz, Ayuda Para el Campesino del Oriente Boliviano (APCIB), helped organize the Central de Pueblos y Comunidades Indígenas del Oriente Boliviano (CIDOB), which in turn organized the Central de Pueblos Indígenos del Beni (CPIB) in the Beni region. These efforts established a new front of Bolivian social and political activism to defend and advance indigenous interests in the eastern lowlands.

In 1981, CIDOB organized a meeting called "Primer Encuentro de Pueblos Indígenos del Oriente Boliviano" and launched a program of local sustainable-development projects and legal land titling for its affiliates. In the Beni case, in the late 1980s CIDDEBENI, Catholic church activists, and indigenous leaders revitalized the traditional cabildo organizations through a series of meetings, seminars, congresses, and training programs culminating in the "Primer Congreso de Pueblos Indígenos del Beni" in 1989. The Beni mobilization effort ultimately paved the way for the historic "March for Territory and Dignity," which enjoyed broad and sympathetic mass media coverage and logistical and political support from some 100 NGO, church, grassroots, and human rights allies. This massive mobilization of indigenous groups and their supporters secured territorial rights to more than three million hectares in the Beni region for the ethnic minorities—Mojenos, Trinitarios, Chimanes, Sirionos, Ignacionos, Movimos, and Yucavaes—inhabiting the area (Contreras 1991; Jones 1990). In a grueling 34-day march, men, women, and children crossed both the tropical lowlands and the eastern slopes of the Andes to reach cheering throngs in the city of La Paz. The march had a favorable impact on public opinion for legitimizing indigenous territorial rights in Bolivia.

In the early 1990s, inspired by and allied with CPIB and CIDOB, small ethnic groups in the remote northeastern Pando department mobilized to form their first federation, the Central Indígena de Región Amazónica de Bolivia (CIRABO). The Cabinellos, Pacaguaros, Cacobos, Rdonos, Tacanos, and Yamilloguas formed the "Primer Consejo Étnico Amazónico" and held their first congress with 184 delegates representing dozens of communities. CIRABO's program also denounced encroaching timber interests and vigorously proclaimed the legitimacy of the indigenous people's territorial rights. The new federation's demands for rights to autonomously governed territory, for the use of indigenous language, and for the freedom to pursue a traditional life-style suggested a stronger sense of ethnic pride than that in many other rural groups in Bolivia (Albó 1990a:xxii). CEPIP and CIDOB in the 1990s jointly produced a draft proposal for the Bolivian congress of a new "Ley Indígena" (indigenous law) that spells out various indigenous rights in the Amazonian lowland areas. This document incorporates the right of direct representation by the leaders and organizations to the state (CIDOB 1992).

## Ethnopolitics at the National Level

The ethnonationalist fervor of recent years has even seeped into the national structures of Bolivia's largest political parties. For reasons of either opportunism or conversion to the cause, or a combination of the two, a variety of leaders and platforms from the most important political parties have shown new appreciation for the multinational composition of the population. An interesting case is the formerly co-governing Movimiento de Izquierda Revolucionario (MIR) party, which, since its founding in the early 1970s, had ignored the ethnic-cultural themes in its party documents and programs. As late as the presidential campaign of 1989, the leader of MIR, Jaime Paz Zamora, had not evinced a particular interest in this political focus. After he had been in office for several years, however, the indigenous cause became one of the central themes in his political discourse, especially in the international arena. The impetus to change came in part from the national consciousness-raising experience of the March for Territory and Dignity. Another stimulus was the growing international context of environmental and Native American concerns and the growing financial resources available to Bolivia for the former. At the same time, Paz Zamora successfully spearheaded a campaign among Latin American presidents for the creation of an international Indigenous Peoples Fund based in La Paz. He also refused to sponsor an official national celebration of Columbus Day in 1992.

The MNR party, architect of the 1952 social revolution—and, according to authors cited in this chapter, sponsor of programs (schools and sindicatos) to assimilate the indigenous population and undermine its cultural identity—also recently discovered indigenous issues. During Bolivia's 1993 presidential election, the MNR convention nominated Víctor Hugo Cárdenas, an Aymara from the minuscule Movimiento Revolucionario Tupak Katari–Liberación party (MRTK–L) as the vice-presidential running mate to Gonzalo Sánchez de Lozada. Cárdenas, one of the leading Aymara intellectuals and ideologues, has added bilingual education, indigenous territorial rights, and a program supporting the legal recognition of traditional indigenous organization to the MNR's political agenda (Cárdenas, personal communication, 1994). During the 1993 campaign, Sánchez de Lozada, for the first time in his political career, espoused Cárdenas's ethnopolitical paradigm in his public discourse on the road to his presidential victory.

On August 5, 1993, an unprecedented, unofficial "inauguration" took place in a La Paz coliseum one day prior to the official event. It brought together 2,000 jilacatas, amautas, caciques, and other indigenous leaders from various regions and included elaborate ritual ceremonies for the installation of the new president and vice president, outfitted for the occasion in Andean ponchos.

The Movimiento de Bolivia Libre (MBL), Bolivia's strongest party of the political left, was the earliest and most impressive in its use of a pro-indigenous discourse. Although MBL's founding platform in 1983 embraced only "social class" issues, by 1985 the multinational character of the Bolivian masses had surged to front and center of its party program (MBL 1988:17).[16] MBL introduced into the national congress a Ley de Comunidades Campesinas y Indígenas that would empower the highland communities with new territorial rights, legal status, and a political role in the state apparatus (Urioste 1991). MBL has advocated the increasingly popular view among indigenous leaders that the Andean community has existed much longer than the state and so is entitled to greater political legitimacy and increased access to resources from the national government. MBL has been the most active among the four principal political parties of Bolivia in advancing debates and proposals on the issue of constitutional reform leading to a "plurinational" state.

The constitutional reform movement for the plurinational and pluricultural state has also gained momentum from the work of independent activists and influential NGOs. UNITAS, the largest network of NGOs in Bolivia, sponsored a series of seminars between 1988 and 1989 in different regions for leaders from dozens of grassroots organizations and NGOs, to deepen the "discovery" of Bolivia's multinational and pluricultural character (UNITAS 1991:161). For UNITAS, the peasantry—Bolivia's largest labor group—had become transformed into the new "nationalities" by the end of the 1980s. With the closure of state mines during the mid–1980s, the combative mine workers' unions, which had been the vanguard of popular movements in Bolivia, went into eclipse. Its demise had a substantial negative impact on these social movements, which suffered from a marked decline in national visibility, political influence, and popular prestige. But by the end of the 1980s, UNITAS had discovered a new road forward for social and political change in the rising ethnonationalism of the countryside.

CIPCA also made a major contribution in advancing the cause of the plurinational and pluricultural state (CIPCA 1992). It assembled a volume that offers a detailed blueprint for restructuring the Bolivian state in rural areas in accordance with their plurinational and pluricultural social character (CIPCA 1992). This 250-page proposal, produced through a series of workshops and seminars with peasant and indigenous leaders and intellectual activists, includes propositions for juridical reform and agricultural, linguistic, educational, and labor policies. The proposal elevates the debate on concepts such as microregional planning units, self-managed indigenous development organizations, state recognition for autonomous indigenous political authorities, and increased indigenous representation in the national seat of power.

The Aymara NGO Comunidad Andino de Desarrollo Agropecuario (CADA), in a 20-page bulletin, formulated a proposal ("anteproyecto de ley de naciones, ayllus, y comunidades") calling for new territorial boundaries in the highlands based on the integration of Andean ecosystems and a political empowering of the Andean ayllu and rural communities.

## Conclusion

Bolivia's cultural revitalization movement has diffused far and wide, and its manifestations reach from the macro down to the micro levels of society. The tempo of related activity increased in recent years in response to social and political activism focused on the 500-year anniversary of Columbus's invasion of the Americas. Many cultural revitalization activities discussed in this chapter emerged during the 1980s. Examples include the rediscovery and recuperation of native languages, textile arts and dyes, tree species, medicinal plants, raised-field agricultural technology, indigenous authority positions and organizations, and Andean crops such as bitter potatoes, coca, and amaranth. That decade witnessed many vigorous revitalization initiatives—the first meetings, assemblies, roundtables, congresses, and festivals—that helped challenge and sometimes modify conventional modernization schemes for rural development and politics. A spirit of renewal, invention, and reinvention has spread in interesting and surprising ways.

The periods in which these initiatives were launched, however, do exhibit some variation. For quinoa and tarwi, seeds were planted in the late 1970s as a spin-off from related activities in neighboring Peru. The revitalization of traditional music and dance via new Andean festivals began in the mid–1970s, but its association with grassroots indigenous mobilization through microregional and regional music festivals emerged more recently.

The activism and changing perspectives of a small but influential group of NGOs has propelled much of the rediscovery and recovery process. Without their appearance on the rural institutional landscape, no doubt many fewer indigenous communities would have organized around these themes, and the state-led rural modernization and political representation models would have remained much less challenged. The existence of this core of culturally conscious NGOs, together with international organizations such as UNICEF, also means that the publications on topics of cultural revitalization discussed in this chapter will be put to use in organizational strategies, programs, and training workshops among indigenous populations. This reduces the likelihood that such publications will languish unopened in libraries or on individuals' bookshelves.

Although adopting one element of the revitalization of rural society (e.g., supporting native food crops) does not necessarily imply that an NGO has embraced other elements (e.g., restoring traditional organizations), it does represent a changing direction with the openness to embrace a wider perspective in the future. In recent years, a growing group of NGOs has broken with imported modernization models to view rural Bolivians and the utilization of local resources in a new way. This is a remarkable change, given the strong mutual reinforcement between Bolivia's internal colonialism and the Western development paradigm imposed between 1940 and 1980. The shift in thinking reflects both the poor results of past rural modernization programs and the external influences of the international environmental movement, worldwide clamor for indigenous rights, and changing funding preferences from more culturally and historically sensitive foreign donors. And despite heavy, continued dependence upon foreign donors, NGOs have been designing imaginative microregional development strategies that emphasize self-reliance and sensitivity to environmental concerns. Just as foreign funding had enormous influence over the misguided rural modernization strategies in the past, western European and United States entities supporting NGOs and grassroots organizations have been contributing to this change in focus toward indigenous resources, values, and knowledge.

The return of liberal democracy to Bolivia in 1982, which restored the rights of free association and free speech, was another key element underlying this continuing cultural revitalization. An important conclusion from this overview is that grassroots organizations have played a central role in the cultural recovery and rediscovery process. Bolivia's return to democracy helped create a national political and social context that opened opportunities for popular participation by the indigenous rural majority.

The Aymara Katarismo movement pushed its ethnonationalist agenda through rural sindicatos and new political parties to help open the gateway to greater grassroots participation by the rural indigenous majority. Subsequently, cultural revitalization accelerated via the active participation of sindicatos, ayllus, cabildos, capitanías, new indigenous federations for the eastern lowlands and the highlands, an indigenous women's organization at the national level, and new producer associations for Andean crops such as tarwi, quinoa, coca, and amaranth. Progress toward an indigenous-based paradigm has advanced impressively thanks to a majority native population that had achieved important citizenship rights through Bolivia's social revolution in 1952. Ironically, export and tourist markets have sometimes played a positive role in encouraging greater local self-reliance and self-respect. The recovery of native textile arts, natural dyes, the coca leaf, and quinoa has been bolstered by these external linkages. Thus, like the influences of the international environmental movement and the Columbian quincentennial, some aspects of Bolivia's external dependency can be turned to its advantage.

The beginnings of a new developmental and political paradigm for Bolivia are under way and gaining force. The national cultural revitalization movement has delivered to Bolivia its first Native American vice president. Various institutions discussed in this chapter have had to unlearn conventional rural modernization and criollo political party strategies. These institutions have begun to relearn and then reaffirm many aspects of indigenous life. The cumulative efforts discussed here might appear meager in the face of the accelerated decline of indigenous communities resulting from prevailing national policies and global economic forces. Yet the evidence suggests that a new path of self-rediscovery has opened, a path that can lead to more profound understanding and appreciation of vital indigenous resources of the past that are still available for the future.

## Notes

1. A pioneering NGO in cultural promotion, which in retrospect appeared to be ahead of its time, was the Instituto de Investigación Cultural para la Educación Popular (INDICEP), based in the altiplano city of Oruro. INDICEP implemented a number of cultural revitalization activities in literacy, popular education, radio shows, rural organizing, and development between 1966 and 1981 (Badani 1991). For example, INDICEP began the altiplano campaign to recognize indigenous heroes such as eighteenth-century anticolonial rebel leaders Tupak Katari and Bartolina Sisa. INDICEP became the forerunner of efforts a decade later to revalorize native languages, history, literature, and music (Bandani 1991). The La Paz office of the Centro de Investigación y Promoción del Campesino (CIPCA) during the 1970s also introduced important radio shows (based upon folktales) with an Andean cultural focus and, through Xavier Albó and Aymara staff members, contributed important publications on Aymara nationalism and offered popular education programs and support for indigenous ethnic identity and a revisionist history.

2. The Katarista phenomenon has been amply documented in the literature on Bolivian peasant movements. The name is taken from that of the anticolonial rebel leader Tupak Katari. Katarismo, led by Aymara nationalists, first emerged in the early 1970s as an underground sindicato movement. Subsequently, in the late 1970s, it spearheaded the "democratization" and independence of the national peasant sindicato movement, which had been manipulated by military governments during a 16-year period. The Katarismo movement also spawned several small political parties that placed two of their members in the national congress between 1985 and 1989. In retrospect, it is apparent that the Kataristas were forerunners of the cultural revitalization covered in this chapter, contributing greatly to the fertile conditions for the recovery of indigenous values latent in the Bolivian countryside. Because of

the ample existing literature, however, I do not analyze here the role of Katarismo during the 1970s and 1980s (see Albó 1983, 1991; Cárdenas 1988; Pacheco 1992; S. Rivera 1987).

3. A recent World Bank study showed that urban indigenous people in Bolivia have 3.4 fewer years in school and earn 60 percent less than the nonindigenous group (Psacharopoulos 1992).

4. Andean archaeological, ethnographic, ethnohistoric, botanical, and agronomy research has shown the impressive sophistication of Andean agricultural management schemes under harsh and varying altitudinal and climatic conditions. The results of such research as described in this book offer a trenchant example. Farming in the rugged Andean environments ranging between 2,000 and 4,000 meters above sea level requires detailed knowledge by indigenous farmers about the microclimatic zones and adaptations of plant species (Brush and Taylor 1993; Mamani 1988). Andean farmers have watched their production systems decline since the European conquest while still developing effective survival strategies and ways to supply 80 percent of the country's agricultural output.

5. It should be mentioned that the educational radio stations under ERBOL in Bolivia have been pioneers in the use of native languages. Their efforts over decades have contributed greatly to a revalorization of this and many other cultural resources (Albó 1977). It is curious, however, that the radio stations did not use native languages in their adult literacy programs.

6. Historically, there have been important experiences in indigenous-focused education in Bolivia, both above and below ground. The teacher's college of Warisata conducted an Andean, ayllu-focused form of training during the 1930s. Also, clandestine pro-indigenous schools were organized in Aymara communities at earlier times in the twentieth century (Cárdenas 1992:6). Albó and Layme (1993:19) identified the use of Aymara song books for short periods in the rural schools.

7. On the streets of Bolivian cities, it is common for indigenous people in traditional ethnic dress to face insults, ridicule, and even physical abuse for showing their cultural identity.

8. The tremendous interest shown by foreign dealers, collectors, and tourists since the 1970s in purchasing nineteenth- and twentieth-century textiles contributed to the revalorization of this ethnic art among Bolivians. This demand created new markets for older textiles in the Bolivian cities of La Paz, Sucre, and Potosí and led middlemen to comb rural fairs and communities in pursuit of textiles that could be resold in high-priced Bolivian and international markets. Also, the recovery of colonial textiles stolen from the Potosí communities of Coroma received considerable media attention, creating greater awareness of the importance of this cultural patrimony among organizations such as CSUTCB. Scholars in the United States have written Ph.D. dissertations on textiles, and a major book was published giving an impressive overview of textile production in Bolivia (Gisbert, Arze, and Cajías 1987). During the late 1980s and early 1990s, textiles appeared more frequently on the covers of Bolivian books, calendars, and posters as expressions of cultural revitalization of this art form.

9. A recent anthology, *Literatura Aymara: Antología* (Albó and Layme 1993), presents an excellent overview and a rich set of examples of colonial prose, origin myths, folktales, historic narratives, political texts, ritual oratory, drama, and radio novels.

10. Public development corporations in the Chuquisaca and Potosí regions also began to sponsor music and dance festivals. These are mostly top-down efforts, however, organized to offer folklore to tourists. During the 1970s, there were many other manifestations of the revitalization of Andean music. Bolivian university students, for example, began to revalorize music and other Andean cultural expressions such as using the poncho worn by indigenous people in the countryside.

11. Albó has argued that some Andean communal practices continued under the guise of the sindicato organizational form, implying that it would be a mistake to label it an alien institution. In the northern altiplano, for example, the sindicato's secretary general is frequently just a new name for the indigenous jilacata (Carter and Albó 1988:486). Similarly, leadership rotational practices bear some resemblance to norms under the ayllus of the nineteenth and twentieth centuries.

12. Sylvia Rivera (1990:100) describes the ayllu as a territorial and kinship unit that is part of a larger ethnic unit in a framework based on a large dual organization of two moieties that are complementary opposites (above-below; masculine-feminine; older-younger). Ayllus exist in the departments of Chuquisaca and Oruro, generally impoverished and geographically isolated areas. According to informed observers, however, the ayllus have undergone modifications over the past centuries. They have suffered a reduction in size, loss of population through the tax and labor policies of the colonial and Republican governments, and losses of some organizational and symbolic principles (Carter and Albó 1988; Rasnake 1988).

13. Sylvia Rivera (1990) offers a blistering critique of some NGOs for supporting sindicatos when ayllus were the most representative social organization available, as well as for being oblivious to deeply seated Andean values and ayllu leadership structures while fostering clientism and political manipulation through the sindicato structure. Another work with material relevant to this argument in the case of Oruro is that about Ayllu Sartani (Aruwiyiri 1992). Sonia Montaño (1992) argues that urban women's clubs set up to distribute international food aid serve as a powerful instrument for assimilating Aymara women into the dominant neocolonial values of Bolivian society.

14. During a hundred-year period beginning in 1667, the Jesuits organized cabildos as civil-religious structures for the inhabitants of the region. Anthropologists such as Jim Jones (1990) who have long experience in the area argue that there are no known pre-Hispanic organizations that could be revived and enable the Beni ethnic groups to participate in a modern political context. Thus, in helping to articulate the cultural forms and social cohesiveness of the Beni communities for 200 years, the cabildos have a strong claim to be both representative and "indigenous."

15. The history of colonialism in the Andes is the story of the breaking down of large ethnic political entities into smaller units of organization. Kingdoms, large ayllus, and even a "confederation" of ayllus called the Charcas Confederation were prominent during the sixteenth century (Abercrombie 1991:102; Rasnake 1988). The effort under way to organize ayllu federations, then, is a reinvention of sorts of an older political unit for a different time and place.

16. MBL's ideological shift toward embracing this ethnonationalism was in part a reflection of its political paradigm in finding new allies once it broke off from the MIR party in 1983. In 1985, MBL began establishing alliances with several small Katarista parties to expand its popular base in the altiplano region (Juan Granada, personal communication, 1993).

# 12

# Theoretical Orientations and Implications of the Proyecto Wila Jawira Research Program

ALAN L. KOLATA

The introductory chapter to this book sketched the fundamental lineaments of our theoretical and interpretive positions concerning Tiwanaku as a state society and, more narrowly, the nature and organization of its sustaining agricultural systems. In this concluding chapter, I want to expand upon some elements of general social theory that influenced the manner in which we framed our research questions—both the specific, empirical question of how Tiwanaku organized its agricultural landscapes and the general interpretive question of what implications these organizational forms held for authority and decision making in the Tiwanaku state. It is my contention that the particular spatio-temporal and social structure of Tiwanaku's sustaining hinterland reflects, both directly and indirectly, pervasive organizational principles in Tiwanaku society, at least in the period of the mature state from about A.D. 400 to 1000.

The organizational principles that govern intensive agricultural production have been a central concern in several influential theoretical formulations regarding the origins and maintenance of archaic states (among others, Boserup 1965; Coward 1979; Downing and Gibson 1974; Hunt 1988; Mitchell 1973, 1977; Sanders and Price 1968; Steward 1955; Wittfogel 1938, 1957). Wittfogel's (1957) hypothesis generated a particularly passionate body of literature (see Mitchell 1973 for an excellent summary). Wittfogel postulated that large-scale irrigation requires centralized management of the hydraulic infrastructure, and he explained the origins of agrarian state societies in arid lands in terms of increased political integration resulting from the need for centralized control of irrigation. The current consensus on the Wittfogel hypothesis rejects both the assumption that large-scale hydraulic works presuppose the presence of centralized authority and the causal inference linking the emergence of state societies with the organizational requirements of such hydraulic infrastructures (Hunt 1988; Mitchell 1973, 1977).

Justifiably, contemporary scholars of early state societies view the degree of centralization in intensive agricultural systems as highly variable, and they demonstrate, in many cases, that the organization of such systems lies outside the purview of state bureaucracies (Netherly 1984) or even excludes explicitly political institutions and authorities from the decision-making apparatus altogether (Lansing 1991). Rather than looking to central authorities for the principles that structured intensive agricultural production in these states (the "top-down" perspective), these scholars emphasize the importance of recognizing the organizational initiatives and context-sensitive strategies of local farmers (the "bottom-up" perspective). In general, scholars immersed in the bottom-up perspective seem to accept that intensive systems of agricultural production require some form of weakly hierarchical organization, but they also believe that these traditional states tended to use the minimum amount of organization necessary to maintain the hydraulic infrastructure while retaining a social mechanism for seeking higher levels of organization when necessary (for regional dispute resolution, disaster response, and the like). Certain recent literature in Andean archaeology and ethnohistory closely follows this new orthodoxy, asserting the dominance of local kin groups rather than hierarchical, supracommunity state authority in the organization of agricultural production (Erickson 1988a; Graffam 1990, 1992; Netherly 1984; see also Schaedel [1988], who extends this analysis to Andean cosmology and worldview).

Although this perspective provides a necessary corrective to a rigid, Wittfogelian formulation, its uncritical application can lead to an equally dogmatic position that overlooks or even denies the reality of centralized state action on local communities in Andean societies. Neither a categorical top-down nor a bottom-up frame of reference alone can account for the multiple forms of social linkages that produced intensive systems of agricultural production and provided for the reproduction of society as a whole. Bureaucratic and nonbureaucratic, centralized and uncentralized forms of organization of intensive agricultural production can, and probably always did, coexist in time and space in most agrarian states. Therefore, at any given point in the history of a state society, it is likely that both frames of reference can provide essential insights into the dynamic interaction between local communities and centralized authorities. The principles and practices determining the exercise of authority in these states were always and everywhere a dynamic, context-specific proposition, set in motion by the multiple historical particularities of place, time, and social identities.

Yet all understanding of the internal dynamics of traditional states is not to be found merely in such particularities, which can be captured only rarely in the haphazardly preserved vignettes of documentary traditions. Underneath this surface of contingency, of almost overwhelming local historical diversity, there is a common fabric of organizational possibilities. This common fabric is what delimits the potential for social complexity and productive capacities in the traditional state. The environmental limits to demographic expansion, the pragmatics of production, and the burden of logistics set real constraints on the scale and complexity of human organization.

These constraints are physical, but they are, of course, culturally and socially mediated. To paraphrase Maurice Godelier (1988:35), the systems of representation that individuals and groups, as members of a given society, make of their environment are the fundamental grounds from which they act upon it, and furthermore, "the social perception of an environment consists not only of more or less exact representations of the constraints upon the functioning of technical and economic systems, but also of value judgements (positive, negative or neutral) and phantasmic beliefs." That is, human perception of the shifting relationship between constraint and possibility is the analytically relevant variable. In this conception, both empirical (that is, sensory-derived) and nonempirical realities hold equivalent weight (Burch 1971). Still, undergirding these perceptions, attitudes, and human psychological states are ultimate limits embedded in the material world. Cognitive processes and psychological states define the human terms of engagement with the environment, but the physical constraints of the material world remain irreducible social facts. These constraints are described, acted upon, understood, and uniquely integrated into the cultural matrix of each society, but they can never be defined away.

Phrased in another way, culture has the power to shape the public perception and social meaning of material constraints—to incorporate and encapsulate them in a system of meaning—but culture cannot significantly alter the *substance* of those constraints. For instance, the chronic drought that we have identified as the proximate cause of the disintegration of Tiwanaku's intensive agroecosystems had an unambiguous impact on the character of altiplano societies in the post–A.D. 1000 social environment. This severe environmental constraint forced widespread deurbanization and population disaggregation. Limited technological responses to these conditions were available to the people of the altiplano, but the physical fact of chronic drought could not simply be symboled away: "pure culture" alone is not instrumentally effective. Although environmental and physical constraints are enormously elastic and subject to cultural manipulation, they remain constraints nonetheless.

Much human, intellectual, and social energy has

been spent precisely on pushing the limits of natural and socially constructed constraints. In agrarian states, this is the instrumental meaning of agricultural intensification. Intensification proceeds both through technological innovation, which facilitates a positive transformation of the natural environment (as viewed from the human frame of reference of increasing capacity to harness energy), and through social innovation, the productive restructuring of human capital. Many of the specifics of Tiwanaku agricultural intensification entailing these two interpenetrating types of innovation have been outlined in this volume.

The top-down versus bottom-up debate (in the Andeanist literature, at least) has been muddled also by terminological confusions and the imputation of inappropriate or excessively narrow meanings to such terms as "bureaucracy" and "centralization of authority." Scholars adhering to the "populist," bottom-up perspective frequently equate the emergence of centralized authority with bureaucracies and then point out, with justification, that formal bureaucracies were exceedingly rare in traditional states. The implications of this argument are straightforward: most decision making in traditional states was decentralized, remaining in the hands of local corporate groups, and therefore the impact of the state on local societies was limited to "surface" extraction of tribute and periodic labor service. From this perspective, the underlying structure and functioning of local social groups remains nearly unaltered by the alien powers of the state.

The notion that an expansive state society would have only superficial impact on local communities strikes me as an oddly anachronistic theoretical framework that, in some senses, echoes the hoary concept of peasant societies as closed, corporate communities encapsulated in a kind of cultural amber seeping out of habitual social action. The concept inappropriately emphasizes the overbearing power of tradition in these societies, denies them history, and renders them motionless. To approach a better understanding of the dynamic relationships between the state and local communities, we must reformulate such static, ahistorical models.

First, it is important to be clear about the various bases and mechanisms that existed for transmitting and exchanging power from city to countryside and from elites to commoners in agrarian states. We must acknowledge that the relationship between such states and local communities was not invariably an oppressive, extractive proposition. As I noted in chapter 1, states and local communities are always counterpoised in a dynamic of mutualism. Centralized states exert directive control over regional economies and in the process impinge on the traditional prerogatives and autonomy of local communities, but they also insert local communities into more inclusive social and economic worlds. States create dynamic interconnections among diverse communities and in doing so accelerate local economic development. States, in turn, by identifying themselves as the agents of development, derive legitimacy, prestige, and an intensification of their social power (Ludden 1985).

Second, the centralization of authority in traditional states does not invariably imply the (Western-style) bureaucratization of power. Still less does it signal the emergence of formal bureaucracies in the modern sense of the term. We can readily conceive of a broad spectrum of institutional possibilities for the expression and exercise of authority that operated simultaneously in early state societies, a spectrum that ran from localized relations of kinship to more remote relations framed around consensual or coerced associations between rulers and subject populations. Indeed, with respect to the relationship between bureaucracies and centralization of authority, I would argue the exact obverse of the position taken by the bottom-up populists. In some sense, rather than being an oppressive vehicle for the centralization of authority and the application of irresistible, arbitrary force, bureaucracies paradoxically generate social relations that are inherently democratizing and decentering. Decision making emanates effectively not from a central locus or personage but from a diffuse penumbra of legitimate authority applied locally and subject to considerable, and potentially idiosyncratic, interpretation by its local agents. Bribes, payoffs, sweetheart deals, favoritism, creative cooking of administrative books, and collusion between taxpayers and petty officials are all standard features of life under "impersonal" bureaucracies. Most people living in bureaucratic systems are articulated with the state at the base level of the administrative hierarchy. That is, they come into contact consistently with the lowest echelon of bureaucrats. These highly variegated, local textures in the administration of bureaucracies open wide the possibilities of covert resistance to state mandates and exactions. The ideal rationality in which bureaucracies efficiently administer edicts from the center withers under the corrosive assault of real life.

A brief digression to explore certain classic sociological concepts of bureaucratic and nonbureaucratic forms of authority will serve to further clarify this central issue. As formulated in Max Weber's defining work, *Wirtschaft und Gesellschaft. Grundrisse der verstehenden Soziologie,* published in English as *Economy and Society,* some salient characteristics of modern bureaucracy include a

principle of official *jurisdictional areas,* which are generally ordered by rules, that is, by laws or administrative regulation. This means: (1) The regular activities required for the purposes of the bureaucratically governed structure are assigned as official duties. (2) The authority to give the commands required for the discharge of these duties is distributed in a stable way and is strictly delimited by rules concerning the coercive means, physical, sacerdotal, or otherwise, which may be placed at the disposal of officials. (3) Methodical provision is made for the regular and continuous fulfillment of these duties and for the exercise of the corresponding rights. . . . Bureaucracy, thus understood, is fully developed in political and ecclesiastical communities only in the modern state. (Weber 1978:956, emphasis in the original)

As Weber (1978:956) comments in continuation:

Permanent agencies, with fixed jurisdiction, are not the historical rule but rather the exception. This is even true of large political structures such as those of the ancient Orient, the Germanic and Mongolian empires of conquest, and of many feudal states. In all these cases, the ruler executes the most important measures through personal trustees, table-companions, or court-servants. Their commissions and powers are not precisely delimited and are temporarily called into being for each case.

I suggest that the situation was similar in native Andean states like Tiwanaku, where permanent agencies with distinct jurisdictions never emerged or were perhaps only weakly developed in the formal network of command.

Weber's concept of the fully modern bureaucracy requires that the state explicitly articulate a rational theory of public administration. That is, the power of the state over the individual is exercised through a system of formal rules, applied abstractly and without conscious reference to the actors' social personae and statuses. This kind of abstract regulation of state affairs is a notion alien to the native states of the Americas and probably to most archaic states of the world. But absence of a rationalizing theory of public administration does not necessarily imply the arbitrary, ad hoc exercise of power, the de facto abrogation of effective power to local authorities, or a lesser degree of centralization of authority. Rather, the principles of the exercise of authority in these traditional states are radically different from those embedded in Western concepts of bureaucracy. What might these alternative principles be?

Again, Weber (1978:1006), drawing on his mastery of the historical sources bearing on the ancient and medieval Western world and on his peculiar acuity in eliciting transcultural, transtemporal sociological categories, provides us with a key insight in his discussion of patrimonial forms of authority as contrasted with bureaucratic forms of domination.

Among the prebureaucratic types of domination, the most important one by far is patriarchal domination. Essentially it is based not on the official's commitment to an impersonal purpose and not on obedience to abstract norms, but on strictly personal loyalty. The roots of patriarchal domination grow out of the master's authority over his household. Such personal authority has in common with impersonally oriented bureaucratic domination stability and an "everyday character." Moreover, both ultimately find their inner support in the subjects' compliance with norms. But under bureaucratic domination these norms are established rationally, appeal to the sense of abstract legality, and presuppose technical training; under patriarchal domination the norms derive from tradition: the belief in the inviolability of that which has existed from time out of mind.

Weber treats patrimonial authority as a special case (and an extension beyond the parochial domain of the household) of the more ubiquitous forms of patriarchal domination. One of his prime examples of patrimonial authority elaborated into an expansive state formation is that of pharaonic Egypt. He also mentions the Incas in passing. Weber comments (1978:1013) that all of the subject territories and populations of pharaonic Egypt might be considered "a single tremendous *oikos* ruled patrimonially by the pharaoh" (*oikos* here refers to the large, authoritarian household of a prince or manorial lord; see Weber 1978:381). As Wheatley notes (1971:52), one of the characteristics of patrimonial authority as conceived by Weber was that the ruler (the supreme patriarch, as it were) "treats all political administration as his personal affair, while the officials, appointed by the ruler on the basis of his personal confidence in them, in turn regard their administrative operations as a personal service to their ruler in a context of duty and respect."

Similarly, with respect to the obligations of the subject populations, Weber (1978:1014) remarks that

> in the patrimonial state the most fundamental obligation of the subjects is the material maintenance of the ruler, just as is the case in a patrimonial household; again the difference is only one of degree. At first, this provisioning takes the form of honorary gifts and of support in special cases, in accordance with the spirit of intermittent political action. However, with the increasing continuity and rationalization of political authority these obligations became more and more comprehensive.

And so the fundamental lineaments of patrimonial authority derive from sentiments of personal obligation reinforced by tradition. The subjects' personal obligations to a ruler may be either coerced or consensual, or they may derive in the first instance from relations of kinship. Consanguineal bonds of kinship within dynastic lines, affinal, indirect, remote, or fictive kinship ties, voluntary association or attachment to households of the royal lineages (mutualism), and violent subjugation and incorporation of subject populations were all pathways for establishing such personal obligations and social linkages between rulers and subjects.

Weber, however, rightly recognized that the principal strut undergirding the patrimonial authority of a ruler (originally identified closely with military action: in short, the power that accrues to a warlord) was "a consensual community which also exists apart from his independent military force and which is rooted in the belief that the ruler's powers are legitimate insofar as they are *traditional*" (1978:1020, emphasis in the original). The importance of this insight cannot be overestimated, for it introduces the issue of the role of ideology in the construction of authority and the emergence of hierarchically organized societies. In a similar vein, Godelier (1978:767) remarks that "the power of domination consists of two indissoluble elements whose combination constitutes its strength: violence and consent," but "of these two components of power, the stronger is not the violence of the dominant, but the consent of the dominated to their domination." Ideology as a shared belief system assumes a central position in maintaining the consent, or, better said, acquiescence, of the dominated social classes to a hierarchical social order.

Why would a dominated class consent to and actively participate in a belief system that serves the interests of an elite, dominating class? Godelier's answer makes great intuitive sense: participation in the societywide belief system also enhances the economic interests of the dominated class. Specifically, Godelier (1978:767) hypothesizes that an elite ideology which reifies hierarchical relations of dominance and exploitation could be promoted and perpetuated only if these relations were cast in the form of an exchange of services between the elite and the dominated. The precise form of this exchange may vary, but Godelier (1978:767) suggests that in the case of early, agrarian-based state formations, the emerging elite class would offer esoteric knowledge of the supernatural realm—of "invisible realities and forces controlling (in the thought of these societies) the reproduction of the universe and of life"—in exchange for the supplementary labor of the commoners. One could also conceive of a variety of other, more directly pragmatic services that an elite class could offer to commoners: adjudication of boundary disputes, maintenance of security, management of redistribution networks, administration of social and economic linkages among diverse local communities, and the like.

Still, as Godelier acknowledges, even if dominated classes share to one degree or another the system of political and economic ideas, beliefs, and symbols promulgated by a dominant class, the threat and the power of coercion hovers in the background. It may be that the most successful (that is, persistent) class-stratified societies arrived at the appropriate balance of force and persuasion. Unmitigated terror leads, in time, to divisiveness, disgust, and revolt; ideological propaganda unreinforced by the potential for sanctions leads, in time, to fragmentation and dissolution of the hierarchical social order.

Embedded in the original structure of Weber's patrimonial states was an incipient hierarchy and an inherent, dynamic process or tendency toward social differentiation. As Weber (1978:1025) points out:

> In the simplest case the prince's great domains comprise his own household, together with a complex of manorial dependencies to which the households of manorial peasants are attached. This already requires an organized administration and hence a suitable division of functions developing in proportion to its size. . . . In this fashion the *patrimonial offices* come into being. The crown offices which originated in the household administration are similar all over the world. (emphasis in the original)

Hierarchy in patrimonial state offices emerges first in the tightly inbred world of the prince's oikos. In a social environment in which personal obligation and fealty are the sine qua non of office, the ruler turns first to his kinsmen and immediate dependents in creating a body of administrative officials. These immediate dependents, even though they may have conflicting loyalties of their own or, for the more highly placed, strategies for usurping princely authority for themselves, are nevertheless more easily manipulated, being, on the whole, resident at court (the extended household of the prince). But, as Weber (1978:1026) implies, the expansion of princely authority beyond a local, parochial domain increases administrative burdens to the point at which the ruler must recruit officials "in an extrapatrimonial fashion." In this manner, of necessity, inner and outer circles of officials develop. These inner and outer "courts" perform similar administrative functions on behalf of the prince's expanding oikos, but they exhibit differential access to, and degrees of dependency on, the ruler. The prince's unwieldy task in such an environment of political intrigue and competition for influence is to maintain sufficient personal contact, or at least the perception of personal contact, with subordinates and clients to reinforce the bonds of personal loyalty and dependence. Personal contact and public demonstrations of reciprocity in the form of gift exchange, reciprocal hosting of banquets, and the like were the lifeblood of this kind of political-administrative system.

Given that personal contact and public appearance were essential to the legitimacy of leadership, it is not surprising to learn that in these patrimonial states the king was often itinerant and that his court moved with him when he was on tour. David Keightley (1983:551–52) offers a particularly incisive description of the role and meaning of the itinerant king in the early Chinese Shang state:

The Shang state . . . was defined by a series of dynastic operations. Orders were issued, but they were the king's, frequently transmitted by him orally. Dependents came to have audience with the king, and the king in turn was concerned about their actions and good fortune and the success of their harvests. Royal gifts, at times conferred when the king was on tour . . . and royal hospitality strengthened ties of mutual obligation. The king displayed his power by frequent travel, hunting, and inspecting along the pathways of his realm, delegating little of his military power and expecting no "legal" or "constitutional" military support in return. . . . If, as the inscriptions suggest, the state was in origin an alliance of independent groups whose tutelary spirits were incorporated into the genealogy and ritual structure of the court as their leaders joined the Shang federation . . . then the king in his travels would have moved through a landscape pregnant with symbolic meaning, sacrificing to the local spirits, giving and receiving power at each holy place, and thus renewing the religious and kin ties (fictive or not) that bound the state together. And the king, as he traveled, would have been a force for cultural as well as political unification, impressing the local populations with his language, his writing system, his sumptuary displays, his weaponry, his tastes, and his beliefs. . . . Power so itinerant in nature suggests in turn that the capital may have been a base of operations, a cult center, a necropolis, and an industrial and artesanal center, rather than a fixed administrative and redistributive center.

In a strikingly similar vein, for an entirely different time and place, Briant (1988) analyzes the periodic migrations of the Achaemenid courts as explicitly political and ritual acts. The migration of the "Great Kings" of Persia served as a public expression of territorial control and subjugation of local populations but also as a mode of governance, a technique of statecraft. As Briant (1988:270–72) phrases it:

It seems quite clear, in fact, that the nomadism of the Achaemenid court carries first of all a political and ideological significance of the highest importance. As it was in fact expressed by Xenophon, one of the major problems confronting the Persians was to "remedy the immensity of the Empire," that is, to find the means to maintain a real control over conquered territories and peoples, or at least over the most important of these. This was one of the functions of the court migrations. . . .

In the Achaemenid period, the king would periodically renew his domination over the great cities of the Empire: the royal protocol imposed on the subject peoples the terms by which their subjugation was to be manifested. . . . During the course of these journeys, the king also may stop at royal resting houses (*basilikoi stathmoi*). Along the royal road, small country populations could witness the majesty, power and wealth of the king, who, on this exceptional occasion, allowed himself to be seen: it was in Persia in particular an occasion to forge a rapport with the simple people, based on the custom of gift-giving and gift-receiving, and to express visually the ideology of the benefactor-king. If we add that, during their travels, the kings' satraps and envoys were greeted in the same way, we must conclude that the subjugated territories were regularly "surveyed" (*arpentés*) by the Achaemenid authorities and that the conquered peoples and towns had to solemnly renew their subjection on a regular basis. Without forcing the sense of the texts, we can conclude then . . . that these "entrances" represent one of the modes of territorial control. . . .

All these texts indicate, then, that the moves by the king and his satraps had a very important political function: to periodically reaffirm their domination over the people and dynasties, to remind them of their obligations, to compel them to publicly declare their subordination, concretely expressed by the presentation of gifts and oaths of loyalty, in short, to mark the limits of their powers on their territories and subjects, powers which cannot be perpetuated but through delegation by a Great King, who was distant, but always capable of visually imposing his presence and authority.

The mobile residential complexes of these itinerant kings were imposing, majestic, and infused with symbols of earthly and divine power. The traveling court constituted the true focus of authority, a capital in motion with the king at its center. And it was explicitly from the person of the king that power emanated. The itinerant capital was, in a sense, a simulacrum of the fixed capital consciously wrought as an awe-inspiring image of sacred and secular authority. These royal capitals, fixed or itinerant, were frequently designed as microcosmic representations of the state, and as cosmograms as well—condensed reflections of the very order of the humanly perceived universe.

The king in motion departed with all the symbols of his power and, inevitably, with the images of the empire's gods: the gods, the king, and the cosmos traveled as one. But such personalized power was fragile, constantly under siege, and threatened by assassination, courtly intrigue, usurpation of authority, and defeat in battle. The king's loss of control over the material symbols of authority with which he was invested at the time of his enthronement (scepters, crowns, bows, shields, idols of the gods) signaled his loss of kingship itself: "Twice Darius had abandoned them [the symbols of kingship] during his flight: Alexander did not fail to proclaim that, through this act, Darius in fact had relinquished the kingdom" (Briant 1988:269). The Persian kings' itinerant capitals were forests of sumptuous tents, with the enormous, multiroom royal tent at the center, overflowing with elaborate furniture and precious objects. As Briant (1988:269) comments,

the moment the victor takes possession of the royal tent symbolically marks the passage of power from one to the other. . . . After the Macedonian victory at Issus: "Having taken possession of Darius' tent, Alexander's pages prepared his bath and his dinner. They lighted a large bundle of torches and waited for the king; after the chase, when he found all of Darius' furnishings nearby, he would see the foreshadow of a hegemony stretching to all of Asia" (Diodorus XVI, 36, 5).

Much of what Keightley and Briant eloquently describe for the king's role in these two diverse imperial societies applies with equal force to the Inca state. Like their Shang and Achaemenid counterparts, Inca kings were constantly in motion. They struck out with glittering retinues of warriors, priests, and camp followers in battle campaigns, on elaborate tours of their provinces, and on ritually prescribed peregrinations to sacred shrines. Some Inca kings were absent from Cuzco for years on end, bringing into question the true political role of Cuzco as an administrative center. It would seem that the administration of the Inca empire was effected not by decision makers resident in a fixed capital but rather by the coterie of kinsmen and dependents clustered around the moving court, in concert with "patrimonial officials" resident in the provinces. But, as was the case with kings of other archaic empires, the Inca's grasp on power was tenuous. Like the great Darius, forcefully dispossessed of kingship by Alexander, the Inca king Atahualpa, on an extended tour through his realm, lost command over the empire when Spaniards took him captive in his itinerant capital on November 16, 1532, and despoiled him there of his kingly symbols.

One intriguing corollary to this insight into the nature of authority in the Inca state is that we can reconceptualize the many "reconquests" that descendants of earlier Inca kings were said to have effected in "rebellious" provinces as an entirely different process altogether. These "reconquests" may in fact have been locally anticipated state visits by the itinerant king and his court. The visits may have been framed in a public idiom that commemorated earlier periods of conflict occasioned by the initial encounter and subjugation of a region into the expanding Inca empire. That is, the king may have appeared in these provinces with his armed retinue in full battle regalia to remind the locals of their relative positions of dominance and subordination, but the actual interaction entailed not reconquest but reaffirmation of established social bonds. Given the historical moment in which the Spanish chroniclers were writing their texts—having before their eyes, as it were, the recent Christian *reconquista* of the Iberian peninsula from the Moors—it is not surprising that they might have understood and recorded the Inca kings' peregrinations throughout their Andean world as if they were episodes of reconquest rather than expressions of a ritualized, recurrent technique of rule. Of course, we cannot doubt that there were genuine instances of resistance, rebellion, and reconquest in Inca provinces, but we must remain sensitive to the possibility that at least some of these "reconquests" were instead cyclical returns of the king to strategic provinces of his domain.

The ritual peregrinations of the Inca kings did not cease even after they died. As Bernabé Cobo (1890–95 [1653]: 339–41) recounts, the members of the kings' royal ayllus (the *panaqas*)

> brought [the royal mummies], lavishly escorted, to all their most important ceremonies. They sat them all down in the plaza in a row, in order of seniority, and the servants who looked after them ate and drank there. . . . In front of the mummies they also placed large vessels like pitchers, called vilques, made of gold and silver. They filled these vessels with maize beer and toasted the dead with it, after first showing it to them. The dead toasted one another, and they drank to the living. . . . This was done by their ministers in their names. When the vilques were full, they poured them over a circular stone set up as an idol in the middle of the plaza. There was a small channel around the stone, and the beer ran off through drains and hidden pipes.

This spectacle in which the descendants of dead kings minister to their ancestors' elaborately costumed, desiccated corpses with offerings of food, drinks, and toasts obscures the subtle political and religious nuances embedded in the cult of the royal mummies. Although grounded in the pan-Andean religious practice of ancestor worship, this elite cult was transformed into something more than the simple veneration of a dead lineage ancestor.

First, the elaborate feasting of the dead royals was organized around and intended as a ceremony of agricultural fertility: "When there was need for water for the cultivated fields, they usually brought out [the dead king's] body, richly dressed, with his face covered, carrying it in a procession through the fields and punas, and they were convinced that this was largely responsible for bringing rain" (Cobo 1979 [1653]: 125). Dead kings were frequently addressed in the protocols of panaqa toasts as Illapa, the weather deity who personified the atmospheric forces of wind, rain, hail, lightning, and thunder—all of the meteorological phenomena responsible for the growth or destruction of agricultural crops.

Second, the public display of the royal mummies during state occasions, arranged in order of seniority, was a graphic affirmation of the legitimacy of Inca dynastic rule. On these occasions, the reigning king would participate in ceremonial processionals quite literally together with the complete line of his royal ancestors, represented by their richly adorned relictual bundles. Who could contest the legitimacy of the Inca when his entire dynasty—the distilled history of his ruling mandate—was constantly visible and present to the nation? By these ritual actions, deceased monarchs and living emperor symbolically became one: embodiments of legitimate power, emblems of agricultural fertility and abundance, and powerful icons of national identity. It would seem that in life as in death the Inca kings were addicted to movement in and through their provinces, to ritual peregrinations to the shrines of the state cults, and to processionals invested with a progression of symbols focused on the figure and body of the king—symbols intended to socialize natural forces and naturalize the social order. As Weber apparently sensed, authority in the Inca state, like that in pharaonic Egypt, was archetypally patrimonial.

Inevitably, the political and psychological realities of the patrimonial state were characterized by varying degrees of fluidity, anxiety, and instability, particularly in territories of the domain beyond the original core holdings under the direct influence of the paramount lord. The legitimacy of kingly office had to be created and recreated anew by intimate contact with subjects. From the strictly administrative point of view, predatory, expansionist patrimonial states such as that of pharaonic Egypt or the Incas rapidly develop highly differentiated patrimonial offices, defined and hierarchized in terms of their degree of relatedness to the paramount ruler. The political coin of the realm, as it were, becomes the ability to demonstrate or argue convincingly for one's real or fictive kinship ties with the paramount. These highly differentiated offices functioned, in effect, as a quasi bureaucracy, or, perhaps more aptly phrased, a patrimonial bureaucracy in which the language of authority was voiced in the idiom of kinship.

This kind of "bureaucratization" of patrimonial office results in the de facto emergence of new status groups, cohorts of local lords and state clients with a commonality of interest focused on desire for recognition and representation at the court of the ruler. These local lords, in turn, operate from a political-economic base that recapitulates on a smaller scale the structural forms of the paramount ruler's oikos. They compete to form their own independent or quasi-independent patrimonial estates through which they extend their influence and control over local populations. Importantly, these local lords frequently seek to appropriate the religious mystique of the paramount's authority by replicating the architectural and symbolic configurations of the paramount's capital. Structurally, the geopolitical landscape of the patrimonial state consists of a congeries of petty polities coalesced around the households of local lords linked only tenuously, if at all, to each other but merged administratively into the oikos of the paramount ruler. That is, political, social, and administrative linkages in such a state structure are strong vertically but weak or incompletely developed horizontally. The personalized, centralizing nature of ultimate authority in such a structure results in a weakening or disintegration of "natural" affinities within ethnic and other traditional local groups in favor of opportunistic gravitation toward the court of the ruler.

Elsewhere, inspired by Weberian categories, I characterized this geopolitical landscape in the Andean world as a "hyper-oikos" (Kolata 1983:367). By this term, I meant that the economy and political influence of the paramount's household extended far beyond the confines of his capital's circumscribed hinterland. The agents of that extension were the elites who governed the provincial settlements. These aristocratic managers were either directly or symbolically related to members of the royal household, and they worked to further the economic and political ends of that household. This is the meaning behind the Inca political device of installing Incas by privilege. The hyper-oikos was essentially a means of building an empire by integrating a class of elites in an extended, fictive kinship system. These elites were bound in a complex network of privilege and obligation that was manipulated by the royal household. As I read Weber, he considered pharaonic Egypt to be, in essence, a hyper-oikos: a gigantic extension of an imperial household ruled through a network of client states and local lords with the twin devices of subtle suasion through the force of sacred tradition and of implicit threat of physical retaliation for rebelliousness from the household's militarized political-administrative center (the court of the warlord-king).

One essential strategy of statecraft in such a hyper-oikos was for the king to confirm the traditional political authority of local lords in dealing with their own communities and subjects. This strategy emerges from simple political pragmatism. Pedro de Cieza de León (1959 [1553]: 57), among other Spanish commentators intrigued by native Andean principles of command, astutely described this phenomenon in his great chronicle of Peru: "And they had another device to keep the natives from hating them, and this was that they never divested the natural chieftains of their power. If it so happened that one of them . . . in some way deserved to be stripped of his power, it was vested in his sons or brothers, and all were ordered to obey them." This system of preserving the local mandate of the native elites has been aptly termed "indirect rule."

For an empire that was rapidly, almost frenetically, expanding and in only the nascent stages of generating formal principles of colonial governance, indirect rule was simple to implement, relatively efficient, and least intrusive in altering the daily rhythms and decision-making autonomy of potentially hostile local communities. The key to the success of indirect rule was the Inca's ability to secure the cooperation and at least overt political loyalty of the local *kurakas*. One strategy for co-opting these local lords was to establish marriage alliances between them and the Inca elite, which established irrevocable bonds of kinship. The ritualized exchange of daughters as marriage partners between Inca and local elites created powerful incentives for provincial political leaders to "buy into" the Inca system; the network of real and fictive kinship ties engendered by these alliances provided rich opportunities to local lords for strategic manipulation of the resulting patron-client relationship.

Of course, this strategy of enticing the local kurakas into the patronage system by promising wealth and enhanced social prestige was effective only so long as the kurakas were able to deliver the labor and productive capacity of their people. The Incas recognized this critical linkage and helped the local kurakas resolve potential conflict with their people through massive displays of state generosity. As described by an anonymous chronicler:

The Incas used to win the benevolence of their vassals by organizing every now and then festivities which many neighboring inhabitants attended; these were the [occasions of] happiness for all these barbarians and there the Inca offered with his own hands *mates* or drinking vases of *chicha* to the *caciques* to drink, which was a great favor; equally he gave them clothes to wear from his proper (deposit), and silver vases and some other things; they were such the subjects that they could not (normally) eat other meat than guinea pig, but during those festivities they were given the meat of alpaca and llama, which is very good meat; and this they took as a great favor and gift. (Anónimo 1925 [1583]: 292, cited in Pärssinen 1992:410–11)

Like the Romans' policy of bread and circuses, intended to diffuse the potential explosiveness of a malcontent underclass, the Inca practice of periodically redistributing warehoused food, drink, and clothing to the commoners during state-sponsored festivals dissipated social tensions and incorporated commoners into the new economic and social order of the Inca world.

Although adopted in the first stages of colonial encounters between cultures as an expedient political strategy, indirect rule, by its very nature, is an evanescent, shifting, tension-plagued device of command. The cultural politics of such encounters necessarily entail transformations, which may take the form of assimilation, of mutual acculturation, or of rapid syncretization in some cultural domains and perduring resistance in others. The inexorability of change is readily predictable, although the depth and direction of such change is not. Paramounts may move to exert increasing control over subordinate lords and the resources of their domains through more direct means such as the imposition of innovative administrative devices. Local lords, on the other hand, may simultaneously seek to strengthen the grip of their authority over their subjects while strategically currying favor with the overlord. Alternatively, they may resist the paramount covertly or, from time to time, through outright rebellion. In short, indirect rule is not an effective *principle* of state governance but an intermediate temporal stage in a process of colonial encounter.

An Andean example of the inevitable transformative processes embedded in the nature of indirect rule is apropos. Late in the historical trajectory of the Inca state, Inca kings were attempting to supersede the techniques of indirect rule by adopting administrative devices designed to consolidate their authority over subject provinces. One of these devices, known as the *mitimae,* held special fascination for the Spaniards, perhaps because they recognized some strategic elements in that institution which echoed their own European traditions of statecraft. Cieza de León (1959 [1553]: 57) provides us with an early, detailed description of the mitimae that vividly captures the essence of the institution:

As soon as one of these large provinces was conquered, ten or twelve thousand of the men and their wives, or six thousand, or the number decided upon, were ordered to leave and remove themselves from it. These were transferred to another town or province of the same climate and nature as that which they left . . . and these were called *mitimaes,* which means Indians come from one land to another. They were given land to work and sites on which to build their homes. And these *mitimaes* were ordered by the Incas to be always obedient to what their governors and captains ordered, so that if the natives should rebel, and they supported the governor, the natives would be punished and reduced to the service of the Incas. Likewise if the *mitimaes* stirred up disorder, they were put down by the natives. In this way these rulers had their empire assured against revolts and the provinces well supplied with food, for most of the people, as I have said, had been moved from one land to another.

In a passage remarkable for its analytical perceptiveness, Cieza de León goes on to distinguish three classes of mitimaes: military, political, and economic. The military mitimaes served an important function as border guards, populating and commanding army garrisons on the fringes of the expanding Inca state. They were essentially groups of soldier-citizens who maintained a military profile on behalf of the Incas while reclaiming and cultivating lands and herding llamas and alpacas on the border zones of the empire. In many respects, these mitimaes fulfilled roles similar to those of the army garrisons and civilian colonies established in frontier areas of the Roman empire. Frequently, rudimentary army camps on the Roman frontier were transformed over time into colonial "new towns" through the actions of legionnaires who remained for many years, establishing farms, roads, markets, and smithies and engaging in a host of other urban occupations.

The second class of transplanted colonists, the political mitimaes, served security functions similar to those of the mitimaes who populated the border outposts. Political mitimaes were more numerous and could be found in every province of the empire. They were forcibly removed from their homelands and resettled in other provinces where they were required to retain their distinctive ethnic costumes, headdresses, customs, and forms of social organization. The strategic goal underlying Inca implantation of political mitimaes was to reduce the chances for rebellion in conquered provinces by shattering traditional patterns of shared ethnic identity among large, contiguous populations. By intermixing local inhabitants with pockets of foreigners in self-contained colonies, the Incas substantially inhibited the potential for subversive political coalitions. In Cieza de León's apt summation

(1959 [1553]: 60): "In this way, all was quiet, and the mitimaes feared the natives, and the natives feared the mitimaes, and all occupied themselves only in obeying and serving."

Cieza de León characterized the third use of mitimae colonists as "stranger" than the others. He went on to describe these economic mitimaes in the following terms (1959 [1553]: 62):

> if, perchance, they had conquered territory in the highlands or plains or on a slope suitable for plowing and sowing, which was fertile and had a good climate . . . they quickly ordered that from near-by provinces that had the same climate as these . . . enough people come in to settle it, and to these lands were given, and flocks, and all the provisions they needed until they could harvest what they planted. . . . For a number of years no tribute was exacted of these new settlers, but on the contrary they were given women, coca, and food so that they would carry out the work of settlement with better will.

To Cieza de León and other Spanish military men, the use of frontier garrisons and colonial outposts was entirely familiar. But the Inca principle of economic mitimaes was alien to these products of an essentially feudal, medieval European tradition. First, it incorporated the unfamiliar Andean ideal of reciprocity. In transplanting populations to reclaim productive lands in a new province, the state was obligated to provide the colonists with a "grubstake": food and coca. Second, these mitimae colonists were exempted from taxation until they could reclaim enough land to sustain themselves and produce a surplus for the state. Finally, few Spanish chroniclers or administrators grasped the significance of the economic mitimaes as state expressions of the Andean principle of economic complementarity. The principal intent of the economic mitimaes was to enhance the productive capacity of the Inca state by reclaiming marginal land and, in some cases, by focusing the labor of thousands of transplanted colonists on the production of a single prestige crop, maize.

One of the most remarkable uses of economic mitimaes occurred during the reign of Huayna Capac. This last independent emperor of the Incas was said to have expelled the autochthonous populations of the Cochabamba Valley, one of the richest and most fertile in Bolivia, in order to install 14,000 new colonists from a variety of ethnic groups who were placed under the direct control of two Inca governors. These multiethnic colonists were brought to Cochabamba explicitly to produce maize for the state. The vast quantities of maize that flowed into the imperial storehouses in Cochabamba were eventually shipped to Cuzco for ultimate consumption by the Inca army.

Huayna Capac completely reorganized the system of land tenure in Cochabamba to accommodate this grand scheme of repopulation and intensive state maize production. He divided the entire valley into 77 long strips, or *suyu,* and then assigned individual ethnic groups to work the land of all or parts of suyus, depending on the topographic context of the designated strip and the population size of each colonizing ethnic group. Only 7 of these strips of land, interspersed among the other 70 suyus, were allotted to the 14,000 colonists for their own subsistence. The remaining portion, over 90 percent of the arable land in the valley, was dedicated to intensive production of maize for the state (Wachtel 1982). As was the case with other multiethnic mitimae colonization schemes, the work assignments and other internal affairs of each ethnic group were governed by its own political leaders. These leaders were then responsible to the two Inca governors who headed up the political hierarchy. In return for their service to the Incas, the various ethnic kurakas were rewarded with small plots of land, with Inca prestige goods such as cotton mantles, and occasionally with women for secondary wives. By Inca governmental decree, each group maintained its own ethnic costume, headdress, and life-style.

It is clear that the Cochabamba economic mitimaes served multiple purposes for the Inca state. Primarily, they were a tremendous economic engine, capable of producing massive quantities of maize for the state in at least two annual crops. More than 2,000 preserved stone storehouses on the hill slopes of the Cochabamba Valley attest to the productive capacity of these transplanted colonists. Secondarily, these colonists performed an important security function: a series of fragmented ethnic groups working side by side in Cochabamba presented a smaller threat to the state than did the potentially unified indigenous inhabitants of the valley whom the Incas deported.

The three categories of Inca mitimaes, then, crosscut each other: political mitimaes frequently served economic functions; military mitimaes were, almost by definition, also political mitimaes; large-scale economic mitimae colonization schemes such as that in the Cochabamba Valley, by their organization and multiethnic composition, became simultaneously effective security devices. Although the principal colonization projects organized by the Incas focused on agricultural development, mitimae colonies were also established to exploit concentrated natural resources such as salt, gold, silver, timber, clay for pottery, semiprecious stones for jewelry, hard stone for construction, and the like. The numbers of colonists relocated in these projects were highly variable, ranging from extended families of a few persons to entire villages and ethnic groups reaching into the thousands, as in the case of Huayna Capac's reorganization of the Cochabamba Valley. We have no precise information on the total number of people in the Inca state removed from their homelands and resettled elsewhere, but all sources indicate that they were a substantial proportion of the population (Rowe 1982).

Such massive transfers of communities and villages that became directly dependent upon the Inca state bureaucracy for political security and for the potential to enhance their own social position and economic well-being resulted in a gradual dissemination of Inca language, values, expectations, and cultural beliefs. Under the impact of this program of population mixing on an imperial scale, old ethnic identities, traditional ayllu affinities, and beliefs began slowly to transform themselves in conformity with the new Inca ideal, enhancing unification of the empire itself (Rowe 1982).

A second innovative administrative device that the Incas attempted to insinuate into their system of command was a more formal, centralized channel of tribute and labor recruitment based on a decimal system of administration (Julien 1988). In this system, labor obligations were assessed on an ascending numerical series of tributary households that began with a minimal unit of 10 households (termed *chunka*) and ended with the maximal unit of 10,000 households (*hunu*). Between these limits, there were decimal groupings for 50, 100, 500, 1,000, and 5,000 tributary households. The Inca state periodically took a census to account for fluctuations in the size and residential patterns of the empire's population. On the basis of the census figures recorded on imperial quipu, or knotted cords, they adjusted membership in these decimal groupings of tributary households to reflect changing demographic realities.

Each decimal unit was headed by an official who, at the lower levels of the household groupings, was drawn from the local community. Officers of the various decimal units were ranked in a formal, pyramid-like hierarchy. Some officials were appointed to their offices by higher-ranking decimal administrators; others appear to have inherited their positions. The chain of command and reporting responsibility began with the chunka leaders and proceeded upward progressively to the hunu officials. Above the rank of hunu, administrative responsibility was vested in individuals with direct consanguineal or political ties to the royal households of Cuzco: these were the surrogates of the emperor himself, serving as provincial governors or as members of the imperial council, which included extremely high-ranking representatives from each of the four quarters of the realm.

In effect, as the Incas began to consolidate their authority in a conquered province, they gradually attempted to streamline the complicated political mosaic of multiple claims to power and traditional prerogatives asserted by local lords by imposing the uniform decimal system of administration. Although this system had clear benefits for the central Inca government, permitting the state to operate with a more "rationalized" form of political organization and labor recruitment in a pluralistic social landscape, it held fewer advantages for the local kurakas. With the emergence of what was essentially an imperial class system of favored officials, those kurakas who were not designated as decimal officers saw many of their social prerogatives and traditional access to local labor pools begin to dissolve. The resulting social tensions were substantial, and we read numerous stories in the chronicles about resentful "natural lords" of the provinces promulgating rebellions against Inca rule at every opportunity. Moreover, these attempts to rationalize principles of labor recruitment and tribute assessment had equally corrosive effects on the traditional kin-based groups of corporate affiliation. Higher-order systems of ayllus (that is, those designated by Platt [1986] from an ethnographic context as major and maximal ayllus) were broken apart through mitimae recolonization schemes or were subsumed under higher-order tributary schemes such as the Incas' decimal-based administrative reorganization of household groups.

We see, then, that the transactional, ambiguous principle of indirect rule, which required uneasy balancing of local autonomy with subordination to increasing tributary demands, rapidly came under pressure from the Inca kings in a number of directions. These efforts to "rationalize" chains of command after the initial colonial encounter bring into sharp relief the provisional and unstable character of the relationships between paramounts and local lords. Processes of rapid political revisionism, instigated by paramounts and local lords alike, appear to be a recurrent feature of patrimonial states, or at least those patrimonial states which took off on a trajectory of territorial expansion. I would argue that the rulers of expansive patrimonial states inevitably attempt to replace indirect rule with more homogenous and "rationalized" principles of command, and that the resulting tensions contribute to the structural fragility of traditional agrarian states.

The attempt to draw an inherent correlation between bureaucracy and political centralization, although perhaps intuitively attractive, is misguided. It may be that some bureaucratized systems lend themselves to political centralization, but this is by no means a sociological and political inevitability. A political system grounded in patrimonial principles of authority, on the other hand, is virtually by definition one that is highly centralized (although frequently unstable) because command decisions and practices are focused on the figure of the king and his court.

In sum, I argue that many, if not all, archaic states operated with patrimonial principles of authority and that such political systems may be characterized organizationally as centralized but nonbureaucratic in nature. With the expansion of these archaic states beyond local hinterlands and parochial political concerns, the patrimonial principles of authority must expand and, of necessity, be transformed in the contact and colonializing process. Frequently, this transformation is an attempt to establish general and more uniform command and control procedures, as in the case of the Inca mitimae and decimal tributary systems cited here. In some sense, this transformation may be characterized as the emergence of a protobureaucracy in that an attempt is made to articulate an abstract theory of public administration. I believe that these theoretical insights into the founding principles of authority in the native Andean state and the transformations of those principles in the dynamic of state expansion can be applied to the specific instance of Tiwanaku.

The spatio-temporal and social structure of Tiwanaku's sustaining hinterland reflects, both directly and indirectly, pervasive organizational principles in Tiwanaku society, at least in the period of the mature state from about A.D. 400 to 1000, with which we have been most concerned. The organization of agricultural production in the Tiwanaku hinterland entailed creation of an artificial landscape of agricultural fields and supporting hydraulic infrastructure of regional scope. This distinctive regional system of production technologies, in turn, was knitted together with a hierarchical settlement network that articulated human populations with the landscape.

When we organized Proyecto Wila Jawira, we began with the proposition that the essential structure of agricultural organization in the research zone during the period of the mature Tiwanaku state involved centralized administration of land and labor. Evidence for the actions of a center-directed political authority in the Tiwanaku hinterland included (1) landscape-scale agricultural reclamation projects, (2) a hierarchical settlement network marked by significant distinctions in settlement size, status, and function, and (3) rural population distributions indicative of a purposive social organization of production explicitly directed toward the extraction of surplus on a regional scale. That is, with respect to regional population distributions throughout the Tiwanaku hinterland, intermediate and small-scale settlements (perhaps more familiarly glossed as village- and hamlet-sized) were distributed in regular clusters along colluvial terraces adjacent to raised-field complexes; they were not found widely distributed among distinct bundles of raised-field plots. Individual "house" mounds among the raised fields can best be interpreted as temporary, perhaps seasonally occupied, encampments for *kamani,* or field guardians (Kolata 1991:115).

To some degree, agricultural production in the Tiwanaku hinterland served the needs of local consumption. But the archaeologically evident instances of capital investment in expanding the reclamation of potentially arable land and in altering and controlling the hydrological regime of the raised-field systems imply the action of a regional political authority. The conjoined data from the spatial and temporal distribution of settlements and field systems, from broad demographic patterns (as these can currently be reconstituted), from estimates of labor input and caloric yields, and from the technological profile of the interconnected aqueduct-reservoir-canal-causeway-field systems in the Tiwanaku sustaining area implicate some form of extractive and channelizing functions performed beyond the purview of local community leaders or political elites.

Although the initial, pioneering construction of raised-field plots was most likely the product of an autonomous, uncentralized social order, the subsequent reshaping of Tiwanaku's hinterland into a regional system of agricultural production under the hegemony of Tiwanaku elites in the period from about A.D. 400 to 1000 entailed the periodic mobilization and coordination of a substantial nonresident labor force. The logistical requirements of repeatedly deploying a concentrated, nonlocal labor force demanded a political order with regional authority to alienate land and co-opt labor.

This interpretation of the organizational framework of production implies that Tiwanaku established proprietary agricultural estates in which ownership and usufruct were vested directly in state institutions, or, perhaps more precisely, in the hands of the elite, dominant classes. These corporate estates or production zones were bound directly to the capital of Tiwanaku through a network of secondary and tertiary urban or urbanized formations with administrative functions. Dispersed, rural hamlets and individual households occur in the Tiwanaku area outside the zone of optimal lacustrine agricultural soils. The inhabitants of these settlements were probably engaged in small-scale subsistence dry farming and localized herding of camelids. Along with commoners in the larger secondary and tertiary centers, they provided a substantial proportion of the corvée, or, more properly, *mit'a* labor for the state fields.

The population of this sustaining area was not distributed uniformly or broadly across the landscape. Rather, a pattern of nodal population clustering has been documented in large urban centers such as Lukurmata and Pajchiri and in intermediate-scale settlements such as Chiripa, Chojasivi, Lakaya, and Yayes, arrayed along the combined geological and human-altered terraces that define the northern and southern borders of the western Catari basin. The regionally integrated agricultural field systems in this same zone were constructed and maintained during the Tiwanaku IV through Tiwanaku V phases (ca. A.D. 400–1000). During Tiwanaku phase V, these field systems achieved their maximum spatial reach. The most technologically advanced manipulation of the reclaimed landscape of raised fields in this area, represented by the construction of interconnected spring, reservoir, and aqueduct water delivery systems, was associated with these same two periods of Tiwanaku's internal development (Kolata 1991, 1993a; Kolata and Ortloff 1989; Ortloff and Kolata 1989).

If local lords, as political leaders of ranked, hierarchically nested corporate groups, were responsible for creating the agricultural landscape of Tiwanaku's northern sustaining area without the control functions of a centralized state, the settlement pattern of the region would look quite different from the way it actually does. For instance, we would expect that relatively substantial settlements would be established at, or associated with, key "break points" in the delivery system that provided freshwater to the raised-field networks. Such strategic break points would include the intakes of principal canals, the origin points of mountain springs that issue from the surrounding terraces of the Lakaya geological formation, and the geographically dispersed but agriculturally critical zones of high groundwater characteristic of that formation. In short, the political-administrative and settlement landscape in the Catari basin would reflect a configuration closer to that hypothesized by Netherly (1984) for the late pre-Hispanic north coast of Peru, in which autonomous sociopolitical groups (*parcialidades*) were arrayed along lands watered by individual canals or segments of canals. Given the marked absence of substantial habitation centers within the raised-field–canal-causeway system of the Catari basin and the complete lack of evidence for local control over, or population clustering in, strategic areas of structural articulation within the hydraulic system as a whole, there remains little alternative but to consider the organization of this essential regional component of Tiwanaku's sustaining area as reflecting state action at a distance.

This analysis can be extended to the Tiwanaku Valley as well, although we have insufficient evidence at present to determine its applicability to the Machaca-Desaguadero region. Ongoing research will eventually determine whether a pattern of centralized extraction similar to that apparent in the Catari basin holds for this southern sustaining area of Tiwanaku or whether there was a different system of organizing agricultural production in this zone. As noted in chapter 8, initial results from intensive survey in the Tiwanaku Valley suggest that there, too, as in the Koani region, agricultural production during the Tiwanaku IV–V phases was organized and managed hierarchically (Albarracín-Jordan 1990; Albarracín-Jordan and Mathews 1990; Mathews 1990).

It may well be that some form of organization similar to the hierarchically ranked moieties that Netherly (1984:230) envisions for the management of large-scale irrigation systems on Peru's north coast played a role in the development of Tiwanaku's agricultural sustaining area. But the principles governing mobilization and control of human labor in Tiwanaku must have been rather different from the principle of relative local autonomy implied in Netherly's treatment of the north coast material. In straightforward terms, the data from the Catari basin implicate a pattern of purposive state development of a distinct, integrated, rural agricultural production zone. The organization of production in this zone was achieved by centralized state action that entailed strategically located installations not under the control of local corporate groups. In great part, the labor force that constructed and maintained these installations was similarly nonlocal, mobilized from a region much broader than that encompassed by the field systems themselves. By about A.D. 500, the Tiwanaku hinterland (at least in the Catari basin) can best be understood as a constructed landscape of state production. The labor invested in shaping that landscape may have been acquired through taxation of both local and nonlocal corporate groups headed by ranked political leaders who acted as intermediaries and surrogates for the Tiwanaku political elite. But given what is known of the settlement distribution in this region, the autonomy of these local kurakas must have been constrained by the needs and prerogatives of the more highly ranked nonlocal elites who resided in the network of urban centers in the greater Tiwanaku sustaining area.

I would argue that the paramount elites of Tiwanaku operated with fluid, context-specific strategies of economic development. On the one hand, the group or perhaps class interests of these elites demanded the creation of strategic, directly controlled production zones that ensured long-term stability in access to surplus crops and commodities. Investment in landscape capital (raised fields, terrace and irrigation systems, aqueducts and dikes) that served the purpose of expanding or stabilizing regional agricultural production went hand in glove with this strategy of direct elite intervention. Economic surpluses generated by these intensification projects were the pediment of the elites' political power. Surplus production furnished them with the means to sustain personal and group prestige through dramatic public expressions of generosity and abundance during the cyclical calendar of agricultural festivals and ritual events. Their opulent lifestyle was a kind of essential social theater that tangibly ratified the elites' personal and positional status within Tiwanaku society.

While social and ideological necessity demanded that Tiwanaku elites carve out corporate estates to ensure a direct supply of surplus agricultural products, political reality dictated that their relationships with most local communities and ethnic groups under their (at times) uncertain dominion follow the path of least resistance. That is, in most instances coercion of local populations and mass alienation of land and labor was not a viable political option. The political and logistical costs of dominating a huge, diverse territory were too great to sustain, and local resistance to the complete encroachment of an authoritarian regime was too great a threat to the social order to justify a posture of unalloyed hostility. Instead, Tiwanaku elites, much like their Inca counterparts some 700 years later, struck a balance between force and persuasion. They established key proprietary estates of production that assured them a stable fund of products which could be invested in sustaining the social roles demanded of them. Outside of these core areas of directly controlled production, they moved by indirection and subtle attention to the local political context. Tributary relationships between the cosmopolitan elites of Tiwanaku and their distant rural counterparts were most likely framed in terms of patron-client exchanges.

The kings and elite interest groups of archaic states assiduously attempt to perpetuate their legitimacy by reconfiguring social space both within their capitals and in the rural reaches of their domains. They create new centers or greatly modify and enhance preexisting ones to proclaim publicly and make tangible the sources of their legitimate right to rule. The kingly warlords and their elite cadre of kinsmen, retainers, and clients construct and inhabit majestic centers, both fixed and itinerant, accoutered with monumental representations of space which they themselves have conceived. These centers are imbued with the signs of sacred authority: enormous plazas for public rituals, visually salient temples, palaces, and thrones, great urban gardens—all for the purpose of symbolically expressing their legitimacy. The elites become dwellers in cities of their own design, and from these cities they circulate into the hinterlands, in effect extending the ideological grounds of their created cosmopolitan culture into the rural interstices. As Lefebvre (1991:235) remarks:

> The city state thus establishes a fixed centre by coming to constitute a hub, a privileged focal point, surrounded by peripheral areas which bear its stamp. From this moment on, the vastness of pre-existing space appears to come under the thrall of divine order. At the same time the towns seem to gather in everything which surrounds it [*sic*], including the natural and divine, and the earth's evil and good forces. As image of the universe (*imago mundi*), urban space is reflected in the rural space that it possesses and indeed in a sense *contains*. Over and above its economic, religious, and political content, therefore, this relationship already embodies an element of symbolism, of image-and-

reflection: the town perceives itself in its double, in its repercussions or echo; in self-affirmation, from the height of its towers, its gates, and its campaniles, it contemplates itself in the countryside that it has shaped—that is to say in its work. The town and its surroundings thus constitute a *texture*. (emphasis in the original)

As Lefebvre recognizes, the city of the archaic state actively shapes its countryside, constituting a fabric or texture of social relations. The city's shaping of its hinterland proceeds conceptually, symbolically, and, of course, materially through commissioned public works, such as the extensive raised-field and regional hydraulic landscape of Tiwanaku or the great irrigated terrace complexes constructed by the Incas, and through the reorganization of autochthonous populations in their provinces.

Although the intensity of this city-country relationship varied over time and space in ancient agrarian states, one of its features remained constant: the city lived off the surrounding countryside by extracting tribute both in kind and in labor service. The latter form of tribute appears to have been emphasized in the Andean world. At the same time, the archaic city-state provided reciprocal services for the countryside, notably economic investment, political security, and an intangible but powerful sense of inclusion and participation in a greater social universe. We might readily imagine that the city introjected into the countryside distinct cultural values and a promise of opportunity that provided welcome relief from the parochial, local perspective of the rural village, its fields, and its pastures. The city opened up new cultural perspectives in the otherwise circumscribed social landscape of the countryside.

But in doing so, the native Andean cities differed from those of most other preindustrial states, and this difference most likely developed in part from the lack of "democratizing" forces inherent in cities possessed of a market-based economy. The cosmopolitan perspective imparted to the rural commoner on pilgrimage to a native Andean capital was limited, controlled, and framed in a discourse of religiosity. Most certainly the elites did not intend to encourage migration to the cities. Relative to cities in other preindustrial societies, Andean capitals exhibited a marked lack of social heterogeneity. In some respects this is functionally related to the lack of marketing services in these cities. There were few economic incentives for rural people to migrate to the city in the ancient Andean world, except as retainers to members of the ruling lineages. The number of such positions was limited, and the bulk of the population—for lack of opportunity and, most likely, for policy reasons exerted by the elites—remained on the land as primary agricultural producers. The result was a notable absence of employment opportunities and social diversity in the cities.

This lack of economic opportunity is clearly reflected in two additional defining characteristics of ancient Andean cities: low urban population size and intense development of instruments of social control within the urban environment. The Andean capitals and their secondary urban settlements were essentially regal and religious in nature. These cities, particularly the capitals of the expansionist states (I would include Cuzco, Chan Chan, and Tiwanaku as three paradigmatic cases in point), were autocratic both in political character and in social composition. They were capitals exclusively of and for elite cultural definition and self-expression. A large, resident population of commoners would have been inimical to the purpose and function of these cities. Apart from the commoners who were incorporated in a retainer capacity, the masses rarely participated in Andean urban culture at all, except on the occasion of public rituals. Not surprisingly, several, and perhaps most, of the Andean fixed capitals were simultaneously regional focal points of pilgrimage. Commoners flowed into these cities at prescribed moments. They can be understood as religious tourists in a kind of elite theme park that was carefully orchestrated to impart to them a sense of emotional participation in, but social segregation from, the esoteric world of the elite.

The foregoing reflections on the nature of the Andean city and its relationship with its sustaining hinterland are meant to foreshadow theoretical and interpretive directions that are developed further in the companion volume to this one. That volume addresses the archaeology of Tiwanaku urban and rural settlement systems and focuses on human occupation and utilization of the Lake Titicaca basin of Bolivia. Here, we have concentrated on examining the environmental and technological context of Tiwanaku agricultural reclamation, expansion, and collapse. We have explored in various degrees of detail how environmental conditions varied over time, how human populations responded to environmental variation, and how, in turn, ecological processes were altered by human-environment interactions. We have analyzed the technological and organizational characteristics of raised-field agriculture, the remarkable system of intensive cultivation that became highly elaborated during the period of the mature Tiwanaku state. We believe that together, the two volumes offer a comprehensive and theoretically explicit portrait of the relationship between the city of Tiwanaku and its hinterland. Our research program is ongoing, and we expect that many of the interpretations we have made here with respect to long-term human-environment interactions in the Lake Titicaca basin and the nature of Tiwanaku intensive agriculture will be modified. We believe, however, that the results presented here reliably furnish part of the conceptual and empirical armature upon which future interpretations by ourselves and others will be constructed.

# References Cited


Aber, J. D., and J. M. Melillo
1991 *Terrestrial Ecosystems.* Philadelphia: Sanders College Publishing.

Abercrombie, T.
1986 *The Politics of Sacrifice: An Aymara Cosmology in Action.* Unpublished Ph.D. dissertation, University of Chicago.
1991 To Be Indian, To Be Bolivian: "Ethnic" and "National" Discourses of Identity. In *Nation-States and Indians in Latin America,* edited by G. Urban and J. Sherzer, pp. 95–130. Austin: University of Texas Press.

Abramowitz, M., and I. Stegun
1964 *Handbook of Mathematical Functions.* National Bureau of Standards, Applied Mathematics Series, no. 55.

Adams, R. E. W.
1980 Swamps, Canals, and the Locations of Ancient Maya Cities. *Antiquity* 54:206–14.

Addiscott, T.
1988 Farmers, Fertilisers and the Nitrate Flood. *New Scientist* 120:50–54.

AGRUCO (Agro-Biología de la Universidad de Cochabamba)
1990 *Agroecología y saber andino.* Cochabamba: AGRUCO, Pratec.

Ahlfeld, F., and L. Branisa
1960 *Geología de Bolivia.* La Paz: Instituto Petrológico.

Albarracín-Jordan, J.
1990 Prehispanic Dynamics of Settlement in the Lower Tiwanaku Valley, Bolivia. In *Tiwanaku and Its Hinterland: Third Preliminary Report of the Proyecto Wila Jawira,* edited by A. L. Kolata and O. Rivera, pp. 276–96. Submitted to the Instituto Nacional de Arqueología de Bolivia, the National Science Foundation and the National Endowment for the Humanities.
1992 *Prehispanic and Early Colonial Settlement Patterns in the Lower Tiwanaku Valley, Bolivia.* Unpublished Ph.D. dissertation, Southern Methodist University, Dallas.

Albarracín-Jordan, J., and J. E. Mathews
1990 *Asentamientos prehispánicos del valle de Tiwanaku, vol. 1.* La Paz: Producciones Cima.

Albó, X.
1977 *Idiomas, escuelas y radios en Bolivia.* La Paz: Cuadernos de Investigación, CIPCA.
1983 Do You Speak English? Reseña de la literatura sobre el mundo rural boliviana en linguas extranjeras. *America Indígena* 43(2):397–412. Mexico.
1987 From MNRista to Katarista to Katari. In *Resistance, Rebellion, and Consciousness in the Andean Peasant World, 18th to 20th Centuries,* edited by S. J. Stern, pp. 379–419. Madison: University of Wisconsin Press.
1990a Introducción. In *Etapa de una larga marcha,* edited by A. Baspiniero Contreras, pp. xiii–xxxviii. La Paz: Asociación Aquí Avance, Educación Radiofónica de Bolivia.
1990b Lo andino en Bolivia: Balance y prioridades. *Revista Andina* 8(2):411–63.
1991 El retorno del indio. *Revista Andina* 9(2):299–331.

Albó, X., and J. Barnadas
1984 *La cara campesina y indígena de nuestro historia.* La Paz: CIPCA.

Albó, X., and F. Layme
1993 *Literatura Aymara: Antología.* La Paz: HISBOL, CIPCA, and Jayma.

Allen, C.
1988 *The Hold Life Has.* Washington, D.C.: Smithsonian Institution Press.

Altieri, M. A.
1987 *Agroecology: The Scientific Basis of Alternative Agriculture.* Boulder: Westview Press.

Altieri, M. A., and S. B. Hecht
1990 *Agroecology and Small Farm Development.* New York: CRC Press.

Alva, J. J., L. Tarifa, and los jampiris de Raqaypampa
1993 *Los jampiris de Raqaypampa.* Cochabamba, Boliva: Centro de Comunicación y Desarollo Andino.

Anderson, I.
1991 Global Warming Rings True. *New Scientist* 21:33.

Anderson, J. M.
1976 An Ignition Method for Determination of Total Phosphorus in Lake Sediments. *Water Research* 10:329–31.

Anderson, N. J.
1990 Spatial Pattern of Recent Sediment and Diatom Accumulation in a Small, Monomictic, Eutrophic Lake. *Journal of Paleolimnology* 3:143–60.

APHA (American Public Health Association)
1985 *Standard Methods for the Examination of Water and Wastewater.* 14th ed. Washington, D.C.: American Public Health Association.

Appleby, P. G., P. J. Nolan, D. E. Gifford, F. Oldfield, N. J. Anderson, and R. W. Battarbee.
1986 $^{210}$Pb Dating by Low Background Gamma Counting. *Hydrobiologia* 143:21–27.

Appleby, P. G., and F. Oldfield
1978 The Calculation of Lead-210 Dates Assuming a Constant Rate of Supply of Unsupported $^{210}$Pb to the Sediment. *Catena* 5:1–8.
1983 Assessment of $^{210}$Pb from Sites with Varying Sediment Accumulation Rates. *Hydrobiologia* 103:29–85.

Aravena, R. B., G. Warner, G. M. MacDonald, and K. I. Hanf
1992 Carbon Isotope Composition of Lake Sediments in Relation to Lake Productivity and Radiocarbon Dating. *Quaternary Research* 37:333–45.

Arce, R. D. A.
1987 *Guerra y conflictos sociales: El caso rural boliviano durante la campaña del Chaco.* Cochabamba: CERES.

Arellano, J.
1973 *El Cuaternario en el valle de Tiwanaku.* Estudio Sedimentológico. La Paz: Instituto Nacional de Arqueología.
1991 The New Culture Contexts of Tiahuanaco. In *Huari Administrative Structure: Prehistoric Monumental Architecture and State Government,* edited by W. H. Isbell and G. F. McEwan, pp. 259–80. Washington, D.C.: Dumbarton Oaks Research Library and Collection.

Argollo, J.
1980 *Los piedemontes de la Cordillera Real entre los valles de La Paz y Tuni Condoriri.* Estudio Geológico, Evolución Plio-Cuaternaria. La Paz: Universidad Mayor de San Andrés.

Argollo, J., P. Gouze, J. F. Saliege, and M. Servant
1987 Fluctuations des glaciers de Bolivie au Quaternaire. *Géodynamique* 2:102–103.

Argollo, J., and L. Ticlla
1991 *Estudio geológico y evaluación de áreas Sukakolleras de la cuenca de Tiwanaku y Kohani Pampa.* Proyecto Agroarqueológico Wila Jawira. Unpublished manuscript on file in the Department of Anthropology, University of Chicago.

Armillas, P.
1971 Gardens on Swamps. *Science* 174:653–61.

Arnold, D.
1987 Kinship as Cosmology: Potatoes as Offspring among the Aymara of Highland Bolivia. *Canadian Journal of Native Studies* 7(2):323–37.

Arnold, D., and J. Jiménez Domingo de Dios Yapita
1992 *Un órden andino de las cosas.* La Paz: HISBOL and ILCA.

Aruwiyiri
1992 *Pachamax Tipusiwa: La Pachamama se enoja.* Oruro, Bolivia: Aruwiyiri and Ayllu Sartanani.

Asamblea de Pueblo Guarani
1992 Pamphlet produced for distribution at the event of the organization's one-hundred-year anniversary.

Ascarrunz, R.
1973 Contribución al conocimiento geológico del área comprendida entre los pueblos de Viacha, Coro Coro, y Umala. *Sociedad Geológica Boliviana* 20:29–64.

Augstburger, F.
1990 Agroecología andina: El concepto y las experiencias de AGRUCO. In *Agroecología y saber andino agro-biología,* compiled by AGRUCO, pp. 11–41. Cochabamba, Bolivia: AGRUCO and Praetec.
1992 Informe de inspección de quinua biológica producida por ANAPQUI en el altiplano sur de Bolivia. Unpublished report.

Badani, T.
1991 Bolivia: La experiencia del INDICEP. In *Etnías, educación y cultura: Defendemos lo nuestro,* compiled by ILDIS-Bolivia, pp. 27–30. La Paz: Editorial Nueva Sociedad.

Bakhmeteff, B. A.
1932 *Hydraulics of Open Channels.* New York: McGraw-Hill.

Barrios de Chungara, D.
1980 *La mujer y la organización.* La Paz: UNITAS, CIDOB, CIPCA.

Bartell, S., and A. L. Brenkert
1988 Spatial-Temporal Modeling of Nitrogen Dynamics in the Walker Branch Watershed. Abstract of paper presented at the third annual meeting of the U.S. chapter of the International Association of Landscape Geology, Albuquerque, New Mexico.

Bastien, J.
1978 *Mountain of the Condor: Metaphor and Ritual in an Andean Ayllu.* St. Paul, Minnesota: West Publishing.

Batchelor, B.
1980 Los camellones de Caymbe en la sierra de Ecuador. *America Indígena* 40:671–89.

Batey, R. A.
1987 Subsurface Interface Radar at Sepphoris, Israel, 1985. *Journal of Field Archaeology* 14:1–8.

Bear, J.
1988 *Dynamics of Fluids in Porous Media.* New York: Dover Publications.

Bear, J., and A. Verruijt
1987 *Modeling Groundwater Flow and Pollution with Computer Programs for Sample Cases.* Boston: D. Reidel.

Bebbington, A. J.
1992 *Searching for an "Indigenous" Agricultural Development: Indian Organizations and NGOs in the Central Andes of Ecuador.* Working Papers no. 45. Cambridge: Centre of Latin American Studies, University of Cambridge.

Bebbington, A. J., and J. Carney
1990 Geographers in the International Agricultural Research Centers: Theoretical and Practical

Considerations. *Annals of the Association of American Geographers* 80(1):34–48.

Benjamin, M. T., N. M. Johnson, and C. W. Naesar
1987 Recent Rapid Uplift in the Bolivian Andes: Evidence from Fission-Track Dating. *Geology* 15:680–83.

Bennett, W.
1934 *Excavations at Tiahuanaco.* Anthropological Papers of the American Museum of Natural History 34(3). New York: American Museum of Natural History.

Benson, L.
1986 The Sensitivity of Evaporation Rate to Climate Change: Results of an Energy-Balance Approach. *U.S. Geological Survey Water Resources Investigations Report,* pp. 86–148. Washington, D.C.

Berglund, B. E.
1986 *Handbook of Holocene Paleoecology and Paleohydrology.* Chichester, U.K.: John Wiley and Sons.

Bermann, M.
1990 *Prehispanic Household and Empire.* Unpublished Ph.D. dissertation, University of Michigan, Ann Arbor.
1994 *Lukurmata: Household Archaeology in Prehispanic Bolivia.* Princeton, New Jersey: Princeton University Press.

Bermann, M., P. Goldstein, C. Stanish, and L. Watanabe
1989 The Collapse of the Tiwanaku State: A View from the Osmore Drainage. In *Settlement and History in the Osmore Drainage, Peru,* edited by D. Rice, C. Stanish, and P. Scarr, pp. 269–85. Oxford: British Archaeological Reports, International Series 545(ii).

Berry, J. K., and J. K. Sailor
1987 Use of Geographic Information System for Storm Runoff Prediction from Small Urban Watersheds. *Environmental Management* 11:21–27.

Beyer, J. L.
1980 Africa. In *World Systems of Traditional Resource Management,* edited by G. A. Kelley, pp. 5–37. London: Arnold.

Binford, M. W.
1983 Ecological History of Lake Valencia, Venezuela: Interpretation of Animal Microfossils and Some Chemical, Physical, and Geological Features. *Ecological Monographs* 52:307–33.
1989 Where Should We Core? Simulating Spatial Patterns of Sedimentation in a Large Complex Lake with Fluctuating Water Level (Lake Huiñamarca, Bolivia-Peru). Poster presented at the Fifth International Symposium on Paleolimnology, Ambleside, Cumbria, U.K.
1990 $^{210}$Pb Dates and Their Associated Uncertainties for PIRLA cores. *Journal of Paleolimnology* 3:253–67.

Binford, M. W., and M. Brenner
1986 Dilution of $^{210}$Pb by Organic Sedimentation in Lakes of Different Trophic States, and Application to Studies of Sediment-Water Interactions. *Limnology and Oceanography* 31:584–95.
1988 Reply to Benoit and Hemond. *Limnology and Oceanography* 33:303–309.
1989 Resultados del estudios del primer año de la limnología en los ecosistemas de Tiwanaku. In *Arqueología de Lukurmata, vol. II,* edited by A. L. Kolata, pp. 213–36. La Paz: Instituto Nacional de Arqueología y Ediciones Puma Punku.

Binford, M., M. Brenner, and D. Engstrom
1991 Patrones de sedimentación temporal en la zona litoral del lago Titicaca Menor (Bolivia). In *Le lac Titicaca: Synthèse des connaissances actuelles,* edited by C. DeJoux and A. Iltis. Toulouse, France: ORSTOM.
1992 Temporal Patterns of Sedimentation in the Littoral Zone of Lake Wiñaymarka (Bolivia). In *Lake Titicaca: A Synthesis of Limnological Knowledge,* edited by C. DeJoux and A. Iltis. Monographiae Biologicae, vol. 68. Dordrecht: Kluwer Academic Publishers.

Binford, M., M. Brenner, and B. Leyden
1987 Paleolimnology of Tiwanaku Ecosystems: Results of Second-Year Studies. In *The Archaeology and Paleoecology of Lukurmata, Boliva: Second Preliminary Report of Proyecto Wila Jawira,* edited by A. Kolata and O. Rivera. Submitted to the Instituto Nacional de Arqueología, La Paz; National Science Foundation, Washington, D.C.; and National Endowment for the Humanities, Washington, D.C.

Binford, M. W., M. Brenner, T. J. Whitmore, A. Higuera-Gundy, E. S. Deevey, Jr., and B. W. Leyden
1987 Ecosystems, Paleoecology, and Human Distur-

bance in Subtropical and Tropical America. *Quaternary Science Reviews* 6:115–28.

Binford, M. W., E. S. Deevey, and T. L. Cisman
1983 Paleolimnology: An Historical Perspective on Lacustrine Ecosystems. *Annual Review of Ecology and Systematics* 14:255–86.

Binford, M. W., K. Hill, and K. Janosky
1990 Testing and Application of Spatially Explicit Models of Land-Water Interactions in Lakes of Acadia National Park, Maine. Paper presented at the fifth annual Landscape Ecology Symposium, Miami, Ohio.

Birbuet, D. G.
1992 *La economía campesina en la microregión de Caquiaviri y Comanche, provincia Pacajes.* La Paz: INVA, SEMTA.

Birks, H. H.
1973 Modern Macrofossil Assemblages in Lake Sediments in Minnesota. In *Quaternary Plant Ecology,* edited by H. J. B. Birks and R. G. West, pp. 173–89. Oxford: Blackwell Scientific Publications.
1980 Plant Microfossils in Quaternary Lake Sediments. *Limnology* 15:1–60.

Birks, H. J. B.
1986 Numerical Zonation, Comparison and Correlation of Quaternary Pollen-Stratigraphical Data. In *Handbook of Holocene Paeloecology and Paleohydrology,* edited by B. E. Berglund, pp. 743–74. Chichester, U.K: John Wiley and Sons.

Birks, H. J. B., and H. H. Birks
1981 *Quaternary Paleoecology.* London: Edward Arnold.

Boersma, L.
1967 Water-Table Fluctuations in the Soil Series of the Willamette Catena. American Society of Agricultural Engineers, *Transactions* 10:405.

Bormann, F. H., and G. E. Likens
1979 *Patterns and Process in a Forested Ecosystem.* New York: Springer-Verlag.

Boserup, E.
1965 *The Conditions of Agricultural Growth: The Economics of Agrarian Change under Population Pressure.* Chicago: Aldine Atherton.

Boulangé, B., and E. Aquize Jaen
1981 Morphologie, hydrographie et climatologie du lac Titicaca et de son bassin versant. *Revue d'Hydrobiologie Tropicale* 14:269–87.

Boulangé, B., C. Vargas, and L. A. Rodrigo
1981 La sedimentation actuelle dans le lac Titicaca. *Revue d'Hydrobiologie Tropicale* 14:299–309.

Bourges, J., J. Cortes, and E. Salas
1992 Hydrological Potential: The Water Resources. In *Lake Titicaca: A Synthesis of Limnological Knowledge,* edited by C. DeJoux and A. Iltis, pp. 523–38. Monographiae Biologicae, vol. 68. Dordrecht: Kluwer Academic Publishers.

Bouysse Cassagne, T.
1987 *La identidad Aymara.* La Paz: Hisbol-IFEA.

Bowen, H. J. M.
1979 *Environmental Chemistry of the Elements.* New York: Academic Press.

Bowman, I.
1909 Physiography of the Central Andes. *American Journal of Science,* series 4–28, vols. 197–217, pp. 373–402.
1916 *The Andes of Southern Perú: Geographical Reconnaissance along the Seventy-Third Meridian.* New York: Henry Holt.

Boyd, C. E.
1982 *Water Quality Management for Pond Fish Culture.* New York: Elsevier.

Bradbury, J. P., B. Leyden, M. Salgado-Labouriau, W. M. Lewis, Jr., C. Schubert, M. W. Binford, D. G. Frey, D. R. Whitehead, and F. H. Weibezahn
1981 Late Quaternary Environmental History of Lake Valencia, Venezuela, *Science* 214:1299–1305.

Bradley, R. S.
1985 *Quaternary Paleoclimatology: Methods of Paleoclimatic Reconstruction.* Boston: Allen & Unwin.

Brady, N. C.
1990 Making Agriculture a Sustainable Industry. In *Sustainable Agricultural Systems,* edited by C. A. Edwards et al., pp. 20–32. Ankeny, Iowa: Soil and Water Conservation Society.

Bray, W.
1983 Report on the 1981 Field Season in Calima. *Pro-calima* 3:2–31.

Brenner, M., and M. W. Binford
1986 Material Transfer from Water to Sediment in Florida Lakes. *Hydrobiologia* 143:55–61.

Brenner, M., C. Schelske, J. Curtis, D. Hodel, M. Binford, and M. Abbott
1993 A High Resolution Paleoclimate Record from Lago Huiñaimarca (Lago Titicaca Menor), Bolivia. *Abstracts of the Sixth International Palaeolimnology Symposium.* Canberra: Australian National University.

Briant, P.
1988 Le nomadisme du Grand Roi. *Iranica Antiqua* 23:253–73.

Briggs, L. T.
1981 Missionary, Patrón, and Radio Aymara. In *The Aymara Language in Its Social and Cultural Context,* edited by M. J. Hardman, pp. 175–84. Gainesville: University of Florida Press.

Brix, H., and H. H. Schierup
1989 The Use of Aquatic Macrophytes in Water-Pollution Control. *Ambio* 18:100–107.

Broadbent, S.
1966 The Site of Chibcha Bogota. *Ñawpa Pacha* 4:135–47.
1968 A Prehistoric Field System in Chibcha Territory, Colombia. *Ñawpa Pacha* 6:1–13.

Brookfield, H.
1961 The Highland People of New Guinea: A Study of Distribution and Localization. *Geographical Journal* 127:436–48.

Browder, J.
1989 *Fragile Lands of Latin America: Strategies for Sustainable Development.* Boulder, Colorado: Westview Press.

Browman, D.
1974 Pastoral Nomadism in the Andes. *Current Anthropology* 15:188–96.
1978 Toward the Development of the Tiwanaku (Tiahuanaco) State. In *Advances in Andean Archaeology,* edited by D. Browman, pp. 327–49. The Hague: Mouton.
1980 Tiwanaku Expansion and Altiplano Economic Patterns. *Estudios Arqueológicos* 5:107–120. Universidad de Chile, Antogasta.
1981 New Light on Andean Tiwanaku. *American Scientist* 69:408–19.
1984 Tiwanaku: Development of Interzonal Trade and Economic Expansion in the Altiplano. In *Social and Economic Organization in the Prehispanic Andes,* edited by D. Browman, R. Burger, and M. Rivera, pp. 117–42. Oxford: British Archaeological Reports, International Series 194.

Brush, S., and E. Taylor
1993 Diversidad biológico en el cultivo de papa. In *Chacra de papa, economía y ecología,* edited by E. Mayer, M. Glave, S. Brush, and E. Taylor, pp. 217–61. Lima: CEPES.

Buechler, H. C., and J.-M. Buechler
1971 *The Bolivian Aymara.* New York: Holt, Rinehart, and Winston.

Burrough, P. A.
1986 *Principles of Geographical Information Systems for Land Resources Assessment.* Oxford: Clarendon Press.
1987 Spatial Aspects of Ecological Data. In *Data Analysis in Community and Landscape Ecology,* edited by R. H. Jongman, C. J. F. ter Braak, and O. F. R. van Tongeren, pp. 213–51. Wageningen, Netherlands: Pudoc Wageningen.

Cabrera, A. L.
1968 Ecología vegetal de la puna. In *Geo-Ecology of the Mountainous Regions of the Tropical Americas,* edited by C. Troll, pp. 91–116. Bonn: Ferd. Dümmlers Verlag.

Cajias, M., and B. Fernández
1987 *Manual de tintes naturales.* La Paz: Manuales Técnicas, SEMTA.

Cajías, M., and L. Girón
1987 *Manual de plantas y preparados medicinales.* La Paz: Manuales Técnicas, SEMTA.

Calnek, E.
1972 Settlement Pattern and Chinampa Agriculture. *American Antiquity* 37:104–15.

Cámara de Senadores, Comisión de Ciencia y Tecnología, and Cámara de Deputados, Comisión de Educación.
1992 *Proyecto de ley.* La Paz: Oficialización de Idiomas.

Campbell, K. E., C. D. Fraily, and L. J. Arellano
1985 The Geology of the Río Beni: Further Evidence for Holocene Flooding in Amazonia. Natural History Museum of Los Angeles County, *Contributions in Science* 364:1–18.

Cárdenas, V. H.
1988 La lucha de un pueblo. In *Raíces de America: El mundo Aymara,* edited by X. Albó, pp. 495–535. Madrid: Alianza Editorial.
1991 Bolivia: Hacia una educación intercultural. In *Etnías, educación y cultura: Defendemos lo nuestro,* compiled by ILDIS-Bolivia, pp. 47–51. La Paz: Editorial Nueva Sociedad.
1992 Prólogo. In *Educación indigena: Ciudadanía o colonización?* edited by R. Choque, V. Soria, H. Mamani, E. Ticona, and R. Conde, pp. 5–16. La Paz: Taller de Historia Oral Andina.

Carmouze, J-P., and E. Aquize Jaen
1981 La regulation hydrique du lac Titicaca et l'hydrologie de ses tributaires. *Revue d'Hydrobiologie Tropicale* 14:311–28.

Carmouze, J-P., C. L. Arce, and J. Quintanilla
1977 La regulation hydrique des lacs Titicaca et Poop. Cahiers ORSTOM, *Serie Hydrobiologie* 11:269–83.
1984 Les bilans hydriques, hydrochimiques et energetiques du lac Titicaca. *Verhandlungen Internationale, Vereinigung für Theoretische und Angewantde Limnologie* 22:1244–45.
1992 Hydrochemical Regulation of the Lake and Water Chemistry of Its Inflow Waters. In *Lake Titicaca: A Synthesis of Limnological Knowledge,* edited by C. DeJoux and A. Iltis, pp. 98–112. Monographiae Biologicae, vol. 68. Dordrecht: Kluwer Academic Publishers.

Carney, H. J.
1984 Productivity, Population Growth, and Physiological Responses to Nutrient Enrichments by Phytoplankton of Lake Titicaca, Peru-Bolivia. *Verhandlungen Internationale, Vereinigung für Theoretische und Angewantde Limnologie* 22:1253–57.

Carney, H. J., M. W. Binford, A. L. Kolata, R. Martin, and C. Goldman
1993 Nutrient and Sediment Retention in Andean Raised-Field Agriculture. *Nature* 364:131–33.

Carney, H. J., P. J. Richerson, and P. Eloranta
1987 Lake Titicaca (Peru/Bolivia) Phytoplankton: Species Composition and Structural Comparison with Other Tropical and Temperate Lakes. *Archiv für Hydrobiologie* 110:365–85.

Carpenter, S. R.
1981 Submerged Vegetation: An Internal Factor in Lake Ecosystem Succession. *American Naturalist* 118:372–83.

Carpenter, S. R., and D. M. Lodge
1986 Effects of Submerged Macrophytes on Ecosystem Processes. *Aquatic Botany* 24:341–70.

Carrizo, E. V.
1993 *Autopsía de la enfermedad: La automedicación y el itinerario terapeútico en el sistema de salud de Vallegrande-Bolivia.* La Paz: Acción Internacional por la Salud (AID); Fundaciones Simon I. Patiño & Pro Bolivia.

Carter, W. E.
1964 *Aymara Communities and the Bolivian Agrarian Reform.* University of Florida Social Sciences Monographs, no. 24. Gainesville: University of Florida Press.

Carter, W., and X. Albó
1988 La comunidad Aymara: Un mini-estado en conflicto. In *Raíces de America: El mundo Aymara,* edited by X. Albó, pp. 451–95. Madrid: Alianza Editorial.

Casaverde, J.
1977 El trueque en la economía pastoral. In *Pastores de puna: Uywamichig Punaruna Kuna,* edited by J. Flores-Ochoa, pp. 171–91. Lima: Instituto de Estudios Peruanos.

CEE (Comisión Episcopal de Educación)
1988 *Educación y transformación social.* La Paz: Comisión Episcopal.

Choque, R., V. Soria, H. Mamani, E. Ticona, and R. Conde
1992 *Educación indígena: Ciudadanía o colonización?* La Paz: Taller de Historia Oral Andina.

Chow, V. T.
1959 *Open Channel Hydraulics.* New York: McGraw-Hill.

Chumiray, G.
1992 La experiencia de la asamblea del pueblo Guarani. In *Futuro de la comunidad campesina,* compiled by CIPCA, pp. 61–79. La Paz: Centro de Investigación y Promoción del

Campesinado (CIPCA), Cuadernos de Investigación 35.

CIDOB (Confederación Indígena del Oriente, Chaco, y Amazonia Boliviana)
1992 *Proyecto de ley de pueblos indígenas del Oriente, Chaco, y Amazonia.* Santa Cruz, Bolivia: CIDOB.

CIEP (Centro de Investigación de Energía y Población)
1990 *Primer encuentro interdepartamental del amaranto.* La Paz: Unidad de Tecnología Alimentaria Boliviana del CIEP.

CIEP-UTAB (Centro de Investigación de Energía y Población and Unidad de Tecnología Alimentaria Boliviana del CIEP)
1991 *Primer encuentro de productores campesinos de amaranto.* La Paz: UTAB.

Cieza de León, Pedro de
1959 [1553] *The Incas.* Translated by H. de Onis. Norman: University of Oklahoma Press.

CIPCA (Centro de Investigación y Promoción del Campesino)
1992 *Futuro de la comunidad campesina.* La Paz: CIPCA, Cuadernos de Investigación 35.

CIRF (Consejo Internacional de Recursos Fitogenéticos)
1981 *Descriptores de quinua.* Rome: CIRF.
1991 *Por una Bolivia diferente: Aportes para un proyecto histórico popular.* La Paz: CIPCA, Cuadernos de Investigación 34.

Clapperton, C. M., and D. E. Sugden
1988 Holocene Glacier Fluctuations in South America and Antarctica. *Quaternary Science Reviews* 7:185–98.

Clement, C. O., and M. Moseley
1989 Agricultural Dynamics in the Andes. In *Ecology, Settlement, and History in the Osmore Drainage,* edited by D. Rice, C. Stanish, and P. Scarr, pp. 435–55. Oxford: British Archaeological Reports, International Series 545(ii).

Cobo, Bernabé
1890–95 [1653] *Historia del nuevo mundo.* 4 vols. M. J. de la Espada, editor. Seville: Sociedad de Bibliofilos Andaluces.
1979 [1653] *History of the Inca Empire: An Account of the Indians' Customs and Their Origin Together with a Treatise on Inca Legends, History, and Social Institutions.* Translated and edited by R. Hamilton. Austin: University of Texas Press.

Colinvaux, P. A.
1987 Amazon Diversity in the Light of the Paleoecological Record. *Quaternary Science Review* 6:93–114.

Collins, J.
1983 Translation, Traditions, and the Organization of Productive Activity: The Case of Aymara Affinal Kinship Terms. In *Bilingualism,* edited by A. M. Miracle, pp. 11–21. Southern Anthropological Society Proceedings no. 16. Athens: University of Georgia Press.

Collins, R. E.
1961 *Flow of Fluids through Porous Media.* New York: Reinhold.

Collot, D., F. Koriyama, and E. García
1983 Répartition, biomasses et production de macrophytes du lac Titicaca. *Revue D'Hydrobiologie Tropicale* 16:241–62.

Condori, A. M.
1989 *Mi despertar.* La Paz: HISBOL.

Contreras, A. B.
1991 *Etapa de una larga marcha.* La Paz: Asociación Aquí Avance, Educación Radiofónica de Bolivia.

Cook, A.
1983 Aspects of State Ideology in Huari and Tiwanaku Iconography: The Central Deity and the Sacrificer. In *Investigations of the Andean Past,* edited by D. H. Sandweiss, pp. 161–85. Ithaca, New York: Cornell University, Latin American Studies Program.

CORDECH-COTESU (Corporación de Desarrollo de Chuquisaca and Corporación Técnica Suiza)
1989 *Informe, evaluación de plantaciones, subregiones: Chuquisaca centro.* Sucre, Bolivia: COTESU.
1992a *Planes operativas 1992 de los 6 nucleos.* Informe Anual. Sucre, Bolivia: CORDECH.

1992b *Plan agroforestal de Chuquisaca.* Informe Anual. Sucre, Bolivia: CORDECH.

Correll, D. S.
1962 *The Potato and Its Wild Relatives: Section Tuberarium of the Genus* Solanum. Texas Research Foundation Botanical Studies, A series, vol. 4. Renner, Texas.

Costanza, R., F. H. Sklar, and M. L. White
1989 Modeling Coastal Landscape Dynamics. *BioScience* 40:91–107.

Coward, E., Jr.
1979 Principles of Social Organization in an Indigenous Irrigation System. *Human Organization* 38(1):28–36.

CSUTCB (Confederación Sindical Única de Trabajadores Campesinos de Bolivia)
1984 *Despues de cuatro siglos de opresión.* La Paz: CSUTCB.
1989 *Debate sobre documentos políticos y asamblea de nacionalidades.* La Paz: CEDLA.

Cusack, D.
1983 Quinua: Grain of the Incas. Paper presented at the annual meeting of the American Association for the Advancement of Science, Detroit.

Custred, G.
1974 Llameros y comercio interregional. In *Reciprocidad e intercambio en los Andes peruanos,* edited by G. Alberti and E. Mayer, pp. 252–89. Peru Problema, 12. Lima: Instituto de Estudios Peruanos.

D'Altroy, T. N.
1992 *Provincial Power in the Inka Empire,* Washington, D.C.: Smithsonian Institution Press.

Dandler, J., and C. Sage
1985 What Is Happening to Andean Potatoes? *Development Dialogue* 1:125–38.

Darch, J. P. (editor)
1983 *Drained Fields of the Americas.* Oxford: British Archaeological Reports, International Series no. 189.

Davalos, J., V. Cereceda, and G. Martínez
1992 *Textiles Tarabuco.* Sucre, Bolivia: FIDA.

Davis, M. B.
1976 Erosion Rates and Land-Use History in Southern Michigan. *Environmental Conservation* 3:139–48.

Davis, M. B., and M. S. Ford
1982 Sediment Focusing in Mirror Lake, New Hampshire, U.S.A. *Limnological Oceanography* 27:137–50.

Dean, W. E., Jr.
1974 Determination of Carbonate and Organic Matter in Calcareous Sediments and Sedimentary Rocks by Loss on Ignition: Comparison with Other Methods. *Journal of Sedimentary Petrology* 44:242–48.

Dearing, J.
1986 Core Correlation and Total Sediment Influx. In *Handbook of Holocene Paleoecology and Paleohydrology,* edited by B. E. Berglund, pp. 247–65. Chichester, U.K: John Wiley and Sons.

Deevey, E. S., D. S. Rice, P. M. Rice, H. H. Vaughan, M. Brenner, and M. S. Flannery
1979 Mayan Urbanism: Impact on a Tropical Karst Environment. *Science* 169:647–54.

Deevey, E., and M. Stuiver
1964 Distribution of Natural Isotopes of Carbon in Linsley Pond and Other New England Lakes. *Limnology and Oceanography* 9:1–11.

DeJoux, C.
1992a The Benthic Populations: Distribution and Seasonal Variations. In *Lake Titicaca: A Synthesis of Limnological Knowledge,* edited by C. DeJoux and A. Iltis, pp. 383–404. Monographiae Biologicae, vol. 68. Dordrecht: Kluwer Academic Publishers.
1992b The Avifauna. In *Lake Titicaca: A Synthesis of Limnological Knowledge,* edited by C. DeJoux and A. Iltis, pp. 460–69. Monographiae Biologicae, vol. 68. Dordrecht: Kluwer Academic Publishers.

DeJoux, C., and A. Iltis (editors)
1992 *Lake Titicaca: A Synthesis of Limnological Knowledge.* Monographiae Biologicae, vol. 68. Dordrecht: Kluwer Academic Publishers.

Delgado, F.
1989 *La agroecología andina dentro de las estra-*

*tegías de desarrollo rural.* Agroecología de la Universidad de Cochabamba, Serie Técnica no. 21. Cochabamba, Bolivia.

D'Emilio, L.
1991a Educación bilingue: Estrategía, conquista, o derecho. *Revista Unitas* 3:21–27.
1991b Bolivia: La conquista de la escuela. El Proyecto Educativo de las Guarani-Chiriguas. In *Etnías, educación, y cultura: Defendemos lo nuestro,* compiled by ILDIS-Bolivia, pp. 37–47. La Paz: Editorial Nueva Sociedad.

Denevan, W. N.
1964 Pre-Spanish Earthworks in the Llanos de Mojos of Northeastern Bolivia. *Revista Geográfica* 32:17–25.
1966 *The Aboriginal Cultural Geography of the Llanos de Mojos of Bolivia. Ibero-Americana.* Berkeley: University of California Press.
1970 Aboriginal Drained-Field Cultivation in the Americas. *Science* 169:647–54.
1980 Tipología de configuraciones agrícolos prehispánica. *America Indígena* 40:619–52.
1982 Hydraulic Agriculture in the American Tropics: Forms, Measures, and Recent Research. In *Maya Subsistence: Essays in Honor of Dennis E. Puleston,* edited by K. V. Flannery, pp. 181–203. New York: Academic Press.

Denevan, W. N., and K. Mathewson
1983 Preliminary Results of the Samborondon Raised Field Project, Guayas Basin, Ecuador. In *Drained Field Agriculture in Central and South America,* edited by J. P. Darch, pp. 167–82. Oxford: British Archaeological Reports, International Series 189.

Denevan, W. N., and B. L. Turner II
1974 Forms, Functions, and Associations of Raised Fields in the Old World Tropics. *Journal of Tropical Geography* 39:24–33.

DeSilva, S. L., and P. W. Francis
1991 *Volcanoes of the Central Andes.* Berlin: Springer-Verlag.

De Vries, T.
1987 A Review of Geological Evidence for Ancient El Niño Activity in Peru. *Journal of Geophysical Research* 92(C13):14,471–79.

Digerfelt, G.
1986 Studies on Past Lake-Level Fluctuations. In *Handbook of Holocene Paleoecology and Paleohydrology,* edited by B. E. Berglund, pp. 127–43. Chichester, U.K: John Wiley and Sons.

Dillon, M., and T. Abercrombie
1988 The Destroying Christ: An Aymara Myth of Conquest. In *Rethinking History and Myth,* edited by J. D. Hill, pp. 50–77. Urbana: University of Illinois Press.

Disselhoff, H. D.
1968 *Oäsestadte und Zaubersteine im Land der Inka. Archaeologische Forschungersreisen im Peru.* Berlin: Sfari-Verlag.

Dobrovolny, E.
1962 *Geología del valle de La Paz.* La Paz: GEOBOL.

Downing, T. E., and M. Gibson (editors)
1974 *Irrigation's Impact on Society.* Tucson: University of Arizona Press.

Duffie, R. C., and W. A. Beckman
1974 *Solar Energy Thermal Processes.* New York: Wiley-Interscience.

Dunn, O., and V. Clark
1974 *Applied Statistics: Analyisis of Variance and Regression.* New York: John Wiley and Sons.

Dunne, T.
1979 Sediment Yield and Land Use in Tropical Catchments. *Journal of Hydrology* 42:281–300.

Dunne, T., and L. B. Leopold
1978 *Water in Environmental Planning.* San Francisco: W. H. Freeman.

Eakins, J. D., and R. T. Morrison
1978 A New Procedure for the Determination of Lead-210 in Lake and Marine Sediments. *International Journal of Applied Radiative Isotopes* 29:531–36.

Eidt, R. C.
1977 Detection and Examination of Anthosols by Phosphate Analysis. *Science* 197:1327–33.
1984 *Advances in Abandoned Settlement Analysis: Application to Prehistoric Anthrosols in Colombia, South America.* Milwaukee: Center for Latin America, University of Wisconsin.

Ellenberg, H.
1975 Vegetationsstufen in perhumiden bis perariden Bereichen der tropischen Anden. *Phytocornologia* 2(3/4):368–87.
1979 Man's Influence on Tropical Mountain Ecosystems in South America. *Journal of Ecology* 67:401–16.

Ellison, R., B. Klinck, and M. Hawkins
1989 Deformation Events in the Andean Orogenic Cycle in the Altiplano and Western Cordillera, Southern Peru. *Journal of South American Earth Sciences* 2:263–76.

Engstrom, D. R., and H. E. Wright, Jr.
1984 Chemical Stratigraphy of Lake Sediments as a Record of Environmental Change. In *Lake Sediments and Environmental History: Studies in Palaeolimnology and Palaeoecology in Honour of Winifred Tutin,* edited by E. Y. Haworth and J. W. G. Lund, pp. 11–67. Minneapolis: University of Minnesota Press.

*En Marcha* (published by Acción Cultural Loyola Sucre [ACLO], Sucre, Bolivia)

Erickson, C.
1984 Waru-Waru: Una tecnología agrícola del altiplano prehispánico. *Boletín del Instituo de Estudios Aymaras,* Serie 2(18):3–37. Puno.
1985 Applications of Prehistoric Andean Technology: Experiments in Raised Field Agriculture, Huatta, Lake Titicaca: 1981–1982. In *Prehistoric Intensive Agriculture in the Tropics, Part 1,* edited by I. Farrington, pp. 209–32. Oxford: British Archaeological Reports, International Series 232(i).
1987 The Dating of Raised-Field Agriculture in the Lake Titicaca Basin, Peru. In *Pre-Hispanic Agricultural Fields in the Andean Region, Part 1,* edited by W. Denevan, K. Mathewson, and G. Knapp, pp. 373–84. Oxford: British Archaeological Reports, International Series 359(i).
1988a *An Archaeological Investigation of Raised Field Agriculture in the Lake Titicaca Basin of Peru.* Ph.D. dissertation, University of Illinois at Urbana-Champaign. University Microfilms, Ann Arbor.
1988b Raised-Field Agriculture in the Lake Titicaca Basin: Putting Ancient Andean Agriculture Back to Work. *Expedition* 30(3):8–16.
1992 Prehistoric Landscape Management in the Andean Highlands: Raised Field Agriculture and Its Environmental Impact. *Population and Environment: A Journal of Interdisciplinary Studies* 13(4):285–300.

Erickson, C., and D. Brinkmeier
1991 Raised-Field Rehabilitation Projects in the Northern Lake Titicaca Basin. Unpublished Report to the Inter-American Foundation.

Erickson, C. L., and K. L. Candler
1989 Raised Fields and Sustainable Agriculture in the Lake Titicaca Basin. In *Fragile Lands of Latin America: Strategies for Sustainable Development,* edited by J. Browder, pp. 230–48. Boulder, Colorado: Westview Press.

Erickson, C., J. Estevez C., W. Winkler C., and M. Michel L.
1991 Estudio preliminar de los sistemas agrícolas precolombiano en el departamento del Beni: Informe de los trabajos de campo efectuados durante el mes de julio de 1990. Unpublished manuscript on file in the Instituto Nacional de Arqueología, La Paz.

FASOR (Federación del Ayllus del Sur de Oruro)
1992 Pamphlet stating FASOR's organization principles and objectives. On file, Inter-American Foundation, Washington, D.C.

Fernández, J.
1989 *Estudio base: Comunidades de las provincias Los Andes y Ingavi.* Plan Internacional Altiplano. La Paz: Documentos Internos.

Fernea, R. A.
1970 *Shaykh and Effendi: Changing Patterns of Authority among the El Shabana of Southern Iraq.* Cambridge: Harvard University Press.

Flores-Ochoa, J.
1983 El cultivo en qocha en la puna sur-andina. In *Evolucion y técnica de la agricultura andina,* edited by A. Fries, pp. 45–79. Cuzco: Instituto Indígena Interamericana.
1987 Cultivation in the *Qocha* of the South Andean Puna. In *Arid Land Use Strategies and Risk Management in the Andes,* edited by D. Browman, pp. 271–96. Boulder, Colorado: Westview Press.

Fontes, J. C., and R. Gonfiantini
1967 Comportement isotopique au cours de l'evaporation de deux bassins sahariens. *Earth and Planetary Science Letters* 3:258–66.

Forman, R. T. T.
1991 Ecologically Sustainable Landscapes: The Role of Spatial Configuration. In *Changing Landscapes: An Ecological Perspective,* edited by I. S. Zonneveld and R. T. T. Forman, pp. 261–78. New York: Springer-Verlag.

Franqueville, A., and G. Aguilar
1988 *El Alto de La Paz: Migraciones y estrategías alimentarias en Bolivia.* La Paz: INAN-ORSTOM.

Frey, D. G.
1969 The Rationale of Paleolimnology. *Verhandlungen Internationale Vereinigung für Theoretische und Angewantde Limnologie* 17:7–18.
1986 Cladocera Analysis. In *Handbook of Holocene Paleoecology and Paleohydrology,* edited by B. E. Berglund, pp. 667–92. Chichester, U.K: John Wiley and Sons.

Galdo Pagaza, R.
1981 Artesanías y pequeñas industrias en el área colindante con el lago Titicaca. In *Acerca de la historia y el universo Aymara,* edited by D. Llanque, pp. 77–106. Lima: Centro de Información, Estudios y Documentación.

Gallagher, J., R. Boszhardt, R. Sasso, and K. Stevenson
1985 Oneota Ridged Field Agriculture in Southwestern Wisconsin. *American Antiquity* 50:605–12.

Gallagher, R. H.
1975 *Finite Element Analysis Fundamentals.* Englewood Cliffs, New Jersey: Prentice Hall.

Garaycochea Z., I.
1987 Agricultural Experiments in Raised Field Agriculture in the Lake Titicaca Basin, Peru. In *Pre-Hispanic Agricultural Fields in the Andean Region,* edited by W. M. Denevan, K. Mathewson, and G. Knapp, pp. 385–98. Oxford: British Archaeological Reports, International Series 359.

Garnsey, P.
1988 *Famine and Food Supply in the Graeco-Roman World: Responses to Risk and Crisis.* Cambridge: Cambridge University Press.

Gasse, F., R. Tehet, A. Durand, E. Gibert, and J. Fontes
1990 The Arid-Humid Transition in the Sahara and the Sahel during the Last Deglaciation. *Nature* 346:141–46.

Gersberg, R. M., B. V. Elkins, and C. R. Goldman
1984 Wastewater Treatment by Artificial Wetlands. *Water Science Technology* 17:443–50.

Gisbert, T., S. Arze, and M. Cajias
1987 *Arte textile y mundo andino.* La Paz: Gisbert y Companía.

Gliessman, S. R.
1990 *Agroecology: Researching the Ecological Basis for Sustainable Agriculture.* New York: Springer-Verlag.

Godelier, M.
1978 Infrastructures, Society and History. *Current Anthropology* 19:763–71.
1988 *The Mental and the Material.* London: Verso.

Godoy, R. A.
1984 Ecological Degradation and Agricultural Intensification in the Andean Highlands. *Human Ecology* 12(4):359–83.
1991 The Evolution of Common Field Agriculture in the Andes: A Hypothesis. *Comparative Studies in Society and History* 33(2):395–414.

Godoy, R. A., and M. Franco
1992 Small Potatoes and Big Ears: Neglect and Biases in Bolivia's Agricultural Research. Copy of manuscript on file, Harvard Institute of International Development.

Goldman, C. R.
1974 *Eutrophication of Lake Tahoe Emphasizing Water Quality.* EPA-600/3-74-034. Washington, D.C.: U.S. Government Printing Office.

Goldschmidt, W.
1982 Toward an Anthropological Approach to Economic Development. *Human Organization* 41(1):80–82.

Goldstein, P.
1989 *Omo, a Tiwanaku Provincial Center in Moquegua, Peru.* Unpublished Ph.D. dissertation, University of Chicago.

Gómez-Pompa, A.
1978 An Old Answer to the Future. *Maxingira* 5:50–55.

Gómez-Pompa, A., H. L. Morales, E. Jiménez Avilla, and J. Jiménez Avilla.
1982 Experiences in Traditional Hydraulic Agriculture. In *Maya Subsistence: Studies in Memory of Dennis Puleston,* edited by K. V. Flannery, pp. 327–42. New York: Academic Press.

Graf, K.
1977 Nuevos datos palinológicos del cuaternario alto de Bolivia. *Boletín del Servico Geológico de Bolivia,* Series A, 1:1–14.
1981a Palynologial Investigations of Two Post-Glacial Peat Bogs near the Boundary of Bolivia and Peru. *Journal of Biogeography* 8:353–68.
1981b Zum Höhenverlauf der Subnivalstufe in den Tropischen Anden insbesondere in Bolivien und Ecuador. *Zeitschrift für Geomorphologie* 37:1–24.
1986 *Klima und vegetationsgeographie der Anden.* Schriftenrenreich Physische Geographie, vol 19. Geographisches Institut der Universitiat Zurich.

Graffam, G.
1990 *Raised Fields without Bureaucracy: An Archaeological Examination of Intensive Wetland Cultivation in the Pampa Koani Zone, Lake Titicaca, Bolivia.* Unpublished Ph.D. dissertation, University of Toronto.
1992 Beyond State Collapse: Rural History, Raised Fields, and Pastoralism in the South Andes. *American Anthropologist* 94(4):882–904.

Grove, J.
1988 *The Little Ice Age.* London: Methuen.

Guillet, D.
1981 Land Tenure, Ecological Zone, and Agricultural Regime in the Central Andes. *American Ethnologist* 8(1):139–56.

Gutierrez, O.
1990 *Reunión del programa nacional de investigación de la papa.* Manuscript on file, Centro de Investigación de la Papa (CIPCA), Cochabamba.

Haas, F.
1955 Molusca: Gastropoda. Report no. 17, Percy Sladen Trust Expedition to Lake Titicaca in 1937. *Transactions of the Limnological Society of London,* Series 3, 1(3):275–308.

Håkanson, L., and M. Jansson
1983 *Principles of Lake Sedimentology.* Berlin: Springer-Verlag.

Hansen, B. C. S., H. E. Wright, and J. P. Bradbury
1984 Pollen Studies in the Junin Area, Central Peruvian Andes. *Geological Society of America Bulletin* 95:1454–65.

Hardman, M. J.
1976 *Andean Women.* AUFS Documentary Film Program: Faces of Change, Film Essay no. 4, The Bolivia Project. Hanover, New Hampshire: Wheelock Education Resources.
1981 Introductory Essay. In *The Aymara Language in Its Social and Cultural Context,* edited by M. J. Hardman, pp. 3–17. Gainesville: University of Florida Press.
1985 Aymara and Quechua: Languages in Contact. In *South America Indian Languages,* edited by H. Klein and L. R. Stark, pp. 617–43. Austin: University of Texas Press.

Harrison, P. D.
1977 The Rise of Bajos and the Fall of the Maya. In *Social Process in Maya Prehistory: Studies in Honour of Sir Eric Thompson,* edited by N. Hammond, pp. 470–508. New York: Academic Press.
1978 Bajos Revisited: Visual Evidence for One System of Agriculture. In *Pre-Hispanic Maya Agriculture,* edited by P. D. Harrison and B. L. Turner II, pp. 247–54. Albuquerque: University of New Mexico Press.

Harwood, R. R.
1990 A History of Sustainable Agriculture. In *Sustainable Agricultural Systems,* edited by C. A. Edwards et al., pp. 3–19. Iowa: Soil and Water Conservation Society.

Hassig, R.
1985 *Trade, Tribute, and Transportation: The Sixteenth Century Political Economy of the Valley of Mexico.* Norman: University of Oklahoma Press.

Hastenrath, S.
1967 Observations on the Snowline in the Peruvian Andes. *Journal of Glaciology* 6:541–50.

Hastenrath, S., and J. Kutzbach
1985 Late Pleistocene Climate and Water Budget

of the South American Altiplano. *Quaternary Research* 24:249–56.

Hastings, C., and M. Moseley
1975 The Adobes of Huaca del Sol and Huaca de la Luna. *American Antiquity* 40:196–203.

Hatch, J.
1976 *The Corn Farmers of Motupe: A Study of Traditional Farming Practices in Northern Coastal Peru.* Land Tenure Center Monograph 1. Madison: University of Wisconsin.
1983 *Nuestros conocimientos: Prácticas agropecuarias tradicionales en Bolivia, vol. 1: Región altiplano.* La Paz: Ministerio de Agricultura y Asuntos Campesinos (MACA), Agencia Internacional de Desarrollo (AID), and Rural Development Services (RDS).

Healy, K.
1989 Coca, the State, and the Peasantry in Bolivia, 1982–88. *Journal of Interamerican Studies and World Affairs* 30(1/2):105–27.
1991 Political Ascent of Bolivia's Peasant Coca Leaf Producers. *Journal of Interamerican Studies and World Affairs* 33(1):87–123.
1992 Back to the Future: Ethno-Development among the Jalq'a. *Grassroots Development* 16(2):22–34.

Hearne, J. W., and C. Howard-Williams
1988 Modeling Nitrate Removal by Riparian Vegetation in a Springfield Stream: The Influence of Land-Use Practices. *Ecological Modeling* 42:178–98.

Heilman, L.
1982 *U.S. Development Assistance to Rural Bolivia, 1941–1974: The Search for a Development Strategy.* Unpublished Ph.D. dissertation, American University, Washinton, D.C.

Henderson, F. M.
1966 *Open Channel Flow.* New York: Macmillan.

Heusser, C. J.
1971 *Pollen and Spores of Chile.* Tucson: University of Arizona Press.

Hilton, J., J. P. Lishman, and A. Millington
1986 A Comparison of Some Rapid Techniques for the Measurement of Density in Soft Sediments. *Sedimentology* 33:777–81.

Hoopes, R. W., and C. Sage
1982 *Limiting Factors in Bolivian Potato Production and Prospects for Improvement.* Working Paper no. 005/82. La Paz, Bolivia: Consortium for International Development (CID).

Hornberger, N. H.
1987 Schooltime, Classtime, and Academic Learning Time in Rural Highland Puno. *Anthropology and Education Quarterly* 18(3):207–21.

Howard-Williams, C., and G. M. Lenton
1975 The Role of the Littoral Zone in the Functioning of a Shallow Tropical Lake System. *Freshwater Biology* 15:391–431.

Huanca, T.
1991a *Jilirinaksan Arsuwipa: Testimonios de nuestros mayores.* La Paz: Taller de Historia Oral Andina.
1991b Bolivia: Bilingualismo y ensenanza bilingüe. In *Etnías, educación y cultura: Defendemos lo nuestro,* compiled by ILDIS, pp. 23–27. La Paz: Editorial Nueva Sociedad.

Huanca, T., and E. Aguilar
1992 *Estudio etnográfico sobre conocimientos y prácticas relacionados con las infecciones respiratorias agudas (IRA) en dos comunidades de Bolivia.* Ministerio de Prevision Social y Salud Pública, Direccion Nacional de Atención a las Personas. La Paz: UNICEF-OPS/OMS.

Huffman, E. W. D., Jr.
1977 Performance of a New Automatic Carbon Dioxide Coulometer. *Microchemical Journal* 22:567–73.

Hunt, R.
1988 Size and Structure of Authority in Canal Irrigation Systems. *Journal of Anthropological Research* 44:335–55.

Hyams, E. S.
1952 *Soil and Civilization.* London: Thames and Hudson.

ILDIS-Bolivia (Instituto Latinoamericano de Investigaciones Sociales)
1991 *Etnías, educación y cultura: Defendemos lo nuestro.* La Paz: Editorial Nueva Sociedad.

Iltis, A.
1988 *Biomasas fitoplanctónicas del lago Titicaca bo-*

*liviano*. ORSTOM en Bolivia, Mission de La Paz, Informe no. 101-06-88. ORSTOM.

1992 Algae: General Floristic Study. In *Lake Titicaca: A Synthesis of Limnological Knowledge,* edited by C. DeJoux and A. Iltis, pp. 176–81. Monographiae Biologicae, vol. 68. Dordrecht: Kluwer Academic Publishers.

Iltis, A., and P. Mourguiart
1991 Repartición y biomasas. In *Lake Titicaca: A Synthesis of Limnological Knowledge,* edited by C. DeJoux and A. Iltis, pp. 251–61. Monographiae Biologicae, vol. 68. Dordrecht: Kluwer Academic Publishers.

Isbell, W. H.
1983 Shared Ideology and Parallel Political Development: Huari and Tiwanaku. In *Investigations of the Andean Past,* edited by D. H. Sandweiss, pp. 186–208. Ithaca, New York: Latin American Studies Program, Cornell University.

Isbell, W. H., and G. F. McEwan (editors)
1991 *Huari Administrative Structure: Prehistoric Monumental Architecture and State Government.* Washington, D.C.: Dumbarton Oaks Research Library and Collection.

Isbell, W. H., and K. Schreiber
1978 Was Huari a State? *American Antiquity* 43:372–89.

Izko, X.
1992 *La doble frontera: Ecología, política y ritual en el altiplano central.* La Paz: HISBOL-CERES.

Jackson, S. T., and D. F. Charles
1988 Aquatic Macrophytes in Adirondack (New York) Lakes: Patterns of Species Composition in Relation to Environment. *Canadian Journal of Botany* 66:1449–60.

James, D. E.
1971 Plate Tectonic Model for the Evolution of the Central Andes. *Geological Society of America Bulletin* 82:3325–46.

Johnson, A. M.
1976 The Climate of Peru, Bolivia, and Ecuador. In *Climates of Central and South America,* edited by W. Schwerdtfeger, pp. 147–218. World Survey of Climatology, vol. 12. Amsterdam: Elsevier.

Johnsson, M.
1986 *Food and Culture among the Bolivian Aymara.* Uppsala Studies in Cultural Anthropology 7. Stockholm: Almquist and Wiskel.

Jones, B. F., and C. B. Bowser
1978 The Minerology and Related Chemistry of Lake Sediments. In *Lakes: Chemistry, Geology, Physics,* edited by A. Lerman, pp. 179–235. New York: Springer-Verlag.

Jones, J.
1990 A Native Movement and March in Eastern Bolivia: Rationale and Response. *Bulletin of the Institute for Development Anthropology* 8(2):1–8.

1993 Environmental Destruction, Ethnic Discrimination, and International Aid. Unpublished paper on file, Inter-American Foundation, Washington, D.C.

Jordan, E.
1985 Recent Glacier Distribution and Present Climate in the Central Andes of South America. *Zeitschrift für Gletscherkunde und Glazialgeologie* 21:213–24.

Julien, C. J.
1988 How Inca Decimal Administration Worked. *Ethnohistory* 35(3):257–79.

Kaiser, A. D., and P. J. Richerson
1988 Ecosystem Consequences of Residual Deep Stratification in Lake Titicaca. Abstract. *EOS* 69:1105.

Keightley, D.
1983 *The Origins of Chinese Civilization.* Berkeley: University of California Press.

Kelts, K., and M. R. Talbot
1989 Lacustrine Carbonates as Geochemical Archives of Environmental Change and Biotic-Abiotic Interactions. In *Ecological Structure and Function in Large Lakes,* edited by M. M. Tilzer and C. Serrya, pp. 290–317. Madison, Wisconsin: Science and Technology Publishers.

Kessler, A.
1970 Über den Jahresgang der potentiellen Verdunstung im Titicaca-Becken. *Archives for Meteorology, Geophysics, and Bioclimatology,* Series B, 18:239–52.

Kessler, A., and F. Monheim
1968 Der Wasserhaushald des Titicacasees nach neueren Messergebnissen. ERDKUNDE, *Archiv für Wissenschaftliche Geographie* 22:275–83.

Kietz, R.
1992 *Compendio del amaranto.* La Paz: ILDIS.

Klein, H. S.
1982 *Bolivia: The Evolution of a Multi-Ethnic Society.* New York: Oxford University Press.

Klinck, B., R. Ellison, and M. Hawkins
1986 *The Geology of the Cordillera Occidental and Altiplano West of Lake Titicaca, Southern Peru.* British Archaeological Survey, Overseas Division, Open File Report.

Knapp, G.
1981 El nicho ecológico llanura humeda en la economía prehistórica de los Andes de altura: Evidencia etnohistórica, geográfica y arqueológica. *Sarance (Ecuador)* 9:83–95.

Knapp, G., and R. Ryder
1983 Aspects of the Origin, Morphology and Function of Ridged Fields in the Quito Altiplano, Ecuador. In *Drained Field Agriculture in Central and South America,* edited by J. P. Darch, pp. 201–21. Oxford: British Archaeological Reports, International Series 189.

Kolata, A.
1983 The South Andes. In *Ancient South Americans,* edited by J. Jennings, pp. 241–85. San Francisco: W. H. Freeman.
1985 El papel de la agricultura intensiva en la economía política del estado de Tiwanaku. *Diálogo Andino* 4:11–38.
1986 The Agricultural Foundations of the Tiwanaku State: A View from the Heartland. *American Antiquity* 51:748–62.
1987a Research Objectives and Strategies: The 1987 Field Season. In *The Technology and Organization of Agricultural Production in the Tiwanaku State,* edited by A. Kolata, C. Stanish, and O. Rivera, pp. 187–94. First annual research report submitted to the National Science Foundation, the National Endowment for the Humanities, and the Instituto Nacional de Arqueología.
1987b Tiwanaku and Its Hinterland. *Archaeology* 40(1):36–41.
1989 Introducción: Objectivos y estrategías de la investigación. In *Arqueología de Lukurmata, vol. 2,* edited by A. Kolata, pp. 13–40. La Paz: Instituto Nacional de Arqueología y Ediciones Puma Punku.
1990 The Urban Concept of Chan Chan. In *The Northern Dynasties: Kingship and Statecraft in Chimor,* edited by M. Moseley and A. Cordy-Collins, pp. 107–44. Washington, D.C.: Dumbarton Oaks.
1991 The Technology and Organization of Agricultural Production in the Tiwanaku State. *Latin American Antiquity* 2:99–125.
1992 Economy, Ideology, and Imperialism in the South-Central Andes. In *Ideology and Pre-Columbian Civilizations,* edited by A. A. Demarest and G. W. Conrad, pp. 65–86. Santa Fe, New Mexico: School of American Research Press.
1993a *Tiwanaku: Portrait of an Andean Civilization.* Oxford: Basil Blackwell.
1993b Understanding Tiwanaku: Conquest, Colonization, and Clientage in the South Central Andes. In *Latin American Horizons,* edited by D. S. Rice and R. Stone, pp. 193–224. Washington, D.C.:Dumbarton Oaks Research Library and Collection.

Kolata, A., and G. Graffam
1989 Los campos elevados de Lukurmata, Bolivia. In *Arqueología de Lukurmata, vol. 2,* edited by A. Kolata, pp. 173–212. La Paz: Instituto Nacional de Arqueología y Ediciones Puma Punku.

Kolata, A., and C. Ortloff
1989 Thermal Analysis of Tiwanaku Raised Field Systems in the Lake Titicaca Basin of Bolivia. *Journal of Archaeological Science* 16:233–63.

Kolata, A., and C. Ponce
1992 Tiwanaku: The City at the Center. In *The Ancient Americas: Art from Sacred Landscapes,* edited by R. Townsend, pp. 317–35. Art Institute of Chicago. Munich: Prestel Verlag.

Kotschi, J., A. Waters-Bayer, R. Adelhelm, and U. Hoesle
1990 *Ecofarming in Agricultural Development.* Tropical Agroecology, no. 2. Wikersheim, Germany: Magraf Scientific Publishers.

Kreith, F.
1973 *Principles of Heat Transfer.* New York: Intext Educational Publishers.

Kus, J.
1984 The Chicama-Moche Canal: Failure or Success? An Alternative Explanation for an Incomplete Canal. *American Antiquity* 49:408–15.

Kutzbach, J. E.
1980 Estimates of Past Climate at Paleolake Chad, North Africa, Based on a Hydrological and Energy-Balance Model. *Quaternary Research* 14:210–23.

Kutzbach, J. E., and F. A. Street-Perrott
1985 Milankovitch Forcing of Fluctuations in the Level of Tropical Lakes from 18 to 0 kyr B.P. *Nature* 317:130–34.

Laba, R.
1979 Fish, Peasants, and State Bureaucracies: The Development of Lake Titicaca. *Comparative Political Studies* 12:335–61.

Lamb, H.
1965 Early Medieval Warm Epoch and Its Sequel. *Journal of Paleogeography, Paleoclimatology, and Paleoecology* 1:13–37.
1982 *Climate and History in the Modern World.* London: Methuen.

Lanning, E.
1967 *Peru before the Incas.* Englewood Cliffs, New Jersey: Prentice-Hall.

Lansing, J.
1987 Balinese "Water Temples" and the Management of Irrigation. *American Anthropologist* 89:326–41.
1991 *Priests and Programmers: Technologies of Power in the Engineered Landscape of Bali.* Princeton, New Jersey: Princeton University Press.

Lauzanne, L.
1992 Fish Fauna, Native Species: The Orestias. In *Lake Titicaca: A Synthesis of Limnological Knowledge,* edited by C. DeJoux and A. Iltis, pp. 405–19. Monographiae Biologicae, vol. 68. Dordrecht: Kluwer Academic Publishers.

Lavenu, A.
1981 Origine et évolution néotectonique du lac Titicaca. *Revue d'Hydrobiologie Tropicale* 14:289–98.
1992 Formation and Geological Evolution. In *Lake Titicaca: A Synthesis of Limnological Knowledge,* edited by C. DeJoux and A. Iltis, pp. 3–15. Monographiae Biologicae, vol. 68. Dordrecht: Kluwer Academic Publishers.

Lavenu, A., M. Fornavi, and M. Sebrier
1984 Existence de deux nouveaux épisodes lacustres quaternaires dans l'altiplano peruvio-bolivien. *Cahiers ORSTOM, Série Géologie* 14:103–14.

Lazzaro, X.
1981 Biomasses peuplements phytoplanctoniques et production primaire du lac Titicaca. *Revue d'Hydrobiologie Tropicale* 14:349–80.

Leach, E.
1959 Hydraulic Society in Ceylon. *Past and Present* 15:2–25.

LeBlond, R.
1983 *Quelques aspects de l'alimentation et de la selection des Proies chez Orestias ispi Lauzanne (Pices, Cyprinodontidae) du lac Titicaca.* La Paz: ORSTOM.

Lefebvre, H.
1991 *The Production of Space.* Translated by D. Nicholson-Smith. Oxford: Basil Blackwell.

Lehman, J. T.
1975 Reconstructing the Rate of Accumulation of Lake Sediment: The Effect of Sediment Focusing. *Quaternary Research* 5:541–50.

Lennon, T. K.
1982 *Raised Fields of Lake Titicaca, Peru: A Pre-Hispanic Water Management System.* Ph.D. dissertation, University of Colorado, Boulder. University Microfilms: Ann Arbor.
1983 Pattern Analysis of Prehispanic Raised Fields of Lake Titicaca, Peru. In *Drained Field Agriculture in Central and South America,* edited by J. P. Darch, pp. 183–200. Oxford: British Archaeological Reports, International Series 189.

Levieil, D. P., and B. S. Orlove
1992 The Socio-Economic Importance of Macrophytes. In *Lake Titicaca: A Synthesis of Limnological Knowledge,* edited by C. DeJoux and A. Iltis, pp. 505–10. Monographiae Biologicae, vol. 68. Dordrecht: Kluwer Academic Publishers.

Lewellen, T.
1978 *Peasants in Transition.* Boulder, Colorado: Westview Press.

Leyden, B. W.
1987 *Late Holocene Pollen Data from Lake Titicaca, Bolivia: Possible Flooding of the Pampa Koani.* Unpublished report on file in the Department of Anthropology, University of Chicago.
1989 Datos polinicos del período Holocino tardio en el lago Titikaka: Una posible inundación en la Pampa Koani. In *Arqueología de Lukurmata, vol. 2,* edited by A. L. Kolata, pp. 263–74. La Paz: Instituto Nacional de Arqueología y Ediciones Puma Punku.

Liddicoat, M. L., S. Tibbits, and E. I. Butler
1975 The Determination of Ammonia in Seawater. *Limnological Oceanography* 20:131–32.

Likens, G. E.
1984 Beyond the Shoreline: A Watershed-Ecosystem Approach. *Verhandlungen Internationale Vereinigung für Theoretische und Angwandte Limnologie* 22:1–22.

Löffler, H.
1986 Ostracod Analysis. In *Handbook of Holocene Paleoecology and Paleohydrology,* edited by B. E. Berglund, pp. 693–702. Chichester, U.K.: John Wiley and Sons.

López, J., W. Flores, and C. Letoureux
1992 *Lliquas Chayantakas.* Programa de Autodesarrollo Campesina (PAC). Potosí, Bolivia: Ruvaltec.

Loubens, G.
1989 Observations sur les poissons de la partie bolivienne du lac Titicaca, 4: *Orestias* spp., *Salmo gairdneri* et problèmes d'aménagement. *Revue d'Hydrobiologie Tropicale* 22:157–77.

Loubens, G., and F. Osorio
1988 Observations sur les poissons de la partie bolivienne du lac Titicaca, 3: *Basilichthys bonariensis* (Valenciennes, 1835) (Pisces, Atherinidae). *Revue d'Hydrobiologie Tropicale* 21:153–77.

Lubchenco, J., and 15 others.
1991 The Sustainable Biosphere Initiative: An Ecological Research Agenda. A Report from the Ecological Society of America. *Ecology* 72:371–412.

Ludden, D.
1985 *Peasant History in South India.* Princeton, New Jersey: Princeton University Press.

Lumbreras, L.
1974 *The Peoples and Cultures of Ancient Peru.* Washington, D.C.: Smithsonian Institution Press.

Lynch, T.
1983 Camelid Pastoralism and the Emergence of Tiwanaku Civilization in the South-central Andes. *World Archaeology* 15:1–14.
1990 Quaternary Climate, Environment, and the Human Occupation of the South-Central Andes. *Geoarchaeology* 5:199–228.

MACA (Ministerio de Asuntos Campesinos y Agropecuario)
1974 *Diagnóstico del sector agropecuario.* 2 vols. La Paz: MACA, Oficina de Planeamiento Sectorial.
1985 *Encuesta de Prognóstico del Sector Agropecuario.* La Paz: MACA, Oficina de Planeamiento Social.

McHarg, I.
1969 *Design with Nature.* New York: Doubleday Natural History Press.

McKenzie, J. A.
1985 Carbon Isotopes and Productivity in the Lacustrine and Marine Environment. In *Chemical Processes in Lakes,* edited by W. Stumm, pp. 99–118. New York: John Wiley and Sons.

Mackereth, F. J. H.
1965 Chemical Investigations of Lake Sediments and Their Interpretations. *Philosophical Transactions of the Royal Society of London,* B, 161:295–309.
1966 Some Chemical Observations on Post-Glacial Lake Sediments. *Philosophical Transactions of the Royal Society of London,* B, 250:165–213.

Mamani, M.
1988 Agricultura a los 4000 metros. In *Raíces de America: El mundo Aymara,* edited by X. Albó, pp. 75–131. Madrid: Alianza Editorial.

Manelis de Klein, H. E.
1973 Los Urus: El extraño pueblo del altiplano. *Estudios Andinos* 7(3):129–50.

Mann, G.
1969 Die Ökosysteme südamerikas. In *Biogeography and Ecology in South America,* edited by E. J. Fittkau, J. Illies, H. Klinge, G. H. Schwabe, and H. Sioli, pp. 171–229. The Hague: W. Junk.

Markgraf, V.
1989 Paleoclimates in Central and South America since 18,000 B.P. Based on Pollen and Lake-Level Records. *Quaternary Science Reviews* 8:1–24.

Markgraf, V., and H. L. D'Antoni
1978 *Pollen Flora of Argentina.* Tucson: University of Arizona Press.

Masuda, S., I. Shimada, and C. Morris (editors)
1985 *Andean Ecology and Civilization: An Interdisciplinary Perspective on Andean Ecological Complementarity.* Tokyo: University of Tokyo Press.

Matheny, R.
1976 Maya Lowland Hydraulic Systems. *Science* 193:639–46.
1978 Northern Maya Lowland Water-Control Systems. In *Pre-Hispanic Maya Agriculture,* edited by P. D. Harrison and B. L. Turner II, pp. 185–210. Albuquerque: University of New Mexico Press.

Mathews, J. E.
1990 Preliminary Report of the Tiwanaku Mid-Valley Survey Project: The North Sierra Zone. In *Tiwanaku and Its Hinterland: Third Preliminary Report of the Proyecto Wila Jawira,* edited by A. Kolata and O. Rivera, pp. 269–75. Submitted to the Instituto Nacional de Arqueología de Bolivia, the National Science Foundation, and the National Endowment for the Humanities.
1992 *Prehistoric Settlement and Agriculture in the Middle Tiwanaku Valley, Bolivia.* Unpublished Ph.D. dissertation, University of Chicago.

Mayer, E.
1979 Land Use in the Andes. *Ecology and Agriculture in the Mantaro Valley of Peru with Special Reference to Potatoes.* Lima: Centro Internacional de la Papa.

MBL (Movimiento Bolivia Libre)
1988 *Un camino nuevo para Bolivia.* La Paz: Imprenta Metodista.

Meggers, B. J.
1954 Environmental Limitations on the Development of Culture. *American Anthropologist* 56:801–24.

Menzel, D.
1964 Style and Time in the Middle Horizon. *Ñawpa Pacha* 2:1–105.
1968 New Data on the Huari Empire in the Middle Horizon Epoch 2A. *Ñawpa Pacha* 6:47–114.
1977 *The Archaeology of Ancient Peru and the Work of Max Uhle.* Berkeley, California: Lowie Museum of Anthropology.

Meybeck, M.
1979 Concentrations des eaux fluviales en éléments majeurs et apports en solution aux océans. *Revue de Géologie Dynamique et de Géographie Physique* 21:215–16.

Miller, S. W.
1985 A Spatial Data Structure for Hydrologic Applications. *Geo-Processing* 2:385–408.

Miracle, A. W., Jr., and J. de Dios Yapita Moya
1981 Time and Space in Aymara. In *The Aymara Language in Its Social and Cultural Context,* edited by M. J. Hardman. University of Florida Social Sciences Monograph no. 67. Gainesville: University of Florida Press.

Miranda, L., and D. Moricio
1992 *Memorias de un olvido: Testimonios de vida Urus-Muratos.* La Paz: HISBOL.

Mitchell, W. P.
1973 The Hydraulic Hypothesis: A Reappraisal. *Current Anthropology* 14(5):532–34.
1977 Irrigation Farming in the Andes: Evolutionary Implications. In *Peasant Livelihood: Studies in Economic Anthropology and Cultural Ecology,* edited by R. Halperin and J. Dow, pp. 36–57. New York: St. Martin's.

Mogravejo, G.
1969 *Estudio geológico-petrográfico de la serranía meridional de Tiwanaku y su relación con la*

*procedencia del material lítico de la ruinas precolombinas.* La Paz: GEOBOL.

Molina, C.
1965 *Estudio geológico de la península de Cumaná y contribuciones al conocimiento de los foraminíferos pérmicos de Yaurichambi, Colquencha y Apilla Pampa.* La Paz: GEOBOL.

Monheim, F.
1956 *Klimatologie und Hydrologie des Titicacabeckens.* Heidelberg Geographische Arbeiten 1.

Montaño, S.
1992 Mujer, donaciones alimentarias, y poder local en la ciudad de El Alto en Bolivia. In *Políticas Sociales, Mujeres, y Gobierno Local,* edited by Dagmar Raczynski, pp. 95–116. Santiago de Chile: Corporación de Investigaciones Económicas para Latinoamérica.

Morales, C. B.
1990 *Bolivia: Medio ambiente y ecología aplicada.* La Paz: Artes Gráficas Latina.

Moreno, E.
1983 *Estudio cuantitativo del zooplanctón de la zona pelágica del lago Titicaca (lago grande).* Thesis, University of San Agustín, Arequipa.

Morlon, P.
1978 *Elementos de descripción frecuencial de las heladas.* Puno: CIDA, Ministerio de Agricultural.
1981 Questions Related to Agriculture on the Peruvian Altiplano: Research Results and Hypotheses for Development. *Ecodevelopment News* 17:23–41.

Morris, H., and J. Wiggert
1972 *Applied Hydraulics in Engineering.* New York: Ronald Press.

Moseley, M.
1975 Prehistoric Principles of Labor Organization in the Moche Valley, Peru. *American Antiquity* 40:191–96.

Moseley, M., R. Feldman, P. Goldstein, and L. Watanabe
1991 Colonies and Conquest: Tiahuanaco and Huari in Moquegua. In *Huari Administrative Structure: Prehistoric Monumental Architecture and State Government,* edited by W. Isbell and G. F. McEwan, pp. 121–40. Washington, D.C.: Dumbarton Oaks Research Library and Collection.

Mourguiart, P.
1987 Les ostracodes actuals de l'altiplano bolivien modèle de répartition. *Géodynamique* 2:102–103.
1992 The Ostracoda. In *Lake Titicaca: A Synthesis of Limnological Knowledge,* edited by C. Dejoux and A. Iltis, pp. 337–45. Monographiae Biologicae, vol. 68. Dordrecht: Kluwer Academic Publishers.

Mourguiart, P., P. Carbonel, J.-P. Peypouquet, D. Wirrmann, and C. Vargas
1986 Late Quaternary Paleohydrology of Lake Huinaymarca (Bolivia). Scenarios Based on Ostracod Fauna. *Hydrobiologia* 143:191–97.

Mujica, E.
1978 Nueva hipótesis sobre el desarrollo temprano del altiplano del Titicaca y sus áreas de interacción. *Arte y Arqueología* 5/6:285–308. La Paz: Revista del Instituto de Estudios Bolivianos.

Murra, J. V.
1960 Rite and Crop in the Inca State. In *Culture in History: Essays in Honor of Paul Radin,* edited by S. Diamond, pp. 393–407. New York: Columbia University Press.
1964 Una apreciación etnológico de la visita. In *Visita hecha a la provincia de Chucuito por Garci Diéz de San Miguel en el año 1567,* pp. 419–44. Documentos Regionales para Etnología y Etnohistoria Andinas, vol. 1. Lima: Casa de la Cultura del Perú.
1965 El Instituto de Investigaciones Andinas y sus estudios en Huánuco, 1963–66. *Cuadernos de Investigación,* 1:7–21. Huánuco, Peru: Facultad de Letras y Educación, Antropología, Universidad Nacional Hermilio Valdizán.
1968 An Aymara Kingdom in 1567. *Ethnohistory* 15:115–51.
1972 El "control vertical" de un máximo de pisos ecológicos en la economía de las sociedades andinas. In *Visita de la provincia de León de Huánuco en 1562, Ortiz de Zúñiga, visitador,* edited by J. Murra, pp. 427–76. Documentos para la Historia y Etnología de Huánuco y la Selva Central, vol. 2. Huánuco, Peru: Universidad Nacional Hermilio Valdizán.

National Research Council
1989 *Lost Crops of the Incas: Little-Known Plants of the Andes with Promise for Worldwide Cultivation.* Washington, D.C.: National Academy Press.

Netherly, P.
1977 *Local Level Lords on the North Coast of Peru.* Ph.D. dissertation, Cornell University. Ann Arbor, Michigan: University Microfilms.
1984 The Management of Late Andean Irrigation Systems on the North Coast of Peru. *American Antiquity* 49:227–54.

Newell, N. D.
1949 Geology of the Lake Titicaca Region, Peru and Bolivia. *Geological Society of America Memoirs* 36:1–111.

Núñez, L., and T. Dillehay
1979 *Movilidad giratoria, armonía social y desarollo en los Andes meridionales: Patrones de tráfico e interacción económica.* Antofagasta, Chile: Universidad del Norte.

Ochoa, C. M.
1990 *The Potatoes of South America: Bolivia.* Cambridge: Cambridge University Press.

Oldfield, F.
1978 Lakes and Their Drainage Basins as Units of Sediment-Based Ecological Study. *Progress in Physical Geography* 1:460–504.

Oliveira, L.
1986 Estudio sedimentológico de testigos del lago Titicaca: Implicaciones paleoclimáticas. Tésis de grado, Universidad Mayor de San Andrés, La Paz.

ONERN (Oficina Nacional de Evaluación de Recursos Naturales)
1965 *Programa de inventario y evaluación de los recursos naturales del departamento de Puno, vol. 1.* Lima: ONERN.

Orlove, B. S., and G. Custred
1980 Agrarian Economies and Social Processes in Comparative Perspective: The Agricultural Production Unit. In *Land and Power in Latin America,* edited by B. S. Orlove and G. Custred, pp. 13–54. New York: Holmes and Meier.

Orlove, B. S., and R. Godoy
1986 Sectoral Fallowing Systems in the Central Andes. *Journal of Ethnobiology* 6:169–204.

Ortloff, C.
1989 A Mathematical Model of the Dynamics of Hydraulic Societies in Ancient Peru. In *Ecology, Settlement, and History in the Osmore Drainage,* edited by D. Rice, C. Stanish, and P. Scarr, pp. 457–77. Oxford: British Archaeological Reports, International Series 545(ii).
1993 Chimu Hydraulics: Technology and Statecraft on the North Coast of Peru, A.D. 1000–1470. In *Research in Economic Anthropology, Supplement 7,* edited by V. Scarborough and B. Isaac, pp. 327–67. Greenwich, Connecticut: JAI press.
1995 Surveying and Hydraulic Engineering of the Pre-Columbian Chimu State: A.D. 900–1450. *Cambridge Archaeological Journal* 5(1)55–74.

Ortloff, C., R. Feldman, and M. Moseley
1985 Hydraulic Engineering and Historical Aspects of the Pre-Columbian Intravalley Canal System of the Moche Valley, Peru. *Journal of Field Archaeology* 12:77–98.

Ortloff, C., and A. Kolata
1989 Hydraulic Analysis of Tiwanaku Aqueduct Structures at Lukurmata and Pajchiri, Bolivia. *Journal of Archaeological Science* 16:513–35.
1993 Climate and Collapse: Agroecological Perspectives on the Decline of the Tiwanaku State. *Journal of Archaeological Science* 20:195–221.

Ortloff, C. R., M. E. Moseley, and R. A. Feldman
1982 Hydraulic Engineering Aspects of the Chimu Chicama-Moche Intervalley Canal. *American Antiquity* 47:572–95.
1983 The Chicama-Moche Intervalley Canal: Social Explanations and Physical Paradigns. *American Antiquity* 48:375–89.

O'Sullivan, P. E.
1983 Annually Laminated Lake Sediments and the Study of Quaternary Environmental Changes: A Review. *Quaternary Science Reviews* 1:245–313.

Pacheco, D.
1992 *El indianismo y los indios contemporáneos en Bolivia.* La Paz: HISBOL and MUSEF.

Palacios Ríos, F.
1977 Pastizales de regadío para alpacas. In *Pastores de Puna,* edited by J. Flores Ochoa, pp. 155–70. Lima: Instituto de Estudios Peruanos.

Papik, B.
1987 *Curaciones simples y eficientes.* 6 vols. La Paz: CALA.

Parenti, L. R.
1981 A Phylogenetic and Biogeographic Analysis of Cyprinodontiform Fishes (Teleostei, Atherinomorpha). *Bulletin of the American Museum of Natural History* 168(4):334–557.
1984 A Taxonomic Revision of the Andean Killifish Genus *Orestias* (Cyprinodontiformes, Cyprinodontidae). *Bulletin of the American Museum of Natural History* 178(2):107–214.

Parkinson, J. A., and S. E. Allen
1975 A Wet Oxidation Procedure for the Determination of Nitrogen and Mineral Nutrients in Biological Material. *Communications in Soil Science and Plant Analysis* 6:1–11.

Parsons, J. J.
1969 Ridged Fields in the Rio Guayas Valley, Ecuador. *American Antiquity* 34:76–80.

Parsons, J. J., and W. Bowen
1966 Ancient Ridged Fields of the San Jorge River Floodplain, Colombia. *The Geographical Review* 56(3):317–43.

Parsons, J. J., and W. Denevan
1967 Pre-Columbian Ridged Fields. *Scientific American* 217:93–100.

Parsons, J. R.
1968 An Estimate of Size and Population for the Middle Horizon at Tiahuanaco, Bolivia. *American Antiquity* 33(2):243–45.
1976 The Role of Chinampa Agriculture in the Food Supply of Aztec Tenochtitlan. In *Cultural Change and Continuity: Essays in Honor of James Bennett Griffin,* edited by C. D. Cleland, pp. 233–62. New York: Academic Press.

Parsons, J. R., M. Parsons, V. Popper, and M. Taft
1982 *Late Prehistoric Chinampa Agriculture on Lake Chalco-Xochimilco, Mexico.* Preliminary report submitted to the National Science Foundation and the Instituto Nacional de Antropología e Historia, Mexico, D.F.

Pärssinen, M.
1992 *Tawantinsuyu: The Inca State and Its Political Organization.* Studia Historica 43. Helsinki: Societas Historica Finlandiae.

Pashkov, N. N., and F. M. Dolgachev
1977 *Máquinas hidráulicas.* Moscow: Editorial Mir. Spanish translation from the Russian, 1985.

Pawley, A. L., and P. J. Richerson
1992 Temporal and Spatial Variation of Zooplankton in Lago Grande. In *Lake Titicaca: A Synthesis of Limnological Knowledge,* edited by C. DeJoux and A. Iltis, pp. 276–84. Monographiae Biologicae, vol. 68. Dordrecht: Kluwer Academic Publishers.

Pearson, F. J., Jr., and T. B. Coplen
1978 Stable Isotope Studies of Lakes. In *Lakes: Chemistry, Geology, Physics,* edited by A. Lerman, pp. 325–39. New York: Springer-Verlag.

Pennington, W.
1981 Records of a Lake's Life in Time: The Sediments. *Hydrobiologia* 79:197–219.

Peterson, B. J., and B. Fry
1987 Stable Isotopes in Ecosystem Studies. *Annual Review of Ecology and Systematics* 18:293–320.

Pflaker, G.
1963 Observations on Archaeological Remains in Northeastern Bolivia. *American Antiquity* 28:372–78.

Pickett, S. T. A., and P. S. White (editors)
1985 *The Ecology of Natural Disturbance and Patch Dynamics.* New York: Academic Press.

Pilskaln, C. H., and T. C. Johnson
1991 Seasonal Signals in Lake Malawi Sediments. *Limnological Oceanography* 36:544–57.

Pinto, J.
1992 Zooplankton Distribution in the Bolivian Part of the Lake. In *Lake Titicaca: A Synthesis of Limnological Knowledge,* edited by C. DeJoux and A. Iltis, pp. 268–75. Monographiae Biologicae, vol. 68. Dordrecht: Kluwer Academic Publishers.

Platt, T.
1986 Mirrors and Maize: The Concept of *Yanantin* among the Macha of Bolivia. In *Anthropologi-*

*cal History of Andean Polities,* edited by J. Murra, N. Wachtel, and J. Revel, pp. 228–59. Cambridge: Cambridge University Press.

1987 The Andean Experience of Bolivian Liberalism, 1825–1900: Roots of Rebellion in 19th-Century Chayanta (Potosí). In *Resistance, Rebellion, and Consciousness in the Andean Peasant World, 18th to 20th Centuries,* edited by S. J. Stern, pp. 180–323. Madison: University of Wiconsin Press.

Ponce Sanginés, C.

1972 *Tiwanaku: Espacio, tiempo y cultura: Ensayo de síntesis arqueológica.* Publicación no. 30. La Paz: Academía Nacional de Ciencias de Bolivia.

1978 *Panorama de la arqueología boliviana.* Publicación 27. La Paz: Instituto Nacional de Arqueología.

1979 *Nueva perspectiva para el estudio de la expansión de la cultura Tiwanaku.* Publicación 29. La Paz: Instituto Nacional de Arqueología.

1980 *Panorama de la arqueología boliviana.* La Paz: Librería y Editorial Juventud.

1989 *Arqueología de Lukurmata, vol. 1: Ensayo de historiación del avance científico (1895–1988).* La Paz: Instituto Nacional de Arqueología y Ediciones Puma Punku.

Powell, T. M., H. Kirkish, P. J. Neale, and P. J. Richerson

1984 The Diurnal Cycle of Stratification in Lake Titicaca: Eddy Diffusion. *Verhandlungen Internationale Vereinigung für Theoretische und Angewandte Limnologie* 22:1237–42.

Pozorski, T., and S. Pozorski

1982 Reassessing the Chicama-Moche Intervalley Canal: Comments on Hydraulic Engineering Aspects of the Chimu-Moche Intervalley Canal. *American Antiquity* 47:851–68.

Price, B.

1971 Prehispanic Irrigation Agriculture in Nuclear America. *Latin American Research Review* 6(3):3–60.

PROCAMPO (Centro para el Desarrollo Rural)

1991 El Tarwi. PROCAMPO, *Revista del Desarrollo Rural* 2(5):9–12.

Prudencio Bohrt, J.

1990 *El caso del trigo.* La Paz: ILDIS.

Psacharopoulos, G.

1992 *Ethinicity, Education, and Earnings in Bolivia and Guatemala.* World Bank Policy Research Working Papers, WPS 1014, Washington, D.C.

Puleston, D. E.

1977 The Art and Archaeology of Hydraulic Agriculture in the Maya Lowlands. In *Social Process in Maya Prehistory: Essays in Honour of Sir Eric Thompson,* edited by N. Hammond, pp. 449–67. New York. Academic Press.

Pyle, R. C.

1981 Aymara Kinship, Real and Spiritual. In *The Aymara Language in Its Social and Cultural Context,* edited by M. J. Hardman. University of Florida Social Sciences Monograph no. 67. Gainesville: University of Florida Press.

Quinn, W. H., V. T. Neal, and S. E. Atúñez de Mayolo

1987 El Niño Occurrences over the Past Four and a Half Centuries. *Journal of Geophysical Research* 92(C13):14,449–61.

Ranaboldo, C.

1986 *Los campesinos herbolarios Kallawayas.* La Paz: Unidad de Investigación SEMTA.

1987 *El camino perdido: Biografía del líder Kallawaya Antonio Alvarez Mamani.* La Paz: Unidad de Investigación SEMTA.

Rasnake, R.

1986 Carnaval in Yura: Ritual Reflections on Ayllu and State Relations. *American Ethnologist* 13(4):662–80.

1988 *Domination and Cultural Resistance, Authority and Power among Andean People.* Chapel Hill, North Carolina: Duke University Press.

Raynal-Roques, A.

1992 Macrophytes: The Higher Plants. In *Lake Titicaca: A Synthesis of Limnological Knowledge,* edited by C. DeJoux and A. Iltis, pp. 223–31. Monographiae Biologicae, vol. 68. Dordrecht: Kluwer Academic Publishers.

Rea, J.

1985 Recursos fitogenéticos agrícolas de Bolivia: Bases para establecer el sistema. Paper presented to the Comité Internacional de Recursos Fitogenéticos, La Paz, Bolivia.

1991 La papa amarga. Paper presented at the Primera Mesa Redonda sobre la Papa Amarga, La Paz, Bolivia.

Reiners, W. A.
1986 Complementary Models for Ecosystem Studies. *American Naturalist* 127:59–73.

Rice, D., and P. Rice
1984 Lessons from the Maya. *Latin American Research Review* 19(3):7–33.

Rice, D., C. Stanish, and P. Scarr (editors)
1989 *Ecology, Settlement and History in the Osmore Drainage, Peru.* Oxford: British Archaeological Reports, International Series 545 (i–ii).

Richards, P.
1985 *Indigenous Agricultural Revolution: Ecology and Food Production in West Africa.* London: Hutchinson.

Richerson, P. J.
1992 The Thermal Stratification Regime in Lake Titicaca. In *Lake Titicaca: A Synthesis of Limnological Knowledge,* edited by C. DeJoux and A. Iltis, pp. 120–30. Monographiae Biologicae, vol. 68. Dordrecht: Kluwer Academic Publishers.

Richerson, P. J., P. J. Neale, R. A. Tapia, H. J. Carney, X. Lazzaro, W. Vincent, and W. Wurtsbaugh
1992 Patterns of Planktonic Primary Production and Algal Biomass. In *Lake Titicaca: A Synthesis of Limnological Knowledge,* edited by C. DeJoux and A. Iltis, pp. 196–222. Monographiae Biologicae, vol. 68. Dordrecht: Kluwer Academic Publishers.

Richerson, P. J., P. Neale, W. Wurtsbaugh, R. Alfaro, and W. Vincent
1986 Patterns of Temporal Variation in Primary Production and Other Limnological Variables in Lake Titicaca, a High Altitude Tropical Lake. *Hydrobiologia* 138:205–20.

Richerson, P. J., C. Widmer, and T. Kittel
1977 *The Limnology of Lake Titicaca (Peru-Bolivia), a Large, High Altitude Tropical Lake.* Institute of Ecology, University of California, Davis, Publication 14.

Riley, T., and G. Freimuth
1979 Field Systems and Frost Drainage in the Prehistoric Agriculture of the Upper Great Lakes. *American Antiquity* 44:271–85.

Riley, T., C. Moffat, and G. Friemuth.
1980 Campos elevados prehistóricos en el medio-oeste superior de los Estados Unidos. *America Indígena* 40:797–815.

Rist, S., and J. San Martín
1991 *Agroecología y saber campesino en la conservación de suelos.* Cochabamba, Bolivia: AGRCUCO.

Rivera, J.
1991 Bolivia: El SENELAP, importancia y limitaciones. In *Etnías, educación y cultura: Defendemos lo nuestro,* compiled by ILDIS-Bolivia, pp. 13–19. La Paz: Editorial Nueva Sociedad.

Rivera, M.
1976 Nuevos aportes sobre el desarrollo cultural altiplánico en los valles bajos del extremo norte de Chile durante el período intermedio temprano. *Anales Universidad del Norte* 10:71–82. Antogafasta, Chile.
1980 Algunos fenóminos de complementaridad económica a través de los arqueológicos en el área centro sur andina: La fase Alto Ramírez reformulada. In *Temas antropológicas arqueológicos* (special edition of *Estudios Arqueológicos*), pp. 71–103. Universidad de Chile, Antofagasta.

Rivera, S.
1987 *Oppressed but Not Defeated: Peasant Struggles among the Aymara and Quechwa in Bolivia, 1900–1980.* Geneva: UNRISD Participation Program.
1990 Liberal Democracy and Ayllu Democracy in Bolivia: The Case of Northern Potosí. In *The Challenge of Rural Democratization: Perspectives from Latin America and the Philippines,* edited by J. Fox, pp. 97–122. Special issue of *Journal of Development Studies* 26(4). London: Frank Cass.

Robinson, D. A.
1964 *Peru in Four Dimensions.* Detroit: Blaine Ethridge-Books.

Roche, M. A., J. Bourges, J. Cortes, and R. Mattos
1992 Climatology and Hydrology of the Lake Titicaca Basin. In *Lake Titicaca: A Synthesis of Limnological Knowledge,* edited by C. DeJoux and A. Iltis, pp. 63–88. Monographiae Biologicae, vol. 68. Dordrecht: Kluwer Academic Publishers.

Romero, E.
1928 *El departamento de Puno.* Lima: Impresa Torres Aguirre.

Rowe, J. H.
1963 Urban Settlements in Ancient Peru. *Ñawpa Pacha* 1:1–27.
1982 Inca Policies and Institutions Relating to the Cultural Unification of the Empire. In *The Inca and Aztec States: 1400–1800,* edited by G. Collier, R. I. Rosaldo, and J. Wirth, pp. 93–115. New York: Academic Press.

Ruttan, V.
1988 Cultural Endowments and Economic Development: What Can We Learn from Anthropology? *Economic Development and Culture Change* 36(3-S):247–71.

Saalman, H.
1968 *Medieval Cities.* New York: George Braziller.

Saavedra, A.
1964 *Mapa regional de la zona de Tiwanaku.* La Paz: Instituto Geográfico Militar.

Sagerlind, L. J.
1976 *Applied Finite Analysis.* New York: John Wiley and Sons.

Sahlins, M.
1972 *Stone Age Economics.* Chicago: Aldine-Atherton.

Salgado López, H.
1986 Investigaciones arqueológicas en el curso medio del río Calima, Cordillera Occidental, Colombia. *Boletín de Arqueología* 1(2):3–15. Fundación de Investigaciones Arqueológicas Nacionales, Bogotá.

Salomon, F.
1987 Ancestor Cults and Resistance to the State in Arequipa, ca. 1748–1754. In *Resistance, Rebellion, and Consciousness in the Andean Peasant World,* edited by S. J. Stern, pp. 144–65. Madison: University of Wisconsin Press.

Salomons, J. B.
1986 *Paleoecology of Volcanic Soils in the Colombian Central Cordillera (Parque Nacional de los Nevados).* Ph.D. dissertation, University of Amsterdam. *Dissertations Botanicae* 95. Berlin: J. Cramer.

Sánchez-Albornos, N.
1978 *Indios y tríbutos en el alto Perú.* Lima: Instituto de Estudios Peruanos.

Sanders, W. T.
1972 Population, Agricultural History, and Societal Evolution in Mesoamerica. In *Population Growth: Anthropological Implications,* edited by B. Spooner, pp. 101–43. Cambridge: Massachusetts Institute of Technology Press.

Sanders, W. T., and B. Price
1968 *Mesoamerica: The Evolution of a Civilization.* New York: Random House.

Sanders, W. T., and D. L. Webster
1978 Unilinealism, Multilinealism, and the Evolution of Complex Societies. In *Social Archaeology: Beyond Subsistence and Dating,* edited by C. L. Redman, M. J. Berman, E. V. Curtin, W. T. Langhorn, Jr., N. M. Versaggi, and J. C. Wanser, pp. 249–302. New York: Academic Press.

Sato, K., T. Fukuhara, and S. Boris
1990 Dynamic Analysis of Heat, Mass and Solute Transfer Due to Evaporation from a Smooth Surface. Paper presented at the fifth International Heat Transfer Conference, Jerusalem.

Scarborough, V.
1983 Raised Field Detection at Cerros, Northern Belize. In *Drained Field Agriculture in Central and South America,* edited by J. P. Darch, pp. 123–36. Oxford: British Archaeological Reports, International Series 189.

Schaedel, R.
1988 Andean World View: Hierarchy or Reciprocity, Regulation or Control? *Current Anthropology* 29(5):768–75.

Schneider, D. M.
1980 *American Kinship.* 2d ed. Chicago: University of Chicago Press.

Seddon, M. T.
1994 *Excavations in the Raised Fields of the Rio Catari Sub-Basin, Bolivia.* Unpublished M.A. thesis, University of Chicago.

Seltzer, G. O.
1990 Recent Glacial History and Paleoclimates of the Peruvian-Bolivian Andes. *Quaternary Science Reviews* 9:137–52.

1992 Late Quaternary Glaciation of the Cordillera Real, Bolivia. *Journal of Quaternary Science* 7:87–98.

Sempere, T., G. Herail, J. Oller, and M. G. Bonhomme
1990 Late Oligocene–Early Miocene Major Tectonic Crisis and Related Basins in Bolivia. *Geology* 18:946–49.

Servant, M.
1977 Le cadre stratigraphique du Plio-Quaternaire de l'altiplano des Andes tropicales en Bolivie. Bulletin AFEQ, *Recherches Françaises sur le Quaternaire, INQUA* 50(1):9–23.

Servant, M., and J-C. Fontes
1978 Les lacs quaternaires des hauts plateaux des Andes boliviennes, premières interpretations paleoclimatiques. *Cahiers ORSTOM, Série Géologie* 10:9–24.

Servant, M., J-C. Fontes, J. Argollo, and J-F. Saliege
1981 Variations du régime et de la nature des précipitations au cours du 15 derniers millinaires dans les Andes de Bolivie. *Cahiers Royal Academie Science Parie,* Series II, 292:1209–12.

Servant-Vildary, S.
1983 Les diatomes de l'altiplano bolivien. *Cahiers ORSTOM, Série Géologie* 11(1):25–35.
1992 Phytoplankton: The Diatoms. In *Lake Titicaca: A Synthesis of Limnological Knowledge,* edited by C. DeJoux and A. Iltis, pp. 163–75. Monographiae Biologicae, vol. 68. Dordrecht: Kluwer Academic Publishers.

Sicilian, J., and C. W. Hirt
1989 *FLOW-3D Computer Code Manual.* Los Alamos, New Mexico: Flow Science, Inc.

Siemens, A. H.
1978 Karst and the Pre-Hispanic Maya in the Southern Lowlands. In *Pre-Hispanic Maya Agriculture,* edited by P. D. Harrison and B. L. Turner II, pp. 117–44. Albuquerque: University of New Mexico Press.
1982 Prehispanic Agricultural Use of the Wetlands of Northern Belize. In *Maya Subsistence: Essays in Honor of Dennis E. Puleston,* edited by K. V. Flannery, pp. 205–25. New York: Academic Press.
1983a Wetland Agriculture in Pre-Hispanic Mesoamerica. *The Geographical Review* 73:66–181.
1983b Modelling Prehispanic Hydroagriculture on Levee Backslopes in Northern Veracruz, Mexico. In *Drained Field Agriculture in Central and South America,* edited by J. P. Darch, pp. 27–54. Oxford: British Archaeological Reports, International Series 189.

Siemens, A. H., and D. E. Puleston
1972 Ridged Fields and Associated Features in Southern Campeche: New Perspectives on the Lowland Maya. *American Antiquity* 37:228–39.

Simmons, R. A.
1974 *Palca and Pucara.* Berkeley: University of California Press.

Smith, C., W. Denevan, and P. Hamilton
1968 Ancient Ridged Fields in the Region of Lake Titicaca. *Geographical Journal* 134:353–67.

Smith, V. H.
1982 The Nitrogen and Phosphorus Dependence of Agal Biomass in Lakes: An Empirical and Theoretical Analysis. *Limnological Oceanography* 27:1101–12.

SOBOMETRA (Sociedad Boliviana de Medicina Tradicional)
1986 *Congreso Nacional de Medicina Tradicional.* El Kallawaya 1(1). La Paz, Bolivia.

Solorzano, L.
1969 Determination of Ammonia in Natural Waters by the Phenolhypochlorite Method. *Limnological Oceanography* 14:799–800.

Spalding, K.
1980 Class Structures in the Southern Peruvian Highlands, 1750–1920. In *Land and Power in Latin America,* edited by B. Orlove and G. Custred, pp. 79–97. New York: Holmes and Meier.

Sprent, J. I.
1987 *The Ecology of the Nitrogen Cycle.* Cambridge: Cambridge University Press.

Squier, E. G.
1877 *Peru: Incidents of Travel and Exploration in the Land of the Incas.* New York: Harper & Brothers.

Stephenson, N. L.
1990 Climatic Control of Vegetation Distribution: The Role of the Water Balance. *American Naturalist* 135:83–118.

Stanish, C.

1989 An Archaeological Evaluation of an Ethnohistorical Model in Moquegua. In *Ecology, Settlement and History in the Osmore Drainage, Peru,* edited by D. Rice, C. Stanish, and P. Starr, pp. 303–20. Oxford: British Archaeological Reports, International Series 545(ii).

1992 *Ancient Andean Political Economy.* Austin: University of Texas Press.

1994 The Hydraulic Hypothesis Revisited: Lake Titicaca Basin Raised Fields in Theoretical Perspective. *Latin American Antiquity* 5:312–32.

Stevens, W. K.

1988 Scientists Revive a Lost Secret of Farming. *New York Times, Science Times Section.* 22 November 1988.

Steward, J. (editor)

1955 *Irrigation Civilizations: A Comparative Study.* Washington, D.C.: Pan American Union.

Street, F. A., and A. T. Grove

1979 Global Maps of Lake-Level Fluctuations since 30,000 yr B.P. *Quaternary Research* 12:83–118.

Strickland, J. D. H., and T. R. Parsons

1972 *A Practical Handbook of Seawater Analysis.* Bulletin 167. Ottawa: Fisheries Research Board of Canada.

Stuiver, M., and P. J. Reimer

1993 Extended $^{14}$C Data Base and Revised CALIB 3.0 $^{14}$C Age Calibration Program. *Radiocarbon* 35:215–30.

Swanson, J. A., and G. J. DeSalvo

1985 *ANSYS Engineering Analysis System User's Manual, Volumes I and II, Rev. 4.2B.* Houston, Pennsylvania: Swanson Analysis Systems.

Swanson, K. E., D. C. Noble, E. McKee, T. Sempere, C. Martínez, and M. Cirbian

1987 Major Revisions in the Age of Rock Units and Tectonic Events in the Northern Altiplano Basin of Bolivia. Paper presented at the 83rd annual meeting of the Geological Society of America, Cordilleran Section. *Abstracts-with-Programs, Geological Society of America* 19(6):456.

Tapia, M.

1990 *Cultivos andinos subexplotados y su aporte a la alimentación.* Lima: Organización de las Naciones Unidades para la Agricultura y la Alimentación, Oficina Regional para America Latina.

ter Braak, C. J. F.

1986 Canonical Correspondence Analysis: A New Eigenvector Technique for Multivariate Direct Gradiant Analysis. *Ecology* 12:83–118.

1987 *CANOCO: A Fortran Program for Canonical Community Ordination by Partial Detrended Canonical Correspondence Analysis, Principal Components Analysis and Redundancy Analysis (Version 2.1).* Wageningen, Netherlands: ITI-TNO.

THOA (Taller de Historia Oral)

1984 *El indio Santos Marka T'ula: Cacique principal de los ayllus de Qallpa y apoderado general de las comunidades originarios de la república.* La Paz: Taller de Historia Oral Andina.

Thompson, L. G., J. Bolzan, H. Brecher, P. Kruss, E. Moseley-Thompson, and K. Jezek.

1982 Geophysical Investigations of the Tropical Quelccaya Ice Cap. *Journal of Glaciology* 28:57–68.

Thompson, L. G., M. Davis, E. Moseley-Thompson, and K. B. Liu

1988 Pre-Incan Agricultural Activity Recorded in Dust Layers in Two Tropical Ice Cores. *Nature* 336:763–65.

Thompson, L. G., L. Hastenrath, and B. Arnao

1979 Climate Ice Core Records from the Tropical Quelccaya Ice Cap. *Science* 203:1240–43.

Thompson, L. G., and E. Moseley-Thompson

1987 Evidence of Abrupt Climatic Change during the Last 1500 Years Recorded in Ice Cores from the Tropical Quelccaya Ice Cap. In *Abrupt Climate Change: Evidence and Implications,* edited by W. Bergen and L. Labeyrie, pp. 99–110. New York: D. Reidel.

1989 *One-Half Millennium of Tropical Climate Variability as Recorded in the Stratigraphy of the Quelccaya Ice Cap, Peru.* Geophysical Union Monograph 55.

Thompson, L. G., E. Moseley-Thompson, J. F. Bolzan, and B. R. Koci

1985 A 1500-Year Record of Tropical Precipitation in Ice Cores from the Quelccaya Ice Cap, Peru. *Science* 229:971–73.

Thornthwaite, C. W., and J. R. Mather
1955 The Water Balance. *Publications in Climatology* 8:1–86.

Tilman, D.
1982 *Resource Competition and Community Structure.* Monographs in Population Biology, no. 17. Princeton, New Jersey: Princeton University Press.

Titus, J. G. (editor)
1988 *Greenhouse Effect, Sea Level Rise and Coastal Wetlands.* EPA-230-05-86-013. Washington, D.C.: Office of Policy, Plannning, and Evaluation.

Tomlin, C. D.
1990 *Geographic Information Systems and Cartographic Modeling.* Englewood Cliffs, New Jersey: Prentice Hall.

Troll, C.
1927 Forschungreisen in den zentralen Anden von Bolivia und Peru. *Petermann's Mittheilungen aus Justus Perthes Geographischer* 73:41–43.
1968 The Cordilleras of the Tropical Americas: Apects of Climatic, Phytogeographical and Agrarian Ecology. In *Geo-Ecology of the Mountainous Regions of the Tropical Americas,* edited by C. Troll, pp. 15–56. Colloquium Geographicum, Band 9. Bonn: Ferd. Dümmlers Verlag.

Tschopik, H., Jr.
1947 The Aymara. In *Handbook of South American Indians, vol. II,* edited by J. H. Stewart, pp. 501–73. Bureau of Ethnology 143(2). Washington, D.C: Smithsonian Institution Press.
1951 The Aymara of Chucuito, Peru. *American Museum of Natural History Anthropological Papers* 4(2):137–308.

Tsukada, M.
1967 Chenopod and Amaranth Pollen: Electron-Microscopic Identification. *Science* 157:80–82.

Turner, B. L., II
1974 Prehistoric Intensive Agriculture in the Maya Lowlands. *Science* 185:118–24.
1978 Ancient Agricultural Land Use in the Maya Lowlands. In *Pre-Hispanic Maya Agriculture,* edited by P. D. Harrison and B. L. Turner II, pp. 163–84. Albuquerque: University of New Mexico Press.
1983 Constructional Systems for Major Agrosystems of the Ancient Maya. In *Drained Field Agriculture in Central and South America,* edited by J. P. Darch, pp. 11–26. Oxford: British Archaeological Reports, International Series 189.

Turner, B. L., II, and S. B. Brush
1987 *Comparative Farming Systems.* New York: Guilford Press.

Turner, B. L., II, and P. D. Harrison
1981 Prehistoric Raised-Field Agriculture in the Maya Lowlands. *Science* 213:399–405.

Turner, V.
1969 *The Ritual Process.* Chicago: Aldine.

Ulpana, F.
1981 *Yachayninchej: El saber agrícola campesino de San Lucas.* Sucre, Bolivia: Talleres Gráficos Qorillama.

UNITAS (Unión Nacional de Instituciones para el Trabajo de Acción Social)
1991 *La revuelta de las nacionalidades.* La Paz: UNITAS.

Unzueta, O.
1975 *Mapa ecológico de Bolivia: Memoria explicativa.* La Paz: MACA, Oficina de Información Técnica.

Urioste, M.
1991 *Proyecto ley de comunidades campesinas e indígenas.* La Paz: Movimiento Bolivia Libre.

USAID (United States Agency for International Development)
1974 *Agricultural Development in Bolivia, a Sector Assessment. Report of the United States AID Mission to Bolivia.* La Paz: USAID.

Vacher, J., E. B. de Thuy, and M. Liberman
1992 Influence of the Lake on Littoral Agriculture. In *Lake Titicaca: A Synthesis of Limnological Knowledge,* edited by C. DeJoux and A. Iltis, pp. 511–22. Monographiae Biologicae, vol. 68. Dordrecht: Kluwer Academic Publishers.

Valdivia, J., and E. Martínez
1993 Diagnóstico, balance, y proyecciones del ser-

vicio nacional de desarrollo de le comunidad. *Procampo* 43:4–8.

van den Berghe, P. L.
1980 Capana: The Demise of an Andean Hacienda. In *Land and Power in Latin America,* edited by B. Orlove and G. Custred, pp. 165–78. New York: Holmes and Meier.

van der Hammen, T., and E. Gonzales
1960 Upper Pleistocene and Holocene Climate and Vegetation of the "Sabana de Bogota" (Colombia, South America). *Leidse Geologische Mededelingen* 25:261–315.

Vaux, P., W. A. Wurtsbaugh, H. Treviño, L. Marino, E. Bustamente, J. Torres, P. J. Richerson, and R. Alfaro
1988 Ecology of the Pelagic Fishes of Lake Titicaca, Peru-Bolivia. *Biotropica* 20:220–29.

Vellard, J.
1992 Associated Animal Communities: The Amphibia. In *Lake Titicaca: A Synthesis of Limnological Knowledge,* edited by C. DeJoux and A. Iltis, pp. 449–57. Monographiae Biologicae, vol. 68. Dordrecht: Kluwer Academic Publishers.

Vincent, W. F., C. L. Vincent, M. T. Downes, and P. J. Richerson
1985 Nitrate Cycling in Lake Titicaca (Peru-Bolivia): The Effects of High Altitude and Tropicality. *Freshwater Biology* 15:31–42.

Vincent, W. F., W. Wurtsbaugh, P. J. Neale, and P. J. Richerson
1986 Polymixis and Algal Production in a Tropical Lake: Latitudinal Effects on the Seasonality of Photosynthesis. *Freshwater Biology* 16:781–803.

Vincent, W. F., W. Wurtsbaugh, C. L. Vincent, and P. J. Richerson
1984 Seasonal Dynamics of Nutrient Limitation in a Tropical High-Altitude Lake (Lake Titicaca, Peru-Bolivia): Applications of Physiological Bioassays. *Limnological Oceanography* 29:540–52.

Vitousek, P. M., J. R. Gosz, C. C. Grier, J. M. Melillo, W. A. Reiners, and R. L. Todd
1979 Nitrate Losses from Disturbed Ecosystems. *Science* 204:469–74.

Vitousek, P. M., and W. A. Reiners
1976 Ecosystem Succession and Nutrient Retention: A Hypothesis. *BioScience* 25:376–81.

Wachtel, N.
1982 The Mitimas of the Cochabamba Valley: The Colonization Policy of Huayna Capac. In *The Inca and Aztec States 1400–1800,* edited by G. Collier, R. I. Rosaldo, and J. D. Worth, pp. 199–235. New York: Academic Press.

Wadell, E.
1972 *The Mound Builders.* American Ethnological Society Monographs. Seattle: University of Washington Press.

Watanabe, L., M. Moseley, and F. Cabieses (compilers)
1990 *Trabajos arqueológicos en Moquegua, Peru: Programa Contisuyu del Museo Peruano de Ciencia de la Salud.* Lima: Editorial Escuela Nueva.

Watts, W. A., and T. C. Turner
1966 Plant Macrofossls from Kirchner Marsh, Minnesota: A Paleoecological Study. *Geological Society of America Bulletin* 77:1339–60.

Waylen, P. R., and C. N. Caviedes
1986 El Niño and Annual Floods on the North Peruvian Littoral. *Journal of Hydrology* 89:141–56.
1988 El Niño and Annual Floods in Coastal Peru. In *Catastrophic Flooding,* edited by L. Mayer and D. Nash, pp. 57–77. Boston: Allen & Unwin.

Weber, M.
1978 *Economy and Society.* Berkeley: University of California Press.

Wendland, W. M., and R. A. Bryson
1974 Dating Climatic Episodes of the Holocene. *Quaternary Research* 4:9–24.

West, R.
1959 Ridge or Era Agriculture in the Colombian Andes. *Proceedings of the 33rd International Congress of Americanists* 33:279–82.

West, T.
1984 El arbusto andiente: Explotación de arbustos nativos para combustible en Bolivia. Unpublished paper on file, Inter-American Foundation, Washington, D.C.

1989 Employment Generation in the Cusco Artisan Market. Unpublished paper on file, Inter-American Foundation, Washington, D.C.

Wheatley, P.
1971 *The Pivot of the Four Quarters.* Chicago: Aldine.

Whitaker, M., and B. Wennergren
1982 Bolivia's Agriculture since 1960: Assessment and Prognosis. In *Modern Day Bolivia, Legacy of the Revolution and Projects for the Future,* edited by J. Ladman, pp. 133–255. Tempe: Arizona State University.

Whitehead, D. R.
1981 Late-Pleistocene Vegetational Changes in Northeastern North Carolina. *Ecological Monographs* 51:451–71.

Wiggens, S.
1976 *Colonización en Bolivia.* Sucre, Bolivia: Acción Cultural Loyola, Iglesia Metodista.

Wilkerson, S. J. K.
1983 So Green and Like a Garden: Intensive Agriculture in Ancient Veracruz. In *Drained Field Agriculture in Central and South America,* edited by J. P. Darch, pp. 55–90. Oxford: British Archaeological Reports, International Series 189.

Winter, T. C.
1981 Uncertainties in Estimating the Water Balance of Lakes. *Water Research Bulletin* 17:82–117.

Winterhalder, B., R. Larson, and R. Thomas
1974 Dung as an Essential Resource in a Highland Peruvian Community. *Human Ecology* 2:89–104.

Wirrmann, D.
1986 *Medios lacustres y estudio del Cuaternario reciente en Bolivia.* Unpublished manuscript on file with OSTROM, La Paz, Bolivia.
1992 Morphology and Bathymetry. In *Lake Titicaca: A Synthesis of Limnological Knowledge,* edited by C. DeJoux and A. Iltis, pp. 16–23. Monographiae Biologicae, vol. 68. Dordrecht: Kluwer Academic Publishers.

Wirrman, D., and P. Mourguiart
1987 Oscillations et paleosalinites des lacs du Quaternaire récent en Bolivie. *Géodynamique* 2:98–101.

Wirrmann, D., and L. F. Oliveira Almeida
1987 Low Holocene Level (7700–3650 Years Ago) of Lake Titicaca (Bolivia). *Paleogeography, Paleoclimatology and Paleoecology* 59:315–23.

Wirrman, D., J. P. Ybert, and P. Mourguiart
1992 A 20,000-Year Paleohydrological Record from Lake Titicaca. In *Lake Titicaca: A Synthesis of Limnological Knowledge,* edited by C. DeJoux and A. Iltis, pp. 40–48. Monographiae Biologicae, vol. 68. Dordrecht: Kluwer Academic Publishers.

Wittfogel, K.
1938 The Theory of Oriental Society. Reprinted 1959 in *Readings in Anthropology,* vol. II, edited by M. Fried, pp. 94–113. New York: Thomas Crowell.
1955 Developmental Aspects of Hydraulic Societies. In *Irrigation Civilizations: A Comparative Study,* edited by J. H. Steward, pp. 43–52. Washington, D.C.: Pan American Union.
1957 *Oriental Despotism: A Comparative Study in Total Power.* New Haven, Connecticut: Yale University Press.

Wolman, M. G.
1967 A Cycle of Sedimentation and Erosion in Urban River Channels. *Geography Annual* 49A:385–95.

Wright, H. T., Jr., and G. Johnson
1975 Population, Exchange, and Early State Formation in Southern Iran. *American Anthropologist* 77:267–89.

Wright, H. E., Jr., D. H. Mann, and P. H. Glaser
1984 Piston Corers for Peat and Lake Sediments. *Ecology* 65:657–59.

Wright, H. E., Jr., G. O. Seltzer, and B. C. S. Hansen
1989 Glacial and Climatic History of the Central Peruvian Andes. *National Geographic Research* 5:439–45.

Wurtsbaugh, W., W. F. Vincent, R. Alfaro, and C. L. Vincent
1984 Nitrogen Limitation in a Tropical Alpine Lake, Lake Titicaca (Peru/Bolivia). Abstract. *Verhandlungen Internationale Vereinigung für Theoretische und Angewantde Limnologie* 22:1252.

Wurtsbaugh, W., W. F. Vincent, R. Alfaro, C. L. Vincent, and P. J. Richerson

1985 Nutrient Limitation of Algal Growth and Nitrogen Fixation in a Tropical Alpine Lake, Lake Titicaca (Peru-Bolivia). *Freshwater Biology* 15:185–95.

Yambert, K. A.

1980 Thought and Reality: Dialects of the Andean Community. In *Land and Power in Latin America,* edited by B. Orlove and G. Custred, pp. 55–78. New York: Holmes and Meier.

Ybert, J. P.

1981 Analyse palynologique de la coupe Holocène du Chiarjahuira sur l'altiplano bolivien. *Cahiers ORSTOM, Série Géologie* 12:125–33.

1984 Diagramme sporopollinique de la coupe Holocène du Chuquiaguillo sur l'altiplano Bolivien. *Cahiers ORSTOM, Série Géologie* 14:29–34.

1985 *Contribución al estudio del Cuaternario del altiplano boliviano: Análisis palinológico del corte Holoceno del río Chiarjahuira.* Paper presented at the Congreso Latinoamerican de Palentología.

1992 Ancient Lake Environments as Deduced from Pollen Analysis. In *Lake Titicaca: A Synthesis of Limnological Knowledge,* edited by C. DeJoux and A. Iltis, pp. 49–62. Monographiae Biologicae, vol. 68. Dordrecht: Kluwer Academic Publishers.

Zienkiewicz, O. C.

1971 *The Finite Element Method in Engineering Science.* New York: McGraw-Hill.

Zucchi, A.

1972 Aboriginal Earth Structures of the Western Venezuelan Llanos. *Caribbean Journal of Science* 12:95–99.

Zuvekas, C.

1977 *Technological Change in Bolivian Agriculture: A Survey.* Working Document Series, General Working Document 4. Washington, D.C.: USAID.

# Index